# ORGANIC CHEMISTRY

HENRY GILMAN, *Editor-in-Chief*

ORGANIC CHEMISTRY

*An Advanced Treatise*

VOLUME  I.  *Second Edition.*  1943
VOLUME  II.  *Second Edition.*  1943
VOLUME  III.  1953
VOLUME  IV.  1953

# ORGANIC CHEMISTRY

## *An Advanced Treatise*

*EDITORIAL BOARD*

HENRY GILMAN, *Editor-in-Chief*

Roger Adams
Hans T. Clarke
Reuben G. Jones
Carl S. Marvel
Gordon J. O'Donnell
David A. Shirley
Harry L. Yale

*CONTRIBUTORS*

P. D. Bartlett
H. E. Carter
L. C. Cheney
J. C. Cowan
R. H. Eastman
H. W. Grimmel
W. E. Hanford
W. Z. Hassid
H. R. Ing
F. A. Miller
C. R. Noller
D. E. Sargent
W. A. Waters
R. H. Wiley
G. F Wright

IN FOUR VOLUMES

Volume III

NEW YORK
JOHN WILEY & SONS, Inc.
London: CHAPMAN & HALL, Limited

PRINTED IN THE UNITED STATES OF AMERICA

# PREFACE TO VOLUMES III AND IV

The general aim and scope of this work are described in the accompanying prefaces to the first and second editions of volumes I and II. Volumes III and IV comprise entirely new material. In the selection of these new chapters, the editors were assisted by suggestions from organic chemists throughout the world. The plan has been to include branches of organic chemistry which have not been covered previously and which are considered of great importance.

The editors are grateful for assistance from many friends for careful reading of the manuscripts. Invaluable help was given by Dr. Robert K. Ingham in connection with the index and the proofs. Thanks are also due to the following: Drs. R. R. Allen, A. G. Brook, F. K. Broome, H. J. Harwood, S. D. Rosenberg, R. J. Vander Wal, T. C. Wu; and Messrs. J. Curtice, S. H. Eidt, G. A. Guter, H. A. Hartzfeld, R. G. Johnson, L. L. Wallen, G. R. Wilder; and Mrs. John F. Speer.

H. G.

AMES, IOWA
*March, 1953*

# PREFACE TO THE FIRST EDITION OF VOLUMES I AND II

Organic chemistry is richly endowed with excellent textbooks. However, there is a need for a general treatise of organic chemistry suitable for instruction at the graduate level. Such a book must focus attention upon new developments. At best, it can but serve the purpose of the moment and provide a point of departure for unceasing revision.

The idea of a collaborative work by specialists in the several branches of the science was developed in 1934. Each author was asked to prepare a chapter dealing with a subject of particular interest to himself. It was hoped to obtain, in this way, an authoritative treatise which would cover most of the important phases of organic chemistry. The execution of this plan has resulted in the present volumes.

For the sake of convenience in revising and expanding the book, the rapidly developing fields of natural products, relationship between physical properties and chemical constitution, valence, and resonance have been grouped together in the second volume. It is planned to revise both volumes at intervals, not only in order to bring the present material up to date, but also to permit the inclusion of new chapters to fill the more conspicuous gaps. For example, chapters on chlorophyll and polymerization will be included in the next edition. Corrections and suggestions will be heartily welcomed.

The contents have been integrated and the accessibility of the information increased by cross references, by individual tables of contents for each chapter, and by a comprehensive subject index which is repeated in each of the two volumes. The inordinate wealth of the literature has made it necessary to restrict references, in general, to a relatively few selected original articles. Researches are cited, as a rule, by reference to the most recent publications; however, sufficient references to early work are given to provide an historical background. Occasional chapters, particularly those in the field of natural products, have abundant citations to original articles, and should be especially useful to research workers. In some chapters the literature has been reviewed up to September, 1937. There is, in addition, occasional mention of work hitherto unpublished. The section General References at the end of each chapter includes mention of some of the more important review articles and books as a guide to collateral reading.

The editors gratefully acknowledge the assistance of many friends in the examination of the manuscripts. Valuable aid was provided by the late Dr. W. H. Carothers, who served on the Editorial Board. Special thanks are due to Drs. G. E. Hilbert, J. F. Nelson, P. T. Parker, A. M. Patterson, G. F Wright, and Messrs. J. C. Bailie, R. L. Bebb, L. C. Cheney, E. J. Crane, W. Harber, A. L. Jacoby, and J. Swislowsky.

H. G.

AMES, IOWA
*December, 1937*

# PREFACE TO THE SECOND EDITION OF VOLUMES I AND II

The purpose, plan, and scope of this Treatise are given in the accompanying preface to the first edition.

This second edition, which represents a significant expansion of the first, contains twenty-six chapters, of which the following eight are new: the reactions of aliphatic hydrocarbons; synthetic polymers; catalytic hydrogenation and hydrogenolysis; organic sulfur compounds; aliphatic fluorides; the chemistry of the porphyrins; chlorophyll; and the redistribution reaction. All the chapters carried over from the first edition have been revised. In some chapters the literature has been reviewed up to September, 1942.

Corrections and suggestions will again be cordially welcomed. The editors are grateful to many friends for the examination of the manuscripts. Particular thanks are due to Messrs. R. K. Abbott, R. W. Leeper, D. S. Melstrom, G. J. O'Donnell, S. M. Spatz, J. R. Thirtle, and L. A. Woods.

H. G.

AMES, IOWA
*October, 1942*

# CONTENTS

## VOLUME III

## VOLUME IV

ix

# CONTENTS OF THE SECOND EDITION OF VOLUME I

# CONTENTS OF THE SECOND EDITION OF VOLUME II

# CHAPTER 1

# THE STUDY OF ORGANIC REACTION MECHANISMS

### Paul D. Bartlett

### *Harvard University*

## CONTENTS

1

# INTRODUCTION

A chemical equation shows the state of a system of molecules before and after reaction. Great interest is attached to the manner in which these changes in state are effected for there is little correlation between the apparent degree of simplicity of an equation and the ease of accomplishing the indicated change. The study of organic reaction mechanisms attempts to visualize the changes in position, order, and manner of linking of the atoms in a system in the course of reaction. When this has been done in a number of cases one may hope to gain some understanding of the factors that make one reaction path favored over another, of the way in which a reaction will respond to changes in external conditions, solvent, catalysts, and reagents. Out of these may grow some command over the means of using known reactions to the best advantage, and some facility in the field of development and invention in organic synthesis.

These goals are qualitative ones. As in structural organic chemistry, progress is made by the study of cases, by comparison and analogy, and success is judged ultimately by the degree of consistency of a large body of interlocking facts and interpretation. The single crucial experiment is a rarity. Research on mechanisms differs from that on structures principally in the degree of usefulness of exact measurements and of physical principles relating to exact measurements and calculations. Appropriate numerical data, never an end in themselves, constitute the sharpest tool at the disposal of the organic chemist interested in the mechanism of chemical change.

**Classification of Reaction Mechanisms.** Reaction mechanisms may be classified broadly into free radical mechanisms, ionic mechanisms, and molecular mechanisms.

In a *free radical mechanism* the bond which is broken separates with unpairing of its bonding electrons, and particles occur in the reaction which have odd numbers of electrons. Such free radicals, and reactions involving them, are generally recognizable by quite characteristic properties.[1] In the absence of stabilizing structural features (see Chapter 6 in Vol. I of this Treatise) or peculiar mechanisms leading to their imprisonment, free radicals are so reactive as to occur only transitorily in chain reactions (see p. 625 in Vol. I of this Treatise). Chain reactions are often induced by light, showing quantum yields greater than 1; they can be induced by the introduction of known free radicals in small amounts, and can be inhibited by small amounts of "inhibitors" (stable free radicals or substances that react with unstable free radicals to yield stable ones). In the gas phase, free radicals can sometimes be trapped by reaction to recognizable products, as in the Paneth-Rice mirror technique (see p. 613 in Vol. I of this Treatise), or recognized by their magnetic and associated properties.[2,3]

Reactions in which a reactant or product is an *ion*, such as the formation of tetramethylammonium iodide from methyl iodide and trimethylamine, obviously involve the unsymmetrical cleavage of a bond, with the electrons remaining paired. In other reactions, such as the

---

[1] See W. A. Waters, "The Chemistry of Free Radicals," Clarendon Press, Oxford (1946), pp. 14–19.

[2] W. A. Waters, *op. cit.*, pp. 21–34.

[3] E. W. R. Steacie, "Atomic and Free Radical Reactions," Reinhold Publishing Corp., New York (1946), p. 61.

bromination of stilbene [4] or of vinyl bromide,[5] there is frequently evidence of participation of ions even though no ions are obviously present as reactants or products.

*Molecular mechanisms* include those which can be shown to occur between molecules without the intermediate formation of either ions or radicals. To show this is not easy, since so many reactions which from their equations appear to be molecular are found to proceed by one of the other types of processes. The first stage of the *ortho*-Claisen rearrangement (preceding the enolization; see p. 72) is a good example of a molecular mechanism, as are probably also the last stage of the $S_N i$ displacement (p. 44) and the last stage of the Tschugaeff dehydration (pp. 52, 53).

It may be noted that the distinction between ionic and molecular mechanisms is a trivial one, based upon the overall charge types of the participants and not upon any sharp difference in the nature of the local process at the seat of reaction. From the latter standpoint the most significant classification of mechanisms would be one based upon the *number of centers* which comprise the reaction system. Such a classification includes the two-center reactions of dissociation and association, the three-center displacement reaction, and four-center reactions involving *cis*-addition and elimination. Various mechanisms of concerted reaction in solution which have been proposed involve larger numbers of centers: five for the bromination of an olefin catalyzed by bromide ion,[6] six and seven, respectively, for the Lowry mechanisms of the enolization of acetone and of the mutarotation of glucose (see below, pp. 88, 90, 94). Because of the varying and important role of the solvent in reactions occurring in solution, and because of the possibility of complexes or prolonged collisions between reactants, it is possible to argue about the number of centers simultaneously suffering a change of bonding in a reaction in solution. Nevertheless, this classification of reactions is a useful one, independent of the type of bond fission taking place.

## SOME GENERAL PRINCIPLES

### Importance of the Displacement Reaction

It is inherent in the kinetic theory that chemical reaction between two molecules is the result of a collision which must have both the right geometrical orientation and the requisite energy for the formation of the new bonds and the breaking of the old ones. For a majority of the

---

[4] P. D. Bartlett and D. S. Tarbell, *J. Am. Chem. Soc.*, **58**, 466 (1936).

[5] K. Nozaki and R. A. Ogg, Jr., *ibid.*, **64**, 697, 704 (1942).

[6] K. Nozaki and R. A. Ogg, Jr., *ibid.*, **64**, 697, 704, 709 (1942).

reactions hitherto studied in the vapor phase, these requirements create an overwhelming probability for two- and three-center reactions in comparison with all other types. This is true to such an extent that most of the simple gaseous reactions, such, for example, as the homogeneous decomposition of acetone to methane and ketene, and the chlorination of methane,[7] which involve changes in more than two bonds, proceed by successions of reactions of the simpler type even though these reactions involve unstable free radicals. Reactions in which one bond is formed and one bond is broken are called "displacement reactions," and it is convenient to apply this term to any reaction that can be represented by the general equation

$$X + Y—Z \rightarrow X—Y + Z$$

regardless of the nature of X, Y, or Z, and regardless of the number of atoms of which each is composed. Such three-center reactions often involve lower total energy changes than the simpler type of dissociation and association in which only a single bond is formed or broken. The latter reactions are of interest principally as initiating and terminating steps in chain reactions.

When displacement and dissociation reactions occur in solution, solvent molecules are present at very high concentrations; these molecules may, and often do, form bonds with the reacting and product species so that it is no longer true that the process of reaction involves the formation and breaking of only one bond at a time. It remains true, however, that most organic reactions in solution whose mechanisms are known proceed by successions of displacement, dissociation, or association reactions, rather than by one-step additions or metatheses. The most important difference between organic reaction mechanisms in the gas phase and in solution arises out of the totally different order of stability of ions in the two kinds of media.

Because the displacement reaction is equally prevalent in the vapor and in solution, and because of the similarities in kinetics in the two types of media, gas-phase analogies have been important in establishing the principles of organic reaction mechanisms, even though most such reactions occur in solution. The homogeneous interconversion of *ortho* and *para* hydrogen by hydrogen atoms has become the classical example of a symmetrical, reversible displacement reaction,

$$\underset{a \quad b \quad c}{H + H—H} \rightleftarrows \underset{a \quad b \quad c}{H—H + H}$$

and was the first chemical reaction to have its absolute rate calculated

[7] E. W. R. Steacie, "Atomic and Free Radical Reactions," Reinhold Publishing Corp., New York (1946), pp. 133, 411.

from a physical picture of the transition state.[8] The simple atomic displacement reaction became a familiar type through the experimental studies of Polanyi [9] on the reactions of sodium vapor with alkyl halides; Bergmann, Polanyi, and Szabo [10] showed the usefulness of extending the concept of the displacement reaction to the behavior of alkyl halides in solution where the reactions were definitely of ionic type. By means of radioactive isotopes the racemization of an optically active iodide by iodide ion was shown to be a displacement of iodine by iodine on carbon.[11] By these steps, and through many other studies of mechanism, the theory of the three-H transition state became the source of the language in which the mechanisms of organic reactions are now discussed.

### The Transition State

For any displacement reaction to occur the reacting molecules must approach each other along some feasible path such that the new bond is gradually formed, the old bond is gradually broken, total energy is conserved, and minimal resistance is encountered to the change. In assessing this resistance, attention is centered upon the most strained and least probable configuration through which the system must pass on its way from reactants to products. This configuration is the so-called *transition state,* or activated complex; in the case of the displacement reaction

$$X + Y\!-\!Z \rightleftarrows X\!-\!Y + Z$$

the transition state must have a linear configuration to meet these conditions. The bond lengths X—Y and Y—Z are both greater in the transition state than is normal for a stable bond and the condition of the complex is such that, depending upon a slight motion in either direction, it can equally well move toward either side of the equation. Because of the existence of such a state, the energy input required for reaction is not as great as that needed to break the original bond between Y and Z. The energy relationships in a displacement reaction are frequently summarized in potential-energy maps such as that shown in Fig. 1, where the contour lines join configurations of equal potential energy, and the coordinates are the two bond lengths concerned, only linear systems being considered. The map expresses the idea that there is a certain set of configurations through which the system may pass

---

[8] H. Pelzer and E. Wigner, Z. physik. Chem., **B15,** 445 (1932).

[9] See, for example, H. v. Hartel and M. Polanyi, *ibid.,* **B11,** 97 (1930).

[10] E. Bergmann, M. Polanyi, and A. Szabo, *ibid.,* **B20,** 161 (1933).

[11] E. D. Hughes, F. Juliusburger, S. Masterman, B. Topley, and J. Weiss, *J. Chem. Soc.,* 1525 (1935). See also below, p. 27.

with minimal input of energy in analogy to the passage of a climber from one valley to another over a mountain pass. For the most part these passes are so narrow, with such steep sides, that transition states deviating appreciably in dimensions from that at the center of the pass need not be considered.[12]

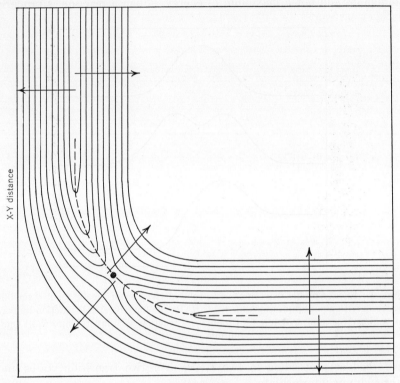

FIG. 1. Schematic energy diagram for a displacement reaction. The contour lines are lines of equal potential energy, and the arrows point uphill with respect to potential energy. The heavy dot represents the transition state and the dotted line the path of least climb by which the reaction may be effected.

The energy difference between the transition state and the starting materials is the energy of activation of the forward reaction; the energy difference between the transition state and the products is the energy of activation of the reverse reaction.

[12] For a detailed physical treatment of the transition-state theory, see S. Glasstone, K. J. Laidler, and H. Eyring, "The Theory of Rate Processes," McGraw-Hill Book Co., New York (1941), Chapter 4; K. J. Laidler, "Chemical Kinetics," McGraw-Hill Book Co. New York (1950), Chapters 3, 13.

The conditions may be such, as they are in the H—H$_2$ reaction, that there is a depression in the pass, corresponding to a somewhat greater stability for the symmetrical configuration than for a slightly unsymmetrical stage leading into or out of it.  In this case the symmetrical stage is not a *transition state* but an *intermediate*, since it represents a minimum and not a maximum of energy.  Such a reaction is properly

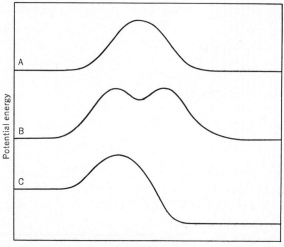

Reaction coördinate

F&#x026A;G. 2.  Energy profile diagrams.  *A*. Profile derived from Fig. 1, for a reversible reaction with equilibrium constant = 1.  *B*. Profile for a reversible reaction by way of an unstable intermediate.  *C*. Profile for a reaction with favorable forward equilibrium constant.

regarded as proceeding in two steps, over two transition states and through one intermediate.

It is not desirable to draw a complete potential-energy diagram like that of Fig. 1 every time we discuss a reaction that involves reactants, products, and a transition state.  It is often convenient, however, to use an abridged representation in which energy is plotted as the ordinate, and *linear distance along the reaction path,* the path of least climb, or its horizontal projection, as the abscissa.  Such an abscissa, often called the "reaction coordinate," has no numerical significance apart from the map from which it is derived, but such a graph conveys at a glance, as in Fig. 2, such important ideas as the existence of intermediates and their number; high or low activation energy; an exothermic or endothermic reaction; and which reaction of a series will have the highest activation energy.  It is clear that, among reactions which are resolvable into familiar types, we can give a reasonable account of the mechanism if we can identify the intermediates (minima on the energy curve) and depict the transition states (maxima on the energy curve), for it is then obvious through what stages the reaction must pass between these points.

## The Principle of Microscopic Reversibility

The concept of the transition state leaves no room for unidirectional mechanisms of thermal chemical change. The configuration of lowest energy for the transition state in a forward reaction must also be the configuration of lowest energy for the reverse reaction. A surface can be constructed on which a billiard ball will make the forward and reverse trips over a hill by different paths, but the properties of such a surface will have no analogs in the known relationships of energy and spatial configuration in thermally reacting systems. It is therefore generally conceded, though not demonstrable by rigorous thermodynamics, that every thermal reaction proceeds forward and backward over exactly the same set of configurations. This principle can be extremely useful, since it allows much information to be gained about the mechanisms of reversible reactions which proceed to an equilibrium too unfavorable for study of the forward reaction.[13]

**Failure of Microscopic Reversibility in Photochemical Reactions.** Photochemical reactions are an important class of reactions showing unidirectional mechanisms. When a halogen molecule absorbs light and is excited to a higher quantum state, the excited molecule often dissociates into atoms which recombine thermally, dissipating their energy kinetically and chemically and not by radiation. Such a reaction cannot be described by a potential-energy diagram having only bond distances as independent variables, since the most important factor determining the energy is the *electronic* energy level of the molecule, affected by the absorption of radiation. The thermal reunion of atoms can be so formulated, but in addition to the dissociation of chlorine envisaged in such a diagram there is a unidirectional passage of material over the hump through light absorption, which proceeds in the direction of dissociation only. Thus it is that the apparent position of equilibrium may vary widely with the illumination in a reversible photochemical reaction.[14] This constitutes an important limitation upon the principle of microscopic reversibility.

[13] See below, p. 104.
[14] See, for example, G. S. Forbes and A. F. Nelson, *J. Am. Chem. Soc.*, **58**, 182 (1936); **59**, 693 (1937).

## The Effect of Medium upon Reaction Rate

A transition state differs from a molecule in that it represents an energy maximum rather than an energy minimum, and accordingly it is always moving in the one direction or the other over the barrier. Despite these points of difference, the transition state is like a molecule in that it possesses definite bonds, geometrical configuration, and distribution of electrical charge. The number of forward-moving transition states existing at any time in the presence of the molecules of starting material in a chemical reaction is governed, just as in a rapid equilibrium, by the changes in energy and entropy associated with the formation of the transition state. For algebraic purposes the unknown factors of solvation and electrical influence entering into a reversible equilibrium in solution are conveniently lumped into an "activity coefficient," $f$, so defined for each medium that in the equilibrium

$$A + B + \cdots \rightleftarrows C + D + \cdots$$

the equilibrium constant

$$K = \frac{(C)f_C(D)f_D \cdots}{(A)f_A(B)f_B \cdots} \tag{1}$$

is independent of the conditions, only the $f$'s varying. It was first proposed by Brönsted [15] that in the special case of reactions between ionic species in dilute aqueous solution a complete prediction of the effect of medium changes upon the rate of reaction should be possible by assigning an activity coefficient to the transition state as if it were a molecule and postulating that a change in medium operates by shifting the "equilibrium" concentration of the transition state. Thus for a reaction between A and B over the transition state X

$$A + B \rightleftarrows X$$

$$K^* = \frac{(X)f_X}{(A)f_A(B)f_B} \tag{2}$$

and the concentration (X) is expressed by

$$(X) = K^*(A)(B)\frac{f_A f_B}{f_X} \tag{3}$$

The rate of the reaction being proportional to the concentration (X) of the forward transition state, the change produced in any reaction rate by a change in medium should be directly proportional to the change in the quotient $f_A f_B / f_X$.

[15] J. N. Brönsted, *Z. physik. Chem.*, **102**, 169 (1922); **115**, 337 (1925).

Eyring has generalized the Brönsted equation to cover all kinds of media and has identified the universal constant expressing the rate of passage of transition states over the barrier as $k'T/h$ ($k'$ = Boltzmann's constant, $T$ = absolute temperature, $h$ = Planck's constant). The Eyring equation also contains a "transmission coefficient," $\kappa$, usually equal to unity, and thus expresses the rate of any reaction between A and B as

$$\kappa \frac{k'T}{h} K^*(A)(B) \frac{f_A f_B}{f_X} \tag{4}$$

It is not in general possible to calculate, from a knowledge of the structures of molecules and transition states, the values of their activity coefficients, so that in many important cases the predictions of the Brönsted equation as to the effect of changing medium on reaction rate cannot be tested. In dilute aqueous solutions, however, it is to be expected that the activity coefficient of an ion will be determined largely by the magnitude of its electrical charge, according to the limiting Debye-Hückel equation

$$\log f = -az^2 \sqrt{\mu} \tag{5}$$

where $f$ is the activity coefficient of the ion, $a$ is a calculable constant approximately equal to 0.5, $z$ is the valence of the ion, and $\mu$ is the ionic strength, defined as $\frac{1}{2} \sum_i c_i z_i^2$ for the concentrations and valences of all the ions present in the solution. Since the overall ionic charge present on the transition state must be equal to the algebraic sum of the charges of its component reactant ions ($Z_X = Z_A + Z_B$), Brönsted was able to derive from equations 4 and 5 the equation

$$\log k = \log k^\circ K^* + 2az_A z_B \sqrt{\mu} \tag{6}$$

$k^\circ K^*$ being independent of the medium.

Equation 6 states that an increase in ionic strength will increase the rate of a reaction between ions of like sign and will decrease the rate of a reaction between ions of unlike sign. The equation also relates the change in rate quantitatively to the product of the charges of the reacting ions.

Equation 6 has proved valid and useful where interactions between singly charged ions are concerned.[16] However, it has been recognized, both experimentally and theoretically, that the forces of interionic attraction are so powerful between oppositely charged ions of higher valence that, when $z_+ z_-$ for any two ions of opposite sign is equal to 4

[16] For some applications of equation 6 see E. Grunwald and S. Winstein, *J. Am. Chem. Soc.*, **69**, 2051 (1947); P. D. Bartlett and C. G. Swain, *ibid.*, **71**, 1406 (1949).

or greater, the limiting form of the Debye-Hückel equation does not hold in any attainable dilution.[17] For example, the reaction between thiosulfate ion and bromoacetate ion, for which $z_A z_B = +2$, yields the correct slope in a plot of equation 6 only when the cations involved in producing the ionic strength are univalent; the use of calcium, barium, magnesium, or lanthanum salts brings large deviations.

A summary [18] of the effect of ionic strength upon the rates of reactions between ions of widely varying charge type showed that the *qualitative* predictions of equation 6 as to the signs and relative magnitudes of the limiting slopes were fulfilled. For the reasons given by La Mer,[17] however, the *quantitative* usefulness of these results in testing the theory is restricted to the cases where $z_A z_B$ does not reach $-4$ for any pair of ions present. Work by Olson and Simonson,[19] though from a quite different viewpoint, tends to confirm the importance of these considerations.

It should be pointed out also that, because of the limited domain of the limiting Brönsted-Debye-Hückel equation, some of its assumptions are not even qualitatively true in many systems of importance to the organic chemist. Thus, in media of low dielectric constant, ions of opposite charge are so far from being independent of one another that they commonly form pairs and clusters.[20] The assumption made in the limit of dilution that the activity coefficient of a molecular species is determined only by its net charge is very far from being generally true, since dipolar ions of zero net charge such as amino acids are powerfully influenced by electrolytes at higher concentrations.[21]

**The Ingold-Hughes Extension of the Brönsted Theory.** Even the seemingly ideal conditions of dilute aqueous solution still do not suffice in general for a far-reaching quantitative test of the Brönsted rate theory. The essential idea of this theory as to the manner in which activities enter into the determination of reaction rates has nevertheless attained wide acceptance, and this idea has been successfully extended to the qualitative interpretation of the effect of ionizing power of the medium on reaction rate by Ingold and Hughes.[22] A uniformly charged spherical body in a medium of dielectric constant $D$ has an electrostatic potential equal to $e^2/2Dr$, where $e$ is the charge and $r$ the radius of the body, and the work of separating two equal and opposite charges from

[17] V. K. La Mer, *Chem. Revs.*, **10**, 179 (1932); references are given there to many original papers.

[18] R. Livingston, *J. Chem. Education*, **7**, 2887 (1930).

[19] A. R. Olson and T. R. Simonson, *J. Chem. Phys.*, **17**, 1167 (1949).

[20] R. M. Fuoss, *Chem. Revs.*, **17**, 27 (1935).

[21] E. J. Cohn in E. J. Cohn and J. T. Edsall, "Proteins, Amino Acids, and Peptides as Ions and Dipolar Ions," Reinhold Publishing Corp., New York (1943), Chapter 11.

[22] See E. D. Hughes, *Trans. Faraday Soc.*, **37**, 608 (1941), and previous references there cited.

distance $r_1$ to $r_2$ in the same medium is $e^2[(1/r_1) - (1/r_2)]/D$. Increasing the dielectric constant will therefore favor reactions in which the transition state has more concentrated charge or larger dipoles than the reactants, and will retard relatively reactions in which the transition state has more diffuse charge or smaller dipoles than the reactants. The field of solvolysis and displacement reactions (see p. 25) affords examples of the general validity of this prediction.

In the reaction between trimethylamine and ethyl iodide to form ethyltrimethylammonium iodide, the initial molecules are uncharged, but the transition state must have considerable separation of charge since it is halfway to the completely ionic quaternary ammonium salt. Ionizing media therefore favor this reaction as shown by the fact [23] that the rate in nitrobenzene is 55 times that in toluene at 100°, whereas for the similar reaction between trimethylamine and $p$-nitrobenzyl chloride [24] the rates in nitromethane and in hexane differ by a factor of 9300. On the other hand, the dissociation of hexaphenylethane into free triphenylmethyl radicals, which involves no ions and no polarization, proceeds at rates in toluene and nitrobenzene which are indistinguishable from each other, and shows an extreme variation in rate of only 2.5-fold in sixteen solvents in which it was studied by Ziegler.[25] It has not proved possible to make quantitative calculations of these effects, but their qualitative interpretation is often useful as a tool in the study of mechanisms.

## Effect of Structure on Reaction Rate and Equilibrium

In the light of the transition state theory it is apparent that the means by which structure affects reaction rate and equilibrium are entirely similar. A substituent that affects the $\Delta S$ and $\Delta H$ of the change from reactants to *products* affects the equilibrium constant of the reaction. When the substituent affects the $\Delta S^*$ and $\Delta H^*$ for the conversion of reactants into *transition state*, the effect is observed on rate of reaction. In each case the effect of structure is most conveniently discussed by comparing the equilibrium constant or the rate constant of a reaction of a compound bearing a substituent X with the equilibrium or rate constant for an identical reaction of the compound having H in place of that X. $\Delta S^*$ is a logarithmic measure of the relative total numbers of energy states available to the reactants and the transition state. Since electronic energy levels are spaced very far apart compared to vibra-

[23] H. G. Grimm, H. Ruf, and H. Wolff, *Z. physik. Chem.*, **B13**, 307 (1931).
[24] H. v. Halban, *ibid.*, **84**, 129 (1913).
[25] K. Ziegler, P. Orth, and K. Weber, *Ann.*, **504**, 131 (1933).

tional, rotational, and translational energy levels of a molecule, the latter contribute practically everything, and the former practically nothing, to the determination of entropy changes. It can therefore be anticipated that a substituent which affects only the electronic state of the molecule will be without influence on $\Delta S^*$, whereas this term will be strongly affected by anything that influences the vibrational and rotational possibilities of the starting materials or transition state. This generalization is not as useful as might at first appear, since there are often stereochemical consequences of the electronic state of a molecule which carry entropy effects with them. (For examples see p. 57.) Bulky substituents or those that alter the relative shapes of starting materials and transition state produce particularly profound effects upon $\Delta S^*$. A group which by its bulk produces congestion in the transition state, or which acts in some way to relieve congestion in the transition state, may be expected to raise or lower the potential energy difference between reactant and transition state as well as affecting the entropy through the kinetic energy levels. Therefore, in general, steric hindrance is not solely an effect on the entropy term of a reaction.

A limitation upon the correlation of substituent effects with $\Delta S^*$ and $\Delta H^*$ is the fact that these quantities are determined experimentally with the assumption that the "constants" of the Arrhenius equation are invariant with temperature. This assumption could be literally correct only in the improbable case where the heat capacity of the transition state was identical with that of the starting materials. Actually, therefore, the constants of the Arrhenius (or the Eyring) equation will not be the same if determined over different temperature intervals, and hence they do not represent a true resolution of a rate into factors of kinetic and potential energy. This limitation is the more insidious because rates of reaction are usually observed only over the rather limited temperature range where they are measurable in convenient lengths of time, and the inconstancy of the Arrhenius parameters is therefore seldom detected directly.

By far the greatest systematic study has been given to the influence of groups which affect the electrostatic energy of the transition state and hence can be expected to affect solely the $\Delta H^*$ term in the rate equation. Theory recognizes three ways in which such an influence may arise: (1) by an electrostatic effect transmitted directly through space; (2) by the effect of the substituent on the nature of the medium through which the electrostatic effect is transmitted; (3) by electronic displacement within the bonds of the molecule.

**The Direct or Electrostatic Field Effect.** If the ionization of succinic acid and of the acid succinate ion is considered to be the same process in all respects in the two cases except for the presence in the acid succinate ion of a negative charge on the carboxylate group, then theory predicts that the work of ionization in the two cases will differ exactly by the electrostatic work of removing a proton from its position on the carboxyl group to infinity against the attraction of the negative charge. For statistical reasons [26] this difference in work of ionization is equal to $RT \ln (K'/4K'')$, where $K'$ and $K''$ are the first and second ionization constants, respectively, of succinic acid.  The electrostatic work of

$$\begin{array}{ccccc} CH_2COOH & & CH_2COO^- & & CH_2COO^- \\ | & \rightleftarrows & | & + H^+ \rightleftarrows & | & + 2H^+ \\ CH_2COOH & & CH_2COOH & & CH_2COO^- \end{array}$$

removing a mole of hydrogen ions to infinity from a starting position at a distance $r$ from the negative charge is $Ne^2/Dr$, where $N$ is Avogadro's number, $e$ is the magnitude of the charge of an electron, and $D$ is the dielectric constant of the medium.  By equating these two expressions for the electrostatic work we obtain the Bjerrum equation [27]

$$RT \ln (K'/4K'') = Ne^2/Dr \qquad (7)$$

which predicts a relation between the interprotonic distance in a dibasic acid and the relative first and second ionization constants of that acid.

For a monobasic acid containing a dipolar substituent, a modified form of the Bjerrum equation can be derived by considering separately the electrostatic work relative to the positive end of the substituent dipole and to the negative end of that dipole.  The result is the equation

$$RT \ln (K/K^\circ) = (Ne\mu \cos \theta)/Dr^2 \qquad (8)$$

where $K$ and $K^\circ$ are the ionization constants of the substituted and unsubstituted acids, $\mu$ is the electric moment of the substituent, and $\theta$ is the angle between this moment and the vector connecting its midpoint with the ionizing hydrogen.  The application of these equations is beset by the difficulty that the electrostatic interaction is over a very small distance, less than the diameter of the molecule, and therefore the gross dielectric constant of the solvent, as one might determine it by standard methods, is not the correct value of $D$ to insert into this equation.

The most successful of many attempts to treat this problem [28] consists in making an estimate of the appropriate value of $D$ by regarding the molecule as a cavity of low dielectric constant surrounded by a medium

[26] E. Q. Adams, *J. Am. Chem. Soc.*, **38**, 1503 (1916).

[27] N. Bjerrum, *Z. physik. Chem.*, **106**, 219 (1923).

[28] J. G. Kirkwood and F. H. Westheimer, *J. Chem. Phys.*, **6**, 506 (1938); F. H. Westheimer and J. G. Kirkwood, *ibid.*, **6**, 513 (1938); F. H. Westheimer and M. W. Shookhoff, *J. Am. Chem. Soc.*, **61**, 555 (1939).

having the normal dielectric constant of the solvent. The values of $D$ so obtained are a sensitive function of the shape of the molecule which constitutes the cavity and are also different for the interaction of a charge with another charge and with a dipole. When such values of $D$ are estimated and inserted into the equation, it is possible to calculate values of $r$ which are entirely reasonable as average distances between protons of dibasic acids which are assumed to exist in solution in randomly disposed chains. The sign and rough magnitude of the effect of chlorine, bromine, fluorine, cyano, nitro, or methyl in the *para* position of benzoic acid on its ionization constant can also be approximately calculated by using the dipole formula, measured dipole moments, and the effective dielectric constants as estimated by the Kirkwood-Westheimer treatment.[29] A similar degree of success can be attained in relating electrostatic effects to reaction rates in favorable cases.[30]

**"Electrostatic Medium" Effect of Substitutents.** Since the transmission of an electrostatic effect from one point to another in a molecule is greatly affected by the effective dielectric constant within that molecule, and this in turn is a sensitive function of the size and shape of the molecule which constitutes a cavity of low dielectric constant within the medium, it follows that substitution that does nothing but alter the size and shape of the molecule may increase or decrease the effectiveness of electric charges or dipoles already present in the molecule. The classical example of this is the effect of four methyl groups in tetramethylsuccinic acid upon the relative values of the first and second ionization constants of the acid. Table I shows the values of these constants.

TABLE I

IONIZATION CONSTANTS OF SUCCINIC ACIDS *

|  | $K' \times 10^4$ | $K'' \times 10^7$ | $K'/K''$ | $r$ calc.,† Å |
|---|---|---|---|---|
| CH$_2$COOH<br>\|<br>CH$_2$COOH | 0.64 | 33.3 | 19.2 | 5.75 |
| (CH$_3$)$_2$CCOOH<br>\|<br>(CH$_3$)$_2$CCOOH | 3.19 | 0.52 | 6135 | 4.80 |

* R. Gane and C. K. Ingold, *J. Chem. Soc.*, 2158 (1931).
† F. H. Westheimer and M. W. Shookhoff, *J. Am. Chem. Soc.*, **61**, 556 (1939).

The methyl groups at one time were supposed to have a great effect in altering the distance between the carboxyl groups in succinic acid. It is now recognized that the effect of the methyl groups is to broaden

[29] F. H. Westheimer, *J. Am. Chem. Soc.*, **61**, 1977 (1939).
[30] F. H. Westheimer and M. W. Shookhoff, *ibid.*, **62**, 269 (1940).

the cavity of low dielectric constant across which the effect of the charge is transmitted and thereby greatly to lower the value of $D$ in the denominator of the right-hand side of equation 7. In the case of dipolar substituents and with reactions other than that of ionic dissociation, it is not known in general how purely electrostatic is the effect of a substituent, and therefore it is sometimes difficult to recognize whether an electrostatic medium effect of an alkyl group is operative or not.

**Internal Electronic Displacement.** *The Inductive Effect.* Almost every bond between two atoms of unlike elements is electrically unsymmetrical and has a dipole moment associated with it. These moments can be detected experimentally in the case of simple compounds, and, from the experimentally measurable resultant moment of the molecule as a whole, approximate assignments of moments to the individual bonds can be made.[31, 32]

Three independent ways are in use of visualizing the nature and origin of these electric moments. According to one way the bond is regarded as an entirely normal covalent one with a permanent displacement of electrons toward the atom which is inherently the more "electronegative." Alternatively, a bond possessing such a displacement may be regarded as a resonance hybrid between a normal and perfectly symmetrical covalent bond and an electrovalent bond in which complete electron transfer is assumed. It has been shown [33] that an extra bond energy is associated with bonds of this sort above what would be calculated from the energies of bonds between pairs of similar atoms. This energy may be regarded as resonance energy. Third, a bond with an electronic displacement may be regarded as modified in the type of its hybridization between $s$ and $p$ orbitals in one or both of the atoms.[34]

In any event such a displacement affecting one carbon atom of the chain would be expected to affect successive carbon atoms in that chain with steadily decreasing intensity since any disturbance of the normal electronic charge on a carbon atom is bound to produce a small electrostatic response in the adjacent carbon atom. The chain of bonded atoms thus produces a totally different medium for the transmission of an effect from an isotropic dielectric or from the model of one dielectric surrounded by another. It has in common with the dielectric medium, however, the property of transmitting an effect with steadily decreasing

[31] C. P. Smyth, "Dielectric Constant and Molecular Structure," Chemical Catalog Co., New York (1931).

[32] G. E. K. Branch and M. Calvin, "The Theory of Organic Chemistry," Prentice-Hall, New York (1941), pp. 126–150.

[33] L. Pauling, "The Nature of the Chemical Bond," Cornell University Press, Ithaca, N. Y. (1948), 2nd ed., Chapter 2; also see pp. 1950 and 1967 in Vol. II of this Treatise.

[34] See A. D. Walsh, *Discussions Faraday Soc.*, **2**, 18 (1947).

intensity as the distance from the source of the effect is increased. Whether the transmission of this so-called inductive effect through a saturated molecule will be more efficient or less efficient than the transmission of the direct electrostatic effect must depend on the one hand upon the polarizabilities of the electronic systems in the bonds of the molecule, and on the other hand on the effective dielectric constant between the source of the displacement and the point at which its effect is observed.  By changing from a solvent of low to one of high dielectric constant it should be possible to increase the importance of inductive effects relative to direct electrostatic effects although, for the reasons just discussed, the change will not be in proportion to the dielectric constants of the pure media.

The polarization in a bond between two atoms of unlike elements is readily thought of as associated with the different electron affinities of the two atoms concerned.  Polarizations in bonds between identical atoms, as in toluene or propylene, require further examination before being classified as inductive effects.[34a]

*Resonance Effects.*  The effect of a chlorine atom upon the direction of substitution in the benzene nucleus [34b] and of the hydroxyl group upon both the orientation and the speed of substitution [34b] is opposite

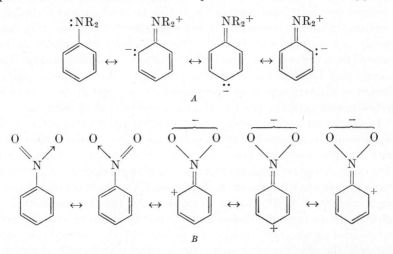

to what would be predicted from the fact that the carbon-chlorine and carbon-oxygen bonds both have the positive ends of their electric moments toward the carbon.  These reactions are examples of cases where the result is determined by some effect obviously different from

[34a] N. N. Lichtin and P. D. Bartlett, *J. Am. Chem. Soc.*, **73**, 5530 (1951).
[34b] See pp. 202 ff. in Vol. I of this Treatise.

either the direct electrostatic effect or the inductive effect internally transmitted. The theory of resonance [35] takes account of the existence of such effects by depicting "hybrid" structures of molecules and transition states capable of representation in more than one electronic distribution. Substituents in benzene which have an electron donor atom bonded directly to the benzene ring increase the electron density at the *ortho* and *para* positions $(A)$, while electron-accepting groups produce electron deficiency at the *ortho* and *para* positions $(B)$. This effect being independent in general of the direction of the electric moment in the substituent group, one does not anticipate any general parallelism between the direction of resonance effects and the direction of direct electrostatic or inductive effects.

Effects classified here as resonance effects are alternatively represented in the notation of molecular orbitals by an attempt to depict directly the electronic distribution in a molecule capable of the effects without relating this distribution to extreme structures. This notation represents a move toward less cumbersome representations of organic structures and it avoids inviting erroneous conceptions of resonance hybrids as oscillating systems.[36] However, there remain certain advantages to the resonance method of representing the structures of compounds with hybrid bonds. One of the greatest of these advantages arises out of the fact that the degree of polarization existing in the permanent ground state of the starting materials may exist to a greater extent in a transition state. Such a time-variable resonance effect (classified by Ingold as an "electromeric" as opposed to the permanent "mesomeric" effect) is then most conveniently described [37] by saying that the transition state receives a greater contribution from a certain extreme structure than does the initial ground state of the system. The second great advantage of the resonance notation is that it is convenient for showing polarizations and distinguishing between those parts of a molecule which are nucleophilic and those which are electrophilic. In a benzene ring or in a conjugated system resonance effects produce alternating polarities in the atoms as opposed to the direct electrostatic or inductive effect which produces a steady decreasing charge increment of the same electrical sign.

**The Hammett Equation.** In very few chemical reactions can the equilibrium constant be related as directly to an electrostatic work term as in the ionization of acids. However, in many reactions the formation

[35] G. W. Wheland, "The Theory of Resonance," John Wiley & Sons, New York (1944); see also pp. 205–213, Vol. I, and Chapter 26, Vol. II, of this Treatise.

[36] M. J. S. Dewar, "The Electronic Theory of Organic Chemistry," Clarendon Press, Oxford (1949), Chapter 1.

[37] C. K. Ingold, *Chem. Revs.*, **15**, 225 (1934).

of the products or transition state can be seen to be attended by an increase or decrease in electrical charge at a critical part of the molecule. Equation 8 would permit the calculation of the effect of substituents on the rates of such reactions provided that the molecular system concerned were rigid, that the effect of the group were an entirely electrostatic one, that the exact magnitude of the charge shift attending the formation of the products or transition state could be known, and, of course, provided that the correct effective dielectric constant for introduction into equation 8 could be estimated. If the effect were transmitted partly by electrostatic interaction through space and partly by an inductive process within the molecule, one would still expect a parallelism between the electric moment of the substituent group and its effect upon the reaction, although equation 8 would no longer suffice for a quantitative estimate of the effect. It is a matter of great interest that the equilibria or rates of over fifty reactions of the *meta* and *para* substituted benzene derivatives obey an equation of the form [38]

$$\log (k/k^\circ) = \sigma\rho \tag{9}$$

in which $k$ is an equilibrium constant or a rate constant, $k^0$ is the same for the unsubstituted compound, $\sigma$ is a constant depending only on the substituent and its position in the benzene ring, and $\rho$ is a constant depending only upon the reaction.

All the reactions that fall within this group occur in a side chain attached to the benzene ring. The failure of the Hammett equation to apply to aromatic substitution is consistent with the great importance of resonance effects influencing alternating positions in this type of reaction. The failure of the Hammett equation to apply to *o*-substituted benzene derivatives is to be connected with the great importance of changes in the entropy of activation which are associated with the introduction of groups at close quarters. The fact that the reactions described by the Hammett equation are influenced by substitution in the manner predicted by equation 8 indicates that, when an effect is transmitted from the *m*- or *p*-positions across a benzene ring into a side chain in one of these typical reactions, the mechanism of the transmission of the effect is largely electrostatic or inductive or both or else that, contrary to the situation in aromatic substitution, all the resonance effects are running parallel to the electrostatic or inductive ones. The equation fails to predict the ionization constant of *p*-nitroaniline and of *p*-nitrophenol, different values of $\sigma$ for the nitro group being required from those established in the other reactions. This is evidently the borderline

[38] L. P. Hammett, "Physical Organic Chemistry," McGraw-Hill Book Co., New York (1940), Chapter 7.

case where resonance interaction between the nitro and amino or hydroxyl groups becomes so extreme as to deviate from the parallelism to the inductive or electrostatic effect observed elsewhere.

It is not possible in general to resolve the effect of a group into an electrostatic portion and a portion transmitted by inductive effect because, in general, the electronic requirements at the seat of reaction are not precisely enough defined nor is the nature of the medium through which the effect is transmitted accurately enough approximated to enable one to compare the observed effect significantly with that predicted from equation 8. In simple cases, however, it has been possible to calculate the $\sigma$ constants by a purely electrostatic treatment [39] with a degree of precision comparable to that of the Hammett fit as a whole. It is therefore quite unclear in most cases just how important electron displacements transmitted through the molecule by the inductive mechanism are.

The values of $\sigma$ and $\rho$ have been assigned by taking $\rho$ for the ionization of benzoic acids in water at 25° as equal to unity. A positive sign of $\sigma$ therefore means that the substituent is one which increases the ionization constants of benzoic acids. A positive sign of $\rho$ means that the reaction in question responds to electron displacements in the same manner as does the ionization of benzoic acids; i.e., that the reaction is accelerated by electron-attracting groups and retarded by electron-releasing groups. Hammett's values of $\sigma$ range from $-0.660$ for the $p$-amino group to $+1.37$ for the $p$-nitro group in derivatives of aniline and phenol. The values of $\rho$ vary from $-3.690$ for the reaction rate of anilines with 2,4-dinitro-1-chloronaphthalene in ethanol at 25° to $+3.99$ for the acidity constants of dimethylanilinium ions in 50% ethanol at 20°. Thus the largest effects are observed in cases where the resonance mechanism for transmission of electron displacements is especially available.

## METHODS OF STUDYING ORGANIC REACTION MECHANISMS

In unraveling the mechanisms of organic reactions the only equipment that is invariably required is a critical attitude in the interpretation of experiments. However, many of the experiments that are useful in this field fall into recognizable types of which one or more will be used in the course of every study of mechanisms. The starting point for any study of mechanisms is *the isolation and identification of all possible products, intermediates, and by-products* of the reaction in question. The results of such a study set limits upon the interpretation of the reaction and can definitely eliminate certain hypotheses. For example, epoxides

[39] F. H. Westheimer, *J. Am. Chem. Soc.*, **61**, 1977 (1939). See also p. 16 above.

have been shown to be intermediates in the hydroxylation of the double bond by peracetic acid; [40] tricyclene was shown *not* to be an intermediate in the rearrangement of camphene hydrochloride by a study of its behavior under the conditions of the reaction.[41] The presence of certain substances in a reaction product is often suggestive without affording actual proof of the role of such substances as intermediates. For very fast reactions, or reactions proceeding over a single energy barrier and hence having no intermediates, this method is not available.

Alcoholic fermentation is an example of a process where the obstacle to study is not its speed but its complexity; here the detailed study of the behavior of possible intermediates has been of service. An example is the fermentation of pyruvic and oxalacetic acids by yeast to acetaldehyde.[42]

*Intercepting an intermediate chemically* has proved useful in the study of certain reaction mechanisms. Examples of this are the use by Ziegler of a secondary amine to detect the presence of 1,4-addition products of alkali metals to conjugated dienes in the "metal-catalyzed" polymerization of the dienes [43] and of pyrogallol to fix the triphenylmethyl-peroxy radical in the autoxidation of hexaphenylethane.[44] In both of these cases the intermediate so detected was far too short-lived to permit its isolation without the aid of an interceptor.

Another type of interception procedure which has been useful is the "cross-over" experiment such as the Claisen rearrangement of a mixture of allyl β-naphthyl ether and cinnamyl phenyl ether.[45] If the rearranging molecules separate into free ions or radicals, they are expected to yield some "crossed products" (cinnamyl- or α-phenylallylnaphthol and allyl-phenol) as well as those observed when each ether is rearranged alone. The absence of such products is then an indication of the intramolecular nature of the reaction if it can be shown in addition that the rates of reaction are such that the two reactions are really occurring simultaneously and not one after the other.

*Kinetics* is a much-used tool in the study of organic reaction mechanisms. Sometimes even the order of a reaction affords important evidence of the mechanism, as in the cases of the first-order halogenation of acetone,[46] the first-order reaction of tertiary chlorides with base,[47]

[40] B. A. Arbusow and B. M. Michailow, *J. prakt. Chem.*, **127**, 1 (1930).
[41] H. Meerwein and K. van Emster, *Ber.*, **53**, 1815 (1920).
[42] C. Neuberg and L. Karczag, *Ber.*, **44**, 2477 (1911).
[43] K. Ziegler, L. Jakob, H. Wollthan, and A. Wenz, *Ann.*, **511**, 64 (1934).
[44] K. Ziegler and L. Ewald, *Ann.*, **504**, 162 (1933).
[45] C. D. Hurd and L. Schmerling, *J. Am. Chem. Soc.*, **59**, 107 (1937).
[46] A. Lapworth, *J. Chem. Soc.*, **85**, 30 (1904); see below, p. 86.
[47] See p. 27.

or the response of the aminonitrile synthesis to changes in the concentrations of the reactants.[48] Usually, however, a kinetic study for the purpose of establishing a mechanism involves extensive comparisons of the rate of the reaction under *variations of conditions* dictated by the hypothesis under test. Such was the study of the rate of the Wagner-Meerwein rearrangement in *solvents* of varying ionizing power,[49] or of the effect of acid and basic *catalysts* upon the mutarotation of glucose.[50]

*Variation of the temperature* of a reaction is a useful tool in kinetic studies, for this makes possible the determination of the energy and entropy of activation. The factor $K^*$ in the Eyring equation (equation 4, p. 11) can be equated to $e^{\Delta S^*/R}e^{-\Delta H^*/RT}$, and $\Delta S^*$ and $\Delta H^*$ can be evaluated from measurements of the rate at two temperatures. A knowledge of the absolute magnitude of $\Delta H^*$ is seldom as informative for a reaction in solution as it is in the gas phase, but a knowledge of $\Delta S^*$ is often helpful in establishing the importance of steric factors [51] or of a cyclic transition state.[52]

In the study of chain reactions, known or suspected, the kinetic effects of *light, initiators,* and *inhibitors* are often individually examined. Such studies contributed to the discovery of the dual mechanism of the addition of hydrogen bromide to the double bond by Kharasch and his co-workers [53] and have been important in the study of polymerization.[54] The insensitivity of ketone halogenation to light is confirmatory evidence of the polar mechanism of this reaction.

Similarly, kinetic studies that show the effect of polar catalysts are equally useful in ruling out free radical mechanisms and pointing to mechanisms of an ionic or polar nature. Examples are the catalysis by aluminum halides of the alkylation and hydride exchange of isoparaffins [55] and the acid catalysis of the decomposition of certain diacyl peroxides.[56] When an irreversible reaction involves an initial reversible dissociation, as in the hydrolysis of $p,p'$-dimethylbenzhydryl chloride [57]

---

[48] T. D. Stewart and C. H. Li, *J. Am. Chem. Soc.*, **60**, 2782 (1938). See below, p. 116.

[49] H. Meerwein and K. van Emster, *Ber.*, **55**, 2507 (1922). See below, p. 56.

[50] J. N. Brönsted and E. A. Guggenheim, *J. Am. Chem. Soc.*, **49**, 2554 (1927). See below, p. 94.

[51] See, for instance, F. P. Price, Jr., and L. P. Hammett, *ibid.*, **63**, 2387 (1941); T. I. Crowell and L. P. Hammett, *ibid.*, **70**, 3444 (1948).

[52] E. G. Foster, A. C. Cope, and F. Daniels, *ibid.*, **69**, 1893 (1947).

[53] See F. R. Mayo and C. Walling, *Chem. Revs.*, **27**, 351 (1940).

[54] See C. C. Price, "Mechanisms of Reactions at Carbon-Carbon Double Bonds," Interscience Publishers, New York (1946), Chapter 4.

[55] P. D. Bartlett, F. E. Condon, and A. Schneider, *J. Am. Chem. Soc.*, **66**, 1531 (1944).

[56] R. Criegee, *Ann.*, **560**, 127 (1948); P. D. Bartlett and J. E. Leffler, *J. Am. Chem. Soc.*, **72**, 3030 (1950).

[57] L. C. Bateman, M. G. Church, E. D. Hughes, C. K. Ingold, and N. A. Taher, *J. Chem. Soc.*, 979 (1940), and immediately preceding papers. See below, p. 28.

or of mustard gas,[58] the fact may be indicated quite specifically by a retarding effect of one of the dissociation products when added to the solution in which the reaction is taking place. This is the so-called mass action, or return, effect of chloride ion in solvolysis.

*Effect of Structure on Kinetic Behavior.* The effect of replacing phenyl by *p*-tolyl is to accelerate the hydrolysis of triphenylmethyl halides and to retard the hydrolysis of triphenylsilyl fluoride.[59] This type of kinetic evidence is a specific way of uncovering contrasts in mechanisms between two similarly appearing reactions. In the case just cited models make it rather clear that the effect of the methyl groups must be an electrical and not a steric effect. Examples of a contrary sort are also to be found. In another example in the field of displacement reactions, the accumulation of substitution at the $\beta$-position of an alkyl halide culminating in the neopentyl structure [60] produces a sharp diminution in the rate of displacement, an effect which is not transmissible through a multiple link [61] and is therefore a steric hindrance specifically located with respect to the seat of reaction.

*Tracers.* Isotopic tracers may be used to detect the existence of a reaction that would not otherwise be observed, such as the oxygen exchange between acetone and water.[62] Isotopic studies are of even wider usefulness in tracing the part played in a reaction by a particular atom. This is done most generally by labeling an atom in the starting material and identifying the form in which it appears in the product. An example is the demonstration that, when carbon monoxide is eliminated from ethyl pyruvate, it is entirely the carbonyl group of the carboxylate that disappears from the molecule.[63] In the special case of hydrogen, deuterium, and tritium, atoms of these isotopes are attacked at such different rates in transfer reactions that a simple comparison in rate between a compound and a deuterated analog will reveal whether the transfer of the hydrogen atom in question is involved in the rate-determining step or not. Thus, Westheimer and Nicolaides [64] have shown that the hydrogen on carbon atom number 2 of 2-propanol is involved in the rate-determining step when this alcohol is oxidized to acetone by chromic acid. Melander [65] has found similarly that the

[58] P. D. Bartlett and C. G. Swain, *J. Am. Chem. Soc.,* **71**, 1406 (1949); A. G. Ogston, E. R. Holiday, J. St. L. Philpot, and L. A. Stocken, *Trans. Faraday Soc.,* **44**, 45 (1948).

[59] C. G. Swain, R. M. Esteve, Jr., and R. H. Jones, *J. Am. Chem. Soc.,* **71**, 965 (1949).

[60] J. Dostrovsky, E. D. Hughes, and C. K. Ingold, *J. Chem. Soc.,* 173 (1946), and preceding papers.

[61] P. D. Bartlett and L. J. Rosen, *J. Am. Chem. Soc.,* **64**, 543 (1942).

[62] M. Cohn and H. C. Urey, *ibid.,* **60**, 679 (1938).

[63] M. Calvin and R. M. Lemmon, *ibid.,* **69**, 1232 (1947).

[64] F. H. Westheimer and N. Nicolaides, *ibid.,* **71**, 25 (1949). See below, p. 76.

[65] L. Melander, *Nature,* **163**, 599 (1949); *Acta Chem. Scand.,* **3**, 95 (1949).

hydrogen atom which is replaced in the nitration of toluene is *not* removed in the rate-determining step.

## THE MECHANISMS OF VARIOUS ORGANIC REACTIONS

In what follows, no attempt will be made to cover all types of organic reactions. Progress to date in the elucidation of mechanisms will be illustrated with certain reactions of non-radical type, chosen chiefly from the chemistry of alcohols and their derivatives and of compounds containing the carbonyl group.

### The Displacement Reaction

The so-called displacement reaction, or substitution at a saturated carbon atom, in which one atom or group is displaced by another of similar polar character, has perhaps been more scrutinized from the standpoint of mechanism than any other reaction type.[66] It may be represented by the general equation

$$Y + RX \rightleftarrows RY + X \qquad (10)$$

where RX and Y may bear electrical charges of either sign, or may be uncharged.

The series of studies [67, 68, 69, 70] referred to on pp. 5–6 has led to the visualization of the transition state for the displacement reaction as I.

$$
\left[
\begin{array}{c}
R \\
| \\
Y\text{----}C\text{----}X \\
\diagup \qquad \diagdown \\
R' \qquad\quad R''
\end{array}
\right]
$$
I

Since evidence is largely limited to displacements in which X and Y are nucleophilic, this conclusion, and much experimental work to which it has led, are also limited to such reactions, called "bimolecular negative substitutions" or "bimolecular nucleophilic substitutions," and abbreviated [71] $S_N2$. These include, among others, the reactions of primary and secondary alkyl halides, sulfates, sulfonates, sulfonium salts, qua-

---

[66] For general reviews see L. P. Hammett, "Physical Organic Chemistry," McGraw-Hill Book Co., New York (1940), Chapter 5; E. D. Hughes, *Trans. Faraday Soc.*, **34**, 203, 185 (1938); **37**, 603 (1941).

[67] M. Polanyi, "Atomic Reactions," Williams and Norgate, London (1932).

[68] F. London, *Z. Elektrochem.*, **35**, 552 (1929).

[69] H. Eyring and M. Polanyi, *Z. physik. Chem.*, **B12**, 279 (1931).

[70] H. Pelzer and E. Wigner, *ibid.*, **B15**, 445 (1932).

[71] E. D. Hughes, *loc. cit.*

ternary ammonium salts, and sometimes certain esters and ethers, with hydroxide and alkoxide ions, the anions of phenols and organic and inorganic acids, ammonia, amines, and thioethers. Most alkylations and dealkylations are representatives of this type.

The transition state (I) lends itself to an explanation of the Walden inversion.[72] Indeed, the proposal of this transition state for displacement reactions of optically active secondary halides represented a return to a suggestion that had been made in various forms for many years but which was first clearly stated by G. N. Lewis.[73] The features that were new at this time were small but important ones. (*a*) Organic reaction mechanisms were emerging from the realm of speculation, largely as a result of work on gas reactions. (*b*) Quantum mechanics had deduced as a geometrical property of the hybridized $sp^3$ orbitals of carbon a slight projection of each orbital on the opposite face of the carbon atom, which suggested the possibility of a smooth transition to an activated complex with three planar $sp^2$ hybrid orbitals and a $p$ orbital.[74, 75] (*c*) Most important, a challenge was now offered to experimental chemistry. According to the theory, the Walden inversion was a special case of a general, if not a universal, mechanism of displacement. It followed that, in a bimolecular nucleophilic displacement occurring at an optically active center, every act of displacement must be attended by inversion of configuration.

Because of limited knowledge of the relation between structure and optical rotatory power, there existed in 1930 only a single one-step reaction in which configurative inversion was definitely known to occur. The first example of this reaction was that [76] shown below; both the RX

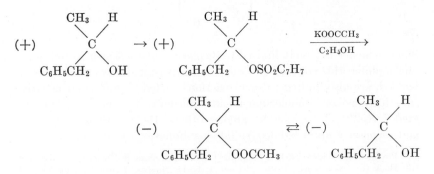

[72] See pp. 264–281 in Vol. I of this Treatise.

[73] G. N. Lewis, "Valence and the Structure of Atoms and Molecules," Chemical Catalog Co., New York (1923), p. 113.

[74] A. R. Olson, *J. Chem. Phys.*, **1**, 418 (1933).

[75] See p. 1954 in Vol. II of this Treatise.

[76] H. Phillips, *J. Chem. Soc.*, **123**, 44 (1923).

and RY of equation 10 could be prepared from ROH without breaking any bond at the asymmetric carbon atom. It was shown in 1934 that the quantitative changes in optical rotation in the reactions of bromosuccinic acid with chloride ion and of chlorosuccinic acid with bromide ion were consistent only with inversion of configuration at every displacement, whether of chlorine by chlorine, of bromine by bromine, or of either one by the other.[77] It was further shown [78] that the conversion of d- into l-2-octyl iodide by potassium radioiodide in acetone proceeded at a rate identical with the uptake of radioiodine by the organic compound and hence consisted of a displacement of iodine by iodine with a Walden inversion. In examples of nucleophilic displacement at a secondary carbon atom, the mechanism of bimolecular inversion was thus established.

In reactions of this type, the hydroxyl ion is such a vigorous reagent that its concentration controls the rate even in the presence of large amounts of hydroxylic solvent. However, many examples are known

$$(CH_3)_3CCl \rightleftarrows (CH_3)_3C^+ + Cl^-$$

$$H_2O \diagdown \diagup Y^- \tag{11}$$

$$(CH_3)_3COH_2^+ \qquad (CH_3)_3CY$$

$$\downarrow H_2O$$

$$(CH_3)_3COH + H_3O^+$$

of displacement reactions whose kinetic order shows that reaction is preferentially with the solvent rather than with such basic reagents. For example, in the reactions of sodium phenylchloroacetate,[79] sodium phenylbromoacetate,[79] α-phenylethyl chloride,[80] and t-butyl chloride [81] with alkali, the reaction of β,β'-dichlorodiethyl sulfide [82] and of the t-butyldimethylsulfonium ion [83] with various negative ions, the rate in hydroxylic solvents is unaffected by variations in the concentration of the ionic reagent. In the customary terminology which neglects the solvent these reactions are referred to as *unimolecular* nucleophilic

[77] A. R. Olson and F. A. Long, *J. Am. Chem. Soc.*, **56**, 1294 (1934).

[78] E. D. Hughes, F. Juliusburger, S. Masterman, B. Topley, and J. Weiss, *J. Chem. Soc.*, 1525 (1935).

[79] G. Senter, *ibid.*, **107**, 908 (1915); G. Senter and S. H. Tucker, *ibid.*, **109**, 690 (1916).

[80] A. M. Ward, *ibid.*, 445, 2285 (1927).

[81] E. D. Hughes, *ibid.*, 255 (1935).

[82] A. G. Ogston, E. R. Holiday, J. St. L. Philpot, and L. A. Stocken, *Trans. Faraday Soc.*, **44**, 45 (1948).

[83] J. L. Gleave, E. D. Hughes, and C. K. Ingold, *J. Chem. Soc.*, 236 (1935).

displacements, abbreviated $S_N1$. It was proposed that the rate of an $S_N1$ reaction is determined by a spontaneous ionization into a negative ion and a reactive carbonium ion, the latter reacting rapidly with solvent or other reagent. Though not unopposed,[84] the ionization mechanism is supported by several lines of evidence besides the order of the reaction.[85]

(a) Increasing the dielectric constant strongly favors $S_N1$ reactions, though it retards $S_N2$ displacements with negative ions. This is normal (see p. 12) for a reaction involving a separation of charge in the transition state.

(b) Displacement reactions of benzhydryl chloride and its homologs [86] and of certain $\beta$-chloroethyl sulfides and amines [87] sometimes show a retardation by chloride ion which is of the proper form to be due to a reversal of the ionization step in equation 11 by competition of the chloride ion with the solvent for reaction with the intermediate carbonium ion.

(c) In mixed water-alcohol solvents the relation between the *rates* and *products* of solvolysis of *t*-butyl chloride is not explicable on the basis of bimolecular reaction between the chloride and solvent molecules.[88]

(d) Finally, the nature of the compounds in which the $S_N1$ reaction appears is consistent with the ionization mechanism: these compounds include tertiary halides, secondary halides in which an ionic charge might be distributed by resonance through phenyl groups or by the aid of electron-donating substituents, and primary halides which can yield ethylenesulfonium or ethyleneimmonium ions.

Of the above lines of evidence, the order of reaction and the effect of dielectric constant (a) are equally compatible with a mechanism involving a direct attack of the solvent according to some such scheme as shown. The "mass action" retardation by chloride ion (b) would be compatible with such a mechanism supplemented by the assumption that the oxonium ion $(CH_3)_3COH_2^+$ is long-lived enough to be re-attacked by an anion. The product criterion (c) does not exclude concerted molecular attack by one solvent molecule on the anion and

[84] See, for example, A. R. Olson and R. S. Halford, *J. Am. Chem. Soc.*, **59**, 2644 (1937); D. R. Read and W. Taylor, *J. Chem. Soc.*, 1872 (1939), and previous papers; R. A. Ogg, Jr., *J. Am. Chem. Soc.*, **61**, 1946 (1939). On the other hand, see L. C. Bateman, E. D. Hughes, and C. K. Ingold, *J. Chem. Soc.*, 881 (1938); E. D. Hughes, C. K. Ingold, and co-workers, *ibid.*, 899, 913, 920, 925, 935, 940 (1940).

[85] See E. D. Hughes, Ref. 66.

[86] L. C. Bateman, M. G. Church, E. D. Hughes, C. K. Ingold, and N. A. Taher, *J. Chem. Soc.*, 979 (1940), and preceding papers.

[87] See p. 39; Ogston *et al.*, Ref. 82.

[88] L. C. Bateman, E. D. Hughes, and C. K. Ingold, *J. Am. Chem. Soc.*, **60**, 3080 (1938).

another on the carbon atom.[89]  The effect of structure $(d)$ is also not uniformly consistent with an ionization mechanism.  However, the sum total of these lines of evidence, together with evidence of electrical conductance [90] which clearly indicates the existence of tertiary and

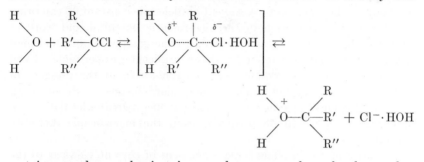

certain secondary carbonium ions, makes any purely molecular mechanism for the $S_N1$ reaction appear cumbersome if not demonstrably incorrect.

The all-importance of the solvent in ionic reactions is emphasized in certain studies of the $S_N1$ reaction.  Dilution of an ethanol solution of benzhydryl chloride with nitrobenzene or acetone, which does not lower the dielectric constant, retards the alcoholysis much more than in proportion to the dilution of the solvent.  Farinacci and Hammett [91] have pointed out that this means the participation of a number of solvent molecules in the ionization process, and also that the solvating efficiency of a solvent is specifically related to its structure and is not a general consequence of its dielectric constant.  The nature of the alcoholysis of benzhydryl chloride suggests that an alcohol is especially effective in solvating the negative ion, through hydrogen bonding and a general orientation in the vicinity of the anion, with the positive end of the O—H dipole directed toward the ion.

If the dilution process is taken to an extreme by carrying out the methanolysis of $p$-methoxybenzhydryl chloride in dilute nitrobenzene solution,[92] reactions can be observed in which the rate-determining step involves two molecules and, finally, a single molecule of methanol. In benzene, however, two molecules of hydroxylic reactant are required to bring about a solvolysis even of triphenylmethyl chloride.[93]  The difference between these systems is probably due to the difference between the solvating powers of benzene and nitrobenzene, the former

[89] S. Winstein, *ibid.*, **61**, 1635 (1939).
[90] P. Walden, *Ber.*, **35**, 2018 (1902).
[91] N. Farinacci and L. P. Hammett, *J. Am. Chem. Soc.*, **59**, 2542 (1937).
[92] P. D. Bartlett and R. W. Nebel, *ibid.*, **62**, 1345 (1940).
[93] C. G. Swain, *ibid.*, **70**, 1119 (1948).

being capable of solvating an anion better than hexane,[94] but not nearly so well as an alcohol or, probably, as nitrobenzene.

The indispensability of solvent in an ionic displacement reaction is not surprising when we recall that spontaneous ionic reactions are unknown in the gas phase. A solvent of dielectric constant 40 can bring about a 40-fold reduction in the electrostatic potential and work of charge separation of ions as compared to the gas phase, and for small ions this work may amount to hundreds of kilocalories per mole. Even this is not enough to produce $S_N1$ reactions without the presence of molecules, or preferably oriented molecular clusters, with solvating power for the ions concerned, i.e., able to produce a greater local diffusion of charge than would be predicted from the macroscopic dielectric constant.

The work of Swain offers some refinement of current views as to the solvation of the carbonium ion. Both methanol and phenol are capable of reacting with triphenylmethyl chloride in dilute (about 0.1 $M$) solution in benzene, the reaction of methanol to yield methyl triphenylmethyl ether being about 50 times as fast as that of phenol giving phenyl triphenylmethyl ether. The presence of phenol in concentration equivalent to the methanol accelerates the formation of the *methyl ether* about 7-fold. All the reactions are kinetically of the third order, involving two molecules of hydroxyl compound and one of triphenylmethyl chloride in the transition state. These facts are accounted for by the postulate that both the triphenylcarbonium ion and the chloride ion require solvation by a hydroxylic molecule in order to be formed, and that the phenol, being the better hydrogen bond former of the two,[95] is the more effective solvating agent for the chloride ion, while the methanol, being the more basic, is the better solvator of the carbonium ion. The solvated carbonium ion is not satisfactorily visualized as involving a covalent link between carbon and oxygen (II), for this would deprive the

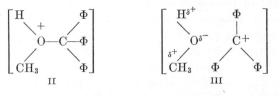

II                III

triphenylcarbonium ion of the special resonance which otherwise accounts for the unique stability of it and its derivatives, and aids in accounting for its color. Rather, the results of Swain focus attention on the *electrovalent solvation* represented by III, which merely represents

[94] C. G. Swain and R. W. Eddy, *ibid.*, **70**, 2989 (1948).
[95] P. D. Bartlett and H. J. Dauben, Jr., *ibid.*, **62**, 1339 (1940).

what remains of a cluster of solvent molecules in the normal solvation complex after all solvent molecules but one have been removed from it. This solvent molecule is highly polarized and may be said to be *electrovalently bonded* to the carbonium ion.

This picture of the $S_N1$ reaction implies that the molecule that solvates the carbonium ion may or may not be the one that enters into the final product. As to the stereochemical outcome of an $S_N1$ displacement, one would expect complete inversion of configuration if the conversion of the electrovalent bond to the solvating molecule into a covalent bond were very rapid following the ionization, and this should be the case with the less stable carbonium ions. However, a relatively stable carbonium ion might persist in the electrovalently solvated condition long enough to undergo a number of exchanges of solvent molecule or to acquire solvation on both sides, with the eventual result of complete racemization. Such data as there are on $S_N1$ reactions of optically active materials support this view: the usual result is a mixture of inversion and racemization, in the absence of special stabilizing features.[96] These considerations are independent of the prevailing belief that the three atoms directly connected to the central carbon of a carbonium ion lie in the same plane with it.[97]

**Effect of Structure on Reactivity in the Displacement Reaction.** Substituents whose overall effect is to attract electrons show, in the $S_N1$ reaction, a depressing effect upon the rate, and the opposite is true of electron-releasing substituents. In the $S_N2$ reaction the situation is not so simple. In the reaction

$$Y^- + R—X \rightarrow R—Y + X^-$$

the transition state IV should be favored by changes in X which make

IV

the C—X bond easily broken, by changes in Y which make the C—Y bond easily formed, and by such substitution in the organic radical as will offer the least resistance to both processes. Within an homologous series, such as $X = {}^-OOCC_6H_4R$, increasing electronegative character of R (increasing ionization constant of $RC_6H_4COOH$) is favorable to

[96] J. Steigman and L. P. Hammett, *ibid.*, **59**, 2536 (1937); E. D. Hughes, C. K. Ingold, and A. D. Scott, *J. Chem. Soc.*, 1201 (1937); W. von E. Doering and A. Streitwieser, *Abst. 119th Mtg., Am. Chem. Soc., Boston, Mass.*, 3 April, 1951.
[97] See p. 57.

the forward and unfavorable to the reverse reaction; or, in other words, high basicity in Y and low basicity in X is favorable to the forward rate. Outside of homologous series, this generalization breaks down and it is not possible to predict rates even roughly from relative basicities of X and Y. For example, a change from X = Cl to X = I in an alkyl halide is favorable to both the forward and reverse rates, but a change of Y from $Cl^-$ to $S_2O_3^=$ will favor the forward rate and lower the reverse rate to the vanishing point. In $S_N2$ displacement reactions with alkyl halides, hydroxyl ion is a more powerful nucleophilic reagent than iodide ion, but toward ethylene oxides the reverse is true.[98, 98a]

## TABLE II

COMPETITION FACTORS $k_Y/k_{H_2O}$ FOR REAGENTS WITH EPOXIDE, β-LACTONE, AND ETHYLENESULFONIUM ION

Reagent reacting with:

| | $(CH_3)_3C^+$ * | $ClCH_2CH_2\overset{+}{S}{<}^{CH_2}_{CH_2}$ * | $^{CH_2*}\!\!{>}OH^+$ (epoxide) | $^{CH_2Cl\dagger}\!\!{>}O$ (epoxide) | $^{CH_2Cl\dagger}\ CH_2{-}C{=}O\ddagger \ /\ CH_2{-}O$ (β-lactone) |
|---|---|---|---|---|---|
| $Cl^-$ | 3.5 | 21 | 24.4 | 27 | 3.3 |
| $Br^-$ | | | 120 | 140 | 10.8 |
| $I^-$ | | 660 | | 2,300 | 54 |
| $SCN^-$ | | 670 | | 1,550 | 68 |
| $CH_3COO^-$ | | 10 | | 14.5 | |
| $OH^-$ | | | 8,000 | | (26,800) § |
| $S_2O_3^-$ | 6.5 | 27,000 | | | 3,300 |

* A. G. Ogston and E. R. Holiday, *Trans. Faraday Soc.*, **44**, 49 (1948).
† J. N. Brönsted, M. Kilpatrick, and M. Kilpatrick, *J. Am. Chem. Soc.*, **51**, 428 (1929).
‡ P. D. Bartlett and G. Small, Jr., *ibid.*, **72**, 4867 (1950).
§ Chiefly attack at the C=O group in normal ester hydrolysis.

Table II presents a typical series of relative nucleophilic reactivities of negative ions, showing the relative rates at which these reagents attack four different RX compounds. Except for the hydroxyl ion,[98a] the

[98] J. N. Brönsted, M. Kilpatrick, and M. Kilpatrick, *J. Am. Chem. Soc.*, **51**, 428 (1929).

[98a] The experiments of Brönsted, Kilpatrick, and Kilpatrick (ref. 98) were not so designed as to afford a measurement of the rate constant for reaction between hydroxyl ion and the ethylene oxides; as a result of their work the reactivity of hydroxyl ion toward epoxides has been regarded as anomalously low (compare Hammett, ref. 66, p. 302). According to more recent measurements [H. J. Lichtenstein and G. H. Twigg, *Trans. Faraday Soc.*, **44**, 905 (1948); C. G. Swain and C. B. Scott, *J. Am. Chem. Soc.*, in press] this reactivity falls in the normal range. The latter authors find that the competition factor of $OH^-$ toward glycidol is about 240.

series is similar toward the ethylenesulfonium ion, ethylene oxides, and $\beta$-propiolactone. It may be surmised that polarizibility is important in determining the relative nucleophilic efficiencies of the halogen ions, but the factors determining these reactivities are far from being understood.

The manner in which structural changes in the "R," or central part, of the transition state affect rates of reaction can best be discussed by reference to the reactions of benzyl chlorides. In the hydrolysis of benzyl chlorides, $p$-alkyl groups accelerate, $p$-nitro groups retard; in the reaction of benzyl chlorides with iodide ion, $p$-nitro groups accelerate; [99] while in the reaction with nitrate ion,[100] nitro groups and alkyl groups all accelerate. In the reaction of benzyl bromides with pyridine in acetone on the one hand and in 90% ethanol on the other, the effects of methyl and nitro substitution [101] are as shown in Table III.

TABLE III

RELATIVE RATE CONSTANTS FOR THE REACTION OF SUBSTITUTED BENZYL BROMIDES WITH PYRIDINE

| | Relative Bimolecular Rate Constant $k$ and Activation Energy $E$ (kcal/mole) | | | |
| | 20°, Acetone | | 30°, 90% Ethanol | |
| Substituent | $k$ | $E$ | $k$ | $E$ |
| --- | --- | --- | --- | --- |
| H | 1 | 12.46 | 1 | 15.3 |
| $p$-CH$_3$ | 1.65 | 11.9 | 2.3 | 16.0 |
| $p$-NO$_2$ | 0.92 | 12.31 | 0.34 | 15.8 |
| 2,4-(CH$_3$)$_2$ | 5.14 | 12.2 | | |
| 2,4-(NO$_2$)$_2$ | 1.87 | 12.4 | 0.42 | 14.4 |

Such facts have been interpreted [102,103] as indicating that there is a gradation in electronic requirements for a displacement reaction occurring by the $S_N2$ mechanism, and not merely a discontinuity between $S_N2$ and $S_N1$. The transition state for reaction with a neutral molecule may be represented [103] by the resonance forms V and that for reaction with a negative ion by the forms VI.

[99] G. M. Bennett and B. Jones, *J. Chem. Soc.*, 1815 (1935).
[100] J. W. Baker and W. S. Nathan, *ibid.*, 236 (1936).
[101] J. W. Baker and W. S. Nathan, *ibid.*, 519, 1840 (1935).
[102] (*a*) J. W. Baker and W. S. Nathan, *ibid.*, 1842 (1935); (*b*) E. D. Hughes, C. K. Ingold, and N. G. Shapiro, *ibid.*, 228 (1936); (*c*) J. W. Baker, *Trans. Faraday Soc.*, **37**, 632 (1941); (*d*) C. G. Swain and W. P. Langsdorf, Jr., *J. Am. Chem. Soc.*, **73**, 2813 (1951).
[103] S. Winstein, E. Grunwald, and H. W. Jones, *ibid.*, **73**, 2700 (1951).

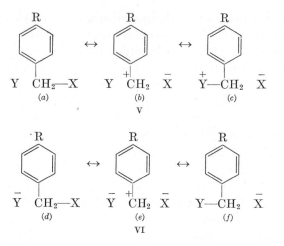

V

VI

Whether the formation of the transition state is facilitated or opposed by the group R must depend upon whether the overall charge on the benzyl group becomes more or less positive during the conversion from reactants to transition state. Because structures $(b)$, $(c)$, and $(e)$ suggest only an increasing positive charge at $CH_2$ during the formation of the transition state, one might anticipate that electron-releasing substituents (alkyl groups) would facilitate displacement. Structures $(a)$, $(d)$, and $(f)$, depending upon the nature of Y, might contribute a diminished positive charge on the benzyl group, relative to that in the reactant, especially in the presence of strongly electron-attracting substituents and a polarizable C—Y bond. Thus there can be a "transition" from a retarding to an accelerating effect of R, either as Y is changed from pyridine to nitrate ion [eliminating the positive charge in $(c)$] or as nitro groups accumulate in the benzyl group in the pyridine reaction (withdrawing electrons more in the polarizable transition state than in the original bromide). It will be noted that the geometry and type of hybridization of orbitals are the same in the benzyl group of these transition states as in the ionization depicted for the $S_N1$ mechanism. The continuum between the $S_N1$ and $S_N2$ mechanisms could be complete if in both there were at least a slight energy minimum at the "symmetrical" state like V or VI, which would imply that the first product of the $S_N1$ process is an ion pair with some integral association between the positive and negative ions. This latter situation has been observed in several cases (see pp. 36, 37), but there is no direct evidence for or against an intermediate in the $S_N2$ mechanism, surrounded by low energy barriers. If there is such an intermediate, then there must always be *two* transition states resembling V or VI, displaced slightly to one side and the other of the configuration of maximum stability. The difference between an $S_N1$ and an $S_N2$ mechanism would then be only the continuously graded one of whether Y is a good solvating agent for a cation and whether its bond to the central atom is largely electrovalent or largely covalent.[103]

When the displacement is not occurring at a saturated carbon atom, as in the reactions of acyl halides, or of triphenylsilyl fluoride,[104] the transition state (VII or VIII) may have an entire negative charge, and

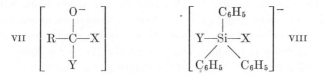

the effect of substituents then registers their ability to aid in the accommodation of this charge; i.e., electron-releasing substituents are unfavorable and electron-attracting ones are favorable.

α-Haloketones, such as the phenacyl halides, which react extremely rapidly with negative ions,[105, 106] may well represent a case in which the ability of the keto group to accept a nucleophilic reagent aids in the direct displacement reaction. Because of the favorable location of the centers concerned, an attacking reagent might interact in a single process with both the carbonyl carbon and its α-neighbor where the displacement occurs (transition state IX).[107]

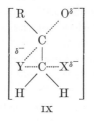

IX

**Displacements in Allylic Compounds.**   The presence of a carbon-carbon double bond in the 2,3-position relative to X is favorable to the displacement reaction; for example, allyl chloride at 50° in acetone reacts with iodide ion 79 times as fast as *n*-butyl chloride.[106] The allylic system can accommodate both positive and negative charges better than

[104] C. G. Swain, R. M. Esteve, Jr., and R. H. Jones, *ibid.*, **71**, 965 (1949).

[105] J. W. Baker, *J. Chem. Soc.*, 445 (1938); *Trans. Faraday Soc.*, **37**, 643 (1941).

[106] J. B. Conant, W. R. Kirner, and R. E. Hussey, *J. Am. Chem. Soc.*, **47**, 488 (1925).

[107] This picture has been suggested by Dr. S. Winstein in discussions and is supported by the relative unreactivity of a phenacyl analog in which IX is stereochemically prohibited (E. N. Trachtenberg, Thesis, Harvard University, 1952).

a saturated system and accordingly facilitates reaction whether the transition state involves increased positive or negative charge on the central carbon atom. Displacements by the $S_N2$ mechanism in unsymmetrically substituted allylic halides normally occur without molecular rearrangement,[108] although exceptions have been observed in the reactions of $\alpha$-methylallyl and $\alpha$-ethylallyl chloride with sodiomalonic ester [109] which lead to 10% and 23%, respectively, of crotyl- and 2-pentenylmalonic esters. Amines and thiourea have also been found to react bimolecularly with rearrangement.[110] This bimolecular mechanism with rearrangement is designated $S_N2'$. Whenever a displacement reaction of an allylic compound proceeds through the ionization mechanism, a mixture of allylic isomers is produced having nearly the same composition as that resulting from the isomer of the starting material: [111]

$$CH_3CHOHCH{=}CH_2 \qquad\qquad CH_3CH{=}CHCH_2OH$$

$$\underset{-20°}{\overset{HBr}{\longrightarrow}}\begin{cases}23.8\% & CH_3CHBrCH{=}CH_2 & 17.6\% \\ 76.2\% & CH_3CH{=}CHCH_2Br & 82.4\%\end{cases}\underset{-20°}{\overset{HBr}{\longleftarrow}}$$

The inequality of composition of the products from the two starting materials can only mean that not all the reacting molecules achieve ionization to the mesomeric carbonium ion; any portion that reacts by direct displacement may yield unrearranged product. This is one of the few promising methods of distinguishing between a true ionization mechanism and a direct displacement with the solvent, which may imitate many of the other characteristics of the ionization mechanism. (See p. 28.)

There are, however, serious complications in the allylic rearrangement; not only has a *bimolecular* rearrangement been discovered, but also a *unimolecular* rearrangement of $\alpha,\alpha$-dimethylallyl chloride not proceeding through a free carbonium ion.[112] The acetolysis, in glacial acetic acid containing acetate ion, of $\alpha,\alpha$-dimethylallyl chloride proceeds at a steadily decreasing rate which eventually becomes and remains that characteristic of the primary isomer, $\gamma,\gamma$-dimethylallyl chloride. Young, Winstein, and Goering were able to show by careful analysis of the kinetic data that the tertiary isomer (X) was undergoing unimolecular conversion into the

[108] W. H. Carothers and G. J. Berchet, *J. Am. Chem. Soc.*, **55**, 2807 (1933); J. D. Roberts, W. G. Young, and S. Winstein, *ibid.*, **64**, 2157 (1942); E. D. Hughes, *Trans. Faraday Soc.*, **37**, 603 (1941).

[109] R. E. Kepner, S. Winstein, and W. G. Young, *J. Am. Chem. Soc.*, **71**, 115 (1949).

[110] W. G. Young, I. D. Webb, and H. L. Goering, *ibid.*, **73**, 1076 (1951).

[111] W. G. Young and J. F. Lane, *ibid.*, **60**, 847 (1938).

[112] W. G. Young, S. Winstein, and H. L. Goering, *ibid.*, **73**, 1958 (1951).

primary isomer (XI) at a rate unaffected by additions of chloride ions, and therefore by a spontaneous mechanism not involving the occurrence of carbonium ions in a state of freedom which would permit chloride ion and acetic acid to compete for them. This constitutes direct evidence for the process as shown which proceeds through an intermediate ion pair

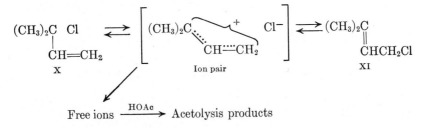

whose charged members are not free from each other. Similar intramolecular isomerizations have been observed with optically active norbornyl $p$-bromobenzenesulfonate,[112a] which undergoes racemization in acetic acid more than 3 times as fast as solvolysis. An internal rearrangement of 2-phenyl-1-propyl $p$-bromobenzenesulfonate into 1-phenyl-2-propyl $p$-bromobenzenesulfonate is likewise detected by kinetic analysis of its acetolysis.[113]

**Displacement with Retention of Configuration.** Since inversion of configuration is now regarded as normal for displacement reactions not proceeding by way of ionization, cases of displacement with retention of configuration attract special interest and require special interpretation. One well-known case of this kind, the reaction of optically active secondary halides with silver oxide, has proved to be complicated kinetically. Particles of solid silver halide act catalytically [114] and preclude the study of a homogeneous system. Studies of other simple displacements with retention of configuration have distinguished two general mechanisms, double inversion and front-side attack, the latter generally involving extrusion of a small molecule from an intermediate compound or complex.

*Participation of Neighboring Groups in Displacement Reactions.* Winstein and Lucas [115] showed that, in the reaction of optically active 3-bromo-2-butanol with hydrogen bromide to yield 2,3-dibromobutane, both asymmetric carbons are involved in the reaction in some manner which causes total loss of optical activity but yields in each case a product unmixed with its diastereomer. The only satisfactory explanation that has been offered for these facts is the occurrence in the reaction of an

[112a] S. Winstein and D. Trifan, *J. Am. Chem. Soc.*, **74**, 1154 (1952).
[113] S. Winstein and K. C. Schreiber, *J. Am. Chem. Soc.*, **74**, 2171 (1952).
[114] E. D. Hughes, C. K. Ingold, and S. Masterman, *J. Chem. Soc.*, 1236 (1937).
[115] S. Winstein and H. J. Lucas, *J. Am. Chem. Soc.*, **61**, 2845 (1939).

ethylene-bromonium ion similar to that originally proposed [116] as an intermediate in bromination of the double bond. The reaction of hydrogen bromide with optically active *threo*-3-bromo-2-butanol is then represented as shown. Similar evidence exists for the participation of neighboring chlorine in displacement reactions.[117]

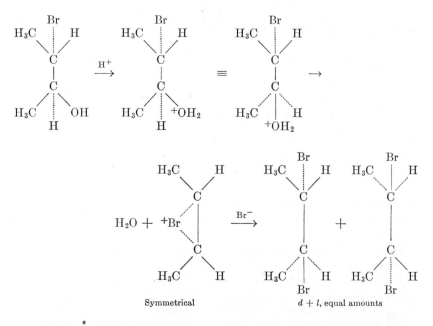

$$H_2O + {}^+Br$$

Symmetrical

$d + l$, equal amounts

Of the isomeric 2-bromocyclohexanols, both the *cis* and the *trans* forms yield *trans*-1,2-dibromocyclohexane by reaction with hydrogen bromide or phosphorus tribromide.[118] Displacements with retention of configuration are also observed when the neighboring group is methoxyl,[119] acetoxyl,[120] or the carboxylate ion.[121]

The original evidence for the occurrence of the ethylene-bromonium ion in the displacement of hydroxyl by bromine requires that this cyclic molecular species be an intermediate (i.e., a stage of minimum potential energy) and not a transition state. In each of the cases cited the cyclic

[116] I. Roberts and G. E. Kimball, *ibid.*, **59**, 947 (1937).

[117] H. J. Lucas and C. W. Gould, Jr., *ibid.*, **63**, 2541 (1941).

[118] S. Winstein, *ibid.*, **64**, 2792 (1942).

[119] S. Winstein and R. B. Henderson, *ibid.*, **65**, 2196 (1943).

[120] S. Winstein and R. E. Buckles, *ibid.*, **64**, 2780, 2787 (1942); S. Winstein, H. V. Hess, and R. E. Buckles, *ibid.*, **64**, 2796 (1942); S. Winstein, C. Hanson, and E. Grunwald, *ibid.*, **70**, 812 (1948).

[121] W. A. Cowdrey, E. D. Hughes, C. K. Ingold, S. Masterman, and A. D. Scott, *J. Chem. Soc.*, 1254 (1937); E. Grunwald and S. Winstein, *J. Am. Chem. Soc.*, **70**, 841 (1948).

intermediate is so short-lived that no evidence of its accumulation is ever found in kinetic studies.

*Driving Forces in Participation of Neighboring Groups.* The formation of the cyclic intermediate might be an intramolecular displacement resembling an $S_N2$ reaction, or it might be a stabilization process following the formation of a carbonium ion by direct ionization. In the former case we might expect the presence of the participating neighboring group to favor the reaction and increase its rate; in the latter case the effect of this group upon the rate would be only its internal effect, as a substituent, upon the rate of ionization. Measurements and theoretical analysis of the results [122] have established the order: $SCH_2CH_2OH > I > NH_2 > O^- > Br > OH$, $OCH_3$, for the driving force provided by these groups toward the formation of the cyclic intermediate. *trans*-2-Iodocyclohexyl *p*-toluenesulfonate undergoes solvolysis in acetic acid 1600 times faster, but the *trans*-2-chloro compound 2500 times more slowly, than unsubstituted cyclohexyl *p*-toluenesulfonate. The stereochemical consequences are the same, but the driving force is very different.

In displacements at a *primary* carbon atom, although stereochemical methods are not available, participation of neighboring groups may be detected by the order and speed of the reaction and by isomerizations attending displacement. $\beta,\beta'$-Dichlorodiethyl sulfide (mustard gas) undergoes displacement with a number of reagents, all at the same approximately *unimolecular* rate, which rate is greater by many powers of 10 than is observed among primary alkyl chlorides.[123] The various anions and neutral molecules that are capable of reacting with mustard gas vary widely in their reactivity, as shown by the results of competition experiments among them (Table II); but none of them is able to attack the primary carbon atom as rapidly as the sulfur atom which is already present at the $\beta$-position in the molecule. This fact causes all displacement reactions of mustard gas to be channeled through the mechanism [124]

$$ClCH_2CH_2SCH_2CH_2Cl \rightarrow$$

$$ClCH_2CH_2\overset{+}{S}\begin{matrix} CH_2 \\ | \\ | \\ CH_2 \end{matrix} \quad Cl^- \overset{X^-}{\longrightarrow} ClCH_2CH_2SCH_2CH_2X + Cl^-$$

[122] S. Winstein, E. Grunwald, and L. L. Ingraham, *ibid.*, **70**, 821 (1948); S. Winstein, E. Grunwald, R. E. Buckles, and C. Hanson, *ibid.*, **70**, 816 (1948); S. Winstein and E. Grunwald, *ibid.*, **70**, 828 (1948).

[123] R. A. Peters and E. Walker, *Biochem. J.*, **17**, 260 (1923); A. G. Ogston and co-workers, *Trans. Faraday Soc.*, **44**, 45 (1948).

[124] The propylenesulfonium ion was postulated in 1937 [F. E. Ray and I. Levine, *J. Org. Chem.*, **2**, 271 (1937)] as an intermediate in the formation of ethylene sulfide from ethylene bromide and dimethyl sulfide.

Confirmation of the existence of a cyclic intermediate in which the carbon atoms originally $\alpha$ and originally $\beta$ are equally exposed to attack has been provided by the conversion of both ethyl 1-hydroxy-2-propyl sulfide and ethyl 2-hydroxy-1-propyl sulfide by hydrochloric acid into ethyl 2-chloro-1-propyl sulfide in the course of conversion into the sulfonium ion and thence into the chloride.[125]

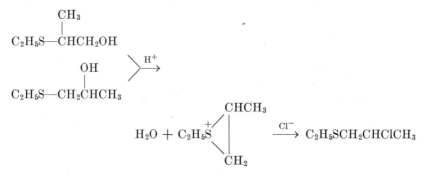

Tertiary $\beta$-chloroethylamines possess a reactive nucleophilic group in the $\beta$-position to the halogen, and this group also participates in displacement reactions of the halogen, yielding a cyclic quaternary ethylene-immonium ion.[126]  The ethylene-immonium ions are stabler than the cor-

$$ R_2NCH_2CH_2Cl \rightleftharpoons R_2\overset{+}{N}\underset{CH_2}{\overset{CH_2}{\diagup\!\!\diagdown}} \; + \; Cl^- $$

responding bromonium or sulfonium ions, and they accumulate in the reacting solutions to an extent depending upon the solvent, the detailed structure of the amine, and the reagents present.  With $\beta$-chloroethyl-diethylamine the rate of formation of the cyclic immonium ion can be followed as a first-order reaction, uncomplicated by secondary processes; the subsequent reactions of this ion with water and other reagents are slow.  Ethyl-*bis*-$\beta$-chloroethylamine yields an ethylene-immonium ion which accumulates in the solution but reacts at a moderate rate with water to produce hydrolysis as the principal overall result.  Methyl-*bis*-$\beta$-chloroethylamine reacts rather rapidly with its own ethylene-immonium ion to yield a cyclic dimer, presumably through a short-lived linear

[125] R. C. Fuson, C. C. Price, and D. M. Burness, *ibid.*, **11**, 477 (1946).

[126] C. Golumbic, J. S. Fruton, and M. Bergmann, *ibid.*, **11**, 518 (1946), and succeeding papers; P. D. Bartlett, S. D. Ross, and C. G. Swain, *J. Am. Chem. Soc.*, **69**, 2971 (1947); **71**, 1415 (1949); P. D. Bartlett, J. W. Davis, S. D. Ross, and C. G. Swain, *ibid.*, **69**, 2977 (1947); B. Cohen, E. R. Van Artsdalen, and J. Harris, *ibid.*, **70**, 282 (1948).

dimer which is cyclized because of the fact [127] that a reaction leading to a six-membered ring occurs faster than the same reaction leading to an acyclic product or to a ring of any other size. Because the ethylene-immonium ions can undergo hydrolysis, displacement, or dimerization at rates comparable to the rate of their formation, they do not in general display simple kinetics. In a few cases the rate constants for the separate stages in their reactions have been evaluated by mechanical and graphical methods.[128] The evidence for the cyclic intermediate has been reinforced by the observation that 1-diethylamino-2-propanol, on conversion into the corresponding chloride followed by alkaline hydrolysis, is converted [129] into 2-diethylamino-1-propanol.

$$CH_3CH\!\!-\!\!\overset{\diagdown}{\underset{O}{/}}\!\!-\!\!CH_2 + HN(C_2H_5)_2 \rightarrow CH_3\underset{\underset{OH}{|}}{CH}CH_2N(C_2H_5)_2 \xrightarrow{SOCl_2}$$

$$CH_3CHClCH_2N(C_2H_5)_2 \xrightarrow{H_2O}$$

$$Cl^- + \quad \underset{CH_2}{\overset{CH_3CH}{\diagdown}}\underset{/}{\overset{|}{\overset{+}{N}(C_2H_5)_2}} \xrightarrow{OH^-} CH_3\underset{CH_2OH}{\overset{N(C_2H_5)_2}{\overset{/}{CH}\diagdown}}$$

The retention of configuration on reaction of alkali with sodium α-bromopropionate (but not with ethyl α-bromopropionate) [130] can be explained by a double inversion involving an unstable α-lactone, a type of compound never isolated. Kinetic studies have not served to decide between the α-lactone (A) and something (B) better describable as a dipolar ion. This distinction may be one of nomenclature only.[131]

$$CH_3\overset{\overset{O}{\diagup\diagdown}}{CH}\!\!-\!\!C\!\!=\!\!O \qquad\qquad CH_3\overset{+}{CH}\!\!-\!\!\overset{\overset{O^-}{|}}{C}\!\!=\!\!O$$
$$A \qquad\qquad\qquad\qquad\qquad B$$

**β-Lactones.** β-Lactones, in contrast to α-lactones, are stable enough to be isolated. They cannot be made from β-hydroxyacids but are obtainable from the salts of β-halogen-substituted acids,[132] by additions to

[127] G. Salomon, *Helv. Chim. Acta,* **16,** 1361 (1933).

[128] P. D. Bartlett, S. D. Ross, and C. G. Swain, *J. Am. Chem. Soc.,* **69,** 2971 (1947); **71,** 1415 (1949); P. D. Bartlett, J. W. Davis, S. D. Ross, and C. G. Swain, *ibid.,* **69,** 2977 (1947).

[129] S. D. Ross, *ibid.,* **69,** 2982 (1947).

[130] W. A. Cowdrey, E. D. Hughes, C. K. Ingold, S. Masterman, and A. D. Scott, *J. Chem. Soc.,* 1254 (1937).

[131] E. Grunwald and S. Winstein, *J. Am. Chem. Soc.,* **70,** 841 (1948).

[132] B. Holmberg, *Ber.,* **45,** 1713 (1912); H. Johansson, *Z. physik. Chem.,* **81,** 573 (1913).

$\alpha,\beta$-unsaturated acids,[133] and by the addition of ketenes to aldehydes and ketones.[134] The ring closure of the salts of $\beta$-halogen-substituted carboxylic acids is an internal displacement reaction apparently analogous to the postulated formation of an $\alpha$-lactone. Actually, in the reaction of thiosulfate with sodium bromosuccinate the rate is controlled by formation of $\beta$-lactone, which subsequently reacts rapidly with the thiosulfate ion,[135] a behavior analogous to the participation of the neighboring sulfur atom in the displacement reactions of mustard gas, resulting in first-order kinetics. In this instance carboxylate groups are available for the formation of either an $\alpha$-lactone or a $\beta$-lactone, but only the $\beta$-lactone is formed. Sodium $\beta$-bromopropionamide-$\beta$-carboxylate, prepared from l-asparagine, shows no interference by the carboxylate group in the normal, bimolecular reaction with thiosulfate. Furthermore, the $\beta$-lactone which is involved in the thiosulfate reaction can be isolated and its rapid reaction with thiosulfate studied kinetically.

$\beta$-Butyrolactone is formed from $\beta$-bromobutyrate ion with a change of sign of optical rotation and apparently also of configuration; the lactone is hydrolyzed by pure water with another change in sign of rotation, but in strong base or strong acid it undergoes normal ester hydrolysis without change in sign of rotation and without isotopic oxygen exchange at the $\beta$-carbon atom.[136] These facts establish that the uncatalyzed attack of water upon this simple $\beta$-lactone proceeds with inversion at the $\beta$-carbon atom, and it is consistent with all these facts to regard the formation of $\beta$-lactones from the salts of $\beta$-bromo acids as proceeding also with inversion. In the more complicated case of 2-bromo-2-benzoylcyclohexane-1-carboxylic acid (XII), careful work by Kohler and Jansen led

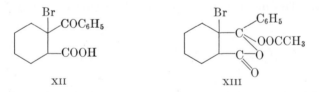

them to a contrary conclusion.[137] The configurations of the geometrically isomeric acids in this case were inferred through the relative ease of formation of cyclic acetates (XIII); only the isomer which formed the ester (XIII) the more slowly yielded a $\beta$-lactone. A later spectro-

[133] D. S. Tarbell and P. D. Bartlett, J. Am. Chem. Soc., **59**, 407 (1937).

[134] F. E. Küng, U. S. pat. 2,356,459 (1944).

[135] F. A. Long and A. R. Olson, J. Phys. Chem., **41**, 267 (1937).

[136] A. R. Olson and R. J. Miller, J. Am. Chem. Soc., **60**, 2687 (1938); A. R. Olson and J. L. Hyde, ibid., **63**, 2459 (1941).

[137] E. P. Kohler and J. E. Jansen, ibid., **60**, 2142 (1938).

scopic investigation of the compounds of Kohler and Jansen [138] revealed subtleties of structure which made it appear probable that the configurations should be reversed, and that the lactonization proceeded with inversion after all.

β-Propiolactone shows a number of bimolecular displacement reactions at the β-carbon atom as well as the normal reactions of an ester.[139] The rates of its displacement reactions with several nucleophilic reagents have been measured;[140] Table II (p. 32) shows a comparison of these with the competition factors of the same reagents for the ethylene-sulfonium ion of mustard gas and for epichlorohydrin. The hydroxyl ion appears to be a disproportionately powerful reagent toward the β-lactone because of the occurrence of normal ester hydrolysis by attack on the carboxylate group.

**Ethylene Oxides.** The most-studied stable analogs of the ethylene-bromonium ion and related intermediates are the ethylene oxides. The stereochemical facts are best interpreted by the view that the formation and opening of the ethylene oxide ring by a displacement reaction always proceed with inversion of configuration.[141]

The acid-catalyzed hydrolysis of cyclohexene oxide and of cycloheptene oxide yields the resolvable and hence *trans*-1,2-diols.[142] Of the isomeric 2-chlorocyclohexanols, only the one produced by addition to cyclohexene in an aqueous medium (conditions normally leading to *trans*-addition) can be converted into cyclohexene oxide.[143] The reaction of cyclohexene oxide with diethylmagnesium yields that isomer of 2-ethylcyclohexanol which shows the lesser steric hindrance in the formation and hydrolysis of esters.[144] The interconversion of *cis*- and *trans*-2-butene, their dibromides, bromohydrins, oxides, and diols [145] forms a consistent pattern with every displacement within the series attended by inversion except those involving neighboring bromine. In this series configurations of the oxides and diols have been established by resolution.

Both ethylene oxide and its conjugate acid, the ion $\begin{array}{c} CH_2 \\ | \end{array}\!\!\!>\!\overset{+}{O}H$, are at-

[138] P. D. Bartlett and P. N. Rylander, *ibid.*, **73**, 4275 (1951).

[139] T. L. Gresham, J. E. Jansen, F. W. Shaver, and R. A. Bankert, *ibid.*, **71**, 2807 (1949) and previous papers.

[140] P. D. Bartlett and G. Small, Jr., *ibid.*, **72**, 4867 (1950).

[141] See S. Winstein and R. B. Henderson, Chapter 1 of R. C. Elderfield, "Heterocyclic Compounds," John Wiley & Sons, New York (1950), Vol. I, pp. 27 ff.

[142] H. G. Derx, *Rec. trav. chim.*, **41**, 312, 333 (1922).

[143] P. D. Bartlett, *J. Am. Chem. Soc.*, **57**, 224 (1935).

[144] P. D. Bartlett and C. M. Berry, *ibid.*, **56**, 2683 (1934); G. Vavon and V. M. Mitchovitch, *Bull. soc. chim. France*, **45**, 961 (1929).

[145] C. E. Wilson and H. J. Lucas, *J. Am. Chem. Soc.*, **58**, 2396 (1936).

tacked by anions in direct displacement reactions.  Table II, p. 32, brings out the fact that the reactivity of a reagent in a nucleophilic displacement reaction is not determined primarily by its basic strength.

Unsymmetrically substituted ethylene oxides are often attacked at different points, depending upon whether the neutral oxide or its conjugate acid is reacting.[146]  Propylene oxide is converted into a mixture of primary and secondary monoethyl ethers in the ratio of 1:1.25 by 1.3% sulfuric acid in ethanol, while 0.7% sodium ethoxide gives an 83% yield of the primary ether.

**Retention of Configuration without Double Inversion.**  $(-)$-$\alpha$-Phenylethanol can be converted into a chloride of the same sign of rotation by thionyl chloride, or into a chloride of the opposite sign of rotation by thionyl chloride and pyridine.[147]  In neither case is there any appreciable racemization.  Only in the presence of pyridine are conditions favorable for ionic attack to produce an inversion; therefore the retention of configuration with pure thionyl chloride as the reagent can scarcely be formulated as involving a double inversion.  It has been proposed [148] that the initially formed $\alpha$-phenylethyl chlorosulfinate, $C_6H_5CH(CH_3)$-OSOCl, if not attacked with inversion as when pyridinium chloride is present, undergoes a decomposition with retention of configuration and extrusion of sulfur dioxide:

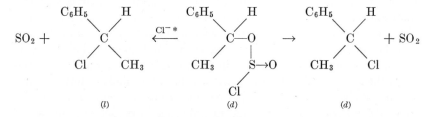

This mechanism has been designated $S_Ni$.  It is observed only in compounds with special structural features such as the $\alpha$-phenyl group and, in the case of phosphorus halides, also an $\alpha$-alkyl group higher than methyl.

[146] P. A. Levene and A. Walti, *J. Biol. Chem.*, **73**, 263 (1927); H. C. Chitwood and B. T. Freure, *J. Am. Chem. Soc.*, **68**, 680 (1946).

[147] A. McKenzie and G. W. Clough, *J. Chem. Soc.*, **103**, 687 (1913); J. Kenyon, H. Phillips, and F. M. H. Taylor, *ibid.*, 382 (1931).

[148] W. A. Cowdrey, E. D. Hughes, C. K. Ingold, S. Masterman, and A. D. Scott, *ibid.*, 1267 (1937).

* The authors cited propose that the chloride ion arises from ionization at the S—Cl bond of the chlorosulfinate, and that it may act upon the intact ester, the ion $C_6H_5$-$CH(CH_3)OSO^+$, or its pyridinium derivative.  The largest source of chloride ion would, however, appear to be the pyridinium chloride, a mole of which is produced simultaneously with the chlorosulfinate.

The necessity of front-side displacement is even more apparent in the conversion of 1-apocamphylamine [149] into the corresponding alcohol by nitrous acid and into the chloro compound with nitrosyl chloride. Here the caged-ring system prohibits attack from the rear, and the total inertness of the products to displacement casts doubt upon ionization as a possible step in the process. An $S_N i$ mechanism here would closely resemble that postulated with thionyl chloride. This mechanism cannot be universal for the reaction of amines with nitrous acid or nitrosyl halides, for often inversion occurs and molecular rearrangements appear suggesting the presence of a carbonium ion.[150]

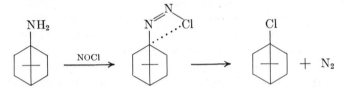

Another case in which the $S_N i$ mechanism may be involved is the conversion of certain alcohols into bromides by hydrogen bromide without solvent. Again it is with $\alpha$-alkylbenzyl alcohols that this phenomenon has been reported.[151] $(-)$-$\alpha$-Phenylethanol is converted by hydrogen bromide at $-80°$ into an unracemized levorotatory bromide; at $-35°$ into completely racemic material; at $-30°$ into an optically impure dextrorotatory bromide; above this temperature the rotation again declines. Arcus [152] has shown that these results could be quantitatively predicted by the superposition of temperature distribution curves for the $S_N 1$, $S_N 2$, and $S_N i$ mechanisms, each one having its maximum importance at a definite temperature and the $S_N i$ predominating at the lowest temperatures. His analysis did not extend to a derivation of the distribution curves on the basis of estimated temperature coefficients for the steps involved in the displacement.

**Electrophilic Displacement.** Displacement reactions at a *saturated* carbon atom in which the attacking and departing groups are electrophilic have not been studied very extensively from the standpoint of mechanism. In the hydrolytic cleavage of unsymmetrical organomercury compounds, relative reactivities have been determined.[153] In the

[149] P. D. Bartlett and L. H. Knox, *J. Am. Chem. Soc.*, **61**, 3184 (1939).

[150] W. Hückel, R. Danneel, A. Gross, and H. Naab, *Ann.*, **502**, 110 (1933); N. Demjanow and M. Luschnikow, *J. Russ. Phys. Chem. Soc.*, **35**, 26 (1903).

[151] P. A. Levene and A. Rothen, *J. Biol. Chem.*, **127**, 237 (1939).

[152] C. L. Arcus, *J. Chem. Soc.*, 236 (1944).

[153] M. S. Kharasch and M. W. Grafflin, *J. Am. Chem. Soc.*, **47**, 1948 (1925); M. S. Kharasch and R. Marker, *ibid.*, **48**, 3130 (1926); M. S. Kharasch and A. L. Flenner, *ibid.*, **54**, 674 (1932).

cleavage of the Hg—C bond by hydrogen bromide and by iodine the reaction proceeds by way of an atomic chain in the absence of special precautions.[154] In a few cases a reaction apparently involving an optically active organoalkali compound has yielded an optically active hydrocarbon with the asymmetric center at the site of the displacement,[155] but more often asymmetry disappears in displacements which depart from the nucleophilic type. The occurrence of normal displacement of lithium by mercury and of mercury by hydrogen or iodine at the bridge-head 4-position of the camphane ring [155a] indicates that attack from the front is more favored here than among nucleophilic displacements.

Aromatic substitution usually involves electrophilic attack upon the benzene ring, but the electronic and stereochemical circumstances of this reaction are sharply different from those in substitution at a saturated atom. (See Chapter 3, Vol. I, of this Treatise.)

Reactions of the so-called positive halogen [156] are electrophilic displacements, and in the special case of the debromination of an $\alpha$-bromoketone the mechanism is known from a study of the reverse reaction.[157]   Where

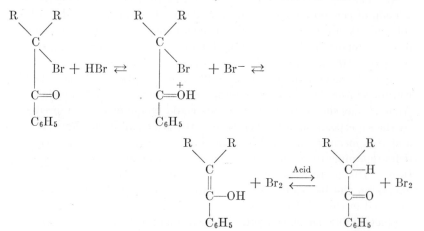

this mechanism is not available, in the debromination of triphenylmethyl bromide, the reaction requires the presence of peroxide for the establishment of equilibrium, which is evidence of an atomic mechanism.

[154] S. Winstein, paper presented at the Third National Conference on Organic Reaction Mechanisms, Evanston, Ill., August, 1950.

[155] E. S. Wallis and F. H. Adams, *J. Am. Chem. Soc.*, **55**, 3838 (1933); see p. 393 in Vol. I of this Treatise.

[155a] S. Winstein, private communication.

[156] T. Seliwanow, *Ber.*, **25**, 3617 (1892); J. Stieglitz, *Am. Chem. J.*, **18**, 758 (1896); W. A. Noyes, *J. Am. Chem. Soc.*, **35**, 767 (1913); T. Henderson and A. K. Macbeth, *J. Chem. Soc.*, **121**, 892 (1922).

[157] R. Altschul and P. D. Bartlett, *J. Org. Chem.*, **5**, 623 (1940).

## Alcohols, Ethers, and Halides

Apart from the displacement reaction there are several types of reactions of alcohols, ethers, and saturated halides which have been the subject of mechanistic study. These include elimination of water and of hydrogen halide, the Wagner-Meerwein, pinacol, and Claisen rearrangements, and the formation of oxonium salts. A start has also been made in the study of the mechanisms of the oxidation of alcohols by chromic acid and other oxidizing agents. Other important reactions, such as esterification and ester hydrolysis and the formation and reactions of acetals, are appropriately considered elsewhere (pp. 115, 118).

**General Character of the Alcohols.** Methyl and ethyl alcohols contain a weakly ionizable O—H bond and are, under comparable conditions, somewhat less ionized than water.[158] The higher alcohols have progressively lower dielectric constants and are poorer ionizing solvents for themselves as well as other substances, although their intrinsic acid strengths may be little different from those of methyl and ethyl alcohols. Secondary and tertiary alcohols behave as substantially weaker acids than primary alcohols.[159]

The oxygen atom of alcohols is weakly basic, being comparable to that of water. Formation of a coördinate bond by the oxygen atom increases the polarity of both the O—H and the C—O bonds. The ethanol-$BF_3$ complex is a strong acid, yielding conducting solutions and undergoing addition to olefins.[160] The hydroxyl group of an alcohol is not subject to displacement by nucleophilic reagents alone,[161] but becomes readily displaceable on coördination with a proton, boron trifluoride, or other electrophilic reagents.

Because coördination enhances the polarity of the O—H bond, the hydrogen-bonded dimer of an unhindered alcohol is more prone to form a further hydrogen bond than is the monomer. This results in a type of multiple association in alcohol, similar to that in water, contrasting with the preference for dimers shown in the association of carboxylic acids.[162] The hydrogen-bonding characteristics of the alcohols determine their special usefulness as ionizing solvents, for instance, for organic and

[158] A. Unmack, *Z. physik. Chem.*, **133**, 45 (1928).

[159] W. K. McEwen, *J. Am. Chem. Soc.*, **58**, 1124 (1936).

[160] H. Meerwein, *Ber.*, **66**, 411 (1933).

[161] The racemization of α-phenylethanol by alkali has been interpreted as a direct displacement with inversion [R. A. Ogg, M. Polanyi, and L. Warner, *Chemistry & Industry*, 614 (1934)]. An alternative explanation is suggested by the work of Doering [W. v. E. Doering and T. C. Aschner, *J. Am. Chem. Soc.*, **71**, 838 (1949)] on hydrogenation-dehydrogenation in ketone-alcohol systems catalyzed by strong bases. See p. 79.

[162] E. N. Lassettre, *Chem. Revs.*, **20**, 259 (1937).

inorganic halides (see p. 29), in comparison with non-hydroxylic compounds of like dielectric constant.

Contrary to an assumption frequently made, the exchanges of protons between the OH-groups of alcohols and water is not an immeasurably fast reaction; indeed, it requires about 18 hours for isotopic equilibrium to become established [163] between pure ethanol and pure water, at 25°.

$$C_2H_5OH + HOD \leftrightarrows C_2H_5OD + HOH$$

In general, in any reversible reaction with an equilibrium constant smaller than $10^{-12}$, the rate constant in one direction must be measurably slow even if the rate constant in the other direction is as fast as any reaction can be according to either the collision or transition-state theory (about $6 \times 10^{12}$). This of course applies to the ionization process in water-alcohol mixtures, and one concludes that this process should proceed with a rate constant of the order of $10^{-6}$ or less. In the presence of a strong base, this limitation is no longer present, and exchange proceeds very rapidly.

The heterogeneous reaction of alcohols with metals in most cases is slow and in some cases requires special treatment of the metal surface. In the scale of very weak acids,[164] alcohols are the weakest acids which will normally react directly with metals, although ammonia and sometimes the amines can be induced to react with sodium by the action of an electrolytic couple, and alkyl sodamides can be made from amines and the organosodium compounds resulting from the attack of sodium on conjugated dienes.[165] For this reason as much as any other, sodium alkoxides are usually the first strong organic bases to be tried in a reaction requiring basic reagents. By going from sodium methoxide to potassium $t$-amyloxide [166] one achieves a substantial increase in basic strength as well as more favorable solubility in ether.

Magnesium methoxide [167] also has basic properties; but the alkoxides of aluminum have a degree of electrophilic character at the metallic atom which makes their solutions in the alcohols acidic rather than basic.[168] Aluminum ethoxide in ethanol is accordingly predominantly in the form $HAl(OC_2H_5)_4$.

[163] W. J. C. Orr, *Trans. Faraday Soc.*, **32**, 1033 (1936).

[164] J. B. Conant and G. W. Wheland, *J. Am. Chem. Soc.*, **54**, 1212 (1932); W. K. McEwen, *ibid.*, **58**, 1124 (1936).

[165] K. Ziegler, L. Jakob, H. Wolltahn, and A. Wenz, *Ann.*, **511**, 64 (1934).

[166] R. G. Gould, Jr., and A. F. Thompson, Jr., *J. Am. Chem. Soc.*, **57**, 340 (1935); W. B. Renfrow, Jr., *ibid.*, **66**, 144 (1944).

[167] H. Lund, *Kgl. Danske Videnskab. Selskab, Mat.-fys. Medd.*, **13**, No. 13 (1935) [*C. A.*, **30**, 1362 (1936)].

[168] H. Meerwein and T. Bersin, *Ann.*, **476**, 120 (1929).

**Dehydration and Dehydrohalogenation.** Alcohols and halides are readily interconvertible in general, and their elimination reactions appear to have much in common as to mechanism. Alcohols with no other functional group are dehydrated homogeneously most generally by acids (sulfuric, sulfonic, phosphoric, and oxalic acids being commonly used) or other electrophilic reagents, such as zinc chloride or, in easy cases, iodine. As a homogeneous method involving no acid, the thermal decomposition of xanthates (Tschugaeff method) is frequently employed. Alcohols having an active hydrogen in the $\beta$-position to the hydroxyl, such as aldols and $\beta$-ketols, may be readily dehydrated by base. The principles of mechanism governing heterogeneous reactions, such as the dehydration of alcohols over hot alumina, are not as well worked out as those in homogeneous reactions, but in general the course of such reactions is more suggestive of polar than of radical mechanisms.

Elimination of hydrogen halide from organic halides is brought about by strong bases or may be effected by converting the halide into a quaternary ammonium salt or a tertiary sulfonium salt and decomposing the salt or its base.

The common basis of simple elimination reactions in polar solvents was considered in an extensive series of papers by Ingold, Hughes, and their co-workers, which was reviewed in 1948.[169] In some ways the simplest system to consider is that in which a base acts upon an alkyl halide to produce an olefin. The reactants are the same as in one of the common displacement reactions, and usually displacement and elimination occur together. Like displacement, elimination may take place with either first- or second-order kinetics, the former being favored in tertiary halides. Mechanisms, known as "$E1$" and "$E2$," have been proposed by Hughes and Ingold, and their implications have been extensively investigated experimentally:

$$E1: \quad CH_3CR_2Br \rightarrow Br^- + CH_3\overset{+}{C}R_2 \xrightarrow{ROH} R\overset{+}{O}H_2 + CH_2{=}CR_2$$

$$E2: \quad B:^- + CH_3CR_2Br \rightarrow B:H + H_2C{=}CR_2 + Br^-$$

According to the $E1$ mechanism, elimination is proceeding through the same intermediate as solvolysis, and the relative amounts of olefin and solvolysis products formed should be largely independent of the concentration of the base and of the nature of the halogen of the starting material. This has been verified in several cases with only second-order differences due to the influence of the departing negative ion upon the carbonium ion. Changes in the nature of the base, however, may af-

[169] M. L. Dhar, E. D. Hughes, C. K. Ingold, A. M. M. Mandour, G. A. Maw, and L. I. Woolf, *J. Chem. Soc.*, 2093 (1948), and earlier references.

fect the relative amounts of elimination and solvolysis resulting from an ionization reaction, since changes in proton-acceptor power and in nucleophilic reactivity do not in general run parallel.[170] It is possible, also, among halides which can react by both the $E1$ and $E2$ mechanisms, to increase the proportion of $E2$ mechanism occurring by increasing the basicity and concentration of the reagent.

The elimination of halogen acid from a simple alkyl halide by excess or equivalent base proceeds irreversibly, since the alkali halides do not add to an isolated carbon-carbon double bond. Under acid conditions, however, such reactions are reversible, the equilibrium being generally favorable to addition at low temperatures and to elimination at higher temperatures. Information concerning the kinetics and mechanism of addition reactions is therefore pertinent to the mechanism of elimination, by the principle of microscopic reversibility (p. 9). Thus, the fact that isobutylene is hydrated at a rate proportional to the concentration of strong acid in aqueous solution [171] is consistent with either an ionization or a concerted addition and elimination involving only water and the ion $H_3O^+$. On the other hand, the higher-order kinetics of the addition of hydrogen chloride to isobutylene in non-polar solvents [172] indicates that the elimination of hydrogen chloride from $t$-butyl chloride in such media can be catalyzed by hydrogen chloride itself. Such eliminations have been observed to occur autocatalytically; and hydrogen chloride is a recognized catalyst for such ionic processes as the rearrangement of camphene hydrochloride (see p. 66).

The debromination of vicinal dibromides is usually carried out by zinc dust in a heterogeneous reaction unfavorable for kinetic study; however, debromination can be brought about at moderate temperatures by the

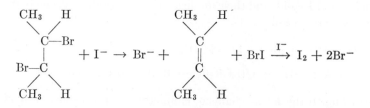

action of iodide ion,[173] with bimolecular kinetics suggesting the mechanism shown. This is an $E2$ mechanism, with iodide ion as the nucleophilic attacking reagent, $Br^+$ being transferred instead of a proton. Al-

[170] See p. 32.

[171] H. J. Lucas and W. F. Eberz, *J. Am. Chem. Soc.*, **56**, 460 (1934).

[172] F. R. Mayo and J. J. Katz, *ibid.*, **69**, 1339 (1947).

[173] R. T. Dillon, W. G. Young, and H. J. Lucas, *ibid.*, **52**, 1953 (1930); previous references cited there.

though this reaction is irreversible because of the ensuing reaction between iodine bromide and iodide ion, its reverse kinetic counterpart has been observed in the bromide-ion-catalyzed additions of bromine to maleic acid and vinyl bromide in acetic acid.[174]

**Stereochemistry of Elimination Reactions.** The dehydration of *cis*-2-phenylcyclohexanol with phosphoric acid yields largely 1-phenyl-1-cyclohexene; its *trans*-isomer yields chiefly 1-phenyl-2-cyclohexene.[175]

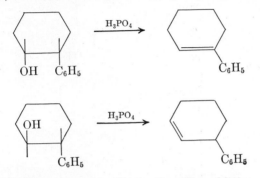

Results of this kind suggest that elimination, like addition, must involve atoms or groups (here, H and OH) situated in the *trans*-relationship to each other. A careful study by Hückel, Tappe, and Legutke [176] has shown that the situation is not in general as simple as this. Ten geometrically pure monocyclic and bicyclic saturated alcohols or the related amines, or both, were examined in different procedures for converting them to olefins. Of three ways of dehydrating alcohols and two ways of deaminating amines, all gave mixtures of isomers except certain reactions of sodium ethoxide on the toluenesulfonate. This strictly second-order reaction yielded no product of *cis*-elimination: i.e., isomer II of *l*-menthyl tosylate (*A*) yielded entirely 2-menthene (*E*), and isomer II of *trans*-α-decalyl tosylate (*B*) yielded entirely $\Delta^{1,2}$-octalin (*F*), although isomer I of *cis*-α-decalyl tosylate (*C*) yielded entirely $\Delta^{1,9}$-octalin (*G*).

Heating the toluenesulfonates in the absence of strong base, which is expected to favor the *E*1 mechanism, yielded mixtures of isomers whose orientation was the same from both *trans*-α-decalol I (*D*) and *cis*-α-decalol I (*C*). This sample of the results illustrates the general conclusion that elimination by the *E*1 process does not require any spatial or configurative relationship between the eliminated atoms or groups and that this mechanism involves a stage in which, as the formulation of a free carbonium ion suggests, the geometrical isomers become equiva-

[174] K. Nozaki and R. A. Ogg, Jr., *ibid.*, **64**, 697, 704 (1942).
[175] C. C. Price and J. V. Karabinos, *ibid.*, **62**, 1159 (1940).
[176] W. Hückel, W. Tappe, and G. Legutke, *Ann.*, **543**, 191 (1940).

52          ORGANIC CHEMISTRY

lent. Reasoning backward, we conclude that the dehydration of 2-phenyl-
cyclohexanol by phosphoric acid is a concerted elimination reaction of
the *E*2 type, with the role of base played by water, a second alcohol
molecule, or a second molecule of phosphoric acid. It is also possible

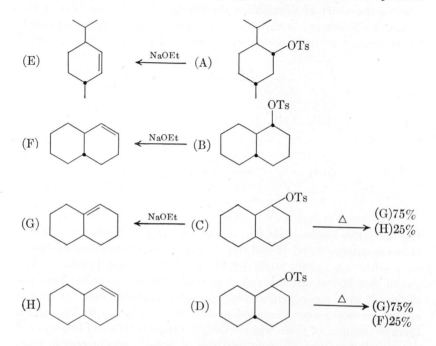

that the dehydration of the *trans*-isomer involves participation of the
phenyl group (see pp. 60, 61) in the formation of a special cyclic ionic
intermediate impossible in the case of the *cis*-isomer.

The decomposition of the quaternary ammonium ion from isomer II
of *l*-menthylamine yielded the same product as the *E*2 treatment of the
toluenesulfonate. The treatment of isomer I of *trans*-α-decalylamine
with nitrous acid yielded a mixture of equal amounts of the two octalins,
a result intermediate between that of the *E*1 and that of the *E*2 reactions
on the toluenesulfonates.

In several cases the Tschugaeff dehydration yielded mixtures of isomers with the opposite preponderance from the mixture resulting from
the reaction with sodium ethoxide. With *l*-menthol II the Tschugaeff
product was the same as that from the *E*1 dehydration; in the case of
*cis*-α-decalol I the Tschugaeff procedure was the only one yielding chiefly
$\Delta^{1,2}$-octalin. From these examples Hückel concluded that the mechanism of the Tschugaeff dehydration involves preferential attack upon a

*cis*-hydrogen atom, and accordingly must proceed through a cyclic intra-molecular process:

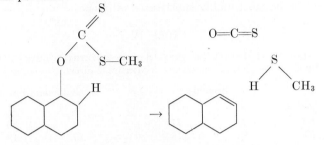

Evidence summarized by Barton [177] indicates that many high-temperature, non-base-catalyzed decompositions of esters, especially xanthates and benzoates, involve unimolecular *cis*-elimination. Careful kinetic study of the homogeneous gas-phase pyrolysis of ethyl chloride and of 1,1-dichloroethane [178] has shown that this reaction is unimolecular, not a chain process, and accordingly involves the kind of transition state which in cases permitting a configurational distinction would lead to *cis*- rather than *trans*-elimination.

In acyclic halides and alcohols in which elimination might involve hydrogen from either of two sites of differing degrees of substitution, the preponderant product is the one involving the elimination of the hydrogen from the more substituted carbon atom (Saytzeff rule). In exhaustive methylation, where a quaternary ammonium hydroxide is decomposed, exactly the opposite rule applies (the Hofmann rule).[179] Hughes and Ingold and their collaborators have established that the Saytzeff rule applies to elimination by the $E1$ mechanism, whether by alcohols, halides, or sulfonium ions, although the last of these are similar to quaternary ammonium ions in their behavior under conditions of bimolecular elimination. Table IV shows the composition of the elimination product from 3-methyl-2-bromobutane and 3-methylbutane-2-dimethylsulfonium ion under conditions shown by kinetic studies to produce bimolecular and unimolecular elimination. Hughes and Ingold have reiterated the view that the important difference between the ammonium and sulfonium ions on the one hand and the alcohols and halides on the other is the presence or absence of a positive charge, which when present makes the greater acidity of primary or secondary hydrogen (as compared to tertiary hydrogen) dominate the point of attack of

[177] D. H. R. Barton, *J. Chem. Soc.*, 2174 (1949).

[178] D. H. R. Barton and K. E. Howlett, *ibid.*, 165 (1949).

[179] For a review see M. L. Dhar, E. D. Hughes, C. K. Ingold, A. M. M. Mandour, G. A. Maw, and L. I. Woolf, *ibid.*, 2093 (1948), and previous papers there cited.

a basic reagent, and when absent allows this to be determined by a sort of olefin-like hyperconjugation in the transition state, which favors the formation of the most highly substituted ethylene.

TABLE IV

PERCENTAGE OF 2-METHYL-2-BUTENE ($A$) AND 2-METHYL-1-BUTENE ($B$) IN PRODUCT OF ELIMINATION FROM 3-METHYL-2-BUTYL COMPOUNDS

| | Bromide | | Sulfonium Ion | |
|---|---|---|---|---|
| Mechanism | $A$ | $B$ | $A$ | $B$ |
| $E2$ | 83 | 17 | 14 | 86 |
| $E1$ | 82 | 18 | 87 | 13 |

The removal of carbon dioxide from a carboxylate ion is a process of the same electronic type as the removal of a proton, except that no acceptor for the carbon dioxide need take part kinetically. Accordingly, the anion of a $\beta$-halogenated carboxylic acid may react unimolecularly to yield an olefin in a concerted decarboxylation which resembles an $E2$ rather than an $E1$ process. Such is the conversion of the dibromide of cinnamic acid to $\beta$-bromostyrene: [180]

$$C_6H_5CH\text{---}CH\text{---}C\text{---}O^- \longrightarrow C_6H_5CH=CHBr \quad CO_2$$
$$\quad\quad\; Br \quad\; Br \quad\; O \quad\quad\quad\quad\quad\quad Br^-$$

The acid-catalyzed decarboxylations of the carboxylactones resulting from some Stobbe condensations [181] may be regarded as examples of coupled eliminations,

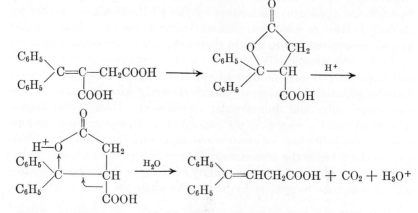

[180] See J. J. Sudborough and K. J. Thompson, *ibid.*, **83**, 683 (1903).
[181] W. S. Johnson, J. W. Petersen, and W. P. Schneider, *J. Am. Chem. Soc.*, **69**, 74 (1947).

or alternatively [182] as reactions proceeding through a carbonium ion and hence analogous to an $E1$ process:

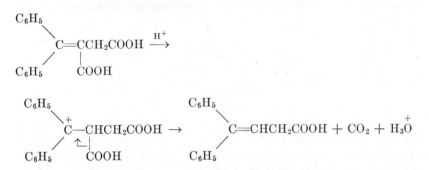

**Wagner-Meerwein Rearrangement** (see Chapter 12, Vol. II). The homogeneous dehydration of pinacolyl alcohol $(CH_3)_3CCHOHCH_3$ by acidic catalysts yields mainly not $t$-butylethylene but the two products of molecular rearrangement, 2,3-dimethyl-2-butene and 2,3-dimethyl-1-butene.[183] The Tschugaeff dehydration, or the thermal decomposition of pinacolyl acetate,[184] will yield dehydration without rearrangement. The essential difference between the rearranging and non-rearranging conditions may well be the occurrence or non-occurrence of carbonium ions produced under conditions of long survival or repeatedly re-formed under reversible conditions. If this is so, then such rearrangements should not be a peculiarity of elimination reactions, but should be capable of occurrence rather generally in either elimination or displacement reactions proceeding by the ionization mechanism. Extensive work by Whitmore and his co-workers has shown that this is so.

Early attempts to formulate the Wagner-Meerwein rearrangement and its special case, the pinacol rearrangement, without any direct migration of alkyl or aryl groups failed, and it became necessary to face the fact that such groups, during an elimination or a displacement, become detached from one position and attached to an adjacent one without going through a stable compound having a three-membered ring. (See Chapter 12, Vol. II, and below.) Thus, the well-studied rearrangement attending the reversible elimination of hydrogen chloride from isobornyl chloride $(A)$ to yield camphene $(C)$, can be observed as an isomerization between the two crystalline compounds isobornyl chloride $(A)$ and cam-

---

[182] W. S. Johnson and W. E. Heinz, *ibid.*, **71**, 2913 (1949).

[183] See F. C. Whitmore and P. L. Meunier, *ibid.*, **55**, 3721 (1933), and previous references given there; also K. C. Laughlin, C. W. Nash, and F. C. Whitmore, *ibid.*, **56**, 1395 (1934).

[184] W. Fomin and N. Sochanski, *Ber.*, **46**, 244 (1913); F. C. Whitmore and H. S. Rothrock, *J. Am. Chem. Soc.*, **55**, 1106 (1933); see above, pp. 52, 53, and Ref. 177.

phene hydrochloride (*B*).[185]   The suspected cyclopropanic intermediate, tricyclene (*D*), has been prepared, and even occurs as a minor by-product in some reactions of this kind; but tricyclene, as is readily

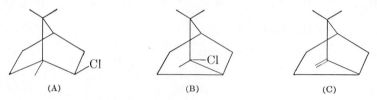

(A)                              (B)                              (C)

seen, has a plane of symmetry, whereas optically active isobornyl chloride can be converted into optically active camphene.   This rules out cyclopropanes as general intermediates in the Wagner-Meerwein rearrangement despite the fact that, in the system in question, there are

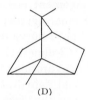

(D)

racemizations which occur under somewhat more drastic conditions and which require special explanation.[186]

The first work to show clearly the ionic nature of the Wagner-Meerwein rearrangement was that of Meerwein and van Emster on the effect of catalysts and solvents on the rearrangement of camphene hydrochloride into isobornyl chloride.   Taking advantage of large differences in the speed with which bornyl and isobornyl chlorides, camphene hydrochloride, and hydrogen chloride react with sodium methoxide, these authors were able to measure the rate of the isomerization and the position of the rapid equilibrium between camphene hydrochloride and its elimination products.   In liquid sulfur dioxide and in cresol the rate of rearrangement is too great to measure; in ether the rate is almost too small to measure; between these extremes, where the rates probably differ by at least four powers of 10, ten organic solvents promote the rearrangement at rates roughly parallel to their dielectric constants. Sulfur dioxide and cresol have dielectric constants of only 15.6 (at 0°) and 5 (at 24°),[187] respectively; but because of their exceptional solvating power for anions they rank among the excellent ionizing solvents for triarylmethyl and other organic halides.[188]   Also metallic halides—

[185] H. Meerwein and K. van Emster, *Ber.*, **B55**, 2507 (1922).

[186] H. Meerwein and F. Montfort, *Ann.*, **435**, 207 (1923).   See also p. 68.

[187] *International Critical Tables*, **6**, 76, 92 (1926).

[188] See, for example, P. Walden, *Ber.*, **35**, 2018 (1902).

stannic, mercuric, zinc, ferric, and antimonic chlorides—which form stable complex anions with chloride ion, and yield halochromic salts with triarylmethyl halides, are powerful catalysts for the rearrangement of camphene hydrochloride.

The evidence amassed by Meerwein was so convincing that the development of the theory of the rearrangement since that time has been largely a matter of detail in the manner in which ionization controls the rearrangement and refinement of the prevailing concepts of the carbonium ion, its chemical and stereochemical characteristics, and the extent to which it is free. On these points there is a good deal of pertinent evidence to be considered.

*Stereochemistry of the Carbonium Ion.* The theory of hybridized orbitals [189] suggests that the carbonium ion, utilizing one $s$ and two $p$ orbitals, should possess a planar configuration as is observed for trimethylboron and the boron halides.[190] The special stability of the triarylcarbonium ions is currently accounted for by resonance structures ($A$–$D$) or

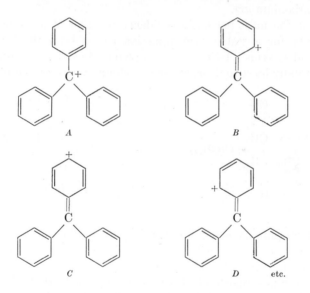

an equivalent molecular orbital representation, which demands coplanarity of the phenyl groups and the central carbon atom.[190a] No facts are known that are in conflict with this postulate, nor are there any direct experiments which clearly demonstrate its correctness. Halochromic

[189] L. Pauling, "Nature of the Chemical Bond," Cornell University Press, Ithaca, N. Y. (1940), p. 88; C. A. Coulson, "Valence," Oxford University Press, 1952, Chapter 8.

[190] H. A. Lévy and L. O. Brockway, *J. Am. Chem. Soc.*, **59**, 2085 (1937).

[190a] G. N. Lewis, T. T. Magel, and D. Lipkin, *ibid.*, **64**, 1774 (1942), offer spectral evidence for two forms of closest approach to planarity in crystal violet.

salts, prepared from optically active triarylmethylthioglycolic acids, are racemic.[191]

Displacement reactions at an asymmetric tertiary carbon atom also show $S_N1$ characteristics and, like $S_N1$ reactions of secondary compounds, result in substantial racemization with, at ordinary temperatures, some excess of inversion over retention of configuration.[192] If there is any continuous transition between the $S_N2$ mechanism, with covalent character in the transition state between the entering solvent molecule and the central carbon, and the $S_N1$ mechanism, with only electrovalent solvation, then the limiting amount of $S_N1$ character has not been reached in the alcoholysis of 2,4-dimethylhexyl-4-phthalate, for dilution of the alcohol with nitromethane lowers the observed amount of inversion in the product from an original 60% down to zero. This is consistent with conclusions reached by others (pp. 33, 34) on continuity of mechanism, and indicates that configurational changes during solvolysis can shed only a limited amount of light on the nature of the "free" carbonium ion.

Perhaps the most persuasive evidence in favor of a requirement of coplanarity for a stable carbonium ion comes from the behavior of bridgehead systems. 1-Chloroapocamphane $(A)$ and 1-bromotriptycene $(B)$ are totally inert to displacement or elimination by basic reagents,[193]

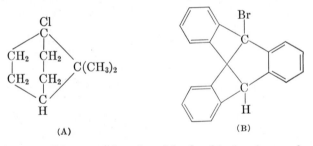

(A)                                      (B)

and 4-chlorocamphane requires for dehydrochlorination such vigorous treatment [194] as boiling with aluminum bromide in cyclohexane or a 50% solution of zinc chloride at 195°.

These results support the idea that restraint against the assuming of a planar form operates against the formation of a carbonium ion. The inertness of the bridgehead compounds might alternatively be ascribed

[191] E. S. Wallis, *ibid.*, **53**, 2253 (1931); E. S. Wallis and F. H. Adams, *ibid.*, **55**, 3838 (1933); M. Gomberg and W. E. Gordon, *ibid.*, **57**, 119 (1935).

[192] P. G. Stevens and N. L. McNiven, *ibid.*, **61**, 1295 (1939); W. v. E. Doering and A. Streitwieser, *Abst. 119th Mtg., Am. Chem. Soc., Boston, Mass.*, 3 April, 1951.

[193] P. D. Bartlett and L. H. Knox, *J. Am. Chem. Soc.*, **61**, 3184 (1939); P. D. Bartlett and E. S. Lewis, *ibid.*, **72**, 1005 (1950).

[194] W. v. E. Doering and E. F. Schoenewaldt, *ibid.*, **73**, 2333 (1951).

to the impossibility of solvation of the carbonium ions from the back side, concerted with the ionization process. In highly branched compounds such as tri-*t*-butylmethyl chloride [195] the carbon atom bearing the halogen is so thoroughly shielded on the back side that no solvent molecule can approach within bond-forming distance of it, yet there is no restraint by ring fusion against these compounds forming coplanar ions. Actually, compounds of this type undergo reaction in hydroxylic solvents with extreme ease,[195, 196] the rate constants being up to 40,000 times that of *t*-butyl chloride. Since this fact shows that rapid ionization may occur even without strong concerted solvation, it seems doubtful that shielding alone is sufficient reason for the inertness of the bridgehead compounds. Brown has expressed the opinion that mutual hindrance of groups on the back side from the functional group provides an additional driving force toward the ionization accompanied by an increase of these bond angles from their normal tetrahedral values to 120°.

In the light of the proposition that the free carbonium ion is planar in form, there must be significance in the fact that, of the two stereoisomeric chlorides, bornyl and isobornyl chlorides, only isobornyl chloride is the direct product of the rearrangement of camphene hydrochloride, even though bornyl chloride is the stabler isomer at equilibrium. It is highly

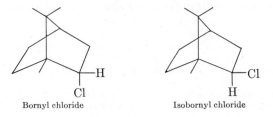

Bornyl chloride        Isobornyl chloride

probable, then, that the bornyl-isobornyl cation never occurs free during the rearrangement. Similar evidence exists in the case of the deamination of certain optically active amino alcohols, and relates to the carbon atom *to* which, rather than the one *from* which, the migrating carbon moves.[197]

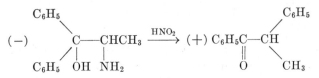

[195] Marguerite S. Swain, *Thesis*, Radcliffe College, 1948. See P. D. Bartlett, *Bull. soc. chim. France*, [5] **18**, 100c (1951).

[196] H. C. Brown and R. S. Fletcher, *J. Am. Chem. Soc.*, **71**, 1845 (1949); see H. C. Brown, *Science*, **103**, 386 (1946).

[197] A. McKenzie, R. Roger, and G. O. Wills, *J. Chem. Soc.*, 779 (1926).

In the latter example it has been shown by Bernstein and Whitmore [198] that an inversion occurred at the carbon to which the phenyl group migrated, and in the former case it was pointed out by Bartlett and Pöckel [199] that, if the configurations are correct as shown,[200] the formation of isobornyl chloride involves an inversion at carbon atom 2 of the camphane ring system, to which the chlorine atom moves during the rearrangement.

Therefore, in these two classical examples of a Wagner-Meerwein rearrangement occurring with replacement at a secondary carbon atom, clean inversion is indicated at the atoms *from* which and *to* which the migration occurs.[200a]

A thorough study [201] of the conversion of 3-phenyl-2-butyl *p*-toluene-sulfonate into the acetate by heating in anhydrous acetic acid has made possible a much more specific picture than hitherto of the migration of a phenyl group in the Wagner-Meerwein rearrangement. 3-Phenyl-2-butanol was obtained in the four possible optically active forms, and an active tosylate from each *dl* pair was heated at 70° in glacial acetic acid containing 1% of acetic anhydride and an amount of sodium acetate sufficient to neutralize the toluenesulfonic acid formed. The results were as shown. One diastereomer underwent complete racemization on conversion into its acetate; the other showed complete retention of sign and magnitude of optical rotation, on conversion by unequivocal

---

[198] H. I. Bernstein and F. C. Whitmore, *J. Am. Chem. Soc.*, **61**, 1324 (1939).

[199] P. D. Bartlett and I. Pöckel, *ibid.*, **59**, 820 (1937). The evidence in this paper concerning a *pinacol* rearrangement has been shown to be incorrect by H. Meerwein, *Ann.*, **542**, 123 (1939).

[200] There is no rigorous way of relating by chemical methods the configurations of bornyl and isobornyl chlorides to those of borneol and isoborneol, which have been established by relation to certain lactones [Y. Asahina, M. Ishidate, and T. Sano., *Ber.*, **69**, 343 (1936)]. However, camphenyl formate, trichloroacetate, etc., rearrange to isobornyl esters whose configurations are certain, since they can be prepared from the alcohols without affecting the asymmetric carbon atom. The so-called isobornyl chloride is therefore similar, in its relationship to camphenyl derivatives, to the entire family of esters with the same configuration as isoborneol, and it would be extraordinary if its configuration were not the same.

[200a] The configuration of the migrating group, on the other hand, remains unchanged during rearrangement. This was established by J. F. Lane and E. S. Wallis, *J. Am. Chem. Soc.*, **63**, 1674 (1941), for the Wolff rearrangement

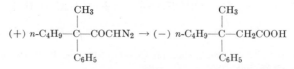

by degrading the product back to the acid from which the starting material was made. There is little reason to doubt the close analogy between the Wolff and Wagner-Meerwein rearrangements as to electronic type of the transition state.

[201] D. J. Cram, *J. Am. Chem. Soc.*, **71**, 3863 (1949); see also *ibid.*, **71**, 3871, 3875 (1949).

methods from the product acetate into the acid phthalate for reference. Consideration of these facts from the standpoint of Winstein's results on the participation of neighboring groups in displacement reactions

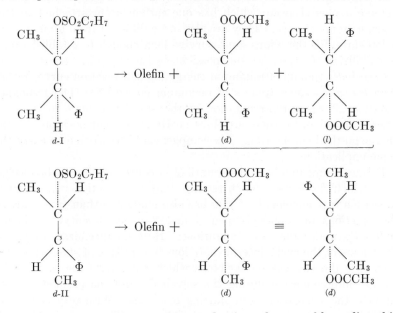

shows that there is one possible mechanism that would predict this behavior, provided that the configurations of the two isomers are as shown. This is the participation of the phenyl group in the displacement of the toluenesulfonate ion in a way similar to the formation of the ethylene-bromonium ion (see pp. 37, 38).

The cyclic intermediate from I has a plane of symmetry and can yield, by attack of acetic acid, only racemic product, although if this attack

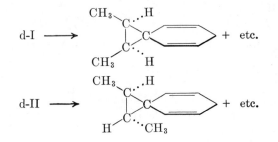

occurs with inversion the relative configurations of the carbon atoms must be the same as in the starting material. The cyclic intermediate from II has no plane of symmetry and can yield only a product with the configuration of d-II, whichever carbon is attacked. Although these intermediates possess three-membered rings, they are quite different from the stable cyclopropanes once envisaged as intermediates in molecular rearrangements, for these intermediates carry a positive charge and involve a phenyl group which has one carbon atom attached to two outside atoms at once. They are also quite different from a mere transition state, for these ions must survive long enough to establish equal probabilities of attack at the possible positions. They are therefore *intermediates* (points of minimum energy along a reaction curve) rather than *transition states* (points of maximum energy).[201a] The resonance notation affords a representation of the stabilizing force in such an intermediate ion, for there are three nearly equivalent positions for the charge on the benzene ring. A $\pi$-complex could be written to carry the same implications.

It is not immediately obvious, until after contemplation of the mechanism which the facts seem to require, that this reaction is a Wagner-Meerwein rearrangement. Cram has also made an exhaustive study of the reactions of 3-phenyl-2-pentyl and 2-phenyl-3-pentyl *p*-toluenesulfonates under the same conditions. Here no racemizations occur, since none of the cyclic intermediate ions has a plane of symmetry. In each case the two carbon skeletons which must yield the same cyclic ion are interconverted during the solvolysis, and the product composition is the same from both starting materials. With respect to part of each product, therefore, the reaction is readily recognizable as a Wagner-Meerwein rearrangement.

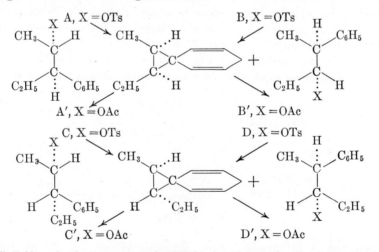

[201a] Evidence has begun to appear in 1952 for the existence also of *unsymmetrical* ions with partial bridging by the phenyl group (D. J. Cram, 4th Conference on Organic Reaction Mechanisms, Bryn Mawr, Pa., discussion Sept. 12, 1952).

The findings of Cram have a direct bearing on the formulation of McKenzie's deamination reaction (p. 59), for they suggest an intermediate that is in accord with the ionic character of the rearrangement and yet assures the preservation of the asymmetry and accounts for inversion of configuration. This intermediate resembles the one in the

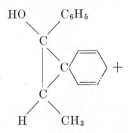

acetolysis of the 3-phenyl-2-butyl toluenesulfonates except that it requires no further displacement reaction in order to yield a stable product. The transfer of a proton from the hydroxyl group to the solvent causes the 3-ring to open between the oxygenated carbon and the benzene ring, and the change of configuration at the site of the original ring closure becomes permanent.

*Homoallylic Systems.* When an aliphatic group migrates in a molecular rearrangement no such resonance-stabilized intermediate can be written, but the question must be examined whether there are any similarities in mechanism between such cases and the migration of a phenyl group. In this connection the *i*-sterol rearrangement [202] is of interest. Cholesteryl *p*-toluenesulfonate (*A*) undergoes unimolecular

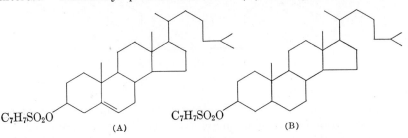

(A)  (B)

solvolysis in methanol at a rate 40 times as fast as its hydrogenation product, cholestanyl *p*-toluenesulfonate (*B*),[203] and 100 times as fast as cyclohexyl *p*-toluenesulfonate.[204] The product, in the presence of potassium acetate, is *i*-cholesteryl methyl ether (*C*),[205] and this compound

[202] See p. 1383 in Vol. II of this Treatise.
[203] W. Stoll, *Z. physiol. Chem.*, **207**, 147 (1932); **246**, 6 (1937).
[204] S. Winstein and Rowland Adams, *J. Am. Chem. Soc.*, **70**, 838 (1948).
[205] E. S. Wallis, E. Fernholz, and F. T. Gephart, *ibid.*, **59**, 137 (1937).

is much more reactive than comparable ethers in saturated ring systems, reacting with ethanol in the presence of acid to yield, first, *i*-cholesteryl ethyl ether and then cholesteryl ethyl ether.[206]   All these facts suggest that some structural feature is providing a driving force for ionization *in both directions* of the rearrangement.   When such a force is

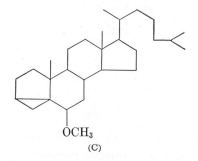

(C)

noted in the allylic rearrangement it is attributed to the formation of a resonance-stabilized cation common to both structures.   The cholesteryl compounds show the additional peculiarity [207] of undergoing certain replacements with retention of configuration, a property that is lost upon hydrogenation to cholestanyl derivatives.   All these facts are most simply interpreted by postulating a mesomeric cholesteryl ion that derives some stabilization from its mesomeric character and that is

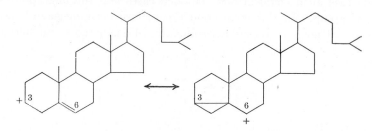

formed from the ionization of either cholesteryl or *i*-cholesteryl derivatives.   As is true of many mesomeric ions, it reacts more rapidly at one position ($C_6$) but yields products more favored at equilibrium by reaction at the other position ($C_3$).

The resonance in the cholesteryl ion bears the same relation to that in an allylic cation as the resonance in diphenylmethane bears to that in diphenyl.   The spectra of diphenylmethane, 9,10-dihydroanthracene, and triptycene show interaction of the phenyl groups in increasing

[206] S. Winstein and A. H. Schlesinger, *ibid.*, **70**, 3528 (1948).
[207] C. W. Shoppee, *J. Chem. Soc.*, 1147 (1946).

degree.[208] This interaction has been formulated in terms of an appreciable resonance of the type shown. Such resonance, involving cyclopropanic bond structures, is of the same type as that in the cholesteryl

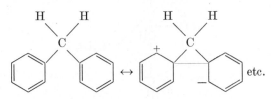

cation. Derivatives of the alcohol, 3-butenol-1, which present the possibility of this type of interaction, are appropriately known as "homoallyl" compounds. Cyclopropylcarbinyl chloride is isomerized entirely into 1-chloro-3-butene (allylcarbinyl chloride) by zinc chloride in concentrated hydrochloric acid.[208a] Less vigorous conditions lead also to cyclobutyl chloride, which is further isomerized to the acyclic chloride. Rates of solvolysis indicate a considerable driving force in the ionization of cyclopropylcarbinyl chloride but not in that of its homoallylic isomer.

*The Camphenyl-Isobornyl Cation.* In camphene hydrochloride there is no unsaturation to provide a driving force for ionization like that in cholesteryl *p*-toluenesulfonate. Nevertheless there exists the same ready interconversion of two isomers, with a complete stereospecificity on the side where configurations have been investigated. The reactivity of

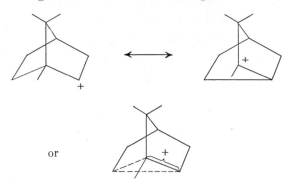

isobornyl chloride [209] is five orders of magnitude greater than that of bornyl chloride, and isobornyl compounds can undergo displacement with retention of configuration. The facts would be consistent with a

[208] P. D. Bartlett and E. S. Lewis, *J. Am. Chem. Soc.*, **72**, 1005 (1950).

[208a] J. D. Roberts and R. H. Mazur, *J. Am. Chem. Soc.*, **73**, 2509 (1951).

[209] J. D. Roberts and H. Harris, unpublished work; see J. D. Roberts, W. Bennett, and R. Armstrong, *J. Am. Chem. Soc.*, **72**, 3329 (1950).

mesomeric camphenyl-isobornyl ion [210] which may also be represented by a $\pi$-complex: [211]

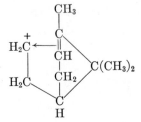

*Kinetics of the Wagner-Meerwein Rearrangement.* Because camphene hydrochloride (**CHCl**) is in equilibrium with camphene (**C**), and hydrogen chloride in all solvents, because hydrogen chloride is a catalyst for the rearrangement, and the dissociation equilibrium is rapidly established compared to the rate of the rearrangement, the rearrangement of the purest camphene hydrochloride shows 3/2 order kinetics. If the dissociation

$$CHCl \rightleftarrows C + HCl$$

is governed by the equilibrium constant

$$K = (C)(HCl)/(CHCl),$$

then

$$(HCl) = (C) = \sqrt{K(CHCl)}$$

and, if the rate of the rearrangement is proportional to the concentrations of reacting substance and of catalyst, it is equal to

$$k(CHCl)(HCl) = kK^{1/2}(CHCl)^{3/2}$$

This expresses the rate of the rearrangement when neither camphene nor hydrogen chloride is present in too great excess.[212] The detailed mechanism of the rearrangement must therefore involve a rate-determining step whose transition state involves the elements of one hydrogen chloride molecule and one camphene hydrochloride molecule. This might be accomplished by postulating that the initial ionization of camphene hydrochloride is rate-determining, and identifying the process with

$$CHCl + HCl \rightarrow CH^+ + ClHCl^-$$

This is unreasonable, however, for it is known that the addition of hydrogen chloride to camphene yields first camphene hydrochloride,

---

[210] T. P. Nevell, E. de Salas, and C. L. Wilson, *J. Chem. Soc.*, 1188 (1939).

[211] M. J. S. Dewar, "The Electronic Theory of Organic Chemistry," Clarendon Press, Oxford (1949), p. 212.

[212] P. D. Bartlett and I. Pöckel, *J. Am. Chem. Soc.*, **60**, 1585 (1938).

although this addition presumably goes through the formation of the camphenyl ion.[213]  Therefore the reversal of the above equation is faster than any other reaction of the camphenyl ion.  This is confirmed by the observation [213] that radiochloride ion is exchanged with camphene hydrochloride about 20 times as fast as the elimination of hydrogen chloride, and this in turn is faster than the rearrangement.  If the rate-determining step is not between camphene hydrochloride and hydrogen chloride, then it must be between some species whose concentrations are proportional to those of the reactant and catalyst.  The camphenyl ion and the (ClHCl)⁻ anion meet this requirement if the above reaction is considered a rapid and reversible one.  Therefore the rate-determining step in the rearrangement of camphene hydrochloride to isobornyl chloride is the reaction shown.  This is required by the kinetics, whether the camphenyl ion is mesomeric or not.

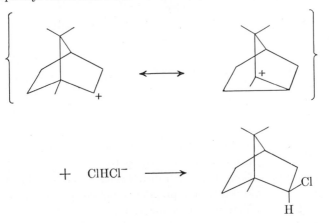

The observation of Nevell, de Salas, and Wilson that deuterium is exchanged by camphene hydrochloride at the same rate as radiochloride ion is not explained by this mechanism, although these authors thought it reasonable that the lone hydrogen atom on the carbon which is the bridgehead in the camphene hydrochloride system should readily exchange when present in the camphenyl ion.

Direct evidence for such a mesomeric ion comes from the work of Winstein and Trifan [213a] on the acetolysis of the isomeric 2-bicyclo-[2,2,1]heptyl (norbornyl) p-bromobenzenesulfonates.  Acetolysis of the exo-isomer (A) is 350 times as fast as that of the endo-isomer (B); the product in each case is the exo-acetate, and optically active starting

[213] T. P. Nevell, E. de Salas, and C. L. Wilson, loc. cit.
[213a] S. Winstein and D. S. Trifan, J. Am. Chem. Soc., **71**, 2953 (1949); **74**, 1147, 1154 (1952).

material leads to a nearly racemic product in the *endo* case and a completely racemic product in the *exo* case. It is obvious that the racemization of a norbornyl compound cannot occur by a simultaneous inversion of all three asymmetric carbon atoms. There are, however, three formal interchanges in the norbornyl cation any one of which will convert it into its mirror image. Formulas $C$, $D$, and $E$ show the distribution of the original atoms in an imaginary norbornyl derivative which has undergone, respectively, a shift of $C_6$ from bonding with $C_1$ to bonding with $C_2$; a shift of hydrogen from $C_3$ to $C_2$; and a shift of hydrogen from $C_6$ to $C_2$.

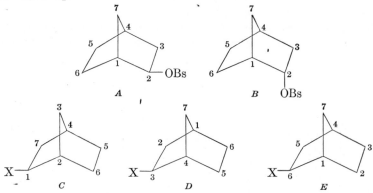

In the solvolysis of a sulfonate of *exo*-norborneol labeled with $C^{14}$ at positions 2 and 3, racemization according to $C$ would establish equivalence between positions 1 and 2 and between 3 and 7. Racemization according to $D$ would establish equivalence between 2 and 3, between 1 and 4, and between 5 and 6. Racemization according to $E$ would establish equivalence between positions 2 and 6 and between 3 and 5. The degradation of the product from an experiment of this kind showed [213b] the following distribution of radioactivity in the several positions of the product: $C_2 + C_3$, 40%; $C_1 + C_4$, 23%; $C_5 + C_6$, 16%; $C_7$, 21%. For $C$ alone we should expect the figures 50, 25, 0, 25; for $D$ alone, 100, 0, 0, 0; for $E$ alone or combined with $D$, 50, 0, 50, 0. The combination of processes $C$ and $D$ would give 40, 40, 0, 20. The combination of $C$ and $E$ would give 33.3, 16.7, 33.3, 16.7, while the combination of all three processes would give complete equivalence of all seven carbon atoms. The experimental figures are well approximated by the calculated distribution of radioactivity for process $C$ followed by a slower process, $E$, which has proceeded only 50% to equilibrium: $C_2 + C_3$, 41.7%; $C_1 + C_4$, 20.8%; $C_5 + C_6$, 16.7%; $C_7$, 20.8%.

[213b] J. D. Roberts and C. C. Lee, *J. Am. Chem. Soc.*, **73**, 5009 (1951).

The *driving force* for reaction of the *exo*-isomer and the stereospecificity of the solvolysis seem to be uniquely accounted for by the formation of a mesomeric bridged ion $F$ which is the camphenyl-isobornyl cation of Wilson stripped of its three methyl groups. The ease of the 6,2-shift indicated by the tracer results is best understood by considering [213a] that the conversion of $F$ into its equivalent $G$ or $H$ involves hardly any greater move of hydrogen than in some of the well-known 1,2-hydride shifts (see below).

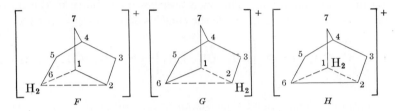

*The Question of a 1,3-Rearrangement.* The migration of a group in the simple cases of the Wagner-Meerwein rearrangement is between adjacent carbon atoms. Sometimes, as in the dimerization of the dehydration products of methyl isopropyl carbinol,[214, 215] the principal products are not those to be expected from one or two migrations between neighboring carbon atoms. Usually in such cases a way can be found to derive the products by a succession of 1,2-shifts, but often the result can be formulated more simply by a 1,3-rearrangement. This is particularly true of the conversion of 4,4-dimethyl-3-ethyl-2-pentanol into 2,4-dimethyl-3-ethyl-2-pentene as the principal product of acidic dehydration.[216]

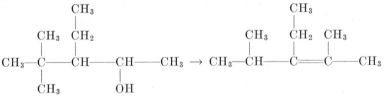

*Hydride Shifts.* The isomerization of a straight-chained into a branched halide under the influence of aluminum chloride has often been interpreted as a simple elimination and readdition of hydrogen chloride:

$$CH_3—CH_2—CH_2Cl \rightarrow (CH_3—CH=CH_2 + HCl) \rightarrow CH_3—CHCl—CH_3$$

[214] N. L. Drake, G. M. Kline, and W. G. Rose, *J. Am. Chem. Soc.*, **56**, 2076 (1934).
[215] F. C. Whitmore and W. A. Mosher, *ibid.*, **63**, 1120 (1941).
[216] W. A. Mosher and J. C. Cox, Jr., *ibid.*, **72**, 3701 (1950).

The isomerization of *n*-propyl chloride by aluminum chloride at 0° in the presence of deuterium chloride has been accomplished without any exchange of deuterium for hydrogen in the resulting isopropyl chloride.[217]  Therefore addition of hydrogen chloride to propylene is no part of the isomerization process, and this reaction is better regarded as a Wagner-Meerwein rearrangement.  Such rearrangements have been formulated by Whitmore [218] as migrations of (H:)⁻ occurring concertedly with, or immediately after, the formation of the electron-deficient center of a carbonium ion.  This view ascribes no stability to the transition state in the migration, while the concept of a π-complex between a

$$CH_3-\underset{\underset{\boxed{H}}{\overset{\cdot\cdot}{\cdot\cdot}}}{\overset{H}{C}}-CH_2:\overset{\cdot\cdot}{\underset{\cdot\cdot}{Cl}}: \longrightarrow \left[ CH_3-\overset{+}{C}H-CH_3 \right] \longrightarrow CH_3-CHCl-CH_3$$

proton and an olefinic bond suggests an intermediate of this form with some stability and even suggests the identification of the carbonium ion related to the product with such a structure.[219]  Dewar proposes that

$$CH_3-CH_2-CH_2Cl + AlCl_3 \rightarrow$$

$$AlCl_4^- + CH_3-CH\overset{\overset{H^+}{\uparrow}}{=\!=}CH_2 \xrightarrow{AlCl_4^-} CH_3-CHCl-CH_3 + AlCl_3$$

the various isomeric carbonium ions and π-complexes have separate existence and are interconverted so rapidly as to be in a state of dynamic equilibrium.

Both 2-cyclohexyl-2-propanol and 1-isopropylcyclohexanol can be converted to bromides by hydrobromic acid without alteration of structure.  The latter bromide is only slowly converted into the former on standing in solution in liquid sulfur dioxide.  Both bromides yield 2-cyclohexyl-2-propyl acetate on treatment with silver acetate in acetic acid, and both yield only olefin on simple solvolysis.[220]

**The Claisen Rearrangement.**[221]  Phenylalkyl ethers can be converted into *o*- and *p*-alkylphenols under conditions that vary with the nature of the alkyl group.  Saturated groups require a strongly acidic or electrophilic catalyst; allylic groups will migrate under the influence of heat alone.  The *sec*-butyl ethers of phenol, *m*-, and *p*-cresol are converted

[217] L. M. Nash, T. I. Taylor, and W. v. E. Doering, *ibid.*, **71**, 1516 (1949).

[218] F. C. Whitmore, *ibid.*, **54**, 3279 (1932).

[219] M. J. S. Dewar, "The Electronic Theory of Organic Chemistry," Clarendon Press, Oxford (1949), pp. 212, 213.

[220] E. B. Lefferts, *Thesis*, Harvard University, 1951.

[221] See p. 189 in Vol. I of this Treatise; D. S. Tarbell, *Chem. Revs.*, **27**, 495 (1940); *Org. Reactions*, **2**, 1 (1944).

by sulfuric acid or zinc chloride in acetic acid into mixtures of butene, sec-butylphenols, and ethers of these phenols.  Racemization accompanies these reactions of optically active sec-butyl ethers: this racemization is complete in the cases where the secondary butyl group enters the ring of an outside ether or phenol,[222] but is incomplete in the intramolecular rearrangements.[223]  The observations are consistent with a predominating ionization mechanism accompanied by a fraction of intramolecular reaction by a mechanism as yet undetermined in its details (see p. 37).

Only in the Claisen rearrangement of aryl allyl ethers into o-allylphenols and the related Cope rearrangement (see below) has the combination of structural and kinetic studies provided a mechanism which appears clear in detail.  Both crotyl and α-methylallyl aryl ethers show rearrangement of the alkyl group itself in the course of overall rearrangement.[224]  Typical Claisen rearrangements are of the first order

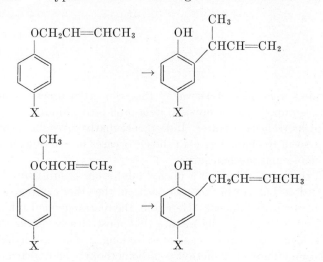

kinetically, and there is no interchange of groups on rearrangement of a mixture of phenols differing in both the allyl and the aryl group.[225] Such evidence points clearly to a strictly intramolecular mechanism involving concerted attachment of the allyl group at the ortho-position and release from the oxygen.

Models show that the stereochemical relations are entirely favorable for the transition state, shown in brackets.  Since three carbon atoms

[222] W. I. Gilbert and E. S. Wallis, J. Org. Chem., 5, 184 (1940).
[223] M. M. Sprung and E. S. Wallis, J. Am. Chem. Soc., 56, 1715 (1934).
[224] W. M. Lauer and P. A. Sanders, ibid., 65, 198 (1943).
[225] C. D. Hurd and L. Schmerling, ibid., 59, 107 (1937).

are changing between the tercovalent and quadricovalent conditions, the form of the transition state should be as nearly as possible compatible with the requirements of both. A model shows how smoothly this change can be accomplished geometrically, with the allylic group occupying a plane below, and almost parallel with, that of the benzene ring, and changes in position at the seats of reaction being somewhat less than those accompanying an ordinary bimolecular displacement.

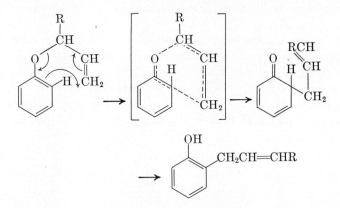

This refutes a surmise of Dewar [226] that concerted processes involving an allylic group should be opposed by a prohibitive hindrance, requiring an all-linear transition state. Indeed, peculiarly favorable geometrical relations seem to characterize all the clear cases of reactions proceeding by intramolecular mechanisms.

When the benzene ring of a phenyl allyl ether is substituted in both *ortho* positions but not in the *para* position, the ether can rearrange into a *p*-allyl-substituted phenol. Here, too, the rearrangement is kinetically of the first order,[227] but the feature that most clearly marks the *ortho*-rearrangement as intramolecular is lacking. The α-ethylallyl and γ-ethylallyl ethers of 2-methyl-6-carbomethoxyphenol rearrange into the same *p*-substituted phenol, indicating that the rearrangement affords an opportunity for structural equilibration of the allylic system.[228] Nevertheless, an ionization mechanism for the *para*-Claisen rearrangement is not entirely satisfactory, for it would seem to demand that a solvent of high nucleophilic reactivity, such as dimethylaniline, should be alkylated under rearranging conditions. Such alkylation is not ob-

[226] M. J. S. Dewar, "The Electronic Theory of Organic Chemistry," Clarendon Press, Oxford (1949), p. 86.

[227] D. S. Tarbell and J. F. Kincaid, *J. Am. Chem. Soc.*, **62**, 728 (1940).

[228] O. Mumm, H. Hornhardt, and J. Diederichsen, *Ber.*, **72**, 100 (1939); Mumm and Diederichsen, *Ber.*, **72**, 1523 (1939).

served.[229]  This reaction belongs to a group of phenomena in the aromatic series which have been considered to demand an ability of a carbonium ion or other electrophilic fragment to be bonded to the $\pi$-electrons of the benzene ring without being bound to a specific position. In this class are the isomerizations of n-alkylbenzenes without change in structure of the alkyl group,[230] and the isomerization of alkylbenzenesulfonic acids.[231]

The close similarities and important differences between the Claisen rearrangements to the *ortho*- and *para*-positions emphasize how easily a small change in structure of a compound or in experimental conditions may make a change in the mechanism by which a reaction occurs.  A reaction mechanism can seldom, if ever, be established by the application of any single simple test but must be scrutinized by a variety of methods and subjected to experimental tests specifically designed to answer the questions pertinent to the case at hand.  In particular, the several respects in which ionic and intramolecular mechanisms are similar render it often quite difficult to distinguish between them with certainty.  For the application of a different criterion of intramolecularity, see the discussion of decarboxylation of dimethylacetoacetic acid, pp. 104–106.

**The Cope Rearrangement.**  Cope and his co-workers have shown that the occurrence of intramolecular rearrangement in strictly carbon chains of the type shown is general, unimolecular, involves "inversion"

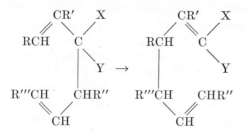

of the substituted allyl group shown in the lower half of the formula, and occurs without interchange of groups between different molecules of the same type rearranging in mixtures.[232]  The rearrangement pro-

[229] D. S. Tarbell, *Org. Reactions*, **2**, 17 (1944).

[230] G. Baddeley and J. Kenner, *J. Chem. Soc.*, 303 (1935).

[231] A. F. Holleman and P. Caland, *Ber.*, **44**, 2504 (1911); for a discussion of $\pi$-complexes see M. J. S. Dewar, *loc. cit.*, and *J. Chem. Soc.*, 406 (1946); A. D. Walsh, *Nature*, **159**, 165 (1947).

[232] (a) A. C. Cope and E. M. Hardy, *J. Am. Chem. Soc.*, **62**, 441 (1940); (b) A. C. Cope, K. E. Hoyle, and D. Heyl, *ibid.*, **63**, 1843 (1941); (c) A. C. Cope, C. M. Hofmann, and E. M. Hardy, *ibid.*, **63**, 1852 (1941); (d) D. E. Whyte and A. C. Cope, *ibid.*, **65**, 1999 (1943); (e) H. Levy and A. C. Cope, *ibid.*, **66**, 1684 (1944); (f) E. G. Foster, A. C. Cope, and F. Daniels, *ibid.*, **69**, 1893 (1947).

ceeds completely in the forward direction at temperatures from 165°
to 185° when X or Y is COOR, COOH, CN, or $C_6H_5$. When X is
methyl and Y is hydrogen, the rearrangement proceeds slowly and incompletely at 300°, the reverse rearrangement being realizable to a
limited extent. It is therefore helpful to the equilibrium and rate for X
or Y to be a group affording strong conjugation with the carbon-carbon
double bond, but even in the absence of such groups there is enough
allylic resonance in the transition state to permit the reaction to proceed
at temperatures far below those for thermal rupture of an ordinary
carbon-carbon bond.

Three Cope rearrangements which were studied kinetically [232f] had
entropies of activation of $-11.1$ to $-14.0$ e.u., consistent with a cyclic
transition state as opposed to a rate-determining step involving cleavage.

A similar rearrangement proceeding with even greater ease is the
conversion of an allylamine oxide into an O-allylhydroxylamine. The
rearrangement of crotylmethylaniline oxide proceeds below 100° with
inversion of the crotyl group: [233]

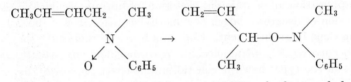

**Oxonium Salts.** The increased water-solubility of ethers and alcohols
which is produced by strong acids is evidence that these compounds
have a basicity which differs from that of amines only in degree. Ethers,
however, do not have the property common to aliphatic tertiary amines
and sulfides of being readily alkylated by a variety of alkylating agents.
The only known alkylating agents that will react with dimethyl or
diethyl ether to yield a tertiary oxonium salt are the very polar complexes of methyl and ethyl fluorides with boron trifluoride.[234]

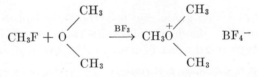

These tertiary oxonium salts are among the strongest known alkylating
agents, being attacked rapidly by every solvent or reagent with any
nucleophilic properties:

$$\overset{+}{(CH_3)_3O} + 2H_2O \rightarrow CH_3OH + H_3O^+ + (CH_3)_2O$$

[233] R. F. Kleinschmidt and A. C. Cope, *ibid.*, **66**, 1929 (1944).
[234] H. Meerwein, G. Hinz, P. Hofmann, E. Kroning, and E. Pfeil, *J. prakt. Chem.*,
[2] **147**, 257 (1937).

Thus the difficulty in dealing with tertiary oxonium salts is twofold: they are very unfavored at equilibrium, and the establishment of equilibrium is rapid even at moderate temperatures. This mobility is perhaps associated with the much greater ionic character in the C—O bond than in the C—N or C—S bond,[235] although ionic character in the "energetic" sense is not what determines the reactivities of the alkyl halides relative to one another or to alcohols.

By distribution of the charge through a benzenoid or other resonating system, as in the pyrylium ion, a tertiary oxonium ion is greatly stabilized.[236]

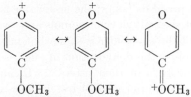

The mobility of formation and decomposition of tertiary oxonium ions may be involved in the mechanisms of some reactions in which the salts are not obtainable as intermediates. Such a reaction is the cleavage of ethers by acetyl iodide,[237] which might be represented:

$$\underset{R}{\overset{R}{\diagdown}}O + CH_3CI \rightarrow \underset{R}{\overset{R}{\diagdown}}\overset{+}{O}CCH_3\,I^- \rightarrow RI + ROCCH_3$$

and thus be analogous to the von Braun cleavage of tertiary amines by cyanogen bromide.[238]

**The Oxidation of Alcohols.** It is often said that the essential step in any oxidation-reduction process is a transfer of electrons. This is so for that large class of oxidation-reduction reactions which occur reversibly at an electrode, including the interconversion of quinones, semi-quinones, hydroquinones, and analogous substances.[239] Attractive ex-

[235] L. Pauling, "Nature of the Chemical Bond," Cornell University Press, Ithaca, N. Y. (1940), p. 64.

[236] A. Baeyer, *Ber.*, **43**, 2337 (1910).

[237] E. L. Gustus and P. G. Stevens, *J. Am. Chem. Soc.*, **55**, 378 (1933).

[238] See pp. 1174–1175 in Vol. II of this Treatise. An illustration is given on p. 1175 of the differing directions of cleavage of a tetrahydroisoquinoline in the von Braun and Hofmann degradations. This difference is the outcome of an $S_N2$ attack (on carbon) adjacent to the nitrogen, in the one case, and an $E2$ attack (on hydrogen) $\beta$ to the nitrogen in the other, on a quaternary ammonium ion. In each case the favored point of attack is that next to the benzene ring, for reasons that have been brought out in this discussion.

[239] For many pertinent references, see J. E. LuValle and A. Weissberger, *J. Am. Chem. Soc.*, **69**, 1567 (1947).

planations of some other organic reactions have been offered involving an electron-transfer step.[240]   In general, however, the definition of oxidation as a process of electron transfer fails to include many of the reactions commonly designated as "oxidations" in organic chemistry. The removal of hydrogen from a simple alcohol to yield an aldehyde or ketone does not occur reversibly at an electrode, and as details of its mechanism begin to appear no stage is found which consists of the removal of one or more electrons from the alcohol unattended by some atoms.

The oxidation of secondary alcohols by chromic anhydride in aqueous acetic acid solution proceeds faster, the less water is present in the solvent.   In a series of six 2-alkylcyclohexanols and two 4-alkylcyclohexanols the oxidation of the *cis*-isomer is somewhat faster than that of the *trans*,[241] thus resembling the dehydration of such isomeric pairs but in contrast to the hydrolysis of their esters.[242]   In aqueous solution the rate of oxidation of isopropyl alcohol by chromic acid is proportional to the isopropyl alcohol concentration, the hydrogen-ion concentration at low acidities and its square in $0.2$–$0.5$ $M$ acid, and the concentration of the acid chromate ion, $HCrO_4^-$.[243]   In connection with their study of the mechanism of this reaction, Westheimer and Nicolaides [244] made an application of tracer elements based upon a *difference*, rather than a *similarity*, between the behavior of two isotopes in an organic compound.

In all reactions involving the transfer of hydrogen from one atom to another the vibrational energy of this bond is converted, in the transition state, partly or wholly into translational energy and thus becomes a contribution toward the energy necessary to produce the transition state.   Because of the difference in mass between light hydrogen and deuterium the vibrational quantum is larger in the former than in the latter and this means a corresponding difference in the zero-point energies.   Depending upon the degree of bonding in the transition state, this will be reflected in the activation energies for the transfer of a proton, deuteron, or a light or heavy hydrogen atom.   The resulting difference in rates is large, amounting to 5- or 6-fold for proton transfer compared to deuteron transfer at ordinary temperatures.   Although such differences were known some years ago,[245] neglect of them has

[240] J. Weiss, *J. Chem. Soc.*, 245 (1942); R. B. Woodward, *J. Am. Chem. Soc.*, **64**, 3058 (1942).

[241] G. Vavon and C. Zaremba, *Bull. soc. chim. France*, **49**, 1853 (1931).

[242] G. Vavon, *ibid.*, **49**, 937 (1931).

[243] F. H. Westheimer and A. Novick, *J. Chem. Phys.*, **11**, 506 (1943).

[244] F. H. Westheimer and N. Nicolaides, *J. Am. Chem. Soc.*, **71**, 25 (1949).

[245] H. S. Taylor and H. Eyring, *Proc. Am. Phil. Soc.*, **72**, 255 (1933); W. F. K. Wynne-Jones, *Chem. Revs.*, **17**, 115 (1935); H. C. Urey and G. K. Teal, *Rev. Modern Phys.*, **7**, 34 (1935).

vitiated the interpretation of some experiments in which incompletely deuterated media were used without correcting for the much greater reaction rate of the protium component as compared to the deuterium component.

In the oxidation of isopropyl alcohol by chromic acid, it was found that 2-propanol-2$d$, $CH_3CDOHCH_3$, was attacked only one-sixth as rapidly as ordinary 2-propanol. This is direct evidence that the hydrogen atom attached to the hydroxylated carbon is transferred in the rate-determining step. Either of two transition states, $A$ or $B$, for the reaction in strong acid, would be consistent with these results. $A$ represents a simpler picture, since it can be produced by a direct collision

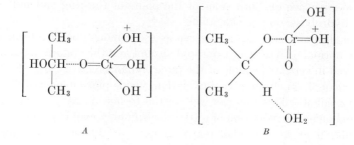

$A$                    $B$

without the necessity of a preliminary formation of the ester, monoisopropyl chromate. However, later work [246] established a strong probability for the occurrence of the chromic ester as an intermediate.

A neutral, bright yellow chromate is extractable into benzene or toluene from aqueous solutions of isopropyl alcohol and chromic acid. This ester is formed very rapidly, is unstable, and its decomposition is accelerated not only by water but also by other bases such as pyridine or dimethylaniline. Indeed, an accelerating effect of pyridine upon the chromate oxidation of isopropyl alcohol is demonstrable even in aqueous solutions of $pH$ between 2 and 3. This basic catalysis brings out the interesting fact that the hydrogen atom which is being attacked in the rate-determining step, though in a position from which transfer of a hydride ion often occurs in other reactions (see p. 80), is here being transferred as a proton. The fact that extraction detects the neutral diisopropyl chromate establishes *a fortiori* the presence in mobile equilibrium of the *acid* chromate ester demanded by the kinetics.

[246] W. Watanabe and F. H. Westheimer, *J. Chem. Phys.*, **17**, 61 (1949); F. H. Westheimer, *Chem. Revs.*, **45**, 419 (1949); F. Holloway, M. Cohen, and F. H. Westheimer, *J. Am. Chem. Soc.*, **73**, 65 (1951).

In the reaction of triphenylsilane with water in piperidine solution

$$(C_6H_5)_3SiH + H_2O \xrightarrow{\text{C}_5\text{H}_{11}\text{N}} (C_6H_5)_3SiOH + H_2$$

the substitution of deuterium for hydrogen on the silicon atom actually increases the rate.[247] This would appear to constitute evidence for a transition state in which the hydrogen is more firmly bonded than in the silane, which shows that conclusions relating to proton transfer cannot be indiscriminately applied to the transfer of deuterons.

The transition state $B$ suggests a reason why, in the experiments of Vavon and Zaremba, the difference between the rates of oxidation of the *cis*- and *trans*-isomers is so small. Processes subject to hindrance are taking place on both sides of the plane of the ring and not, as in ester hydrolysis, on one side alone.

The chromic ester can also serve as a common type of intermediate in the normal oxidation of isopropyl alcohol and the abnormal oxidation observed in certain alcohols of the pinacolyl and related types.[248] Pinacolyl alcohol, on chromic acid oxidation, yields pinacolone and 6% of *t*-butyl alcohol. This fact, as well as the formation of a phenol and a benzophenone on oxidation of a triaryl carbinol,[249] could be conveniently formulated as a molecular rearrangement or $\beta$-fission attending the cleavage of the chromic ester at the O—Cr bond:

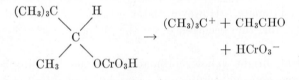

$$(CH_3)_3C^+ + 2H_2O \rightarrow (CH_3)_3COH + H_3O^+$$

Waters[250] and Fieser[251] have observed the absorption of small amounts of oxygen during the course of chromic acid oxidation. Waters has suggested that this may point to a radical-chain mechanism for the oxidation, but in the light of the findings of Westheimer it is highly probable that the oxygen is being absorbed by lower oxidation states of chromium and not by organic fragments.

**The Equilibration of Alcohols and Ketones by Alkali Alkoxides.** A secondary alcohol can often be converted into a stereoisomer by heating

[247] H. Gilman, G. E. Dunn, and G. S. Hammond, *J. Am. Chem. Soc.*, **73**, 4499 (1951).

[248] W. A. Mosher and F. C. Whitmore, *ibid.*, **70**, 2544 (1948); W. A. Mosher and E. O. Langerak, *ibid.*, **71**, 286 (1949).

[249] See P. D. Bartlett and J. D. Cotman, Jr., *ibid.*, **72**, 3096 (1950).

[250] W. A. Waters, *J. Chem. Soc.*, 1151 (1946).

[251] L. F. Fieser, *Discussions Faraday Soc.*, **2**, 245 (1947).

with a sodium alkoxide.   This reaction was interpreted by Hückel [252] as the establishment of a hydrogenation-dehydrogenation equilibrium between the alcohol and the related ketone, the rehydrogenation being accomplished in both stereochemical senses.   Thus for isoborneol: [253]

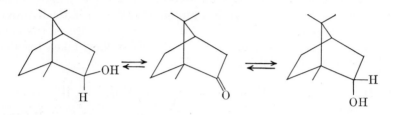

Convincing proof of the correctness of this view has been brought by Doering and his co-workers [254] in the case of the isomerization of quinine into quinidine, epiquinine, and epiquinidine, and in several other racemizations, epimerizations, and reductions.   Optically active phenyl-methyl carbinol (A) is stable against racemization in boiling toluene with sodium t-butoxide unless an oxidizing substance is added.   Fluorenone in the amount of 5 mole per cent based on the alcohol makes racemization easy under these conditions.   This is evidence that alkali does not act directly to change the configuration at the alcoholic carbon atom but is effective only through promoting equilibrium with acetophenone (B), by a hydrogenation-dehydrogenation equilibrium with some ketone originally present.

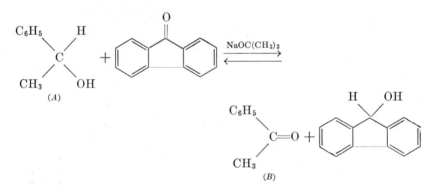

[252] W. Hückel and H. Naab, *Ber.*, **64**, 2137 (1931); see W. Hückel, "Theoretische Grundlagen der organischen Chemie," Akademische Verlagsgesellschaft, Leipzig (1949), 6th ed., Vol. 1, pp. 393 ff.

[253] G. Wagner and W. Bryckner, *J. Russ. Phys. Chem. Soc.*, **35**, 537 (1903).

[254] W. E. Doering and T. C. Aschner, *J. Am. Chem. Soc.*, **71**, 838 (1949); W. E. Doering, G. Cortes, and L. H. Knox, *ibid.*, **69**, 1700 (1947).

The manner in which the hydrogen is transferred from the carbon of the alcohol to that of the carbonyl group in the ketone is indicated by deuterium-exchange experiments. Optically active 2-methyl-1-butanol-1d (C) is racemized by an alkali alkoxide in the presence of a ketone without losing any deuterium to the solvent. This cannot happen if the hydrogen appears at any stage as a proton, in water, or in the hydroxyl group of an alcohol. It is possible if the transfer of hydrogen from one carbon to another is as hydride ion, H:$^{-}$. These facts taken together lend support to the following mechanism:

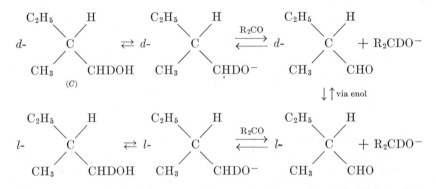

In the case of quinine the situation is complicated by several facts: (1) Quinine has a sufficiently hindered structure so that it will not enter into direct hydrogenation-dehydrogenation equilibria with its own related ketone, quininone (B); therefore the addition of a little quininone alone is not sufficient to convert quinine into the isomeric alcohols. (2) Quininone has an asymmetric carbon atom in the α-position and is rapidly enolized by strong bases with the establishment of equilibrium between it and epiquininone (C). Of the four possible diastereomeric alcohols the two most rapidly equilibrated with each other are quinine (A) and quinidine (D), which are the more rapidly formed reduction products of the ketones (B) and (C), respectively, the equilibrium B ⇌ C being the most rapidly established of all. (3) The quinine molecule contains a hydrogen-acceptor center in the quinoline ring, and in the presence of strong base a substantial amount of the quinine is oxidized irreversibly to quininone, although no rehydrogenation of this ketone by unchanged quinine occurs. (4) Epiquinine (E) and epiquinidine (F), though formed more slowly from the ketones than their isomers, are dehydrogenated still more slowly, and gradually accumulate as overall equilibrium is approached.

Partial asymmetric reduction of isobutyrophenone in optically active sec-butylcarbinol affords confirmatory evidence that the reductant is not

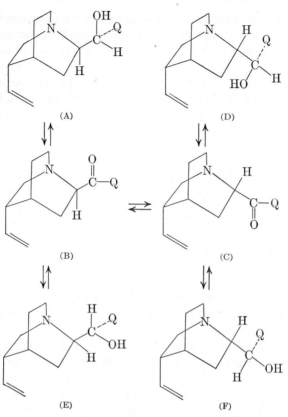

(A)          (D)

(B)     ⇌     (C)

(E)          (F)

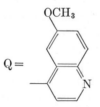

$Q=$

the optically inactive alkoxide originally added to the reaction but rather an alkoxide ion with asymmetry of its own. The necessity of ketones, even when present in small amounts, in the racemization of optically active secondary alkoxide can account for discrepancies such as that between the work of Rometsch and Kuhn [255] and that of Doughty and Kenyon [256] as to the racemizability of sec-butyl alcohol by sodium.

[255] R. Rometsch and W. Kuhn, *Helv. Chim. Acta*, **29**, 1488 (1946).
[256] M. Doughty and J. Kenyon, *ibid.*, **30**, 2142 (1947).

**The Cannizzaro Reaction.** A special case of the foregoing mechanism is possible when a strong base acts upon an aldehyde having no active hydrogen in the $\alpha$-position. The conversion of a portion of the aldehyde at equilibrium into the addition product of the hydroxyl ion endows this product with all the necessary properties of an alkoxide ion. It can then transfer its C-hydrogen to another aldehyde molecule, being itself converted irreversibly into acid, which becomes fixed as the negative ion:

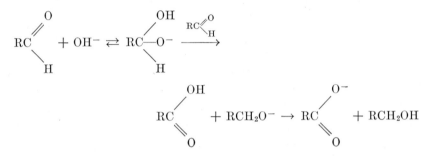

The fact that hydrogen in the aldehyde does not exchange with the solvent during the Cannizzaro reaction [257] is a point of similarity demanded by this mechanism.

**Hydrogenation-Dehydrogenation between Ketones and Aluminum Alkoxides.**[258] Treatment of a ketone with aluminum isopropoxide will establish equilibrium between these reactants, acetone, and the aluminum derivative of the hydrogenation product of the ketone (Meerwein-Ponndorf-Verley reduction). Similarly, an alcohol can be dehydrogenated by conversion into its aluminum derivative with aluminum $t$-butoxide and treatment with a ketone (Oppenauer oxidation). In general, quinones and aromatic ketones tend to be better oxidants, i.e., lead to more favorable equilibria in dehydrogenation of an alcohol, than do saturated ketones.[259] However, the rate of attainment of equilibrium may be very much greater for systems with less hindrance, irrespective of the equilibrium relations. For example, fluorenone gives more rapid dehydrogenations by a rate factor of two powers of 10 than the somewhat better oxidant benzophenone, and quinine cannot be dehydrogenated to quininone by means of the Oppenauer technique with aluminum $t$-butoxide and a ketone.[260]

These similarities and differences between the Meerwein-Ponndorf-Verley-Oppenauer equilibration and that brought about by strong bases

[257] H. Fredenhagen and K. F. Bonhoeffer, *Z. physik. Chem.*, **A181**, 379 (1938).
[258] See A. L. Wilds, *Org. Reactions*, **2**, 178 (1944).
[259] R. H. Baker and H. Adkins, *J. Am. Chem. Soc.*, **62**, 3305 (1940).
[260] R. B. Woodward, N. L. Wendler, and F. J. Brutschy, *ibid.*, **67**, 1425 (1945).

suggest that the mechanism of this reaction also involves a hydride transfer, but in the less ionic conditions of the close molecular complexes which are favored with aluminum compounds. Such a mechanism

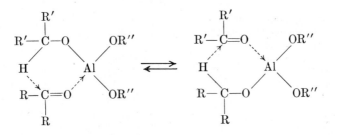

would explain the greater susceptibility of the aluminum alkoxide reduction to steric hindrance. The aluminum alkoxide procedure is preferable with condensable ketones, where strong bases must be avoided, whereas the use of alkali alkoxides is preferable with hindered ketones where danger of condensation is small.

If the transfer of hydride ion in the equilibration of a ketone and an alcohol can be effected either by donation from a negative ion or by an internal cyclic process within a coördinate complex, as these two examples suggest, then the reduction of carbonyl compounds by lithium aluminum hydride in ether [261] is a borderline case. The solubility of the reagent in ether would seem to place it with the less ionic type.

## Some Reactions of the Carbonyl Group

**Basic Strength.** Ketones, like alcohols and ethers, have unshared electrons and accordingly are bases. In many of the reactions of the carbonyl group this basicity can be recognized as playing an important part in the mechanism. Table V shows the basic strengths of some compounds containing the carbonyl group expressed as $pK_A$, the negative logarithm of the ionization constant of the conjugate acid $BH^+$ where

$$R_2C{=}O + H^+ \rightleftarrows R_2C{=}OH^+$$
$$\text{(B)} \qquad\qquad \text{(BH}^+\text{)}$$

$$K_A = \frac{[H^+][R_2C{=}O]}{[R_2C{=}OH^+]} = \frac{a_{H^+}c_B f_B}{c_{BH^+}f_{BH^+}}$$

$a$ = activity, $c$ = concentration, and $f = a/c$ = activity coefficient. Such constants have been estimated chiefly by two methods.

[261] R. F. Nystrom and W. G. Brown, *ibid.*, **69**, 1197 (1947).

## TABLE V

BASIC STRENGTHS OF OXYGEN COMPOUNDS EXPRESSED AS $pK_A$ FOR $BH^+$

| | $H_2SO_4$—$H_2O$ * | IR † |
|---|---|---|
| Benzalacetophenone | −5.61 | |
| β-Benzoylnaphthalene | −5.92 | |
| β-Benzoylbiphenyl | −6.19 | |
| Anthraquinone | −8.15 | |
| ΦCOOH | −7.25 ‡ | |
| ΦCOCH₃ | | −6.00 |
| ΦNO₂ | −11.26 § | −10.4 |
| ΦCHO | | −5.1 |
| Acetone | | −3.7 |
| EtOAc | | −5.1 |
| i-Pr₂O | | ⌒−2 |

* L. P. Hammett and A. J. Deyrup, *J. Am. Chem. Soc.*, **54**, 2721 (1932); L. P. Hammett, *Chem. Revs.*, **16**, 67 (1935); L. P. Hammett and M. A. Paul, *J. Am. Chem. Soc.*, **56**, 827 (1934).

† W. Gordy and S. C. Stanford, *J. Chem. Phys.*, **8**, 175 (1940).

‡ L. P. Hammett, A. Dingwall, and L. Flexser, *J. Am. Chem. Soc.*, **56**, 2010 (1934).

§ J. C. D. Brand, *J. Chem. Soc.*, 997 (1950).

In the method of Hammett [262] a series of simple basic indicators which undergo a color change on conversion to their conjugate acids are examined colorimetrically in a series of mixtures of water and strong acid, usually sulfuric. In each solution the proportion of the indicator that is in its acidic form is governed by the equation

$$\frac{c_{BH^+}}{c_B} = \frac{a_{H^+}f_B}{K_A f_{BH^+}} \quad \text{or} \quad \log\frac{c_{BH^+}}{c_B} = pK_A - pH + \log\frac{f_B}{f_{BH^+}}$$

Therefore over the range of composition of the acid mixture where this fraction is measurable, i.e., not too near zero or 100%, it is possible to compare the acid mixtures with respect to the property ($pH - \log f_B/f_{BH^+}$). This quantity is defined as the "acidity function" and is designated by the symbol $H_0$. The acidity function is assumed to be independent of the nature of B so long as B remains uncharged. By choosing a series of basic indicators whose measurable ranges overlap, it has been possible to assign values of $H_0$ to mixtures of water and sulfuric or other strong acid up into the regions of extremely high hydrogen-ion activity where the solutions are very non-ideal. If now the conversion of any basic substance into its conjugate acid is associated with a change of light absorption either in the visible or in the ultra-

[262] L. P. Hammett, "Physical Organic Chemistry," McGraw-Hill Book Co., New York (1940), pp. 262–273.

violet, it is possible to assign a value to the ionization constant for that substance by knowing the $H_0$ of any solution in which the base is converted to its conjugate acid to a measurable extent.

The second method is that of Gordy.[263] It has been established that the formation of a hydrogen bond between a basic substance and water or an alcohol causes a shift in the position of the infrared band due to the O—H vibration. Empirically the magnitude of this shift is proportional to the logarithm of the basicity constant of the base where this is independently known. Favorable conditions for observation with weak bases exist in deuterium-bond formation with deuteromethanol and with heavy water since the absorptions to be observed in these cases do not interfere with others normally present. Still weaker bases have been evaluated by observing the HCl stretching band in solutions of hydrogen chloride in the compound in question.

It will be observed from Table V that the ketones are very weak bases indeed and that the strength of benzoic acid as a base falls between that of $p$-benzoylbiphenyl and that of anthraquinone. A ketone with $pK_A$ of $-6$ would exist in water solution containing 0.01 $N$ sulfuric acid to the extent of only one-millionth of 1% in the form of its conjugate acid. Nevertheless, as will appear below, this small fraction of the conjugate acid may be all-important in certain mechanisms of reaction.

**The Keto-Enol Equilibrium.** $\beta$-Diketones and $\beta$-keto esters having at least one hydrogen atom between the two carbonyl groups and certain $\alpha$-diketones and carbonyl compounds with special conjugation exist in

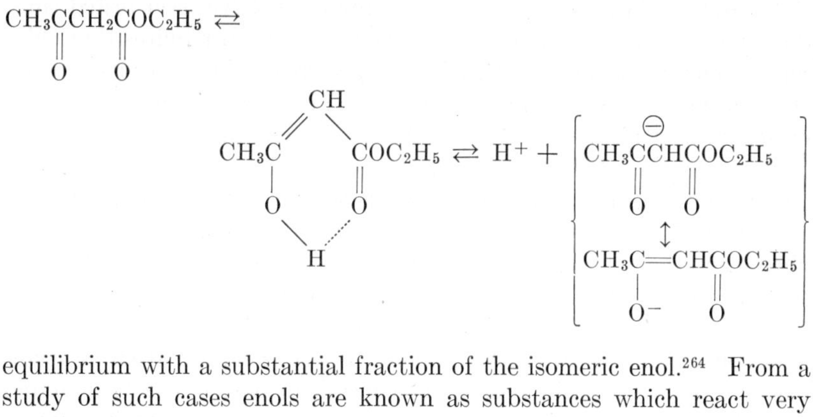

equilibrium with a substantial fraction of the isomeric enol.[264] From a study of such cases enols are known as substances which react very rapidly with halogens,[265] are measurably acidic, and yield anions which

[263] W. Gordy and S. C. Stanford, *J. Chem. Phys.*, **9**, 204 (1941); W. Gordy, *ibid.*, **9**, 215, 440 (1941).

[264] See pp. 1040 and 1041 in Vol. I of this Treatise.

[265] K. H. Meyer, *Ber.*, **45**, 2846 (1912).

are reactive both at the oxygen and at the carbon in the $\alpha$-position to the hydroxyl group. The enolate anion is an example of a molecular species best represented as a resonance hybrid. The enols themselves have a perfectly definite molecular structure since interconversion with their ketonic isomers involves a change in bonding of a hydrogen atom.

Simple ketones enolize to an extremely small extent at equilibrium ($2.5 \times 10^{-4}\%$ in the case of acetone),[266] but a study of the kinetics of certain of their reactions early indicated the occurrence of enolization. Hydrogen in the $\alpha$-position to the carbonyl group is replaced by halogen much more easily than hydrogen elsewhere in the molecule. The rate of halogenation of acetone is proportional to the concentration of the ketone and of acidic and basic substances present but is independent of the concentration of halogen.[267] When a participant in the overall chemical equation is not involved in the kinetic equation it can only mean that the reaction proceeds in at least two steps and that the step which determines the rate is one not involving that participant. In the case of the bromination of acetone the kinetic evidence is interpreted as indicating the following mechanism:

$$
\begin{array}{c}
CH_3 \\
| \\
C\!\!=\!\!O \\
| \\
CH_3
\end{array}
\xrightarrow[\text{Slow}]{\text{Acid or base}}
\begin{array}{c}
CH_2 \\
\| \\
C\!\!-\!\!OH \\
| \\
CH_3
\end{array}
\xrightarrow[\text{Fast}]{Br_2}
\left[
\begin{array}{c}
CH_2Br \\
| \quad\diagup OH \\
C \\
| \quad\diagdown Br \\
CH_3
\end{array}
\right]
\rightarrow
\begin{array}{c}
CH_2Br \\
| \\
C\!\!=\!\!O \\
| \\
CH_3
\end{array}
+ HBr
$$

A number of corollaries of this interpretation have been tested since the original work of Lapworth. (1) The mechanism requires that chlorine, bromine, and iodine, though differing greatly in reactivity, should all react with acetone at the same rate. (2) It is also obvious that in the presence of very powerful catalysts enolization might become faster than bromination; then the concentration of the halogen would begin to enter into the rate equation. Such is the case with the iodination of acetophenones in 51% sulfuric acid [268] and the chlorination of acetophenone in the more basic aqueous solutions.[269] (3) An enol can have no asymmetry about the $\alpha$-carbon atom. Therefore the same catalysts that promote the halogenation of acetone should bring about the racemization of an optically active ketone whose $\alpha$-carbon atom is asymmetric. This has been repeatedly confirmed, and it has been found that the rates of halogenation and of racemization of such ketones as

[266] G. Schwarzenbach and C. Wittwer, *Helv. Chim. Acta*, **30**, 669 (1947).

[267] A. Lapworth, *J. Chem. Soc.*, **85**, 30 (1904).

[268] L. Zucker and L. P. Hammett, *J. Am. Chem. Soc.*, **61**, 2785 (1939).

[269] P. D. Bartlett and J. R. Vincent, *ibid.*, **57**, 1596 (1935).

2-o-carboxybenzyl-1-indanone (A)[270a] and d-phenyl-sec-butyl ketone (B)[270b] are identical within the experimental error. (4) The ketonization of an enol in a deuterated medium affords an opportunity for the binding of deuterium to the α-carbon atom, and this process is found to be still another way of measuring the rate of enolization.[271] (5) Other

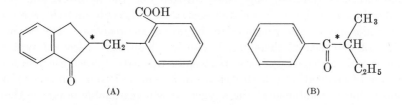

(A)                                                    (B)

reactions proceeding through enolization are the conversion of an unsymmetrical benzoin into its isomer,[272] the autoxidation and racemization of benzoins,[273] and the equilibration between α,β- and β,γ-unsaturated ketones.[274] (6) Finally, evidence from kinetics and tracers

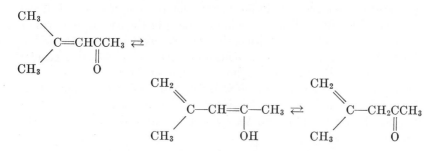

points to enolization as the rate-determining step in certain aldol condensations. (See pp. 102–104.)

*Kinetics of Enolization.* The kinetics of enolization has been investigated chiefly through the iodination of acetone in water. This reaction proceeds at a rate which is the sum of a contribution from each acidic molecular species and each basic molecular species present in the so-

[270] (a) C. K. Ingold and C. L. Wilson, *J. Chem. Soc.*, 773 (1934); (b) P. D. Bartlett and C. H. Stauffer, *J. Am. Chem. Soc.*, **57**, 2580 (1935).

[271] S. K. Hsü, C. K. Ingold, and C. L. Wilson, *J. Chem. Soc.*, 78 (1938).

[272] E. M. Luis, *ibid.*, 2547 (1932).

[273] A. Weissberger, H. Mainz, and E. Strasser, *Ber.*, **62B**, 1942 (1929); A. Weissberger, E. Strasser, H. Mainz, and W. Schwarze, *Ann.*, **478**, 112 (1930); A. Weissberger, A. Dörken, and W. Schwarze, *Ber.*, **64B**, 1200 (1931); A. Weissberger, *Ber.*, **65B**, 1815 (1932); *J. Chem. Soc.*, 223 (1935); and other papers.

[274] G. A. R. Kon, *J. Chem. Soc.*, 1616 (1930); *Ann. Repts. Chem. Soc.*, **29**, 138 (1932); see pp. 1041–1044 in Vol. I of this Treatise. F. H. Stross, J. M. Monger, and H. de V. Finch, *J. Am. Chem. Soc.*, **69**, 1627 (1947).

lution.[275]  For example, the reaction proceeds substantially faster in an acetic acid and sodium acetate buffer solution having the components present at a concentration of 0.1 $M$ than in a buffer solution of identical $p$H but with the components present at only 0.01 $M$ concentration. This is characteristic of the so-called general acid and basic catalysis [276] and indicates that not only the hydrogen ion, the hydroxyl ion, and water but also the undissociated acetic acid molecule and the acetate ion make specific contributions to the rate of the reaction.  The mechanism of enolization, therefore, is one in which any species of proton donor and any species of proton acceptor can participate.  Since in the course of enolization a hydrogen atom is removed from the $\alpha$-position and becomes combined at the oxygen, it is a reasonable inference that proton acceptors (bases) attack the proton at the $\alpha$-position while proton donors (acids) are concerned with the delivery of a proton to the oxygen.  Simple as this concept is, a detailed mechanism consistent with all the experimental facts has not been found.

Brönsted [277] interpreted general acid-base catalysis as indicating that the transfer of a proton might be the rate-determining step in a chemical reaction.  This fits well with the known facts in the case of removal of a proton from combination with carbon or delivery of a proton to carbon. However, except for very weak acids and bases (see p. 48), it is general experience that the transfers of protons between oxygen atoms are too fast to measure, and this makes it difficult to assign a mechanism to *acid*-catalyzed enolization which involves slow proton transfer to the oxygen.  Lowry [278] suggested that acid-base catalysis always involves

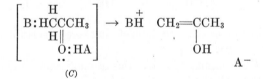

a proton donor acting at one point in the molecule and a proton acceptor acting simultaneously at another point (the "push-pull" theory).  The kinetic demands of this interpretation are quite specific; the Lowry view would require each contribution to the rate to result from a triple *

[275] H. M. Dawson and J. S. Carter, *J. Chem. Soc.*, 2282 (1926); H. M. Dawson, G. V. Hall, and A. Key, *ibid.*, 2844 (1928); H. M. Dawson, C. R. Hoskins, and J. E. Smith, *ibid.*, 1884 (1929); H. M. Dawson and E. Spivey, *ibid.*, 2180 (1930).

[276] J. N. Brönsted, *Chem. Revs.*, **5**, 281 (1928); L. P. Hammett, "Physical Organic Chemistry," McGraw-Hill Book Co., New York (1940), pp. 215–224.

[277] J. N. Brönsted, *Chem. Revs.*, **5**, 281 (1928).

[278] T. M. Lowry and I. J. Faulkner, *J. Chem. Soc.*, **127**, 2883 (1925).

* There is no kinetic distinction between a triple collision and a collision between one molecular species and a complex formed from two others.

collision, in the case of enolization a collision between a ketone molecule, an acid, and a base (either of which may be a solvent molecule), the transition state being ($C$) as shown. The experimental facts seem at first sight to require a combination of both mechanisms. In acetate buffers [279] the rate constant of iodination of acetone is expressed by

$$k = 1.3 \times 10^{-6}[\text{HOAc}] + 3.3 \times 10^{-6}[\text{OAc}^-]$$

$$+ 3.5 \times 10^{-6}[\text{HOAc}][\text{OAc}^-] + 5.6 \times 10^{-4}[\text{H}_3\text{O}^+] + 7[\text{OH}^-] + 6 \times 10^{-9}$$

which corresponds to six catalytic processes, five of them interpretable as involving a single catalyst molecule, and one clearly involving an acid and a base at once. To Pedersen [280] and to Hammett [281] it has seemed most satisfactory to disregard the one third-order term, which represents at most 14% of the rate (for [HOAc] = [OAc$^-$] = 0.2), and to account for the five second-order terms by reactions 1 and 2–3. It will be noted that in the sequence describing the acid catalysis the rate-

$$
\begin{array}{cc}
\text{CH}_3 & \\
| & \\
\text{CO} + \text{B} \rightarrow \text{BH}^+ + 
\left[
\begin{array}{cc}
\text{CH}_2^- & \text{CH}_2 \\
| & \| \\
\text{CO} & \text{CO}^- \\
| & | \\
\text{CH}_3 & \text{CH}_3
\end{array}
\leftrightarrow
\right]
\xrightarrow[\longleftarrow]{\text{Acid or H}_2\text{O}}
\begin{array}{c}
\text{CH}_2 \\
\| \\
\text{COH} \\
| \\
\text{CH}_3
\end{array}
& (1)
\end{array}
$$

$$
\begin{array}{c}
\text{CH}_3 \\
| \\
\text{CO} + \text{HA} \underset{}{\overset{\text{Fast}}{\rightleftarrows}} \text{A}^- + 
\begin{array}{c}
\text{CH}_3 \\
| \\
\text{C}=\text{OH}^+ \\
| \\
\text{CH}_3
\end{array} \\
| \\
\text{CH}_3
\end{array}
\qquad (2)
$$

$$
\begin{array}{c}
\text{CH}_3 \\
| \\
\text{C}=\text{OH}^+ + \text{A}^- \underset{}{\overset{\text{Slow}}{\rightleftarrows}} \text{HA} + 
\begin{array}{c}
\text{CH}_2 \\
\| \\
\text{COH} \\
| \\
\text{CH}_3
\end{array} \\
| \\
\text{CH}_3
\end{array}
\qquad (3)
$$

determining step is actually the attack of a basic substance upon the $\alpha$-position of the conjugate acid of acetone.* However, this is kinetically indistinguishable from a reaction between the ketone and the original acid because the equilibrium represented in line 2 is assumed to be rapid and there is therefore a permanent proportionality between the product (acetone)(HOAc) and the product (acetone·H$^+$)(OAc$^-$). In this way

[279] H. M. Dawson and E. Spivey, *ibid.*, 2180 (1930).

[280] K. J. Pedersen, *J. Phys. Chem.*, **38**, 581 (1934).

[281] L. P. Hammett, "Physical Organic Chemistry," McGraw-Hill Book Co., New York (1940), pp. 236–237.

* It should be noted that the A$^-$ in (3) need not be the same individual, nor even the same species, as the A$^-$ in (2) by which the ketone became protonated.

no step is postulated which involves a slow transfer of a proton to or from oxygen.

In later work by Pedersen [282] examples of enolization were observed in which a third-order term is the dominant one and cannot possibly be explained as due to the method of analysis of the data. The bromination of acetoacetic ester in the presence of cupric ion proceeds at a rate chiefly determined by the product of the concentration of ester, cupric ion, and base. It has been pointed out by Swain [283] that every one of the terms in the equation of Dawson and Spivey might be interpreted as due to a concerted termolecular attack of certain equivalent acid-base pairs upon the ketone, and the results are fitted nearly as well by the equation

$$k = 2.5 \times 10^{-12}\{[H_2O] + 1.5 \times 10^4[OAc^-] + 3 \times 10^{10}[OH^-]\}$$

$$\cdot \{[H_2O] + 1 \times 10^2[HOAc] + 2.5 \times 10^6[H_3O^+]\}$$

which is now entirely in accord with the view of Lowry [278] requiring a concerted push and pull upon the substrate.

*Stable Enols.* Enols stable enough to be isolated occur in $\alpha$-diketones such as benzyl phenyl diketone, $\beta$-diketones such as acetylacetone and dibenzoylmethane, $\beta$-keto esters such as ethyl acetoacetate, phenols, and numerous similar cases which have in common some degree of stabilization of the enolic double bond by conjugation. Here the equilibrium is much more favorable to the enolic tautomer than it is with the simple monoketones. Table III on p. 1041 in Vol. I of this Treatise shows some examples of the position of the equilibrium between keto and enol isomers as determined by bromine titration. Enols of monoketones, though present only to a minute extent at equilibrium with their keto isomers, can nevertheless be isolated in certain cases where extreme steric hindrance is present. Thus the enolic form of benzhydrylacetomesitylene [284] is directly isolated from the hydrolysis of its magnesium

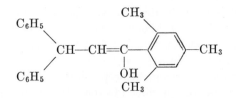

derivative and is slowly isomerized into the keto form by acidic or basic catalysts. The very slow isomerization of highly hindered vinyl alco-

[282] K. J. Pedersen, *Acta Chem. Scand.*, **2**, 252, 385 (1948).
[283] C. G. Swain, *J. Am. Chem. Soc.*, **72**, 4578 (1950).
[284] E. P. Kohler and R. B. Thompson, *ibid.*, **59**, 887 (1937).

hols and enediols has been shown by Fuson and his co-workers [285] to be quite general. The *cis-trans* isomerism of compounds of this type has been investigated,[286] whereas the enol of acetoacetic ester is known only in the *cis* hydrogen-bonded form.[287] In this example it is reasonable to

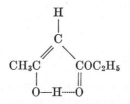

expect that a *trans* form in which the hydroxyl group would be free to undergo hydrogen bonding with neighboring molecules would have a higher boiling point than the keto form of acetoacetic ester, whereas in fact the normal enol boils lower than the keto form.[288]

**Addition Reactions of the Carbonyl Group.** The addition of hydrogen cyanide is a rather general reaction of ketones and aldehydes, although

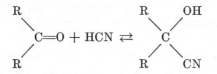

ketones of the level of reactivity of camphor, benzophenone, anthrone, and xanthone fail to yield appreciable quantities of cyanhydrin under conditions where menthone, fluorenone, and phenyl *t*-butyl ketone react to measurable equilibria.[289] The reaction of ketones and aldehydes with pure hydrogen cyanide is very slow but is rendered too fast for convenient measurement by the presence of a small concentration of cyanide ion.[290] Lapworth deduced from this that the rate-determining step in the formation of a cyanhydrin is the attack of the cyanide ion upon the carbon of the carbonyl group. This reaction has proved to be

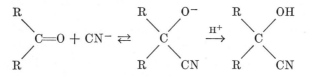

[285] R. C. Fuson and J. Corse, *ibid.*, **61**, 975 (1939); R. C. Fuson and T. L. Tan, *ibid.*, **70**, 602 (1948), and earlier papers.
[286] A. M. Buswell, W. H. Rodebush, and R. McL. Whitney, *ibid.*, **69**, 770 (1947).
[287] N. V. Sidgwick, *J. Chem. Soc.*, **127**, 907 (1925).
[288] K. H. Meyer and V. Schoeller, *Ber.*, **53**, 1410 (1920).
[289] A. Lapworth and R. H. F. Manske, *J. Chem. Soc.*, 2533 (1928); 1976 (1930).
[290] A. Lapworth, *ibid.*, **83**, 995 (1903).

an illuminating prototype of addition reactions of the carbonyl group, for in most such reactions the ability of the carbonyl group to react at all appears to be related to its rather high polarity expressible in the structure

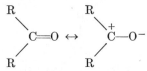

and reflected in the dipole moments of 2.70 to 2.90 D which characterize aldehydes and ketones generally.[291]  As the resonance formula for a ketone suggests, many addition reactions proceed like the cyanhydrin reaction by direct attack of a nucleophilic reagent upon the carbon atom. It may also be anticipated from this formula that the formation of a coördinate bond between the oxygen of the carbonyl group and some electrophilic substance will enhance the polarization of the carbonyl group and make the carbon a more favorable point of attack for nucleophilic reagents.   Some addition reactions to the carbonyl group may then well be catalyzed by proton donors and by other electrophilic reagents.   Because of its generally great speed the formation of cyanhydrins has not been studied in sufficient detail to rule out the possibility that water, alcohol, or hydrogen cyanide itself may be playing an essential role in the kinetics by coördination at the oxygen of the carbonyl group.

The *addition of sodium bisulfite* to aldehydes and ketones is another simple addition reaction whose rate-determining step may be regarded as the attack of a nucleophilic ion upon the carbon.   The equilibrium

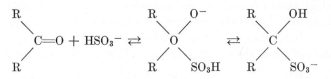

of formation of bisulfite addition compounds depends upon structure in a somewhat similar way to that of cyanhydrin formation.[292]   The bisulfite reaction presents an important contrast to the cyanhydrin reaction in that the equilibrium of the latter can be frozen by acidification, which prevents the occurrence of sufficient cyanide ion or cyanhy-

[291] G. E. K. Branch and M. Calvin, "The Theory of Organic Chemistry," Prentice-Hall, New York (1941), p. 146.

[292] W. Kerp, *Arb. kaiserl. Gesundh.*, **21**, 180 (1904) [*Chem. Zentr.*, **75** II, 57 (1904)]. See I. M. Kolthoff and N. H. Furman, "Volumetric Analysis," John Wiley & Sons, New York (1928), Vol. I, pp. 177 ff.   Compare this Treatise, Vol. I, p. 645.

drin anion to mobilize the forward and reverse reactions. Therefore cyanhydrins can be isolated even though the equilibrium of their formation may be unfavorable. Bisulfite derivatives, however, will approach equilibrium with bisulfite and carbonyl compounds under all conditions of acidity and basicity. It is therefore feasible to isolate the bisulfite compounds only in cases of rather favorable equilibrium. It is also obvious that if the above equation represents a reversible reaction then the addition of either acid or base to the system will displace this equilibrium toward the left by converting the bisulfite ion into sulfurous acid or sulfite ion.

*Hemiacetals and the Mutarotation of Glucose.* Aldehydes form addition products with alcohols, the hemiacetals, which are in general even more difficult to isolate than the bisulfite addition compounds. That hemi-

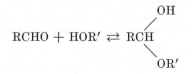

acetals are generally formed is confirmed by such observations as the disappearance of the ultraviolet carbonyl absorption band of propionaldehyde on standing for 45 minutes in solution in alcohol,[293] but open-chain hemiacetals are stable enough to be isolated only in special cases such as that of chloral hemiacetal. The situation here is similar to that with the bisulfite compounds in that the equilibrium is mobile enough under all conditions so that most hemiacetals begin dissociating during the process of separating them from their dissociation products.

Hydroxy aldehydes and hydroxy ketones which can yield hemiacetals with five- or six-membered rings commonly exist preferentially in the hemiacetal form. This phenomenon was discovered and has been most carefully studied in the sugar series (see Vol. II, p. 1546), where it is the cause of the mutarotation of freshly prepared solutions of α- or β-glucose.

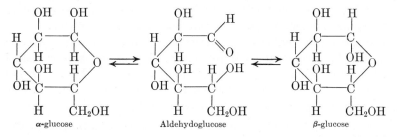

α-glucose        Aldehydoglucose        β-glucose

---

[293] W. Herold and K. L. Wolf, *Z. physik. Chem.*, **B12**, 165 (1931); see also W. Herold, *Z. Elektrochem.*, **39**, 566 (1933).

The mutarotation of glucose has been an important subject of kinetic investigations because it can be accurately followed either by measurements of optical rotation [294] or by the use of a dilatometer, taking advantage of the change in density on interconversion of the $\alpha$- and $\beta$-isomers.[295] Studies of this kind have shown that hemiacetal formation, like enolization, is subject to general acidic and basic catalysis, the rate being representable as the sum of a specific rate for each species of proton donor and each species of proton acceptor present in the solution. For the mutarotation of glucose in buffers of acetic acid and sodium acetate at 25°, Brönsted and Guggenheim found the rate equation

$$k = 8.8 \times 10^{-5} + 2.4 \times 10^{-3}[H_3O^+] + 4 \times 10^{-5}[HOAc]$$
$$+ 4.4 \times 10^{-4}[OAc^-] + \leqslant 1 \times 10^2[OH^-]$$

In this reaction it is clear that the rate-determining step must be one involving the breaking of a carbon-oxygen bond but the only transfers of protons taking place on glucose are to and from oxygen atoms. It seems necessary to conclude from the experimental facts that the breaking of the carbon-oxygen bond actually occurs either in synchronism with the delivery and removal of protons by acids and bases or else as a spontaneous reaction of a non-ionized complex between glucose and a proton donor or proton acceptor.

A more fundamental problem concerning mutarotation again involves the question of possible simultaneous attack by an acid and a base. The equation of Brönsted and Guggenheim appears to deny such simultaneous attack, for there is in it no term proportional to the concentrations of both an acid and a base. Lowry and Faulkner,[296] however, were led to advocate the simultaneous "push-pull" picture by observations on mutarotation of tetramethyl glucose in the acidic solvent cresol, the basic solvent pyridine, and solvents consisting of mixtures of the two. Mutarotation is very slow in cresol alone, which is a stronger acid but weaker base than water. Mutarotation is also very slow in pyridine alone, which is a stronger base but weaker acid than water. In mixtures of pyridine and cresol, however, rates of mutarotation are obtained as much as 20 times the rate observed in pure water.

The apparently conflicting requirements of these two sets of observations can be reconciled by a reinterpretation of the kinetic data of Brönsted and Guggenheim.[297] The rate attributed by these workers to molecular acetic acid might in fact be due to acetic acid acting as an acid and water acting as a base simultaneously, or to oxonium ion acting as

[294] See p. 1548 in Vol. II of this Treatise; C. S. Hudson and J. K. Dale, *J. Am. Chem. Soc.*, **39**, 320 (1917).
[295] J. N. Brönsted and E. A. Guggenheim, *J. Am. Chem. Soc.*, **49**, 2554 (1927).
[296] T. M. Lowry and I. J. Faulkner, *J. Chem. Soc.*, **127**, 2883 (1925).
[297] See C. G. Swain, *J. Am. Chem. Soc.*, **72**, 4578 (1950).

an acid and acetate ion acting as a base. Similar considerations applied to each term lead to an equation of the type

$$k = 2.9 \times 10^{-8}\{[H_2O] + 2.8 \times 10^2[OAc^-] + \leqslant 6.3 \times 10^7[OH^-]\}$$
$$\times \{[H_2O] + 25[HOAc] + 1.5 \times 10^3[H_3O^+]\}$$

which, as in the case of iodination of acetone, fits the data satisfactorily.

There remains the question of why, if protons are transferred with extreme rapidity from one oxygen to another, the mutarotation of glucose does not proceed as a spontaneous reaction of the dipolar ion. That it

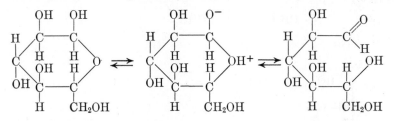

does not in fact do so is readily seen from the fact that the concentration of this dipolar ion must bear a constant ratio to that of neutral glucose at all $p$H's and in the presence of all catalysts and mutarotation would appear as a non-catalytic reaction if this were its mechanism. It has been suggested by Westheimer [298] that the dipolar ion, even though its equilibrium were rapidly established, is present at so low a concentration that it would have to undergo ring opening at almost the greatest rate possible for a unimolecular reaction of zero activation energy in order to account for the observed rates of mutarotation. It remains possible that some fraction of the so-called water rate of mutarotation, which is independent of the $p$H, may be due to a mechanism of this kind, but the catalytic rates observed are faster than this because they do not depend upon such a rare and unfavored molecular species for their occurrence.

By the principle of microscopic reversibility (see p. 9) the studies of mutarotation lead to possible mechanisms of hemiacetal formation. Of these the most unambiguous is the push-pull mechanism, whose reversibility is apparent:

$$\text{RCHO} + \text{R}'\text{OH} + \text{HA} + \text{B} \rightleftarrows$$

$$\left[ \begin{array}{c} \overset{\text{H}}{\underset{\text{RC}}{|}} \overset{\text{O}\cdot\text{HA}}{\diagup} \\ \diagdown \\ \overset{}{\text{O}-\text{H}\cdots\text{B}} \\ \text{R}' \end{array} \right] \rightarrow \overset{\text{H} \quad \text{OH}}{\underset{\text{OR}'}{\text{RC}}} + \text{A}^- + \text{BH}^+$$

[298] F. H. Westheimer, private communication.

From this reaction it would appear that the attachment of an electrophilic reagent, and especially of a proton, to the oxygen of the carbonyl group must bring about a great increase in its polarization and in the electrophilic reactivity at the carbon atom. This is apparently the basis of the reversible trimerization of aldehydes which is observed in the presence of a strong proton donor and under circumstances where the aldehyde itself is the strongest base present. The product, paraldehyde,

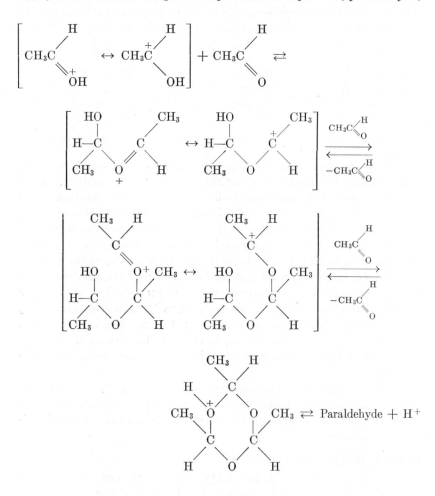

is entirely stable in the absence of acids but is readily detrimerized when strong acid is present.

*Grignard Reagents and Organolithium Compounds* (see Vol. I, pp. 495–520 and 646). The addition of organolithium compounds and Grignard reagents to ketones and aldehydes is normally such a rapid reaction as to preclude studies of its kinetics. Studies of the mechanism of this reaction have been based largely upon an investigation of the relation between structure of the reagent or carbonyl compound and the nature of the products and the relative reactivities as determined in competition experiments and by tests for residual organometallic compound. It has been shown [299] that reactivity toward phenylmagnesium bromide is in the order: acetone > acetaldehyde > benzaldehyde > acetophenone > phenyl isocyanate > benzoyl fluoride > benzophenone > benzoyl chloride > benzoyl bromide > ethyl benzoate > benzonitrile. In the case of the least reactive compound of this series, benzonitrile, the reaction with butylmagnesium bromide has been shown to be strictly of the second order.[300]

It would seem a reasonable assumption that the reaction between a Grignard reagent and a ketone is also of the second order, but there are qualitative observations which indicate that the mechanism is not entirely simple. It has often been observed that, on the addition of Grignard reagents in deficient amount to ketones such as benzophenone, complexes are precipitated from which the ketone can be recovered upon hydrolysis.[301] By the addition of Grignard reagent in excess these complexes are brought back into the solution, whereupon normal reaction occurs with the formation of tertiary alcohols. Whitmore [302] has suggested that the complex shown, which undoubtedly involves a coördinate link between magnesium and oxygen, is intermediate in both

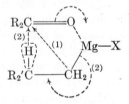

normal addition of and reduction by Grignard reagents. In the former case an alkyl group undergoes 1,3-migration from magnesium to the carbon atom (process 1). In the case of reduction, which becomes a prominent side reaction with certain ketones and Grignard reagents, the reaction consists of a transfer of hydride ion from the $\beta$-position of the

[299] C. E. Entemann, Jr., and J. R. Johnson, *J. Am. Chem. Soc.*, **55**, 2900 (1933); M. S. Kharasch and J. H. Cooper, *J. Org. Chem.*, **10**, 46 (1946).

[300] C. G. Swain, *J. Am. Chem. Soc.*, **69**, 2306 (1947).

[301] J. Leroide, *Compt. rend.*, **148**, 1611 (1909); E. Fischer and K. Hess, *Ber.*, **45**, 912 (1912); H. Gilman and R. G. Jones, *J. Am. Chem. Soc.*, **62**, 1243 (1940).

[302] F. C. Whitmore, paper presented before the Atlantic City Meeting of the American Chemical Society, September, 1941.

Grignard reagent to the carbonyl carbon (process 2), being closely similar to the controlling step in the Meerwein-Ponndorf and Oppenauer equilibrations.  If the transition state in the addition of a Grignard reagent to a ketone involves, as shown, partial bond formation both at oxygen by an electrophilic center and at carbon by a nucleophilic center, then it is clear why the order of reactivity of ketones in this reaction is not simply the order of basicity or the inverse of this order.  Any substitution in the ketone will produce simultaneous opposite effects upon its reactivity at these two sites.

It is interesting that the order of reactivity of Grignard reagents toward benzophenone is, where comparable data are available, opposite to that toward benzonitrile.  Toward benzophenone the tertiary butyl, methyl, phenyl, and $\alpha$-naphthyl Grignard reagents are in that descending order of reactivity.[303]  Toward benzonitrile the order is phenyl > ethyl > tertiary butyl, the relative "reaction times" for disappearance of the qualitative test for these three Grignard reagents [304] being 1.00, 2.7, and 81.  Stereochemically an intramolecular rearrangement of a complex between a nitrile and a Grignard reagent is not favored as in the case of a ketone since we must suppose that the carbon, nitrogen, and magnesium lie along a straight line unless the bonding state of the CN group in the complex is entirely different from what it is in the free nitrile.  Likewise the relative reactivities of nitriles toward phenylmagnesium bromide [305] are the opposite of the expected order of basicity (*para*-chlorophenyl > phenyl > *meta*- or *para*-tolyl > *ortho*-tolyl > *para*-diethylaminophenyl) and suggest that the reactivity in this case is dominated by electrophilic character in the carbon and is not affected equally by complex-forming ability of the nitrile.

Reducing Action of the Grignard Reagent.  In many cases a Grignard reagent, instead of undergoing simple addition to a ketone, yields the magnesium derivative of the secondary alcohol related to the ketone and an olefin derived from the Grignard reagent.  In some cases the proportion of reduction, relative to addition, drops sharply with decreasing temperature.[306]

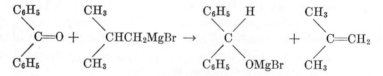

[303] M. S. Kharasch and S. Weinhouse, *J. Org. Chem.*, **1**, 209 (1936).

[304] H. Gilman, E. L. St. John, N. B. St. John, and M. Lichtenwalter, *Rec. trav. chim.*, **55**, 577 (1936).

[305] H. Gilman and M. Lichtenwalter, *ibid.*, **55**, 588 (1936).

[306] C. R. Noller, W. E. Grebe, and L. H. Knox, *J. Am. Chem. Soc.*, **54**, 4690 (1932).

The reduction often comes to the fore in ketones in which some steric hindrance to addition would be anticipated, and the reduction has therefore been regarded as an essentially slow mode of reaction which predominates only when there is specific hindrance.[307,308] Kharasch and Weinhouse, however,[303] found that the relative amounts of reduction of benzophenone by a series of Grignard reagents are not inversely correlated with the relative rates of attack of these Grignard reagents upon a ketone. *t*-Butyl, *i*-butyl, and *n*-butyl Grignard reagents fall in descending order of reactivity, and these Grignard reagents yield 0%, 91%, and 58.6% reduction of benzophenone, respectively. Kharasch and Weinhouse sought some relation between the rates of both addition and reduction and the "electronegativities" of the organic radicals in the Grignard reagents. Such a correlation is understandably rough in view of the varying sizes and shapes of the organic radicals in the series and of the fact that the reduction process involves the introduction of an olefinic bond which may be favored by influences having no importance in the addition reaction. For example, the phenyl and benzyl Grignard reagents, which do not possess $\beta$-hydrogen, cannot react by the above equation whatever the "electronegativity" of the group.

Kharasch and Cooper [309] have pointed out that the order of reactivity of ketones and aldehydes toward Grignard reagents is not parallel to that toward semicarbazide as measured in aqueous or alcoholic buffer solution. Toward Grignard reagents acetone, acetaldehyde, and cyclohexanone have relative reactivities of 15.5, 10.8, and 1, whereas toward semicarbazide in a phosphate buffer of $p$H 7 in water the relative reactivities of these same compounds are 1, 60, and 6, respectively. There are several possible reasons for such a lack of correlation: (*a*) Semicarbazone formation is a condensation reaction whose rate-determining step may not be addition. (*b*) Different carbonyl compounds do not fall in the same order of rate of semicarbazone formation when examined in different buffers.[310] (*c*) The order of reaction of a Grignard reagent and a ketone has not been established, and the fact that complexes are formed which may be subject to attack by an extra molecule of Grignard reagent may be of importance here.

Free Radical Reactions of Grignard Reagents. Pure methylmagnesium bromide will add to benzophenone to give a 95% yield of diphenylmethyl carbinol. This yield is not appreciably affected by the presence of magnesium, cuprous chloride, or manganous chloride. However, the

[307] J. B. Conant and A. H. Blatt, *ibid.*, **51**, 1227 (1929).
[308] See pp. 646, 647 in Vol. I of this Treatise.
[309] M. S. Kharasch and J. H. Cooper, *J. Org. Chem.*, **10**, 46 (1945).
[310] F. H. Westheimer, *J. Am. Chem. Soc.*, **56**, 1962 (1934).

presence of small amounts of ferric chloride or cobaltous chloride will cause the formation of 65% and 95%, respectively, of benzpinacol, the yield of addition product being correspondingly reduced.[311]  In numerous other investigations metallic chlorides have been found to be similarly effective in amounts as little as 1 mole % in completely altering the course of the Grignard reaction.  Such effectiveness of very small amounts of material is one of the characteristic marks of a chain reaction, and Kharasch and his co-workers have proposed the general explanation that an interchange of Grignard reagent with the metallic chloride produces an unstable new organometallic compound.

$$RMgX + CoCl_2 \rightarrow MgClX + RCoCl$$

Decomposition of this organometallic compound yields a coupling product of the organic radical of the Grignard reagent and highly reactive products containing the metal in a lower valence state.

$$2RCoCl \rightarrow R—R + 2CoCl$$

The fate of these fragments varies with the reaction at hand, but in the present case it is likely that the overall process is

$$2\Phi_2CO + 2CoCl \rightarrow \begin{array}{c} \Phi_2COCoCl \\ | \\ \Phi_2COCoCl \end{array} \xrightarrow{2MgClX} \begin{array}{c} \Phi_2COMgX \\ | \\ \Phi_2COMgX \end{array} + 2CoCl_2$$

The cobalt-free reaction of $i$-butylmagnesium bromide with benzophenone is not addition but reduction to benzhydrol.  In this case 2 mole % of manganous chloride changes the course of the reaction to yield more than 90% of benzpinacol instead of more than 90% of benzhydrol.[312]  The normal reaction of methylmagnesium bromide with benzalacetophenone yields a mixture of 1,2- and 1,4-addition products.[313]

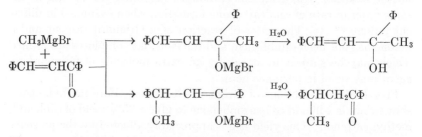

The presence of metallic chlorides does not affect the ratio of 1,2- and 1,4-addition, but 1 mole % of cobaltous chloride leads to a product con-

[311] M. S. Kharasch and F. L. Lambert, *ibid.*, **63**, 2315 (1941).
[312] M. S. Kharasch, S. C. Kleiger, J. A. Martin, and F. R. Mayo, *ibid.*, **63**, 2305 (1941).
[313] See pp. 672 ff. in Vol. I of this Treatise.

taining 82% of the dimolecular reduction product of benzalacetophenone, 1,3,4,6-tetraphenyl-1,6-hexanedione.[314]   The fate of the radical of the

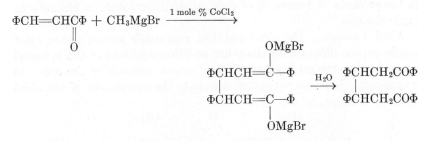

Grignard reagent in these halide-induced reactions is most clearly shown in studies of the coupling reaction between the Grignard reagent and organic halides.[315]   In each case the radicals of the Grignard reagent are coupled to one another while the radical of the halide has undergone disproportionation, coupling, or chain transfer.

Any discussion of organic reaction mechanisms would be misleading without some examples of how far experiment frequently runs ahead of theory.   The reaction of methylmagnesium bromide with isophorone

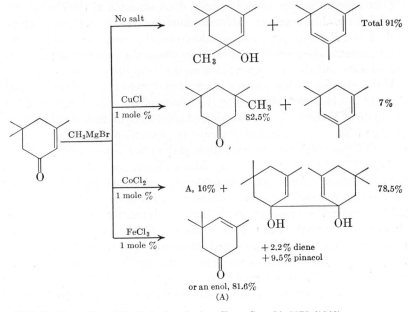

or an enol, 81.6%
(A)

[314] M. S. Kharasch and D. C. Sayles, *J. Am. Chem. Soc.*, **64**, 2972 (1942).

[315] M. S. Kharasch and E. K. Fields, *ibid.*, **63**, 2316 (1941); M. S. Kharasch and M. Kleiman, *ibid.*, **65**, 491 (1943); M. S. Kharasch, D. W. Lewis, and W. B. Reynolds, *ibid.*, **65**, 493 (1943).

can be made to take no less than four different courses, each in good yield, according to whether it is conducted without added substances or in the presence of 1 mole % of cuprous chloride, cobaltous chloride, or ferric chloride.[316]

*Aldol Addition.* The aldol addition, commonly known as the aldol condensation, differs from the other addition reactions of the carbonyl group in that the adding reagent is a second molecule of the carbonyl compound. It is convenient to designate the component of the aldol

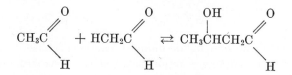

addition to whose carbonyl group an addition occurs as the *A* component and the one which functions as an addition reagent as the *B* component.[317] It is obvious from the equation that only carbonyl compounds having hydrogen in the α-position can act as *B* components in the aldol addition.

Fundamental kinetic work has been done on some of the simpler examples of the aldol reaction. Most illuminating have been the case where both *A* and *B* components are acetaldehyde, the case where both *A* and *B* components are acetone, and the case where the *A* component is carbon dioxide and the *B* component is methyl isopropyl ketone.

If the reaction took place in a single step it would be anticipated that the rate would be proportional to the square of the concentration of the aldehyde or ketone. In the reaction of acetaldehyde to form aldol with hydroxyl ion as the catalyst the rate is proportional only to the first power of the aldehyde concentration and to the concentration of the catalyst.[318] The catalysts for the aldol addition are the same as those for enolization. Although Bell originally suggested that the rate of aldolization was determined by the dehydration of an aldehyde hydrate, it is now considered more probable that in this reaction, as in the iodination of acetaldehyde, the rate-determining step is the formation of an enol. The fact that aldol prepared from ordinary acetaldehyde in solution in heavy water contains no deuterium bound to carbon [319] indicates at least that enolization cannot be faster than aldol addition, for enolization provides a means of deuterium exchange at the α-positions of

[316] M. S. Kharasch and P. O. Tawney, *ibid.*, **63**, 2308 (1941).
[317] C. R. Hauser, *ibid.*, **60**, 1957 (1938).
[318] R. P. Bell, *J. Chem. Soc.*, 1637 (1937).
[319] K. F. Bonhoeffer and W. D. Walters, *Z. physik. Chem.*, **A181**, 441 (1938).

carbonyl compounds. A similar conclusion has been drawn in the case of the formation of ketohexoses by the addition of dihydroxyacetone to glyceraldehyde.[320] If the enolization of dihydroxyacetone determines the rate of this addition an explanation is provided at the same time for the ability of glyceraldehyde to yield ketohexoses by reaction with itself, for glyceraldehyde (A) and dihydroxyacetone (C) have a common enol (B).

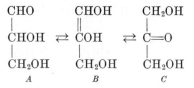

Although in general the formation of an enediol such as B affords a path for the interconversion of isomeric hydroxycarbonyl compounds, the enediol is not necessarily intermediate in all such interconversions. When glucose is converted into fructose in the presence of alkali at room temperature in heavy water, the product contains no deuterium on carbon,[321] although deuterium is taken up in the reaction conducted above 40°. This fact suggests that there is a hydride-shift mechanism as well

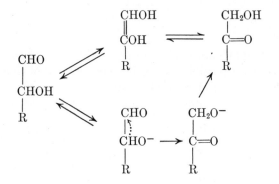

as one involving enolization as shown. A direct demonstration of the role of the enol in the aldol addition was provided by Meyer and Lenhardt,[322] who isolated the enol form of oxalomesityl oxide and showed that it reacted readily with benzaldehyde and piperidine, whereas the keto form gave no reaction under the same conditions. In this particu-

[320] W. D. Walters and K. F. Bonhoeffer, *ibid.*, **A182**, 265 (1938).

[321] H. Fredenhagen and K. F. Bonhoeffer, *ibid.*, **A181**, 392 (1938).

[322] K. H. Meyer and S. Lenhardt, *Ann.*, **398**, 56 (1913).

lar instance aldol addition is immediately followed by intramolecular transesterification leading to a lactone.

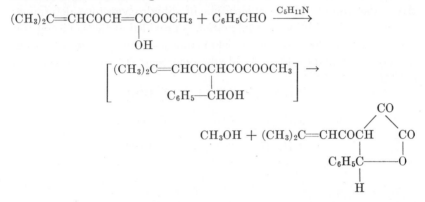

The aldolization of acetone to yield diacetone alcohol is a reversible reaction with an equilibrium very unfavorable to the addition product. The same is true of the carbonation of methyl isopropyl ketone to yield $\alpha,\alpha$-dimethylacetoacetic acid. It is therefore not feasible to study these

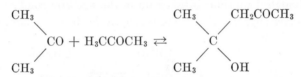

examples of the aldol addition kinetically in the forward direction. Fortunately it is again possible to invoke the principle of microscopic reversibility (see p. 9) and to apply conclusions from the study of the reverse reaction to the interpretation of the forward mechanism. In a

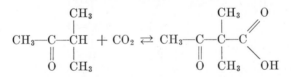

beautiful study of the decarboxylation of dimethylacetoacetic acid Pedersen [323] has shown that in ordinary aqueous buffer solutions the rate is determined by the $pH$ and is not subject to general acidic and basic catalysis. There is one rate constant for the decarboxylation of the negative ion $CH_3COC(CH_3)_2COO^-$ and another rate constant, greater by two powers of 10, for the decarboxylation of the neutral acid. Although neither dimethylacetoacetic acid nor methyl isopropyl ketone is

[323] K. J. Pedersen, *J. Am. Chem. Soc.*, **60**, 595 (1938).

brominated at all rapidly under the conditions of these experiments, if
the acid is subjected to decarboxylation in the presence of bromine, 1
mole of bromine is consumed for each mole of acid which decarboxylates
and the product is methyl α-bromoisopropyl ketone.   This can be ex-

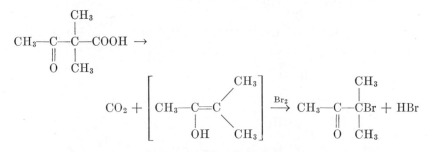

plained only if the direct products of the decarboxylation are carbon
dioxide and trimethylvinyl alcohol, the enol of methyl isopropyl ketone.
In accord with the principle of microscopic reversibility, this is in har-
mony with the independent evidence that the forward mechanism for an
aldol addition requires the conversion of the B component into its enol.

Although the decarboxylation of dimethylacetoacetic acid is not subject to general acidic and basic catalysis it is subject to specific catalysis
by primary and secondary (but not tertiary) amines.   These facts are
consistent with either of two pictures of the course of the reaction.   In
the first the rate is regarded as proportional to the concentration of a
dipolar ion.   The rate-determining step would then be the cleavage of

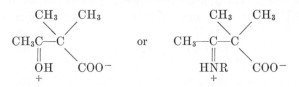

the carbon-carbon bond accompanied by an appropriate electronic re-
allocation to form the products, as shown.   According to the second in-

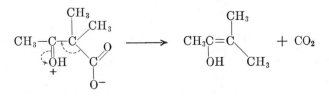

terpretation there might be no such separation of charge as is suggested
in the dipolar ion formula but rather the carboxyl group might be in-

volved in the formation of a chelate ring with a hydrogen bond to the keto group. The transition state would then involve the concerted breaking of a carbon-carbon and an oxygen-hydrogen bond.

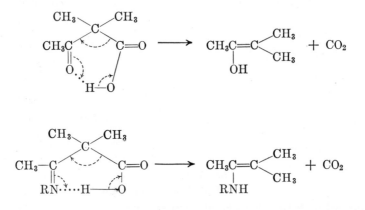

It will be seen that the choice here is not between two mechanisms, since in each case the transition state is the same chemically and geometrically. The question is simply one of the extent of charge separation in the transition state, since the second picture calls for a charge separation amounting to very little, and possibly even zero, whereas the first picture implies a somewhat greater dipolar character. Persuasive evidence in favor of a very small separation of charge in the transition state is provided by the observation of Westheimer and Jones [324] that the rate of decarboxylation of dimethylacetoacetic acid is not notably affected by a variation from 75% methanol (rate constant 1.72) to pure water (rate constant 1.83). Such a change in medium with its accompanying change in dielectric constant should distinctly modify the electrostatic work of activation if the transition state differs from the starting material in the degree of charge separation. It would then appear that the specific catalysis by primary and secondary amines is associated with their ability to form addition or condensation products at the keto group of the reactant and through these to yield more effective chelate transition states for the reaction.[324a]

[324] F. H. Westheimer and W. A. Jones, *ibid.*, **63**, 3283 (1941).

[324a] A simpler alternative picture of this catalysis would assign to the amine the role of a bifunctional catalyst, simultaneously donating a proton to the carbonyl oxygen and removing one from the carboxyl group. The transition state, having two quasi-hydrogen bonds, would be in the shape of an irregular hexagon and not unduly strained. Certain bifunctional catalysts with appropriate spacing of acidic and basic centers are very effective in the mutarotation of glucose [C. G. Swain and J. F. Brown, Jr., *J. Am. Chem. Soc.*, **74**, 2538 (1952)].

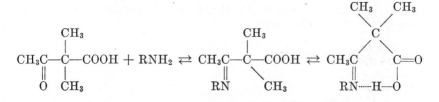

The reverse aldol addition in which diacetone alcohol is cleaved to acetone, like the decarboxylation of dimethylacetoacetic acid, is catalyzed by primary and secondary amines but not in general by bases. Unlike the decarboxylation,[325] the rate of reaction of neutral diacetone alcohol is negligible compared with that of the negative ion $(CH_3)_2CCH_2COCH_3$.

$$\underset{O^-}{|}$$

The primary amine-catalyzed dealdolization is as little affected by the dielectric constant of the medium as the neutral decarboxylation,[326] and parallel conclusions about its mechanism appear to be warranted.

Although these two examples of addition reactions to the carbonyl group are studied kinetically only through the reverse processes, these studies afford important information about the additions themselves. From the equilibrium constant measured for aqueous solutions

$$K = \frac{(\text{diacetone alcohol})}{(\text{acetone})^2} = 0.037 \text{ L/mole}$$

at 25° by Koelichen,[327] and his dealdolization rate constant $k_1 = 0.0111$ minute$^{-1}$ for 0.051 $N$ hydroxyl ion, the bimolecular rate constant for the forward reaction in 1 $N$ hydroxyl ion can be estimated as 0.008 L/mole minute, and in a solution 1 $M$ in acetone, aldolization occurs at a rate of 0.008 mole per minute. Enolization, however, under the same conditions, occurs with a rate constant of 25;[328] therefore with acetone, in contrast to acetaldehyde, enolization occurs about 3000 times as fast as aldol addition. This difference reflects the fact that aldehydes undergo addition reactions much faster than ketones; possibly acetaldehyde is little more than reactive enough to combine with its enolate anion as fast as the anion is formed.

The fact that neutral dimethylacetoacetic acid undergoes decarboxylation more rapidly than its negative ion might seem to suggest that the

[325] F. H. Westheimer and H. Cohen, *ibid.*, **60**, 90 (1938).
[326] F. H. Westheimer and W. A. Jones, *loc. cit.*
[327] K. Koelichen, *Z. physik. Chem.*, **33**, 129 (1900).
[328] H. M. Dawson and A. Key, *J. Chem. Soc.*, 543 (1928).

reverse reaction, carbonation, should occur more easily with the enol than with its enolate anion:

$$CH_3COC(CH_3)_2COOH \underset{k_2}{\overset{k_1 = 7 \times 10^{-5}}{\rightleftarrows}} CO_2 + CH_3C{=}C(CH_3)_2$$
$$\qquad\qquad\qquad\qquad\qquad\qquad\qquad\qquad\qquad | $$
$$\qquad\qquad\qquad\qquad\qquad\qquad\qquad\qquad\quad OH$$

$$CH_3COC(CH_3)_2COO^- \underset{k_2'}{\overset{k_1' = 1.5 \times 10^{-8}}{\rightleftarrows}} CO_2 + CH_3C{=}C(CH_3)_2$$
$$\qquad\qquad\qquad\qquad\qquad\qquad\qquad\qquad\qquad | $$
$$\qquad\qquad\qquad\qquad\qquad\qquad\qquad\qquad\quad O^-$$

This, however, is far from being the case. The equilibrium constants, $K$ and $K'$, of these two decarboxylations must be related by the equation

$$K/K' = K_a/K_k,$$

where

$$K = \frac{[CO_2][CH_3C(OH){=}C(CH_3)_2]}{[CH_3COC(CH_3)_2COOH]}$$

$$K' = \frac{[CO_2][CH_3COC(CH_3)_2{}^-]}{[CH_3COC(CH_3)_2COO^-]}$$

$$K_a = \frac{[H^+][CH_3COC(CH_3)_2COO^-]}{[CH_3COC(CH_3)_2COOH]}$$

$$K_k = \frac{[H^+][CH_3COC(CH_3)_2{}^-]}{[CH_3C(OH){=}C(CH_3)_2]}$$

$K_a$ has the value $3.08 \times 10^{-4}$ at $25°$.[329] If we assume that $K_k$ is similar to the ionization constant of a phenol, or about $10^{-10}$, we can estimate the relative magnitudes of $k_2$ and $k_2'$ thus:

$$\frac{k_2}{k_2'} = \frac{k_1 K'}{k_1' K} = \frac{k_1 K_k}{k_1' K} = \frac{7 \times 10^{-5} \times 10^{-10}}{1.5 \times 10^{-8} \times 3 \times 10^{-4}} = 1.5 \times 10^{-3}$$

Therefore, toward carbon dioxide an enolate anion is much more reactive than a neutral enol, even though a relatively favorable mechanism exists for addition of the enol. Where no such enolic mechanism exists, as in the carbonation of methane and decarboxylation of acetic acid, only the anionic addition and cleavage are realized in practice.

The work discussed thus far has identified three mechanistic cases in the base-catalyzed aldol addition. If the $A$ component is very reactive, as with acetaldehyde, the rate-determining process is enolization, subject to general acid-base catalysis. If the $A$ component is less reactive, the rate is determined by its reaction with either of two enoloid species present at equilibrium: the enolate anion, whose concentration is then

[329] K. J. Pedersen, J. Am. Chem. Soc., 58, 246 (1936).

determined by the $pH$, or an enamine in equilibrium with the $B$ component and ammonia, a primary or secondary amine. For the aldol reaction promoted by *acid* catalysts [330] the mechanism must be quite different from that promoted by bases. Kinetic studies of acid-catalyzed dealdolization are complicated by the ease of dehydration of $\beta$-hydroxy ketones. In view of the slow reaction between an enol and a ketone, rapid addition in acid can be explained only as enhancement by the acid

$$CH_3-\overset{\overset{+}{O}H}{\underset{CH_3}{\overset{\|}{C}}} \leftarrow CH_3=\overset{OH}{\overset{|}{C}}-CH_3 \rightleftharpoons CH_3-\overset{OH}{\underset{CH_3}{\overset{|}{C}}}-CH_2-\overset{\overset{+}{O}H}{\overset{\|}{C}}-CH_3$$

of the reactivity of the carbonyl group. By the dehydrating action of strong acid, the product of this reaction is mesityl oxide. The reaction is thus driven forward despite an unfavorable equilibrium of aldolization. If the addition of a non-ionized enol to a keto group can be strongly

$$CH_3-\overset{OH}{\underset{CH_3}{\overset{|}{C}}}-CH_2\overset{O}{\overset{\|}{C}}CH_3 \xrightarrow{H^+} H_2O + (CH_3)_2C{=}CH\overset{O}{\overset{\|}{C}}CH_3$$

catalyzed by acid in this way, it is not surprising that mild acid catalysis also becomes important in the amine-catalyzed aldol condensation. The self-condensation of crotonaldehyde to yield polyenols [331] is catalyzed effectively by piperidinium acetate, or by piperidine in the presence of a small amount of any carboxylic acid. In the absence of the acid the reaction fails. The criterion of Westheimer and Jones for the possible cyclic nature of the transition state has not been applied to this case where a larger ring is in question.

It has long been an interesting question why the aldol addition stops after only two molecules of aldehyde have reacted together, despite the fact that the aldol itself should be entirely capable of acting as $A$ component in a further reaction of linear polymeric type. Hibbert [332] surmised that the reason for this might be the formation of a compound between one molecule of aldol and one of aldehyde, and he even proposed a structure for such a compound. Twenty-eight years later such a compound was isolated and a common structure, different from Hibbert's,

[330] K. H. Meyer, *Ann.*, **398**, 57 (1913).
[331] R. Kuhn, W. Badstübner, and C. Grundmann, *Ber.*, **69**, 98 (1936); R. Kuhn and C. Grundmann, *Ber.*, **70**, 1318 (1937).
[332] H. Hibbert, *J. Am. Chem. Soc.*, **37**, 1760 (1915).

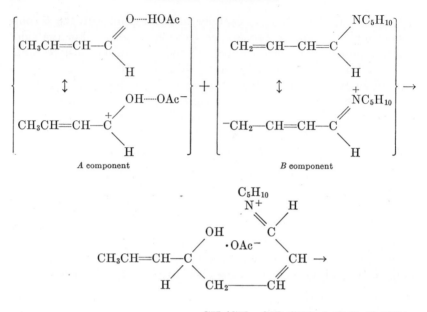

A component          B component

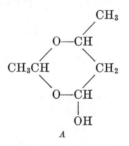

$$CH_3(CH=CH)_3CHO + C_5H_{10}N \cdot HOAc$$

was assigned to it almost simultaneously in three laboratories.[333] The aldol-aldehyde compound has the structure of a sesquiacetal, $A$, being thus a cyclic acetal of the aldehyde and a hemiacetal of the aldol. Like other hemiacetals with six-membered rings, this compound is stable

$$
\begin{array}{c}
CH_3 \\
| \\
O\!-\!CH \\
\diagup \qquad \diagdown \\
CH_3CH \qquad CH_2 \\
\diagdown \qquad \diagup \\
O\!-\!CH \\
| \\
OH
\end{array}
$$

A

enough to be distilled but is in a sufficiently mobile equilibrium with aldol and aldehyde so that the aldehyde can be removed by continuous passage of nitrogen at 50° through a water solution of the compound.[334]

[333] E. Hanschke, *Ber.*, **76B,** 180 (1943); E. Späth, R. Lorenz, and E. Freund, *Ber.*, **76B,** 57 (1943); R. H. Saunders, M. J. Murray, F. F. Cleveland, and V. I. Komarewsky, *J. Am. Chem. Soc.*, **65,** 1309 (1943); R. H. Saunders, M. J. Murray, and F. F. Cleveland, *ibid.*, **65,** 1714 (1943).

[334] E. Späth, R. Lorenz, and E. Freund, *loc. cit.*

On long standing the dissociation of this compound to an equilibrium leads to the production of "paraldol," $B$,[335] in which the acetalized component is aldol instead of acetaldehyde. The occurrence and relative

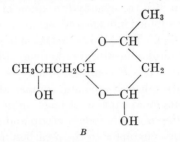

$B$

stability of these cyclization products account for the characteristic absence of absorption due to the carbonyl group in the ultraviolet or infrared spectra of aldol. In the presence of strong base, polymeric aldol condensation does take place because of the great activity imparted to the small amount of acetaldehyde present at equilibrium in the dissociation of the sesquiacetal.

*The Benzoin Condensation.* The benzoin condensation is a reaction of the aldol type in which the active hydrogen of the $B$ component is

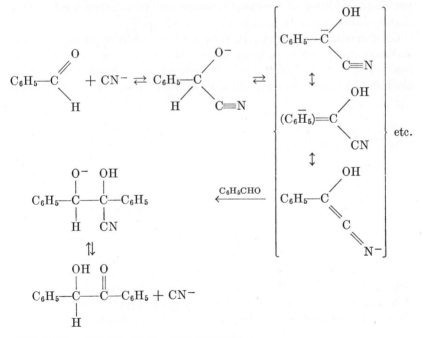

[335] E. Späth and H. Schmid, *Ber.*, **74B**, 859 (1941).

originally the hydrogen of an aldehyde group. Such hydrogen is not normally available for aldol addition and is rendered so in the benzoin condensation only by the temporary conversion of the benzaldehyde by means of cyanide ion into the cyanhydrin anion in which the hydrogen is activated by the combined influence of the nitrile and phenyl groups.[336]

*The Michael Reaction.* The Michael reaction is an addition in which the *A* component is an $\alpha,\beta$-unsaturated ketone, aldehyde, ester, nitrile, or similar compound. The *B* component may be a ketone, aldehyde, ester, nitrile, aliphatic nitro compound, amine, alkali alkoxide, alkali cyanide, or other compound capable of reacting in a nucleophilic sense. Because the interaction of the carbonyl group and the ethylenic double bond imparts the same character to the $\beta$-carbon as belongs to the carbon of the carbonyl group every reagent capable of adding to the

$$RCH{=}CHCR' \leftrightarrow RCH{=}CH\overset{+}{C}{-}R' \leftrightarrow \overset{+}{R}CH{-}CH{=}CR'$$
$$\underset{O}{\|} \qquad\qquad \underset{O^-}{|} \qquad\qquad\qquad \underset{O^-}{|}$$

carbonyl group is capable of attachment to the $\beta$-carbon atom of an $\alpha,\beta$-unsaturated ketone. The Michael reaction is often distinguished from the simple addition of the same *B* component to a carbonyl group by a slightly lower reactivity and less ready reversibility.

**Condensation Reactions.** In certain of the addition products to the carbonyl group, such as hemiacetals, the hydroxyl group is *activated toward displacement.* Thus, under strongly acidic conditions in anhydrous alcohol, aldehydes form acetals with elimination of water. Formalde-

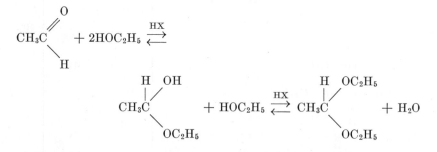

hyde is especially prone to enter into reaction sequences in which aldolization is followed by the displacement of active hydroxyl. The formation of hexamethylenetetramine involves a series of rapidly reversible additions and displacements, taking the course it does doubtless because of

[336] A. Lapworth, *J. Chem. Soc.*, **83**, 995 (1903).

the limited solubility of the highly symmetrical product. In the *chloro-methylation* of aromatic compounds the direct addition product of the

$$6CH_2O + 4NH_3 \longrightarrow \text{(structure)} + 6H_2O$$

aromatic compound to formaldehyde possesses active hydroxyl which is displaced by chlorine. The *Mannich reaction* is another important

$$CH_3\text{-C}_6H_4 + CH_2O + HCl \rightleftarrows$$

$$CH_3\text{-C}_6H_4\text{-}CH_2OH + HCl \rightleftarrows CH_3\text{-C}_6H_4\text{-}CH_2Cl + H_2O$$

preparative sequence in which displacement of active hydroxyl is an essential step, although it is not clear in individual cases whether the amino alcohol (*A*) or the methylene ketone (*B*) is directly intermediate:

$$R'COCH_3 + CH_2O + R_2NH \cdot HCl \rightleftarrows R'COCH_2CH_2NR_2 \cdot HCl + H_2O$$

$$R_2NCH_2OH \qquad\qquad R'COCH{=}CH_2$$
$$A \qquad\qquad\qquad\qquad B$$

A second way in which condensations result is by *elimination of water* from the carbon atom of the original carbonyl group and an adjacent position. This occurs when the hydroxyl group is activated, as in the addition products of amines and hydrazines to aldehydes and ketones, and it also happens when a hydrogen atom adjacent to the carbon of the original carbonyl is activated for any reason. Thus the aldols, RCHOHCHRCHO, are readily dehydrated under much milder conditions than suffice for the dehydration of an ordinary alcohol. When R is aromatic the dehydration is so easy as to proceed under the influence of even the basic catalyst for the aldol addition (Claisen-Schmidt and Perkin condensations). In most condensation reactions of this type the intermediate hydroxyl compound is not isolated and its presence is inferred through the study of model reactions of similar type and because there appears to be no other demonstrable reaction sequence leading to elimination of the oxygen of a carbonyl group.

A third way in which condensation reactions arise is by entrance of the hydroxyl group of the primarily formed aldol into an intramolecular reaction involving the O—H bond. Examples of this include the *Darzens condensation,* and various cases of intramolecular transesterification such as the example given on p. 104 of the reaction between benzaldehyde

$$RCHO + ClCH_2COR' \xrightarrow{\text{Base}} \left[ \begin{matrix} RCH—CHClCOR' \\ | \\ OH \end{matrix} \right] \xrightarrow{\text{Base}} RCH\underset{O}{\diagdown\diagup}CHCOR'$$

and the enol of oxalomesityl oxide. In the *Stobbe condensation* [337] even a relatively hindered ketone like benzophenone functions as an efficient *A* component because the usual high degree of reversibility of the addition step is counteracted by ready intramolecular transesterification.

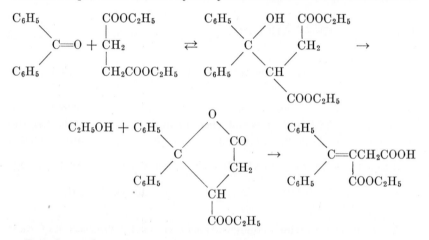

Fourth, condensation reactions may occur by elimination of an anionic group which is originally attached to the carbonyl group. This process gives rise to the whole group of reactions of carboxylic acids and their derivatives: esterification, transesterification, hydrolysis of esters, acylation by acid anhydrides and halides, aminolysis of esters, the Claisen condensation, etc. The haloform cleavage of trihalomethyl ketones, and cleavages of certain other ketones by strong alkali, are also examples of this process.

Kinetic work on four reactions will serve to illustrate the study of condensation reactions of three of the types just mentioned. The formation and hydrolysis of acetals and the aminonitrile reaction, involving the displacement of active hydroxyl, the formation of semicarbazones, involving dehydration of an addition product, and the formation and hydrolysis of esters, involving the elimination of an anionic group, have all been studied in some detail.

*The Acetal Reaction.* The hydrolysis of acetals [338] is a reversible reaction whose opposing process is the acetal condensation. Accurate measurements have been made of the rates of hydrolysis of a number of acetals, and it is found that these rates are directly proportional to the hydrogen-ion concentration. Since the position of the equilibrium is not

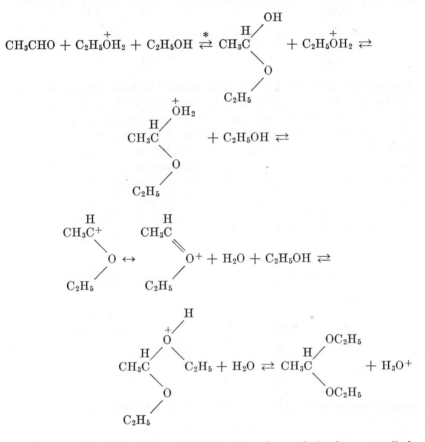

shifted by acid it follows that the *formation* of acetals is also controlled by the hydrogen-ion concentration. The absence of general acid catalysis speaks in favor of a mechanism such as shown by the equations. In the presence of very high concentrations of hydrogen chloride the hy-

[338] J. N. Brönsted and W. F. K. Wynne-Jones, *Trans. Faraday Soc.,* **25,** 59 (1929); J. N. Brönsted and C. Grove, *J. Am. Chem. Soc.,* **52,** 1394 (1930).

* For the mechanism of hemiacetal formation see pp. 93–95. This portion of the reaction must come to equilibrium more rapidly than the latter stages, for otherwise the general acid-base catalysis which characterizes the formation of hemiacetals would be apparent in the acetal reaction.

droxyl group of the hemiacetal is displaced by chlorine instead of ethoxyl and the product is an α-chloro ether.[339]

*The Aminonitrile Reaction.* The treatment of an aldehyde or simple ketone with ammonia and hydrogen cyanide simultaneously leads to the formation of an aminonitrile:[340]

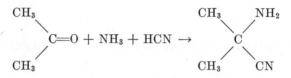

The question as to which hydroxyl compound undergoes conversion into the final product, the amino alcohol $(CH_3)_2C(OH)NH_2$ or the cyanhydrin $(CH_3)_2C(OH)CN$, was answered by Stewart and Li by a careful kinetic study[341] of the related reaction in which acetone cyanhydrin and diethylamine are taken as reactants. In alcohol as solvent the rate of reaction is proportional not to the concentrations of these starting materials but to the concentrations of amine and acetone. This result and others are interpreted as showing that the cyanhydrin does not possess active hydroxyl but that the amino alcohol does, the kinetics being consistent with the mechanism given. The activating effect of an oxygen

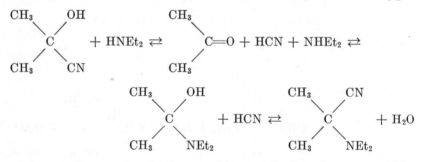

atom or a nitrogen atom in the α-position on a hydroxyl group would be

expected to encourage either direct $S_N2$ displacement of the hydroxyl or the formation of a substituted carbonium ion $(CH_3)_2\overset{+}{C}NH_2$ ↔

[339] F. M. Litterscheid and K. Thimme, *Ann.*, **334**, 49 (1904); E. Wedekind, *Ber.*, **36**, 1383 (1903).

[340] W. Gulewitsch, *Ber.*, **33**, 1900 (1900); W. Gulewitsch and T. Wasmus, *Ber.*, **39**, 1181, 1726 (1906).

[341] T. D. Stewart and C. H. Li, *J. Am. Chem. Soc.*, **60**, 2782 (1938).

$(CH_3)_2\overset{+}{C}=NH_2$ capable of reacting rapidly with the electron-donor substances present.

*The Formation of Semicarbazones.* In important respects the formation of semicarbazones is probably typical of the formation of hydrazones, arylhydrazones, and oximes, the case of semicarbazones having been most studied because of analytical advantages.[342] Semicarbazide is a base which is half converted into the corresponding ammonium ion at $pH$ 3.7. At progressively lower $pH$ values the reactive semicarbazide is increasingly converted at equilibrium into the unreactive ion, and both the equilibrium and rate become unfavorable to semicarbazone formation. On the other hand, the formation of semicarbazones is subject to general acid catalysis, and hence solutions of high $pH$ are also unfavorable to the rate of the reaction. The most favorable rates are obtained in solutions of $pH$ close to that of half-neutralized semicarbazide and in the presence of moderate concentrations of organic acids. The rates and equilibria, which are quantitatively in accord with this description, support some such mechanism as the following, illustrated for the case of acetone:

$$\begin{array}{c} CH_3 \\ \diagdown \\ C{=}O + HA + H_2NNHCONH_2 \underset{\longleftarrow}{\overset{(1)}{\longrightarrow}} \\ \diagup \\ CH_3 \end{array}$$

$$\begin{array}{c} CH_3 \\ \diagdown \\ C{=}O\cdot HA + H_2NNHCONH_2 \underset{\longleftarrow}{\overset{(2)}{\longrightarrow}} \\ \diagup \\ CH_3 \end{array} \qquad \begin{array}{c} CH_3 \quad \overset{+}{N}H_2NHCONH_2 \\ \diagdown \diagup \\ C \qquad\qquad\qquad + A^- \underset{\longleftarrow}{\overset{(3)}{\longrightarrow}} \\ \diagup \diagdown \\ CH_3 \quad OH \end{array}$$

$$\begin{array}{c} CH_3 \quad NHNHCONH_2 \\ \diagdown \diagup \\ C \\ \diagup \diagdown \\ CH_3 \quad OH \end{array} + HA \underset{\longleftarrow}{\overset{(4)}{\longrightarrow}} \begin{array}{c} CH_3 \quad NHNHCONH_2 \\ \diagdown \diagup \\ C \\ \diagup \diagdown \\ CH_3 \quad OH\cdot HA \end{array} \underset{\longleftarrow}{\overset{(5)}{\longrightarrow}}$$

$$\begin{array}{c} CH_3 \\ \diagdown \\ C{=}\overset{+}{N}HNHCONH_2 + H_2O + A^- \underset{\longleftarrow}{\overset{(6)}{\longrightarrow}} \\ \diagup \\ CH_3 \end{array}$$

$$\begin{array}{c} CH_3 \\ \diagdown \\ C{=}NNHCONH_2 + H_2O + HA \\ \diagup \\ CH_3 \end{array}$$

[342] J. B. Conant and P. D. Bartlett, *ibid.*, **54**, 2881 (1932); F. H. Westheimer, *ibid.*, **56**, 1962 (1934).

It would be consistent with the kinetics for any one of the steps 2–6 to be rate determining, but it is most probable that the rate is determined by either 2 or 5 since these steps involve the formation and breaking of bonds other than those of hydrogen to oxygen or nitrogen.  For a discussion of the comparative aspect of the work in question, see Vol. I of this Treatise, pp. 1049–1052.

*Esterification and Ester Hydrolysis.*  Carboxylic acids can be converted into esters by several classes of procedures, which differ so markedly in their characteristics that it has been apparent from the first that they represent different reaction paths.  The first category includes the reaction between the carboxylic acid and an alcohol, catalyzed by acids, and the reaction between the acid chloride and an alcohol, catalyzed by acids or bases.  The second category includes esterification of the acid by diazoalkanes, or of a salt of the acid by an alkyl halide or other alkylating agent.  The third class, applicable only in special cases, consists of esterification by pouring a solution of the acid in concentrated sulfuric acid into the alcohol.

From the fact that the first class of reactions is subject to sharp steric hindrance from groups close to the carbonyl group whereas the second class is not, it was recognized early [343, 344, 345] that these two procedures differed in that only the first involved addition to the carbonyl group. The isolation of a crystalline addition compound of sodium methoxide and methyl benzoate [346] or ethyl benzoate [347] lent credence to the view that the addition of alcohol to the carbonyl group of an acid or the addition of water to that of an ester was a step in the establishment of esterification-hydrolysis equilibrium.  As demanded by this reaction path,

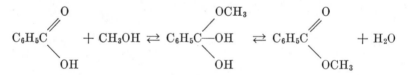

configuration is always retained in the esterification of an optically active saturated alcohol; and tracer experiments show that oxygen from the water is not found in the alcohol produced in alkaline hydrolysis of esters.[348, 349, 350]

[343] L. Henry, *Ber.*, **10**, 2042 (1877).
[344] R. Wegscheider, *Ber.*, **28**, 1468, 3127 (1895).
[345] H. v. Pechmann, *Ber.*, **31**, 501 (1898).
[346] L. Claisen, *Ber.*, **20**, 649 (1887).
[347] H. v. Pechmann, *loc. cit.*, p. 501.
[348] M. Polanyi and A. L. Szabo, *Trans. Faraday Soc.*, **30**, 508 (1934).
[349] S. C. Datta, J. N. E. Day, and C. K. Ingold, *J. Chem. Soc.*, 838 (1939).
[350] I. Roberts and H. C. Urey, *J. Am. Chem. Soc.*, **61**, 2584 (1939).

When the attack of a base on the carbonyl group of an ester leads to reaction, the base becomes a part of the product. Therefore, the only base other than water that can *hydrolyze* an ester is the hydroxyl ion; the only base that can produce a methyl ester by transesterification is the methoxide ion; etc. The role of acids is more reversible, and it is found that esterification and ester hydrolysis are subject to general acid catalysis.[351-354] The following mechanism for acid-catalyzed esterification and ester hydrolysis is consistent with these facts.

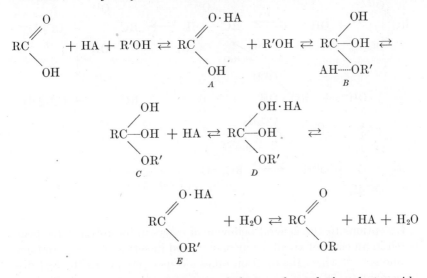

It will be noted that assignment of the usual catalytic role to acids involves postulating the addition product $C$ of alcohol to acid as a true intermediate. In the basic mechanism there would appear to be a possible short cut, from $F$ to $H$ and $I$, without the completion of the addition product. It has proved possible to show by isotopic studies [355] that the equivalence of the $O^{18}$ and $O^{16}$ in $F$ is established, either through a rapid equilibration of $F$ with $G$, or by the actual formation of $C$, in which an oxygen atom derived from the solvent is situated equivalently to one originally present in the keto group of the ester being hydrolyzed. Recovery of the unhydrolyzed ester after various amounts of hydrolysis have taken place has shown that isotopic oxygen exchange occurs be-

[351] L. P. Hammett, "Physical Organic Chemistry," McGraw-Hill Book Co., New York (1940), pp. 356–359.
[352] H. M. Dawson and W. Lowson, *J. Chem. Soc.*, 2444 (1927); H. M. Dawson, E. R. Pycock, and E. Spivey, *ibid.*, 291 (1933).
[353] H. Goldschmidt, *Ber.*, **29**, 2208 (1896); *Z. Elektrochem.*, **15**, 4 (1909).
[354] A. C. Rolfe and C. N. Hinshelwood, *Trans. Faraday Soc.*, **30**, 935 (1934).
[355] M. L. Bender, *J. Am. Chem. Soc.*, **73**, 1626 (1951).

tween the ester and the water at a rate equal to 1/4.8 of the rate of hydrolysis for ethyl benzoate, and relatively faster for isopropyl benzoate. The figure observed for acid hydrolysis of ethyl benzoate was similar, 1/5.2. These results prove that the symmetrical intermediate $C$ or an equivalent structure is formed at least 20% of the time in the alkaline hydrolysis of ethyl benzoate, and the simplest assumption is that it is the common intermediate in isotopic exchange and in ester hydrolysis.

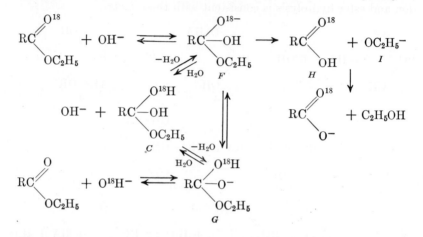

Exceptions to the general behavior of esters in hydrolysis have been noted in an ester of an allylic alcohol,[356] and in certain esters of tertiary alcohols,[357,358] where the reaction takes a course resembling the $S_N1$ displacement (p. 58).

In the preparation of esters by alkylation of the anion of the acid, the process is clearly a displacement with the acid anion retaining its integrity throughout. Alkylation by diphenyldiazomethane has been the subject of a careful kinetic study,[359] one of whose conclusions is that there exists a one-step reaction between the diazo compound and benzoic acid,

$$(C_6H_5)_2CN_2 + HOOCC_6H_5 \rightarrow (C_6H_5)_2CHOOCC_6H_5 + N_2$$

which is not analogous to either a normal esterification or any of the familiar mechanisms for the displacement reaction.

2,4,6-Trimethylbenzoic acid, dissolved in concentrated sulfuric acid, gives a freezing-point depression corresponding to four dissolved par-

[356] J. Kenyon, S. M. Partridge, and H. Phillips, *J. Chem. Soc.*, 85 (1936).

[357] S. G. Cohen and A. Schneider, *J. Am. Chem. Soc.*, **63**, 3382 (1941).

[358] W. v. E. Doering and A. Streitwieser, *Abst. 119th Mtg., Am. Chem. Soc., Boston, Mass.*, 3 April, 1951.

[359] J. D. Roberts, W. Watanabe, and R. E. McMahon, *J. Am. Chem. Soc.*, **73**, 760 (1951).

ticles for each acid molecule.  This proves [360] to be due to ionization of
the form indicated by the equation.  That *ortho* substitution favors this

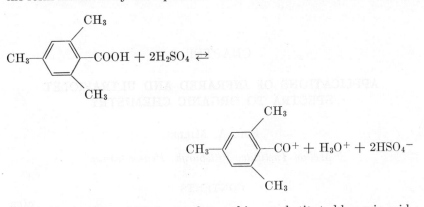

mode of ionization, which is not observed in unsubstituted benzoic acid,
must be due to the steric effect of the *ortho* groups on the relative stabil-
ities of the ions as shown.  Newman was able to verify the prediction

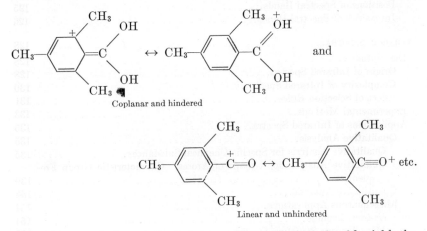

that such a solution, poured into excess methanol, should yield the
hindered ester immediately and in good yield.[361]  Indeed, an ester can
probably be prepared more quickly from some of the classical examples
of sterically hindered acids than from acids of any other type.

[360] H. P. Treffers and L. P. Hammett, *ibid.*, **59**, 1708 (1937).
[361] M. S. Newman, *ibid.*, **63**, 2431 (1941).

CHAPTER 2

# APPLICATIONS OF INFRARED AND ULTRAVIOLET SPECTRA TO ORGANIC CHEMISTRY

FOIL A. MILLER

*Mellon Institute, Pittsburgh, Pennsylvania*

CONTENTS

## INTRODUCTION

### Outline of Molecular Spectra.  Scope of the Chapter

This chapter deals primarily with the use of infrared and ultraviolet spectra in determining the structure of organic molecules.  Certain other applications of considerable utility to the chemist have also been described.  The goal has been to give the student a general survey of the application of these methods to organic chemistry, so that he may have some acquaintance with these important techniques and may be able to judge when and how they can be of use in solving his problems.

Since this discussion will treat only a portion of the broad field of spectroscopy, it is necessary to define clearly the subject area.  Molecular spectra may be divided into three categories: rotational spectra, vibrational spectra, and electronic spectra.  Each of these will be described briefly in order to provide a background for the later discussions and to allow the scope of the chapter to be delineated.

1. *Rotational spectra* result from the absorption of photons by molecules with the complete conversion of the energy of the photons into energy of molecular rotation.  This rotational energy is *quantized;* i.e., a molecule cannot possess any arbitrary energy of rotation, but only certain discrete values.  These values are referred to as energy levels and are often represented as horizontal lines spaced along a vertical energy axis.  Only those photons can be absorbed whose energies are exactly equal to the difference between two rotational energy levels.  Consequently the spectrum consists of discrete lines.

These energy differences are very small; they usually correspond to absorption of wavelengths in the range 0.01–10 cm. (far infrared and microwave regions). As yet pure rotational spectra have had little direct application to organic chemistry, and so no further mention will be made of them.

2. *Vibrational spectra* occur when the absorption of radiant energy produces changes in the energy of molecular vibration. Again, only certain discrete energies are permitted the molecule, and the absorption of light corresponds to a transition between two of these energy levels. Thus, vibrational spectra also are discrete rather than continuous.

The energy differences evidenced in vibrational spectra are approximately 100 times greater than those in rotational spectra. Usually, a change in vibrational energy is accompanied by simultaneous changes in rotational energy. Since the latter are relatively small, they have the effect of widening the vibrational "line" into a band which is therefore termed a *vibration-rotation band.*

Most vibrational absorption bands appear in the range from 2 to 100 $\mu$.* This discussion will deal only with the range 2–25 $\mu$, since this region has been most widely used because of its accessibility to prism spectrometers. It is part of the near infrared, which is considered to extend from the long-wavelength limit of the visible, 0.75 $\mu$, to about 25 $\mu$.

Vibrational spectra can also be obtained from the *Raman effect.* The types of information furnished by the vibrational Raman and infrared spectra are essentially the same, although the experimental techniques are quite different. Much of what will be said about infrared spectra, therefore, is also true for Raman spectra, but only the former will be discussed explicitly. Reference may be made to the excellent chapters in Harrison, Lord, and Loofbourow's book [1] for a good comparison of the two.

3. *Electronic spectra* arise from the absorption of radiant energy and its complete conversion into increased energy of certain electrons. The kind of electrons concerned, and the nature of the molecular states between which transitions occur, will be described later under "The Origin of Electronic Spectra." These electronic energies are also quantized. Transitions between the electronic energy levels require some 10–100 times more energy than vibrational transitions. Associated with each electronic level of the molecule is a series of vibrational levels, and with each vibrational level is a series of rotational levels. Electronic transitions usually involve these sublevels, so that there are simultaneous

---

* Units of wavelength are defined in the following section.

[1] G. R. Harrison, R. C. Lord, and J. R. Loofbourow, "Practical Spectroscopy," Prentice-Hall, New York (1948).

changes in electronic, vibrational, and rotational energies. Since there are many possible vibrational and rotational sublevels from which an electronic transition can start, and since for any initial level there are many possible terminal levels in the upper electronic state, electronic spectra are highly complex. In the vapor phase the spectra often appear as a sequence of vibration-rotation bands, but in solution these bands are usually smeared out so that only a relatively broad and structureless absorption is observed.

Electronic spectra occur in the visible and ultraviolet regions, from about 7500 to 100 Å. The most widely used portions of this range are

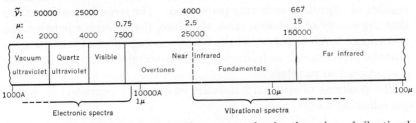

Fig. 1. A portion of the electromagnetic spectrum, showing the regions of vibrational and electronic spectra. (The wavelength scale is logarithmic.)

the *visible*, from 7500 to 4000 Å, and the *quartz ultraviolet*, from 4000 to 2000 Å. The discussion of electronic spectra will be restricted to these two regions. They will be collectively termed "ultraviolet" for brevity.

Figure 1 indicates graphically the infrared and ultraviolet regions that will be under discussion.

## Methods of Expressing Spectroscopic Data

Spectroscopic determinations generally provide two different types of numerical data: the positions of lines or bands in the electromagnetic spectrum, and the intensities of these bands.*

**Positions of Spectral Bands.** The positions of spectral bands may be expressed as wavelengths ($\lambda$) or as frequencies ($\nu$). To show the relationship of these terms to one another and to energy, let us define the following symbols.

$c$ = velocity of light (cm. sec.$^{-1}$).
$\lambda$ = wavelength (cm., $\mu$, Å).
$\nu$ = frequency (sec.$^{-1}$).
$\tilde{\nu}$ = wavenumber (cm.$^{-1}$) = $1/\lambda$ (cm.).

* Other data, such as the extent of polarization, are helpful in certain studies with molecular spectra but need not be considered here.

$E'$, $E''$ = energies (in ergs) of the upper and lower levels involved in a spectral transition.

$E_p$ = energy of photon (ergs).

$h$ = Planck's constant (erg-sec.).

These quantities are related by the following important equations:

$$c = \lambda\nu \tag{1}$$

$$E_p = E' - E'' = h\nu = hc/\lambda = hc\bar{\nu} \tag{2}$$

The first equation says that the velocity of light (i.e., the distance traversed in 1 sec.) is equal to the wavelength of one vibration times the number of vibrations occurring per second. The second equation states that the energy of a photon (and, therefore, the difference between the two energy levels involved in the corresponding spectral transition) is directly proportional to frequency and to wavenumber, but inversely proportional to wavelength.

The positions of spectral bands are customarily expressed in one of the following units:

a. Units of wavelength.
  1. Micron ($\mu$). $\qquad$ $1\ \mu = 10^{-6}$ meter $= 10^{-3}$ mm.
  2. Millimicron (m$\mu$). $\quad$ $1\ m\mu = 10^{-3}\ \mu = 10^{-6}$ mm. $= 10^{-7}$ cm. $= 10$ Å.
  3. Angstrom (Å). $\qquad$ $1$ Å $= 10^{-8}$ cm. $= 0.1$ m$\mu$.

b. Units of frequency.
  1. Reciprocal seconds ($\nu$). Too large to be convenient.
  2. Wavenumber ($\bar{\nu}$). $\quad \bar{\nu}$ (cm.$^{-1}$) $= 1/\lambda$ (cm.) $= 10^4/\lambda$ ($\mu$) $= 10^8/\lambda$ (Å).

For infrared spectra, both wavenumbers and microns are convenient units. For electronic spectra the millimicron is currently most popular. It is preferred over the angstrom because one less significant figure is indicated. For example, 275 m$\mu$ gives a fairer picture of the accuracy of measurement than 2750 Å. Wavenumbers assume values between 13,000 and 50,000 for electronic spectra, and therefore they too indicate more significant figures than are justified. Consequently, more and more authors are using cm.$^{-1} \times 10^{-2}$. Wavenumbers have the great advantage of being directly proportional to energy and are, therefore, to be preferred over units of wavelength for theoretical work in both infrared and ultraviolet spectra.

**Intensities of Spectral Bands.** The intensity at a given wavelength is occasionally given in purely arbitrary terms such as the deflection of a galvanometer or the blackening of a photographic plate. A somewhat better expression is *transmittance*, defined by

$$T = I/I_0 = \text{transmittance} \qquad 100T = \text{per cent transmittance}$$

Here $I_0$ and $I$ are the intensities of radiant energy of a given wavelength incident on, and emergent from, the sample, respectively.

For absorption spectra the intensity can be formulated much more precisely by means of the *Lambert-Beer law*,

$$\log_{10}(I_0/I) = \log_{10}(1/T) = kcl = A \tag{3}$$

where $I_0$ and $I$ are defined as above; $c$ = concentration of absorbing material; $l$ = path length through sample; $k$ = proportionality constant (a function of wavelength that is characteristic of each molecular species); $A$ = absorbance (this has often been called *optical density*, symbol $D$). This equation is derived in many textbooks of physical chemistry.[2,3]

The proportionality constant $k$ is given various names, depending on the units of concentration and the system of logarithms. The two most important cases for chemists are the following (with $l$ in centimeters, and using $\log_{10}$):

1. $A = \epsilon cl$, where $c$ is in moles per liter, and $\epsilon$ is termed the *molecular extinction coefficient*. Thus $\epsilon$ may be regarded as the absorbance of a sample 1 cm. thick and having a concentration of 1 mole per liter. This is a useful form of the equation because $\epsilon$ provides a comparison of intensity for equal numbers of molecules.

2. $A = E^{1\%}_{1\,\mathrm{cm.}} \, cl$, where $c$ is in per cent wt./vol., and $E^{1\%}_{1\,\mathrm{cm.}}$ is termed "$E$, 1%, 1 cm." This is convenient when the molecular weight is not known or when quantitative analyses are to be made.

A number of other forms of the Lambert-Beer law are given in references 3 and 4. Because of the deplorable confusion of the terminology connected with spectrophotometry, it is highly desirable that the units and the base of the system of logarithms be stated explicitly when the Lambert-Beer law is employed.

The *absolute intensity* of an absorption band may be expressed by giving the absolute value of $\epsilon_{\max}$, the molecular extinction coefficient at maximum absorption. This quantity can be determined by means of the Lambert-Beer law, provided that the slit widths employed are sufficiently narrow.[4a,5] This criterion can usually be fulfilled when measuring the ultraviolet spectra of solutions but seldom is satisfied for infrared spectra.

[2] See, for example, F. Daniels, "Outlines of Physical Chemistry," John Wiley & Sons, New York (1948), pp. 78–79.

[3] Harrison, Lord, and Loofbourow, ref. 1, pp. 363–367, 369.

[4] E. A. Braude, *Ann. Repts. on Progress Chem. (Chem. Soc. London)*, **XLII**, 105–130 (1945).

[4a] W. West, in Weissberger's "Physical Methods of Organic Chemistry," Interscience Publishers, New York (1949), 2nd ed., Vol. I, Part II, pp. 1303–1305.

[5] R. N. Jones and K. Dobriner, "Infrared Spectrometry Applied to Steroid Structure and Metabolism," "Vitamins and Hormones," Academic Press, New York (1949), Vol. VII, pp. 294–363.

Consequently it is customary to report $\epsilon_{max}$ for ultraviolet bands, but not for those in the infrared. The absolute intensity may also be expressed as the *integrated absorption intensity*, $2.303 \int \epsilon_a \, d\nu$, where 2.303 is the conversion factor from $\log_{10}$ to $\log_e$, $\epsilon_a$ is the absolute molecular extinction coefficient, $\nu$ is the frequency in cycles per second, and the integration is carried out over the entire frequency range of the band. This is more readily measured for infrared spectra than the absolute value of $\epsilon_{max}$, and it promises to be of considerable importance in elucidating chemical structure.[5,6] For example, Jones and Dobriner[5] have shown that the integrated intensity of the carbonyl stretching frequency in the infrared for a number of steroids depends on the type of carbonyl (ketone, acetate) and its position, and that the intensity is additive when two carbonyl groups are present. Consequently a measurement of this intensity provides information concerning the structure of a steroid. These authors have given a brief discussion outlining the methods of measurement and the experimental difficulties. References to more complete discussions may be found there.

## INFRARED SPECTRA

This discussion will attempt to describe how vibrational infrared spectra may be of assistance to the organic chemist. Emphasis will be placed on the fairly complex molecules with which he deals in his day-to-day work. The discussion will not treat the problem of analyzing infrared spectra in terms of normal vibrations or the related problem of determining the symmetry of relatively simple molecules. These topics have been admirably discussed by Herzberg.[7]

### Description

**Origin of Infrared Spectra.** It has already been mentioned that molecules can absorb photons whose energies are exactly equal to the difference between two vibrational energy levels and that a vibrational absorption spectrum results. It is helpful to have a physical model for picturing this process, and fortunately a simple one is available.

To a rather good approximation a molecule can be regarded as an assembly of balls and springs, the balls representing the nuclei and the springs the chemical bonds. Such a system can vibrate according to a

[6] R. E. Richards and W. R. Burton, *Trans. Faraday Soc.*, **45**, 874 (1949).

[7] G. Herzberg, "Infrared and Raman Spectra of Polyatomic Molecules," D. Van Nostrand Co., New York (1945).

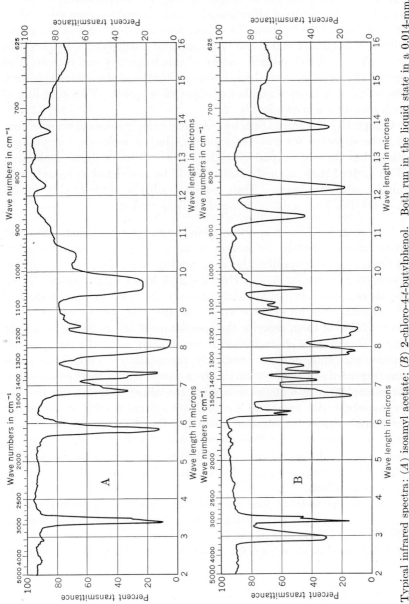

FIG. 2. Typical infrared spectra: (A) isoamyl acetate; (B) 2-chloro-4-t-butylphenol. Both run in the liquid state in a 0.014-mm. cell.

vast number of complex patterns. It can be shown, however, that any one of these patterns can be synthesized by the proper superposition of a relatively few forms of vibration which are termed "normal vibrations" or "fundamental vibrations." [8] Each normal vibration has associated with it a frequency called the "fundamental frequency." In general a molecule can absorb radiant energy of this frequency and convert it to energy of vibration. One thus obtains a vibrational absorption spectrum consisting of a discrete number of absorption bands. Two examples of such spectra are shown in Fig. 2.

**Complexity of Infrared Spectra.** A fairly complex absorption spectrum is to be expected for most compounds, since a molecule containing $n$ atoms has $3n - 6$ normal vibrations ($3n - 5$ for a linear molecule). With each of these normal vibrations will be associated a characteristic fundamental frequency. Thus, toluene, with $n = 15$, has 39 fundamental vibrations and 39 fundamental frequencies.

The quantity $3n - 6$ is obtained in the following manner. In order to describe completely the motion of the nuclei of a molecule, three coordinates must be specified for each nucleus, e.g., the $x$, $y$, and $z$ Cartesian coördinates for each. Thus, for a molecule with $n$ atoms, $3n$ coördinates are required in all, and the molecule is said to have $3n$ degrees of freedom. Not all of these are vibrational degrees of freedom, however. Three of them describe the translation of the molecule as a rigid unit. This may be characterized completely by using the three coördinates of the center of mass. Similarly, the rotation of a non-linear molecule (regarded as a rigid system) is given completely by three coördinates, for example, the two angles describing the orientation of a line fixed in the molecule with regard to a coördinate system fixed in space, and a third angle describing rotation about this line. The remaining $3n - 6$ degrees of freedom must then describe motions of the nuclei relative to each other, with the system as a whole fixed in space—that is, they describe vibrational motions. Hence, there is a total of $3n - 6$ fundamental vibrations.

For a *linear molecule* (one for which the equilibrium positions of all the nuclei are on the same straight line), there are $3n - 5$ fundamental vibrations. This is due to the fact that only two angles are needed to describe rotation, since rotation about the molecular axis is not measurable.

One must not expect to observe exactly this number of bands in the spectrum, however. The number may be increased by bands which are

[8] *Ibid.*, pp. 67–71.

not fundamentals, namely combination tones, overtones, and difference tones.* Conversely, the number of observed bands may be diminished by the following effects:

(*a*) If the molecule is highly symmetrical it is probable that selection rules will forbid the appearance of some of the frequencies in the infrared spectrum. This will be explained more fully in the next section.

(*b*) High symmetry also often requires that certain pairs or triads of the fundamental frequencies be exactly identical. They are then said to be *degenerate* and are, of course, observed as only one band.

(*c*) Some vibrations may happen to have frequencies so nearly alike that they are not separated by the spectrometer (accidental degeneracy).

(*d*) Some fundamental bands may be so weak that they are not observed.

(*e*) Some of the fundamentals may occur at such low wavenumbers that they fall outside the range of the usual infrared spectrometer.

In summary, then, a fairly complex infrared spectrum can be expected for most organic compounds. Between 5 and 30 bands are usually observed.†

**Effect of Selection Rules.**[9] It has been mentioned that some vibrational frequencies are forbidden to appear in the infrared spectrum by the action of selection rules. These selection rules are most restrictive for highly symmetric molecules. *The general requirement for infrared activity of a vibration is that the vibration must produce a (periodic) change in the dipole moment.* If no such change occurs, the vibration is "forbidden in the infrared." The molecule can still carry out the vibration, of course, but the vibration cannot be activated by the absorption of infrared radiation and therefore cannot be detected in the infrared spectrum.

---

* A *combination tone* is the sum of two or more different frequencies, such as $\bar{\nu}_1 + \bar{\nu}_2$. (The absorbed photon excites both vibrations 1 and 2 simultaneously.) An *overtone* is a multiple of a given frequency, as $2\bar{\nu}_1$ (first overtone), $3\bar{\nu}_1$ (second overtone), etc. A *difference tone* is the difference between two frequencies, such as $\bar{\nu}_1 - \bar{\nu}_2$. (The molecule is already in one excited vibrational state $[\bar{\nu}_2]$ and absorbs enough additional radiant energy to raise it to another excited vibrational state $[\bar{\nu}_1]$.)

† The spectrum of a purified mineral oil such as Nujol is a notable exception to the above remarks. It is undoubtedly a complex mixture of many rather large molecules, all of low symmetry, and yet its spectrum from 650 to 3500 cm.$^{-1}$ consists of only 5 bands. This is most fortunate, for it makes Nujol an excellent "mulling" agent for preparing powdered samples (see p. 133). The simplicity of the spectrum is due partly to the combined operation of *c*, *d*, and *e* above. Other reasons are mentioned briefly by A. Elliott, E. J. Ambrose, and R. B. Temple, *J. Chem. Phys.*, **16**, 877 (1949), especially pp. 879–880.

[9] The theory of selection rules is discussed fully by Herzberg, ref. 7, pp. 251 ff. A summary of the working formulas and an example of their application are given in a paper by A. G. Meister, F. F. Cleveland, and M. J. Murray, *Am. J. Phys.*, **11**, 239 (1943).

As an illustration of the operation of selection rules, let us consider a molecule which has a *center of symmetry*. This is a point such that a straight line drawn from the equilibrium position of any atom of the molecule to this point, and then extended an equal distance beyond, encounters the equilibrium position of an identical atom. Ethylene, carbon dioxide, benzene, and *trans*-1,2-dichloroethylene all have centers of symmetry; water and methane (and indeed most molecules) do not.

Figure 3 gives schematic pictures for two of the normal vibrations of *trans*-1,2-dichloroethylene which will be used as examples. The circles indicate the equilibrium positions of the atoms; the arrows indicate the

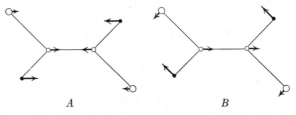

A            B

Fig. 3. Two normal vibrations of *trans*-1,2-dichloroethylene (schematic): (*A*) symmetric to center of symmetry; (*B*) antisymmetric to center of symmetry. The arrows represent displacements of the nuclei from their equilibrium positions. (For diagrams of the remaining ten normal vibrations, see Herzberg, ref. 7, p. 331.)

displacements of the atoms during one phase of each vibration. During the other phase the displacements are exactly opposite in direction.

Fundamental vibrations are always either symmetric or antisymmetric to a center of symmetry.[10] A vibration which is symmetric to the center of symmetry is one for which the displacement vector for every atom will, when reflected at the center of symmetry, coincide with the vector of the corresponding mirror atom (Fig. 3*A*). For an antisymmetric vibration, each displacement vector will, when reflected at the center of symmetry, be the negative of the actual displacement vector for the mirror atom (Fig. 3*B*). Vibrations which are symmetric to the center of symmetry obviously cannot produce a change in the dipole moment. The dipole moment is zero for the equilibrium configuration, and it remains zero throughout the entire vibration because a displacement by any one atom is counterbalanced by the displacement of its opposite. (See Fig. 3*A*.) Such vibrations are therefore forbidden in the infrared. Conversely, the vibration shown in Fig. 3*B* does produce a change in the dipole moment. The moment is zero in the equilibrium position, but it is certainly not zero at either extreme of the vibration. Therefore, this vibration is allowed in the infrared.

[10] G. Herzberg, ref. 7, pp. 83, 97–98.

## Experimental Methods

Infrared spectra are almost invariably measured as absorption spectra. The sample is placed in a beam of radiation and the proportion of the energy absorbed from the beam at various wavelengths is measured. It does not seem appropriate to describe here the apparatus that is employed. Several good introductory discussions are available,[1, 11] and a paper by Williams [12] gives an excellent review of the subject.

It does seem desirable to describe the preparation of the sample, since this is often of considerable interest to the organic chemist. Substances may be studied as gases, liquids, or solids. Solutions may also be used, but the solvent must be carefully selected for transparency to infrared radiation in the region to be studied. No solvent is completely transparent throughout the infrared. The two best solvents in this respect are carbon disulfide and carbon tetrachloride, and by using solutions in each the entire range from 2 to 15 $\mu$ can be covered. Unfortunately, many of the polar compounds are not sufficiently soluble in these solvents to give usable concentrations. A number of other liquids may be used in limited portions of the spectrum. A list of many of them with their regions of transparency is given in a paper by Torkington and Thompson.[13]

It may be noted that liquid water absorbs very strongly throughout much of the near infrared, and, consequently, aqueous solutions can seldom be used. An exception to this is found in the work described by Gore, Barnes, and Petersen,[14] in which the spectra of several amino acids and their salts were measured in aqueous solutions at various $p$H's. It is necessary, however, that the solubility of the sample be relatively high if the absorption of water is not to hide the absorption of the solute. This same paper demonstrates the usefulness of heavy water as a complementary solvent to ordinary water. It is good practice to dry all samples because of the strong absorption of water and because water will rapidly etch the sodium chloride or potassium bromide of which cell windows are usually made.

Solids are best studied in the form of suspensions, or "mulls," in a purified mineral oil such as Nujol. A mull can be prepared very easily by putting a small amount of the finely ground sample on a sodium chloride plate, adding a small drop of mineral oil, and then placing a

[11] R. B. Barnes, R. C. Gore, U. Liddel, and V. Z. Williams, "Infrared Spectroscopy," Reinhold Publishing Corp., New York (1944). This material, except for the extensive bibliography, appeared originally in *Ind. Eng. Chem., Anal. Ed.*, **15**, 659–709 (1943).

[12] V. Z. Williams, *Rev. Sci. Instruments*, **19**, 135–178 (1948).

[13] P. Torkington and H. W. Thompson, *Trans. Faraday Soc.*, **41**, 184 (1945).

[14] R. C. Gore, R. B. Barnes, and E. Petersen, *Anal. Chem.*, **21**, 382 (1949).

second salt plate on top and rubbing the two together until the suspension is homogeneous.  The mineral oil reduces the loss of transmitted light due to scattering from the small crystal surfaces.  The sample should be finely ground to avoid the orientation effects described on p. 139.  If the C—H bands of the sample are to be examined, Nujol cannot be used.  One of the completely fluorinated hydrocarbons which are now available can then be employed in its place.*  Another technique which is sometimes useful involves melting the solid between the two salt plates by heating carefully and then allowing it to cool.  This procedure may have to be repeated in order to get a preparation that does not scatter the light excessively.

Some other substances, such as rubber and some of the plastics, are conveniently studied in the form of a film which can be made by putting a few drops of a suitable solution on a salt plate and allowing the solvent to evaporate.

The size of the sample required is 1–5 mg., although less can be used if necessary.† The sample can be recovered by rinsing the salt plates with carbon tetrachloride or some other suitable solvent.

Infrared data are usually presented as a plot of per cent transmittance vs. wavenumbers or microns (cf. Fig. 2).  In some cases a line graph is convenient.  This is an array of vertical lines spaced along a wavenumber scale to indicate the positions of the bands, the heights of the lines affording a rough measure of their intensity.

Present usage is about equally divided between wavenumbers and microns; the author strongly favors the use of wavenumbers.  They have the advantage of being directly comparable to Raman displacements.  Furthermore, combination tones and difference tones are much more easily calculable in terms of wavenumbers than of wavelengths.

When making a visual comparison of the intensities of analogous bands in two different spectra, one must recall that the transmittance is an exponential function of the concentration and cell length: $T = 10^{-kcl}$ (see equation 3).  It is, therefore, helpful if the sample thicknesses are the same.  Since this is virtually never true of mulls, the relative in-

---

* Perfluorokerosene, made by du Pont, and Fluorolube, by the Hooker Electrochemical Co., have proved to be very satisfactory for the region above 1450 cm.$^{-1}$

† Micro cells having a total volume of about 0.05 ml. are available as accessories from several manufacturers of infrared instruments.  For solute concentrations of 1%, a 0.5-mg. sample is sufficient.  It is also possible to obtain the infrared spectra of samples of microscopic size by using a reflecting microscope in conjunction with a conventional infrared spectrometer.  Blout, Bird, and Grey [J. Optical Soc. Am., **40**, 304 (1950)] have given an extensive discussion of the problems involved and have shown that good spectra may be obtained from minute crystals, single fibers, and small tissue sections.  Minimum sample size for their instrument was 50 $\mu$ by 50 $\mu$, with the thickness dependent on the absorption coefficient.  Such microscopes are also available commercially.

tensities of two or more bands within one spectrum must be compared with the relative intensities of the same bands in another spectrum.

## Applications of Infrared Spectra

The applications of infrared spectra to be considered here may be grouped into three major types: qualitative analyses, quantitative analyses, and miscellaneous applications. (A fourth type, the analysis of a spectrum in terms of fundamental frequencies and the determination of molecular symmetry, will not be treated.) This discussion will deal primarily with the first type.

**Qualitative Analysis.** Qualitative analysis by infrared spectra may be further subdivided into two kinds: analysis for specific chemical substances, and analysis for certain groups or bonds within molecules.

*Qualitative Analysis for Specific Chemical Substances.* This type of analysis is based on the fact that the infrared spectrum is one of the most specific molecular properties known. The specificity may be explained by reference to the ball and spring model. The vibrational frequencies of this system will be altered if (*a*) the mass of one of the balls is changed, (*b*) the strength of one of the springs is altered, or (*c*) the springs are rearranged geometrically, as in changing from a straight chain to a branched chain. Similarly, molecular vibration frequencies are sensitive to changes in the masses of the nuclei, in the strengths of bonds, and in the geometrical arrangement of nuclei and bonds. As a result the infrared spectrum is, in general, a much more specific and characteristic property than the ultraviolet spectrum, melting point, boiling point, density, or refractive index. This is a consequence of the sensitivity of the spectrum to changes in molecular structure, and of the multiplicity of numerical values associated with this property (the positions and intensities of the bands).

Some limitations on this specificity must be acknowledged, however. The infrared spectrum is not a completely specific property in the sense that every different compound has a measurably different spectrum. For example, it is doubtful whether one could detect any differences in the spectra of the molecules $CH_3$—$(CH_2)_x$—$CH_3$ if $x$ were varied from, say, 15 to 16 to 17. The changes made by introducing additional methylene groups in this vibrating system are relatively small. The added methylene groups do not add any kinds of bonds that are not already present in large numbers, nor do they change the structural geometry of the molecule. It is, therefore, not surprising that the spectra should be little affected. One can also look at the matter in another way. In these long chainlike molecules the most important vibrations are those involving relatively short units of the chain, like single methylene groups and short segments of the chain containing up to four or five carbon atoms. Inserting one more methylene group in a long series of such groups will, therefore, not change the spectrum appreciably.

Another limitation is exemplified in the butadiene-styrene copolymer system (GRS rubber). The infrared spectrum will indicate the presence

$x$ $CH_2$=CH—CH=$CH_2$ + $y$ $C_6H_5$CH=$CH_2$ →

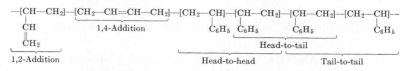

of butadiene and styrene units and will provide some information about the relative amounts of $(a)$ 1,2- and 1,4-addition of the butadiene,[15-17] and $(b)$ *cis* and *trans* configuration of the butadiene.[17] However, it is at present impossible to get any information about whether the styrene units are regularly spaced along the chain; whether addition is, or is not, head-to-head; or where and how much cross linking may be present.

In spite of these limitations the specificity of infrared spectra is still very high—sufficiently high so that it is almost always possible to distinguish between compounds having different functional groups or different geometrical structures. For example, the spectra of structural isomers such as butane and isobutane, or *o*-, *m*-, and *p*-xylene, are distinctly different. This is also true of stereoisomers such as *cis-trans* isomers, *syn-anti* isomers, and optical isomers which are not enantiomorphs (i.e., which are not mirror images of one another). The spectrum thus constitutes a powerful tool for differentiating between these isomers. (The problem of deciding which isomer a given sample may be is usually much more difficult to settle, however. The case of *cis-trans* isomers will be discussed on p. 154, after a consideration of characteristic group frequencies.)

*The influence of optical isomerism* on the infrared spectrum is frequently a question of interest. In the gaseous, liquid, or solution phases the spectra of enantiomorphs will be exactly identical. Spectra of diastereoisomers (forms differing in the spatial distribution of substituent groups) will, in general, differ from one another no matter what the

[15] J. E. Field, D. E. Woodford, and S. D. Gehman, *J. Applied Phys.*, **17**, 386 (1946); *Rubber Chem. Technol.*, **19**, 1113 (1946); H. A. Robinson's "High Polymer Physics," Chemical Publishing Co., New York (1948), p. 28.

[16] W. B. Treumann and F. T. Wall, *Anal. Chem.*, **21**, 1161 (1949).

[17] E. J. Hart and A. W. Meyer, *J. Am. Chem. Soc.*, **71**, 1980 (1949).

physical state may be. The nature of the differences cannot be predicted, but they will probably be small in most cases.

In the solid phase the spectra of enantiomorphs are often found to exhibit differences. These are usually rather small for the simpler enantiomorphs but may become quite marked in complex molecules like methionine. They are frequently constant enough to be useful for identification. Gore and Petersen describe such a case involving D(−) and L(+) threonine [*Ann. N. Y. Acad. Sci.*, **51**, 924 (1949)]. The differences are probably attributable to impurities or to polymorphism (p. 139).*

The identity of the spectra of enantiomorphs (in vapor, liquid, or solution) may be explained in the following manner. Vibrational energy levels are determined by the potential function of the molecule, which is a mathematical expression giving the potential energy as a function of the displacement of the nuclei from their equilibrium positions. Consider now two molecules that are identical except for being mirror images of one another. As a consequence of this their potential functions must also be mirror images. This means that the mathematical expressions for the two potential functions can be made identical (instead of being mirror images) by choosing properly the positive direction of that Cartesian coördinate axis which is perpendicular to the mirror plane. But this choice of direction is arbitrary and cannot change the physical state of the molecule. Since the potential functions of the two isomers can be made identical in this manner, it follows that their vibrational energy levels must be identical and, therefore, their vibrational spectra.

The ability of the infrared spectrum to discriminate between different molecular structures has a host of applications in qualitative analysis. Some of these are described below.

1. Characterizing and identifying substances. Obviously the infrared spectrum is a useful physical property for characterizing a compound and for identifying it either when pure or when in a mixture. For example, it is possible to distinguish between most of the forms of natural and synthetic rubber regardless of whether they are pure elastomers or cured samples.[18]

2. Testing the purity of a compound. If the spectrum of a sample that is known to be of good purity is available, the presence of impurities in another sample can be detected from the additional bands in its spectrum. The minimum detectable amount of impurity varies enormously from one case to another, but 1 mole per cent may be taken as a typical value.

* The author is indebted to Dr. R. C. Gore for the information in this paragraph.
[18] H. L. Dinsmore and D. C. Smith, *Anal. Chem.*, **20**, 11 (1948).

It is also possible to obtain a rough idea of the purity from the overall appearance of the infrared spectrum. As a general rule, a pure compound gives a spectrum consisting of sharp, well-resolved bands. Conversely, in a crude product the bands are more numerous, and they tend to overlap one another to give a smeared appearance. One soon learns to recognize the two types. There are some compounds, such as the amino acids, that exhibit ill-defined spectra even when pure, but they are exceptional. The spectra of proteins are also notorious in this respect, but proteins may be regarded as highly impure in the sense that they are composed of many different amino acids within any one giant molecule.

3. Following the isolation of a desired product. The spectrum provides a convenient means for following the isolation of a desired substance by a purification procedure such as distillation or chromatographic adsorption. It is not necessary to know what the compound is in this application, since the concentration of an unknown substance can be traced by observing some characteristic infrared band. This procedure proved very fruitful in the hands of Dobriner and his colleagues in the separation and identification of a number of urinary ketosteroids.[19] Incidentally, this paper contains the spectra of four steroids which differ only in being stereoisomers of one another. They provide a striking example of how such differences affect the infrared spectrum.

4. Proof of identity. The infrared spectrum also provides convincing evidence for proving or disproving the identity of two substances. An example may be cited from the work on penicillin, where the infrared spectrum played an important role in establishing the identity of synthetic and natural benzylpenicillin (penicillin-G).[20, 21] This method is particularly valuable when melting points cannot be obtained, as for salts and other substances that melt with decomposition.

In this connection it may be noted that there are often minor changes in the spectrum of a substance when its physical state is altered or when different solvents are used. Band positions may shift by 0–20 cm.$^{-1}$ (or more if hydrogen bonding is involved), and band intensities may be affected.[22-24] Consequently it is desirable to have samples in the same physical state if their spectra are to be critically compared.

Further caution is required in applying this technique for proof of

[19] K. Dobriner, S. Lieberman, C. P. Rhoads, R. N. Jones, V. Z. Williams, and R. B. Barnes, *J. Biol. Chem.*, **172**, 297 (1948).

[20] V. du Vigneaud, F. H. Carpenter, R. H. Holley, A. H. Livermore, and J. R. Rachele, *Science*, **104**, 431–433, 450 (1946).

[21] H. T. Clarke, J. R. Johnson, and R. Robinson, "The Chemistry of Penicillin," Princeton University Press, Princeton, N. J. (1949), pp. 382–414.

[22] R. S. Halford and O. A. Schaeffer, *J. Chem. Phys.*, **14**, 141 (1946).

[23] T. A. Kletz and W. C. Price, *J. Chem. Soc.*, 644 (1947).

[24] R. E. Richards and H. W. Thompson, *Proc. Roy. Soc. (London)*, **A195**, 1 (1948).

identity if the samples are solids. Although identity of the spectra constitutes good evidence that two substances are chemically the same, the converse is not always true in the solid state. The infrared spectrum is sensitive to crystal structure and to crystal orientation. If, for example, a substance can crystallize in several different forms (*polymorphism*), these forms may exhibit rather striking differences in a few details of their spectra. Such a case has been observed with 5-pregnen-3($\beta$)-ol-20-one, which was convertible into at least two, and possibly

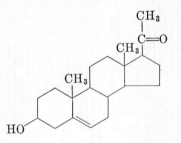

three, different crystalline forms having noticeably different infrared and x-ray spectra.[25]

Another possibility is that the crystals may be oriented differently in two different samples, resulting in dissimilar spectra. Benzylpenicillin provides an example.[26] It has been observed that when this compound is crystallized from a certain solvent the crystals are in the form of platelets. In making a mull these platelets become preferentially oriented parallel to the salt plates. As a result the relative intensities of the bands are not the same as in a finely ground sample where orientation is random. Some bands may be weakened because the changing dipole moment produced by the vibration is in such a direction in the oriented sample that it cannot interact effectively with the electric field of the radiation. Conversely, other bands may be intensified.

The effects of crystal structure and crystal orientation can be eliminated by using a solution or by keeping the sample molten. This should be attempted whenever two solid samples are suspected to be the same but their spectra show small differences.

*Qualitative Analysis for Groups of Atoms. Characteristic Group Frequencies.* It has been found empirically by studying many related molecules that certain groups of atoms have characteristic vibrational frequencies in the infrared and Raman spectra. For example, the OH, NH, and CH groups exhibit frequencies at about 3500, 3400, and 3000 cm.$^{-1}$, respectively. Often, the exact value of the frequency may give

[25] W. J. Haines, M. P. Goodwin, G. Pish, and F. A. Miller, unpublished research.

[26] R. B. Barnes, R. C. Gore, E. F. Williams, S. G. Linsley, and E. M. Petersen, *Anal. Chem.*, **19**, 620 (1947).

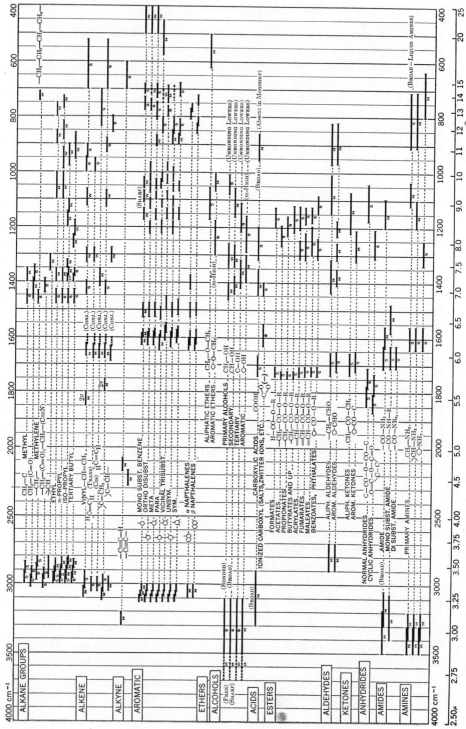

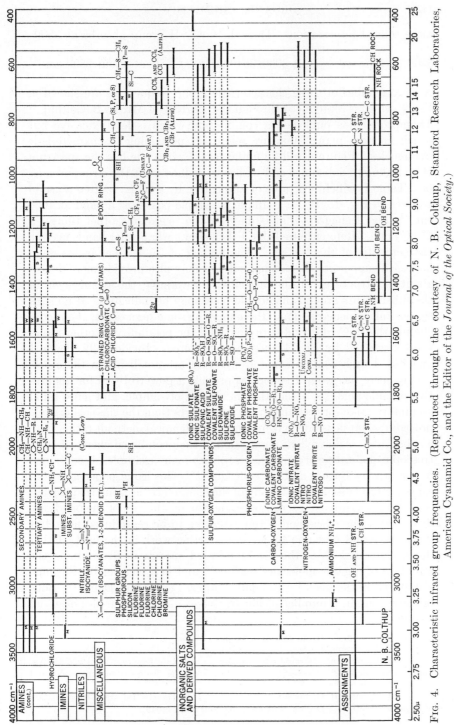

FIG. 4. Characteristic infrared group frequencies. (Reproduced through the courtesy of N. B. Colthup, Stamford Research Laboratories, American Cyanamid Co., and the Editor of the *Journal of the Optical Society*.)

141

more refined information. Thus the $\equiv$C—H group absorbs at 3300–

3200, olefinic $=$C—H at 3030–3010, and —C—H at about 2890 cm.$^{-1}$

A large number of these characteristic group frequencies are shown in Fig. 4, which is reproduced through the courtesy of Mr. N. B. Colthup.[27] Thompson [28] has published a compilation which is less extensive but which includes many literature references pertaining to characteristic frequencies. Figure 4 will be found useful when one has the spectrum of an unknown substance and wishes to deduce what the structure may be. Table I, which is a table of absorption by groups, is often a useful adjunct to Fig. 4. If, for example, a sample possesses a band at 1650 cm.$^{-1}$, Fig. 4 suggests that it may be due to (among other things) a C$=$C bond. Reference to Table I then shows what other bands may be characteristic of this linkage. The finding of these other bands gives increased support to the assignment and may also provide more details about the structure. In the case cited, for example, the arrangement of the substituents around the double bond may be indicated. If no such supporting evidence is found, there must be some reservation about concluding that a C$=$C bond is present and the possibility of other structures suggested by Fig. 4 must be considered. Incidentally, Table I and Fig. 4 each contain some groups that are not listed in the other.

Obviously the group frequencies provide a powerful tool for qualitative organic analysis, a tool that is sparing of sample, and more rapid and informative for certain structural features than the classical organic procedures. It is usually a complement to chemical methods rather than a substitute. An excellent description of such combined chemical-spectroscopic qualitative organic analyses, with many examples, is contained in a paper by Barnes and his colleagues.[26] This same paper also contains a helpful discussion of many of the characteristic group frequencies. Such details as intensities, contours, and the reliabilities of the bands are described. The discussion is too extensive to be reproduced here, but it will be found of value by anyone starting work in the field. Other detailed discussions of the use of infrared spectra in determining the structure of organic molecules may be found in a chapter by Rasmussen,[28a] and in the book by Randall, Fowler, Fuson, and Dangl.[29] Both of these contain a number of illustrative examples and tables of group frequencies.

[27] N. B. Colthup, *J. Optical Soc. Am.*, **40**, 397 (1950).

[28] H. W. Thompson, *J. Chem. Soc.*, 328 (1948).

[28a] R. S. Rasmussen, "Infrared Spectroscopy in Structure Determination and Its Application to Penicillin," in L. Zechmeister's "Progress in the Chemistry of Organic Natural Products," Springer-Verlag, Vienna (1948), pp. 331–386.

[29] H. M. Randall, R. G. Fowler, N. Fuson, and J. R. Dangl, "Infrared Determination of Organic Structures," D. Van Nostrand Co., New York (1949).

## TABLE I

CHARACTERISTIC INFRARED ABSORPTION BANDS

(Arranged by atomic groups)

| R = alkyl group | Ar = aryl group | Ph = phenyl group | ~ = approximately |
|---|---|---|---|
| (s) = strong | (m) = medium | (w) = weak | (b) = broad |

| Group | Range (cm.$^{-1}$) | Range ($\mu$) | Reference |
|---|---|---|---|
| **1. O—H** | | | |
| A. Stretching frequencies | | | |
| —O—H (free) | 3730–3520 | 2.68–2.84 | e(a) |
| —O—H (associated) | 3520–3100 (b) | 2.84–3.22 (b) | e(a) |
| B. Deformation frequencies | 1080–1030 | 9.26–9.71 | |
| | | | |
| **2. N—H** | | | |
| A. Stretching frequencies | | | |
| —NH$_2$ (free) | 3550–3420, | 2.82–2.92, | |
| | 3450–3320 | 2.90–3.01 | |
| N—H (associated) | 3500–3100 (b) | 2.86–3.23 (b) | |
| =N—H | 3400–3300 | 2.94–3.03 | |
| B. Deformation frequencies | | | |
| —NH$_2$ | 1645–1550 | 6.08–6.45 | |
| —NH— | 1580–1510 | 6.33–6.62 | |
| | | | |
| **3. C—H** | | | |
| A. Stretching frequencies | | e | |
| ≡C—H (acetylenic) | 3310–3200 | 3.02–3.12 | |
| =CH$_2$ (olefinic) | 3080 ± 10, | 3.25 ± 0.01, | e(c) |
| | 2975 ± 10 | 3.36 ± 0.01 | |
| $\overset{\mid}{=}$C—H (olefinic) | 3020 ± 10 | 3.31 ± 0.01 | e(c) |
| Ar—H | 3090–3000 | 3.24–3.33 | e(b), e(d) |
| CH$_3$—C | 2960 ± 15, | 3.36–3.39, | e(c) |
| | 2870 ± 5 | 3.48–3.49 | |
| —CH$_2$— | 2926 ± 5, | 3.41–3.43, | e(c) |
| | 2850 ± 5 | 3.50–3.52 | |
| —$\overset{\mid}{\underset{\mid}{C}}$—H | 2890 | 3.46 | e(c) |
| B. Deformation frequencies | | | |
| —CH$_2$— | 1475–1425 | 6.78–7.02 | |
| —CH=CH$_2$ (see also C=C) | 1420–1395 | 7.04–7.17 | |
| CH$_3$—C * | 1375 ± 10 | 7.27 ± 0.05 | g, h, y |
| —CH$_3$ of isopropyl | 1380 (w), | 7.25 (w), | |
| | 1370 (w) | 7.30 (w) | |
| —CH$_3$ of t-butyl (see also C—C) | 1380 (w), | 7.25 (w), | |
| | 1370 (s) | 7.30 (s) | |

* May shift if CH$_3$ is attached to an atom other than C.

## TABLE I

CHARACTERISTIC INFRARED ABSORPTION BANDS (*Continued*)

(Arranged by atomic groups)

R = alkyl group    Ar = aryl group    Ph = phenyl group    $\sim$ = approximately
(s) = strong       (m) = medium       (w) = weak           (b) = broad

| Group | Range (cm.$^{-1}$) | Range ($\mu$) | Reference |
|---|---|---|---|
| 4. S—H | $\sim$2580 (w) | $\sim$3.88 (w) | g |
| Si—H | $\sim$2240 | $\sim$4.46 | h |

5. Deuterium
   All D stretching frequencies (O—D, N—D, C—D,
     S—D, etc.) $\simeq 0.71 \times$ corresponding H stretch-
     ing frequencies (in cm.$^{-1}$).

| | | | |
|---|---|---|---|
| 6. C≡C | 2250–2150 | 4.44–4.65 | |
| H—C≡C—R | 2140–2100 | 4.67–4.76 | i |
| R$_1$—C≡C—R$_2$ | 2260–2190 | 4.42–4.57 | i |

7. C=C
   A. Stretching frequencies

| | | | |
|---|---|---|---|
| =C= (1,2-dienoid) | 2200–1960 (s) | 4.55–5.10 (s) | |
| C=C (unconjugated) | 1650–1600 | 6.06–6.25 | |
| C=C (conjugated) | 1610–1580 | 6.21–6.33 | |

   B. Also

| | | | |
|---|---|---|---|
| CH$_2$=CH—R    (R = alkyl or aryl.) †,‡ | 990 ± 5, 910 ± 5 | 10.10 ± 0.05, 11.00 ± 0.06 | j, k |
| CH$_2$=CH—G    (G = functional group other than ester, amide, or nitrile.) | 990, 926 | 10.10, 10.80 | |
| CH$_2$=CH—E    (E = ester group.) | 990, 812 | 10.10, 12.32 | |
| CH$_2$=CR$_1$R$_2$ | 890 ± 5 | 11.24 ± 0.06 | j, k |
| CH$_2$=C⟨ (Terminal double bond on ring.) | 875 | 11.43 | |
| R$_1$CH=CHR$_2$ (*trans*) | 1325–1275 (m), 980–965 (s) | 7.55–7.85 (m), 10.20–10.35 (s) | j, k, l |
| R$_1$CH=CHR$_2$ (*cis*) | 1410–1350 (m), 715–685 | 7.10–7.40 (m), 14.0–14.6 | |
| R$_1$CH=CR$_2$R$_3$ | 840–800 | 11.9–12.5 | j, k |
| C. Phenyl ring | 1625–1575, 1520–1480 | 6.15–6.35, 6.58–6.75 | |
| (1) Benzoyl (Ph—CO—) | 1600, 1584 | 6.25, 6.32 | |

† Aryl group sometimes shifts 910 band.
‡ Sometimes overtone at 1830–1805 cm.$^{-1}$, 5.46–5.54 $\mu$.

## TABLE I

CHARACTERISTIC INFRARED ABSORPTION BANDS (*Continued*)

(Arranged by atomic groups)

R = alkyl group     Ar = aryl group     Ph = phenyl group     $\sim$ = approximately
(s) = strong         (m) = medium       (w) = weak            (b) = broad

| Group | Range (cm.$^{-1}$) | Range ($\mu$) | Reference |
|---|---|---|---|
| (2) Substituted phenyl | | | |
|   (a) Monosubstituted | 760–740 | 13.2–13.5 | *m, n* |
|   (b) *ortho*-Disubstituted | 750–740 | 13.3–13.5 | *m, n* |
|   (c) *meta*-Disubstituted | 790–770 | 12.7–13.0 | *m, n* |
|   (d) *para*-Disubstituted | 830–810 | 12.0–12.3 | *m, n* |
|   (e) 1,2,3-Trisubstituted | 770–760 | 13.0–13.2 | *m, n* |
|   (f) 1,2,4-Trisubstituted | 815–800 | 12.3–12.5 | *m, n* |
|   (g) 1,3,5-Trisubstituted | 835–825 | 12.0–12.1 | *m, n* |
| D. Naphthalenes | | | |
|   $\alpha$-Naphthalenes | 800–780, 780–755 | 12.5–12.8, 12.8–13.2 | |
|   $\beta$-Naphthalenes | 855–830 (m), 830–800 (s), 760–720 | 11.7–12.0 (m), 12.0–12.5 (s), 13.2–13.9 | |
| 8. C—C | | | *f, o* |
|   —(CH$_2$)$_x$—  ($x \geq 4$)  (Singlet in liquid, doublet in solid paraffins. Actually due to CH$_2$ deformation.) | 740–720 | 13.5–13.9 | |
|   (CH$_3$)$_2$CH— | 1170 $\pm$ 3, 1145 $\pm$ 5 | 8.55 $\pm$ 0.02, 8.73 $\pm$ 0.04 | *o* |
|   (CH$_3$)$_3$C— | 1250 $\pm$ 2, 1208 $\pm$ 6 | 8.00 $\pm$ 0.02, 8.28 $\pm$ 0.04 | *o* |
|   C—CH(CH$_3$)—CH(CH$_3$)—C | 1140–1110 | 8.77–9.01 | |
| 9. C≡N | 2400–2100 | 4.17–4.76 | *p* |
|   R—C≡N | 2260–2240 (s) | 4.43–4.47 (s) | |
|   Ar—C≡N, R—C≡N (conj.) | 2240–2215 (s) | 4.47–4.52 (s) | |
|   —S—C≡N | $\sim$2160 | $\sim$4.63 | |
|   R—N≡C (isocyanide) | 2200–2100 | 4.55–4.76 | *p* |
| 10. C=N | | | |
|   —N=C=S | $\sim$2100 | $\sim$4.76 | |
|   —N=C=N— | $\sim$2100 | $\sim$4.76 | |
|   —N=C$\diagdown$ | 1660–1610 | 6.02–6.21 | |
| 11. C—N | | | |
|   C—N—C (C saturated) | 1150–1100 | 8.70–9.09 | |
|   C—N—C (C unsaturated or aromatic) | 1330–1250 | 7.52–8.00 | |
|   N—CH$_3$ | 1370–1310 | 7.30–7.63 | |

## TABLE I

CHARACTERISTIC INFRARED ABSORPTION BANDS (*Continued*)

(Arranged by atomic groups)

R = alkyl group    Ar = aryl group    Ph = phenyl group    $\sim$ = approximately
(s) = strong    (m) = medium    (w) = weak    (b) = broad

| Group | Range (cm.$^{-1}$) | Range ($\mu$) | Reference |
|---|---|---|---|
| 12. C=O | | | |
| A. Stretching frequencies § | | | |
| Anhydrides —CO—O—CO— | 1860–1800, | 5.38–5.56, | |
| | 1800–1750 | 5.56–5.71 | |
| Acid chlorides (unconjugated) | 1850–1780 | 5.41–5.62 | q |
| Azlactones | 1820–1810 | 5.49–5.52 | |
| Chlorocarbonate RO—CO—Cl | 1800–1770 | 5.56–5.65 | |
| Lactones, $\gamma$ | 1800–1760 | 5.56–5.68 | q |
| Lactones, $\delta$ | Normal ester position | | q |
| Esters | 1760–1720 | 5.68–5.81 | q, r |
| Unconjugated | 1755–1735 | 5.70–5.76 | q |
| Conjugated | $\sim$1720 | $\sim$5.81 | q |
| Also other bands as follows: | | | |
| (1) Formates | 1185, 1160 | 8.44–8.62 | r |
| (2) Acetates | 1245, 665–635, | 8.03, 15.0–15.7, | r |
| | 615–580 | 16.3–17.2 | |
| (3) Propionates | 1275, | 7.84, | r |
| | 1200–1190 (s), | 8.33–8.40 (s), | |
| | 1080, 1020, 810 | 9.26, 9.80, 12.3 | |
| (4) $n$-Butyrates | 1255, 1190, 1100 | 7.97, 8.40, 9.09 | r |
| (5) Isobutyrates | 1260, 1200, 1160, | 7.94, 8.33, 8.62, | r |
| | 1080 | 9.26 | |
| (6) Isovalerates | 1195 | 8.37 | |
| (7) Phthalates | 1285–1265, | 7.78–7.90, | |
| | 1130–1110, | 8.85–9.01, | |
| | 1075–1065 | 9.30–9.39 | |
| Aldehydes | 1730–1675 | 5.78–5.97 | |
| Ketones | | | r, s, t, u, v |
| (1) Unconjugated | 1720–1705 | 5.81–5.86 | s |
| (2) $\alpha,\beta$-Conjugated (including aryl ketones) | 1700–1665 | 5.88–6.00 | s |
| (3) $\alpha,\beta,\alpha',\beta'$-Conjugated (including diaryl ketones) | 1670–1650 | 5.99–6.06 | s |

§ These are lowered by conjugation and by hydrogen bonding, and are raised by ring strain. See discussion.

## TABLE I

CHARACTERISTIC INFRARED ABSORPTION BANDS (*Continued*)

(Arranged by atomic groups)

R = alkyl group    Ar = aryl group    Ph = phenyl group    $\sim$ = approximately
(s) = strong      (m) = medium     (w) = weak       (b) = broad

| Group | Range (cm.$^{-1}$) | Range ($\mu$) | Reference |
|---|---|---|---|
| (4) All methyl ketones but acetone (not stretching frequencies) | 1460, 1420, 1370, 1170, 595 | 6.85, 7.04, 7.30, 8.55, 16.8 | r |
| Carboxylic acids, —COOH (see also O—H) | 1740–1650 | 5.75–6.06 | |
| B. Nitrogen-containing carbonyl compounds | | | |
| Amino acid ions, $NH_3{}^+RCOOH$ | 1750–1700 | 5.71–5.88 | |
| $\beta$-Lactam (strained ring carbonyl) | 1825–1750 | 5.48–5.72 | |
| Ureido | 1720–1670 | 5.81–5.99 | |
| Amides | | | |
| (1) R—CO—NH₂ (see also N—H) | 1690–1650, 1630–1620 | 5.92–6.06, 6.13–6.17 | w |
| (2) R—CO—NHR (see also N—H) | 1680–1640, 1570–1530 | 5.95–6.10, 6.37–6.54 | w |
| (3) R—CO—NR₂ | 1650 | 6.06 | w |
| C. Miscellaneous carbonyl-containing groups | C=O stretching frequency plus the following: | | |
| Benzoyl, Ph—CO— | 1600, 1584 | 6.25, 6.31 | u |
| Acetate, CH₃—CO—O | 665–635, 615–580 | 15.0–15.7, 16.3–17.2 | |
| Acetyl, CH₃—CO— | 615–580 | 16.3–17.2 | |
| 13. C—O salts | | | |
| Carboxylate ion, —COO⁻ | 1630–1550, 1465–1400 | 6.13–6.45, 6.82–7.14 | q |
| $CO_3{}^=$ | 1470–1400, 880–810, 730–675 | 6.80–7.14, 11.4–12.3, 13.7–14.8 | |
| $HCO_3{}^-$ | 1680–1610, 1465–1400, 1025–970, 880–810, 730–675 | 5.95–6.21, 6.82–7.14, 9.75–10.3, 11.4–12.3, 13.7–14.8 | |

## TABLE I

CHARACTERISTIC INFRARED ABSORPTION BANDS (*Continued*)

(Arranged by atomic groups)

R = alkyl group    Ar = aryl group    Ph = phenyl group    $\sim$ = approximately
(s) = strong      (m) = medium      (w) = weak        (b) = broad

| Group | Range (cm.$^{-1}$) | Range ($\mu$) | Reference |
|---|---|---|---|
| 14. C—O | | | |
| —O—CH$_3$ | 1340–1280 | 7.46–7.81 | |
| Ethers, unsaturated | 1260–1200 | 7.94–8.33 | |
| =C—O—C— (including aryl ethers) | | | |
| Ethers, saturated | 1150–1070, 580–540 | 8.70–9.35, 17.2–18.5 | |
| Triglycerides | $\sim$1240 (m), 1170 (s), 1110 (w) | $\sim$8.06 (m), 8.55 (s), 9.01 (w) | |
| 15. C—F | | | |
| —CF$_2$— and —CF$_3$ | 1350–1200, 1200–1080 | 7.41–8.33, 8.33–9.26 | |
| =C—F | 1230–1100 | 8.13–9.09 | |
| —C—F | 1120–1010 | 8.93–9.90 | |
| 16. C—Cl | 730–630 | 13.7–15.9 | |
| C—Cl (overtone?) | 1510–1480 (w) | 6.62–6.76 (w) | |
| —CCl$_2$— | 845–795, $\sim$620 | 11.8–12.6, $\sim$16.1 | |
| 17. C—Br | 525–475 | 19.0–21.1 | |
| 18. Silicon-containing groups | | | *x, y, z* |
| Si—H | $\sim$2240 | $\sim$4.46 | *h* |
| —Si—CH$_3$ | 1410, 1260 (s) | 7.09, 7.94 (s) | *h, x, y, z* |
| —Si—C$_2$H$_5$ | 1460, 1410, 1375, 1240, 1010, 960 | 6.85, 7.09, 7.27, 8.06, 9.90, 10.4 | *y* |

## TABLE I

CHARACTERISTIC INFRARED ABSORPTION BANDS (*Continued*)

(Arranged by atomic groups)

| R = alkyl group | Ar = aryl group | Ph = phenyl group | $\sim$ = approximately |
|---|---|---|---|
| (s) = strong | (m) = medium | (w) = weak | (b) = broad |

| Group | Range (cm.$^{-1}$) | Range ($\mu$) | Reference |
|---|---|---|---|
| —Si—Ph (with two vertical bonds on Si) | 1590, 1490, 1430, 1190, 1120, 1030, 995 | 6.29, 6.71, 6.99, 8.40, 8.93, 9.71, 10.05 | y |
| —O—Si— (with vertical bonds) | 1100–1000 | 9.1–10.0 | z |
| —Si(CH$_3$)$_3$ | 840, 755 | 11.9, 13.2 | z |
| —Si(CH$_3$)$_2$— | 800 (s), 700 | 12.5 (s), 14.3 | z |
| **19. Sulfur-containing groups** | | | g, aa, bb |
| S—H | $\sim$2580 (w), 1000–900 | $\sim$3.89 (w), 10.0–11.1 | g |
| >C=S | 1550–1410 | 6.45–7.09 | |
| —C—S— (with vertical bonds) | 700–600 | 14.3–16.7 | g |
| —S—S— | $\sim$500 (?) | $\sim$20.0 (?) | g |
| Sulfoxide —S→O | 1060–1030 (s) | 9.43–9.71 (s) | bb |
| Sulfones —SO$_2$— | 1350–1300, 1160–1120 | 7.41–7.69, 8.62–8.93 | aa, bb |
| Sulfonates R—SO$_2$—OR | 1200–1150 | 8.33–8.70 | aa |
| SO$_4$$^=$ | 1530–1450 | 6.54–6.90 | |
| S=P | 610–570 | 16.4–17.5 | |
| **20. Miscellaneous groups** | | | |
| —NO$_2$ (nitro) | 2500–2400, 1590–1540, 1380–1320 | 4.00–4.17, 6.29–6.49, 7.25–7.58 | |
| —N—O— (with vertical bond) | $\sim$1000 | $\sim$10.0 | |
| NO$_3$$^-$ (nitrate) | 1420–1370, 845–815, 740–715 | 7.04–7.30, 11.8–12.3, 13.5–14.0 | |
| P=O | 1380–1320 | 7.25–7.58 | |
| Phosphites | 870 | 11.5 | |
| Phosphonates | 940 | 10.6 | |

## TABLE I

CHARACTERISTIC INFRARED ABSORPTION BANDS (*Continued*)

(Arranged by atomic groups)

| R = alkyl group | Ar = aryl group | Ph = phenyl group | $\sim$ = approximately |
|---|---|---|---|
| (s) = strong | (m) = medium | (w) = weak | (b) = broad |

| Group | Range (cm.$^{-1}$) | Range ($\mu$) | Reference |
|---|---|---|---|
| 21. Compounds of interest | | | |
| Nujol | 2918, 2861, 1458, 1378, 720 (w) | 3.427, 3.495, 6.859, 7.257, 13.89 (w) | |
| Liquid water (very thin) | $\sim$3430, 1650–1600 | $\sim$2.92, 6.06–6.25 | |
| Atmospheric water vapor | $\sim$1944–1320 (much fine structure) | $\sim$5.14–7.58 | |
| Atmospheric $CO_2$ | 2367, 2336, 721 (w), 667 (s) | 4.225, 4.281, 13.87 (w), 14.99 (s) | |

## GENERAL REFERENCES FOR TABLE I

[a] Barnes, Gore, Stafford, and Williams, *Anal. Chem.*, **20**, 402 (1948).

[b] Thompson, *J. Chem. Soc.*, 328 (1948).

[c] Randall, Fowler, Fuson, and Dangl, "Infrared Determination of Organic Structures," D. Van Nostrand Co., New York (1949), Chapters 3 and 4.

[d] Rasmussen, "Infrared Spectroscopy in Structure Determination and Its Application to Penicillin," in L. Zechmeister's "Progress in the Chemistry of Organic Natural Products," Springer-Verlag, Vienna (1948), pp. 331–386.

## SPECIFIC REFERENCES FOR TABLE I

[e] Fox and Martin, (a) *Proc. Roy. Soc.* (*London*), **A162**, 419 (1937); (b) **A167**, 257 (1938); (c) **A175**, 208 (1940); (d) *J. Chem. Soc.*, 318 (1939).

[f] Rasmussen, *J. Chem. Phys.*, **16**, 712 (1948).

[g] Trotter and Thompson, *J. Chem. Soc.*, 481 (1946).

[h] Thompson, *ibid.*, 289 (1947), especially p. 293.

[i] Wotiz and Miller, *J. Am. Chem. Soc.*, **71**, 3441 (1949).

[j] Rasmussen and Brattain, *J. Chem. Phys.*, **15**, 120, 131 (1947); Rasmussen, Brattain, and Zucco, *ibid.*, **15**, 135 (1947).

[k] Sheppard and Sutherland, *Proc. Roy. Soc.* (*London*), **A196**, 195 (1949).

[l] Treumann and Wall, *Anal. Chem.*, **21**, 1161 (1949).

[m] Whiffen and Thompson, *J. Chem. Soc.*, 268 (1945).

[n] Thompson and Torkington, *Trans. Faraday Soc.*, **41**, 246 (1945).

[o] Simpson and Sutherland, *Proc. Roy. Soc.* (*London*), **A199**, 169 (1949).

[p] Sheppard and Sutherland, *J. Chem. Soc.*, 453 (1947).

[q] Rasmussen and Brattain, *J. Am. Chem. Soc.*, **71**, 1073 (1949).

[r] Thompson and Torkington, *J. Chem. Soc.*, 640 (1945).

[s] Cromwell, Miller, Johnson, Frank, and Wallace, *J. Am. Chem. Soc.*, **71**, 3337 (1949).

[t] Jones, Dobriner, and co-workers, *ibid.*, **70**, 2024 (1948); **71**, 241 (1949). Jones and Dobriner, "Vitamins and Hormones," Academic Press, New York (1949), Vol. 7, pp. 294–363.

[u] Rasmussen, Tunnicliff, and Brattain, *J. Am. Chem. Soc.*, **71**, 1068 (1949).

[v] Hartwell, Richards, and Thompson, *J. Chem. Soc.*, 1436 (1948).

[w] Richards and Thompson, *ibid.*, 1248 (1947).

[x] Wright and Hunter, *J. Am. Chem. Soc.*, **69**, 803 (1947).

[y] Young, Servais, Currie, and Hunter, *ibid.*, **70**, 3758 (1948).

[z] Richards and Thompson, *J. Chem. Soc.*, 124 (1949).

[aa] Schreiber, *Anal. Chem.*, **21**, 1168 (1949).

[bb] Barnard, Fabian, and Koch, *J. Chem. Soc.*, 2442 (1949).

When two identical bonds are near enough to each other in a molecule so that they can interact mechanically, there is usually a one-to-one correspondence between the number of observed stretching frequencies and the number of bonds. For example, two N—H stretching frequencies can be observed in the spectrum of an unsubstituted amide, R—CO—NH$_2$. (One is due to a stretching of the two N—H bonds in phase with one another, the other to stretching out-of-phase.) On the other hand, a monosubstituted amide, R—CO—NHR, exhibits only one N—H stretching band. This is useful for distinguishing between the two.[30] In general, mechanical interaction will occur between identical bonds (*a*) if the bonds are attached to the same atom, or (*b*) if they are conjugated to one another, as in the structure C=C—C=C. In most other cases the frequencies of identical bonds will be so nearly alike that they will not be separated experimentally, and the only effect will be to intensify the one observed band characteristic of them.*

Several cautions should be borne in mind when using the compilations of group frequencies. The first concerns the reliability of the bands as evidence for or against certain structures. It is well known that vibrational frequencies may be divided into two broad types: those characteristic of small groups of atoms within the molecule, and those due to vibrations of essentially the entire molecule (assuming the molecule to be not too large). It is frequencies of the former type that are now being considered. They may be further divided rather arbitrarily into stretching and bending frequencies, as shown to a limited extent in Fig. 4 and Table I. In general, the stretching frequencies are the more re-

[30] R. E. Richards and H. W. Thompson, *J. Chem. Soc.*, 1248 (1947).

* Dr. R. N. Jones has kindly pointed out that, in steroids containing two carbonyl groups, the two carbonyl stretching frequencies are measurably different unless the two carbonyl groups are separated by three or more saturated carbon atoms. See ref. 5, and also p. 17 of ref. 29.

liable for indicating structure; the bending vibrations, which are almost always less than about 1400 cm.$^{-1}$, should usually be regarded as confirmative in nature.

Secondly, these compilations describe *average* results for the compounds investigated; it is not expected that they should fit every conceivable case. The range of frequencies given for any group is a compromise between making this range wide enough to include all known cases and yet keeping it narrow enough to convey some ability to discriminate this group from others. In most cases the frequencies due to a given group will be found to spread considerably less than Fig. 4 suggests.

Thirdly, several special circumstances can appreciably alter either the frequencies or the intensities of characteristic group vibrations: conjugation, hydrogen bonding, strained rings, and selection rules. They will be described in that order.

*a.* Effect of conjugation. If two unsaturated bonds are conjugated with each other, the characteristic frequencies of *both* bonds are usually lowered. For example, the carbonyl stretching vibration in ketones is affected by conjugation as shown in the tabulation.[31–33] (Further ex-

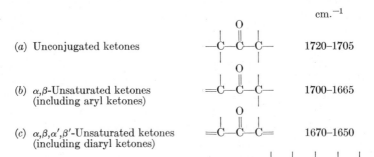

cm.$^{-1}$

(a) Unconjugated ketones                1720–1705

(b) α,β-Unsaturated ketones            1700–1665
(including aryl ketones)

(c) α,β,α',β'-Unsaturated ketones       1670–1650
(including diaryl ketones)

tension of the conjugation to the $\gamma,\delta$ bond as in —C=C—C=C—C=O has little additional effect on the position of the carbonyl band.) Similarly the C=C frequency is found to be lowered some 30 cm.$^{-1}$ by conjugation to another double bond. A reasonable explanation for these observations is that resonance structures of the type *b* and *c* are rela-

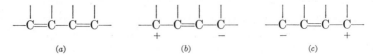

(a)                (b)                (c)

[31] H. W. Thompson and P. Torkington, *J. Chem. Soc.*, 640 (1945).

[32] R. S. Rasmussen, D. D. Tunnicliff, and R. R. Brattain, *J. Am. Chem. Soc.*, **71**, 1068 (1949).

[33] N. H. Cromwell, F. A. Miller, A. R. Johnson, R. L. Frank, and D. J. Wallace, *ibid.*, **71**, 3337 (1949).

tively important to the ground state and impart some single-bond character to the double bonds. This means a lower force constant (weaker spring) and, hence, a lower frequency. Conversely, the frequency of the single-bond vibration should be increased, but this has not been verified. The lowering by conjugation is usually 20–50 cm.$^{-1}$ Two carbonyl groups in conjugation seem to be an exception to this general rule.[32] For example, diacetyl, $CH_3$—CO—CO—$CH_3$, exhibits an infrared band at 1718 cm.$^{-1}$, which is in the range for unconjugated carbonyl groups. The appearance of only one of the two stretching frequencies in the infrared may be due to the fact that the *trans* form is the stable one at room temperature. This form has a center of symmetry, and therefore the symmetrical C=O stretching vibration is forbidden in the infrared.[32]

*b. Effect of hydrogen bonding.* If an OH or an NH group is involved in hydrogen bonding, the characteristic stretching band will be markedly lowered and broadened. The extent of the lowering (500 cm.$^{-1}$ or more in extreme cases) is a measure of the strength of the hydrogen bond. The "free" OH and NH frequencies in Fig. 4 and Table I are for the gaseous state or for extremely dilute solutions in non-polar solvents. Conversely, the OH bending frequency near 1100 cm.$^{-1}$ is increased by hydrogen bonding. If a hydrogen bond is formed to a C=O group, the carbonyl stretching frequency is also lowered by 10–30 cm.$^{-1}$ [33] Fortunately, these results can usually be predicted in advance from a knowledge of the compounds or can be detected from the spectrum. Conversely, of course, the infrared spectrum has afforded a fruitful method of studying hydrogen bonding.[34-35a]

*c. Effect of ring strain.* For cyclic ketones the carbonyl frequency increases as the size of the ring diminishes. Thus, in the series cyclohexanone, cyclopentanone, and cyclobutanone the C=O frequencies have values near 1710, 1740, and 1775 cm.$^{-1}$, respectively. The same trend is found in lactones and lactams.[36]

*d. Effect of selection rules.* Selection rules affect the intensity but not the position of absorption bands. It has been mentioned that they are most restrictive when a molecule has high symmetry. Suppose, for example, that a molecule possessing a center of symmetry has a C=C bond or a C≡C bond across this center of symmetry. Ethylene, *trans*-butene-2, and acetylene serve as examples. The frequencies associated with stretching these bonds will not appear in the infrared spectrum,

[34] L. Pauling, "The Nature of the Chemical Bond," Cornell University Press, Ithaca, N. Y. (1940), 2nd ed., pp. 316–327.

[35] J. A. Leermakers and A. Weissberger in H. Gilman, "Organic Chemistry," John Wiley & Sons, New York (1943), 2nd ed., Vol. II, pp. 1778–1783.

[35a] W. C. Sears and L. J. Kitchen, *J. Am. Chem. Soc.*, **71**, 4110 (1949).

[36] R. S. Rasmussen and R. R. Brattain, *ibid.*, **71**, 1073 (1949).

since the stretching vibration does not produce a change in the dipole moment.   One might thus be easily misled into concluding that the compounds have no unsaturation.

Even though a frequency is formally allowed by selection rules, its intensity may be so low that it is still not observed.   These cases usually cannot be predicted except from experience.   An interesting example occurs in the normal heptyne compounds $C_7H_{11}Y$, where Y may be H, OH, Cl, Br, CN, or $COOCH_3$.   It has been observed that, unless the $C\equiv C$ bond is either adjacent or next adjacent to one end or the other of the chain, its intensity is so low that it is scarcely detected.[37]   Apparently when it is near the middle of the chain the stretching of the triple bond produces virtually no change in the dipole moment.   This might lead to the erroneous conclusion that no triple bond is present in these molecules.   Similar results have been observed for olefinic compounds. The more symmetrically the substituents are arranged around the double bond of an olefin, the weaker the $C=C$ band is in the infrared.[38]

**Quantitative Analysis.**   Only passing mention will be made of this application since it is outside the scope of this chapter.   Good discussions will be found in several places.[1, 11, 12, 38a]   The method depends on the fact that in a mixture of compounds that do not interact (a) the spectrum of the mixture is the sum of the spectra of the individual components, and (b) the absorbance due to any component is proportional to its concentration.   The method is especially applicable to mixtures of geometrical isomers, where most other methods fail.   It is a useful complement to analysis by distillation, since distillation essentially separates non-polar substances according to their molecular weights but does not discriminate well between isomers.   As an example of a typical quantitative analysis by infrared absorption, a mixture of toluene and o-, m-, and p-xylenes may be cited.   For an interesting application to a mixture of solids, the reader is referred to the paper of Barnes and co-workers dealing with the analysis of penicillins.[26]

**Miscellaneous Applications.**   *cis-trans Isomers.*   If both isomers are available it is often possible to say which is *cis* and which *trans*.   When the double bond is astride a center of symmetry in the *trans* form the matter is simple; the *trans* form will not exhibit the $C=C$ frequency, whereas the *cis* will because it has no center of symmetry.   Furthermore, the spectrum of the *trans* form will generally be less rich in bands than that of the *cis* because of the selection rules already discussed.   If the

[37] J. H. Wotiz and F. A. Miller, *ibid.*, **71**, 3441 (1949).

[38] T. A. Kletz and A. Summer, *J. Chem. Soc.*, 1456 (1948).

[38a] M. G. Mellon, ed., "Analytical Absorption Spectroscopy," John Wiley & Sons, New York (1950), pp. 493–513 (by L. J. Brady).

double bond is not astride a symmetry center, one may be able to use the observation that the C=C frequency in the *trans* form of hydrocarbons is usually about 20 cm.$^{-1}$ higher than in the *cis* form.[39, 39a] For structures of the type R—HC=CH—R′, a band at 970 cm.$^{-1}$ is characteristic of the *trans* form but not of the *cis;*[16] this is often a useful criterion. In this manner it has been shown that vaccenic acid (11,12-octadecanoic acid) possesses the *trans* configuration.[40] By using this band it has also been possible to get a quantitative estimate of the amount of *trans* configuration in polybutadiene.[17] If only one of the two isomers is available, the problem is usually much more difficult except for the very special case when the double bond is known to be at a center of symmetry in the *trans* form.

*Miscellaneous Structure Studies.* Miller and Koch [41] have shown that the infrared spectrum of diketene, $(CH_2CO)_2$, changes markedly and reversibly with temperature. This is interpreted as showing that diketene exists in an equilibrium mixture of two or more forms; it is the shift of this equilibrium that alters the spectrum. Similarly, evidence for the formation of hemiacetals has been obtained from the observation that the additive spectrum of an alcohol and aldehyde is not the same as the spectrum of a mixture of the two.[42]

Another type of structure study depends on the use of the characteristic group absorption frequencies. It is sometimes possible to determine the simultaneous presence of both keto and enol tautomers, since the keto form will have a C=O absorption band and the enol a C=C and an O—H band.* As another example, it has been shown that in

(a)                    (b)

pyridazine the double bonds are not fixed to give either form *a* or *b* but that there is resonance between the two forms analogous to that in benzene.[43]

*Kinetic Studies.* The infrared spectrum can be used like any other physical property to follow chemical changes as a function of time. An

[39] M. R. Fenske, D. H. Rank, *et al., Anal. Chem.,* **19,** 700 (1947).

[39a] Reference 28a, p. 348.

[40] P. C. Rao and B. F. Daubert, *J. Am. Chem. Soc.,* **70,** 1102 (1948).

[41] F. A. Miller and S. D. Koch, *ibid.,* **70,** 1890 (1948).

[42] A. Ashdown and T. Kletz, *J. Chem. Soc.,* 1454 (1948).

* R. J. W. Le Fevre and H. Welsh have determined the keto-enol ratio of ethyl acetoacetate in several solvents by infrared analysis [*J. Chem. Soc.,* 2230 (1949)].

[43] R. C. Lord, A. L. Marston, and F. A. Miller, to be published.

interesting example is the *in situ* study of the thermal decomposition of ethylene oxide at temperatures up to 470°.[44] Another is the measurement of the rate of hydrogen-deuterium exchange between $D_2O$ and *p*-nitrotoluene.[14]

*The detection of hydrogen bonding* has already been mentioned (p. 153).

**The Value of Infrared Spectra in Following Chemical Operations.** It is usually desirable to obtain an infrared spectrum after each chemical reaction. This often gives prompt warning that a reaction has not taken the expected course or that a large amount of some impurity has been obtained. The spectrum also often affords a convenient means of deciding whether a purification has been effective. The great advantage of using it in such work is that it applies to completely new, hitherto unknown compounds almost as well as to those for which spectra are already available. The routine use of spectra in this manner has been found to be extremely valuable and is highly recommended.

**Applicability of Infrared Studies to Inorganic Compounds.** A brief mention will be made of this topic because the organic chemist does occasionally deal with inorganic compounds. If the bonds within a molecule or an ion are covalent, the molecule will possess a characteristic infrared absorption spectrum. Examples are $H_2O$, $CO_2$, $SnCl_4$, $HNO_3$, $N_2O$, $SiF_4$, $CO_3^=$, $PO_4^{-3}$, $NO_3^-$, and $NH_4^+$.* If the only bonds within a solid are electrostatic, as is the case in $NaCl$ and $CaF_2$, infrared absorption is due only to "lattice vibrations." The bands are then very broad and are responsible for the long-wavelength cutoff in transmission for such crystals. Salts like $CuSO_4$ and $LiNO_3$ exhibit absorption due to both the internal vibrations of the polyatomic ions and to the lattice vibrations. The latter are usually of low frequency (below 600 cm.$^{-1}$).

Characteristic frequencies have been found for many polyatomic inorganic ions.[44a] Their usefulness in qualitative analysis is obvious. In a series of crystals such as $Na_2CO_3$, $K_2CO_3$, and $CaCO_3$, bands will be found in each case characteristic of the $CO_3^=$ ion. These may be shifted slightly from one salt to another because of the different electrical fields of the various positive ions, so that it is often possible to identify not only the polyatomic ion but also the particular salt.

Two experimental difficulties may be pointed out. Since the atoms in many inorganic molecules are relatively heavy, the vibrations often have

---

[44] G. L. Simard, J. Steger, T. Mariner, D. J. Salley, and V. Z. Williams, *J. Chem. Phys.*, **16**, 836 (1948).

* Homonuclear diatomic molecules ($O_2$, $N_2$, $Cl_2$, etc.) are a notable exception to this statement because for them selection rules forbid infrared absorption. These molecules have only one vibration, the stretching mode ($3n - 5 = 1$). Since this vibration is symmetric to the center of symmetry, it is inactive in the infrared.

[44a] F. A. Miller and C. H. Wilkins, *Anal. Chem.*, in press.

low frequencies. This may put them beyond the range of the usual infrared spectrometer. Also, it is quite difficult to use aqueous solutions because of the extremely strong absorption of water.

## Compilations of Vibrational Spectra

Although a compilation of infrared spectra of pure compounds would obviously be very useful, there is at present no extensive published collection. Several sources are listed below with a few descriptive remarks.

1. "Catalog of Infrared Spectrograms," American Petroleum Institute Research Project 44, Carnegie Institute of Technology, Pittsburgh, Pa. Especially good for petroleum hydrocarbons.

2. Barnes, Gore, Liddel, and Williams, "Infrared Spectroscopy," Reinhold Publishing Corp., New York (1944). About 360 spectra covering only the range 800 or 1000 cm.$^{-1}$ to 2000 cm.$^{-1}$ Contains an excellent bibliography listing 2700 papers.

3. Randall, Fowler, Fuson, and Dangl, "Infrared Determination of Organic Structures," D. Van Nostrand Co., New York (1949). About 350 spectra.

4. "Catalog of Infrared Spectrograms," Samuel P. Sadtler and Son, Philadelphia 3, Pa. Several thousand spectra.

For spectra not contained in these collections, one must have recourse to the original literature. The annual reviews by Gore on infrared spectroscopy are a great aid in searching the literature.[44b] These continue the bibliography of Barnes, Gore, Liddell, and Williams' book (ref. 11). Papers by H. W. Thompson and by G. B. B. M. Sutherland and their co-workers contain rather extensive surveys of many related compounds. For steroids, the papers of Furchgott,[45] and of Dobriner and Jones and their colleagues,[5, 19, 46] are outstanding. The spectra of a number of organosilicon compounds have been reported.[47–49] The bibliography appearing in a paper by Thompson[28] and that in Table I of this chapter may be of help when looking for a particular type of compound, such as an amide or a mercaptan.*

[44b] R. C. Gore, *Anal. Chem.*, **21**, 7 (1949) (with R. B. Barnes); **22**, 7 (1950); **23**, 7 (1951).

[45] R. F. Furchgott, H. Rosenkrantz, and E. Shorr, *J. Biol. Chem.*, **163**, 375 (1946); **164**, 621 (1946); **167**, 627 (1947); **171**, 523 (1947).

[46] R. N. Jones, V. Z. Williams, M. J. Whalen, and K. Dobriner, *J. Am. Chem. Soc.*, **70**, 2024 (1948); R. N. Jones, P. Humphries, and K. Dobriner, *ibid.*, **71**, 241 (1949).

[47] N. Wright and M. J. Hunter, *ibid.*, **69**, 803 (1947).

[48] C. W. Young, P. C. Servais, C. C. Currie, and M. J. Hunter, *ibid.*, **70**, 3758 (1948).

[49] R. E. Richards and H. W. Thompson, *J. Chem. Soc.*, 124 (1949).

* Other papers concerned with the infrared spectra of various types of compounds include the following: (a) Cyclopropane and cyclobutane hydrocarbons: Derfer, Pickett, and Boord, *J. Am. Chem. Soc.*, **71**, 2482 (1949) (21 spectra). (b) Position of substitution on the benzene nucleus: Young, DuVall, and Wright, *Anal. Chem.*, **23**, 709 (1951). (c) Polynuclear aromatics: Orr and Thompson, *J. Chem. Soc.*, 218 (1950) (30 spectra). (d) Carboxylic acids: M. St. C. Flett, *ibid.*, 962 (1951) (60 spectra). (e) Long-chain fatty acids, esters, and alcohols (including triglycerides): Shreve, Heether, Knight, and Swern,

Since the Raman effect provides another experimental method of determining vibrational spectra, Raman data can sometimes be used to advantage. Some references to the more extensive collections of Raman data are given below.[50-56]

## VISIBLE AND ULTRAVIOLET SPECTRA

An enormous mass of data dealing with the visible and ultraviolet spectra of organic molecules has been accumulated in the literature of chemistry. These observations are somewhat more difficult to describe in general terms than those for infrared spectra, largely because the theory of electronic spectra is less well understood. Nevertheless, electronic spectra are highly useful to the organic chemist. The subject has already been touched on in this Treatise,[57, 58] but the approach here will be rather different and there will be no duplication.

The reader is reminded that "electronic spectra" and "visible and ultraviolet spectra" are synonymous and that only the region 2000–7500 Å is under consideration.

## The Origin of Electronic Spectra

Electronic spectra arise from transitions between two different electronic states. The principal effect of a transition is to change the energy of a relatively few electrons. It is, therefore, instructive to consider

*Anal. Chem.*, **22**, 1498 (1950) (19 spectra). (*f*) Epoxy compounds: (1) Field, Cole, and Woodford, *J. Chem. Phys.*, **18**, 1298 (1950); (2) Shreve, Heether, Knight, and Swern, *Anal. Chem.*, **23**, 277 (1951) (22 spectra). (*g*) Peroxides, hydroperoxides: Shreve, Heether, Knight, and Swern, *ibid.*, **23**, 282 (1950) (11 spectra). (*h*) Sugars, sugar derivatives, cellulose derivatives: L. P. Kuhn, *ibid.*, **22**, 276 (1950) (79 spectra). (*i*) Organic sulfur compounds: N. Sheppard, *Trans. Faraday Soc.*, **46**, 429 (1950). (*j*) Organic phosphorus compounds: (1) Meyrick and Thompson, *J. Chem. Soc.*, 225 (1950) (10 alkyl esters of phosphorus oxyacids); (2) Daasch and Smith, *Anal. Chem.*, **23**, 853 (1951) (60 spectra).

[50] "Catalog of Raman Spectral Data," American Petroleum Institute Research Project 44, Carnegie Institute of Technology, Pittsburgh, Pa.

[51] M. R. Fenske, W. G. Braun, R. V. Wiegand, D. Quiggle, R. H. McCormick, and D. H. Rank, *Anal. Chem.*, **19**, 700–765 (1947) (spectra of 172 pure hydrocarbons).

[52] J. H. Hibben, "The Raman Effect and Its Chemical Applications," Reinhold Publishing Corp., New York (1939).

[53] K. W. F. Kohlrausch, "Der Smekal-Raman Effekt," Julius Springer, Berlin (1931); "Ergänzungsband" to above (1938).

[54] K. W. F. Kohlrausch, "Ramanspektren," Academische Verlag, Leipzig [reprinted by Edwards Brothers, Ann Arbor, Mich. (1943)].

[55] G. Glockler, *Revs. Modern Phys.*, **15**, 111 (1943) (a review covering 1939–1942).

[56] J. Weiler, "Landolt-Bornstein Tabellen," 3. Erg., Vol. II, Julius Springer, Berlin (1935) (about 1500 Raman spectra, complete to 1935).

[57] J. A. Leermakers and A. Weissberger in H. Gilman, "Organic Chemistry," John Wiley & Sons, New York (1943), 2nd ed., Vol. II, pp. 1783–1794.

[58] L. Pauling, *ibid.*, pp. 1981–1983.

the nature and locale of the electrons that are involved in electronic spectra. Following this the electronic states will be described.

**Nature of the Electrons Involved in Electronic Spectra.** The electrons in molecules are divisible into three groups: those belonging to one atom, those belonging to two atoms, and those belonging to more than two atoms. Each of these will be considered in turn.

*Electrons belonging to one atom* are those in the completed inner electron shells, and those in the outer shell that are not involved in chemical bonding (for example, the unshared outer electrons of fluorine in $CH_3F$). These electrons are held rather strongly, and their excitation requires considerable energy. As a result their spectra occur in the vacuum ultraviolet (below 2000 Å) and are characteristic of the atom rather than of the molecule. Such spectra will not be considered further.[59]

*Electrons belonging to a pair of atoms* sometimes give rise to absorption in the quartz ultraviolet. Such electrons usually occur in multiple bonds.* For example, the carbonyl group (—C=O) has a characteristic absorption at 2800 Å, and the nitroso group (—N=O) at 3000 and 6650 Å. Such groups are termed *chromophores*, meaning "color bearers."

*Electrons belonging to more than two atoms* occur in conjugated systems and in some free radicals (e.g., triphenylmethyl). In a conjugated system the unsaturation, or $\pi$, electrons behave in many ways as though they belonged to the entire system rather than to a particular atom or bond. Such a system can absorb light in the visible or ultraviolet regions and is regarded as a chromophore. These electrons are the most important of the three types for absorption above 2000 Å.

**Description of Electronic States.** Each electronic state of a given molecule has a characteristic (and different) spatial distribution of the electrons among the atomic nuclei. This electron density distribution in the normal state is represented by the conventional valence bond structure. In a similar manner other, less stable states may be represented by other valence bond structures. For example, the electronic state of lowest energy (the *ground state*) of butadiene is well described by the usual formula a. Structures b and c might be thought to repre-

$$CH_2=CH-CH=CH_2 \quad \overset{+}{C}H_2-\overset{-}{C}H-CH=CH_2 \quad \overset{+}{C}H_2-CH=CH-\overset{-}{C}H_2$$
$$(a) \qquad\qquad (b) \qquad\qquad\qquad (c)$$

sent excited states. (See, however, the following paragraphs.) These structures differ from the ground state in the distribution of a few of the

[59] An excellent review of the spectroscopy of organic molecules in the vacuum ultraviolet has been given by J. R. Platt and H. B. Klevens, *Revs. Modern Phys.*, **16**, 182–223 (1944).

* $Cl_2$ and $Br_2$ provide two exceptions.

bonding electrons, which causes a rearrangement of the chemical bonds and produces a less stable molecule.

The electronic transition, then, is the process of altering the electron density distribution. There are many excited electronic states. Usually only one or two, and at most five or six, are involved in absorption above 2000 Å.

The concept of resonance [60] is in many cases a helpful device for formulating a mental picture of electronic states.[61] It is well known that the ground state of some molecules, such as benzene, cannot be represented satisfactorily by a single valence bond structure. Similarly, a single valence bond structure is often (indeed usually) a poor representation of an excited state. In particular, if two or more valence bond structures can be written that have the same, or nearly the same, energy (as is the case for the two Kekule structures for benzene), neither one represents an actual state of the molecule very well. Instead, these two structures "interact" or "resonate," and two new states are formed. In this formal mathematical process the original energy levels act as though they repelled each other, so that one of the new states has a lower energy and the other a higher energy than the original. To a first approximation (a) the splitting is symmetrical about the average value of the two original energies, and (b) the splitting is greater the smaller the difference in energy between the two original valence bond structures. Resonance may also occur between more than two valence bond structures, of course. There are always as many new states formed by resonance as there were original valence bond structures.

In view of this it is necessary to modify the previous picture of the excited electronic states of butadiene. There are four excited structures of type b, namely $\overset{\pm}{CH_2}\text{—}\overset{\mp}{CH}\text{—}CH\text{=}CH_2$ and $CH_2\text{=}CH\text{—}\overset{\mp}{CH}\text{—}\overset{\pm}{CH_2}$, where the signs indicate that the positive charge may be written on any one of the four carbon atoms and the negative charge is then on the other designated carbon. These structures have nearly equal energies. There are also two structures of type c, $\overset{\pm}{CH_2}\text{—}CH\text{=}CH\text{—}\overset{\mp}{CH_2}$, whose energy will be close to that of the preceding four. Finally, there is a non-ionic structure that is analogous to the Dewar structures for benzene. Wheland [61] represents it as $CH_2\text{—}CH\text{=}CH\text{—}CH_2$. Its energy is somewhat lower than that of the ionic forms. Since these seven

[60] L. Pauling in H. Gilman, "Organic Chemistry," John Wiley & Sons, New York (1943), 2nd ed., Vol. II, pp. 1943–1983.

[61] The use of resonance in describing the ground and excited electronic states of organic molecules has been well discussed by G. W. Wheland, "The Theory of Resonance," John Wiley & Sons, New York (1944), pp. 146–160.

hypothetical structures have roughly the same energy, they interact to give seven new energy levels. The lowest of these is lower than any one of the original seven and is the first excited electronic state of butadiene.

It is thus seen that the description of an excited electronic state in terms of the classical valence bond structures may become rather complex. In principle, however, it is no different from the description of the ground state of benzene.

The nature of electronic states may perhaps be further clarified for the reader by expressing them as linear combinations of valence bond structures. Let:

$A, B, C, \cdots$ = valence bond structures which can be written for a given spatial assembly of atoms (e.g., structures such as $a$, $b$, and $c$ for butadiene).

$\psi_A, \psi_B, \psi_C, \cdots$ = the wave equations for structures $A, B, C, \cdots$.

$a, b, c, \cdots$ = numerical coefficients.

Subscripts $0, 1, 2, \cdots$ refer to the ground state, the first excited electronic state, etc.

Then the actual wave function for the ground electronic state may be written as

$$\psi_0 = a_0\psi_A + b_0\psi_B + c_0\psi_C + \cdots$$

The coefficients $a_0$, $b_0$, etc., may be either positive or negative. The square of a given coefficient represents the magnitude of the contribution of the corresponding structure to the actual state of the molecule.

This linear combination may be visualized in the following manner. Structure $A$ represents a certain electron density distribution in the molecule. This distribution will be represented on a piece of transparent paper by a properly shaded map. The density of shading will be weighted proportionally to $a_0{}^2$. On other pieces of paper are electron density maps for structures $B$, $C$, etc., each one weighted proportionally to its coefficient. When these are superimposed, one obtains a composite map of the actual electron density distribution (in two dimensions).

Each electronic state is represented by a different set of coefficients. Thus, the first excited state is given by

$$\psi_1 = a_1\psi_A + b_1\psi_B + c_1\psi_C + \cdots$$

and similarly for the second, the third, and so on.

Some states may be represented very well by a single valence bond structure (e.g., the ground state of butadiene). Then the corresponding coefficient in the linear combination is much larger than all the others.

In other cases no coefficient predominates, but rather several different ones have about the same magnitude. It is then that resonance occurs.

This approach is described more fully by: (a) L. Pauling, ref. 34, pp. 8–12, 35; (b) G. W. Wheland, ref. 61, pp. 26–28.

The ground state is the initial state in the vast majority of observed electronic transitions in organic molecules.* The chemist, therefore, already has a good mental picture of one of the states which is concerned in practically every electronic transition. There remains to be considered only which of the many excited electronic states is likely to be involved. For this we turn to some results due to Mulliken.

**Qualitative Prediction of Transitions.** Mulliken has made a theoretical study of electronic transitions in polyatomic molecules,[62] and from his papers the following three generalizations can be drawn. They apply to molecules containing multiple bonds.

*The more probable transitions are to ionic states.* In dienes and polyenes the lowest excited electronic state to which transitions are allowed has a considerable probability of opposite charges occurring on or near the ends of the chain. For butadiene, for example, the wave functions corresponding to ionic forms $\overset{\pm}{C}H_2$—CH=CH—$\overset{\mp}{C}H_2$ make important contributions to this state.[63]

If the ground state itself is a resonance hybrid of ionic forms, the absorption is particularly intense. This is the case for many dyes.[58, 61]

*The greater the extension of the conjugated system, the smaller the energy difference between the ground level and the first excited electronic level to which transitions are allowed.* Consequently, the long-wavelength absorption maximum shifts to longer wavelengths ("toward the red") as the number of conjugated bonds increases. The concept of resonance furnishes a reasonable explanation. Compare 1,3,5-hexatriene with 1,3-butadiene. The ground state of hexatriene is well represented by the single structure a. The first excited electronic state with appreciable ionic character can be pictured as a resonance hybrid of structures like b through e.

(a)   $CH_2$=CH—CH=CH—CH=CH_2$

(b)   $\overset{\pm}{C}H_2$—$\overset{\mp}{C}H$—CH=CH—CH=CH_2$ and

$CH_2$=CH—CH=$\overset{\pm}{C}H_2$—$\overset{\mp}{C}H$—CH_2$

---

* The reason for this is that such transitions are almost always measured by the absorption of light. The molecules are then in their ground electronic state initially because the next highest electronic state has so much greater energy that the molecules cannot reach it by thermal activation.

[62] R. S. Mulliken, *J. Chem. Phys.*, **7**,(a) p. 14; (b) 20; (c) 121 (especially 134–135); (d) 339; (e) 353; (f) 364; (g) 570 (1939).

[63] Reference 62f, pp. 369–370.

(c)  $\overset{\pm}{C}H_2$—CH=CH—$\overset{\mp}{C}H$—CH=CH$_2$ and

$$CH_2=CH—\overset{\pm}{C}H—CH=CH—\overset{\mp}{C}H_2$$

(d)  $\overset{\pm}{C}H_2$—CH=CH—CH=CH—$\overset{\mp}{C}H_2$

(e)  $CH_2=CH—\overset{\pm}{C}H—\overset{\mp}{C}H—CH=CH_2$

The energy of this state is closer to that of the ground state than it is in butadiene because there are many more ionic structures of about this same (relatively low) energy which can interact, thus enhancing the splitting of the energy levels. Consequently, the lowest of the resulting excited ionic states is closer to the ground state for hexatriene than for butadiene. (See Table IIC.)

Lewis and Calvin have proposed an interesting alternative explanation for the shift in the position of absorption.[64, 65] It is based on a formal analogy between a conjugated system and an harmonic oscillator. From their results the long-wavelength absorption bands for the members of several series of polyenes can be predicted rather accurately.

*The greater the increase in the polarity of the molecule in the excited state, the greater the intensity of absorption.* Transitions to ionic states are therefore intense. Also, other things being equal, a greater elongation of the molecule produces a greater intensity of absorption.[62f] (This fact will be used later in discussing the spectra of *cis-trans* isomers.)

### Experimental Results

The electronic spectra of all but the simplest molecules are almost invariably measured as absorption spectra by placing the sample in a beam of radiation and subsequently determining the extent of absorption at various wavelengths. The samples are usually in dilute solution in transparent solvents such as water, ethyl alcohol, 1,4-dioxane, hexane, cyclohexane, or isoöctane (2,2,4-trimethylpentane). Good descriptions of the spectroscopic apparatus may be found in several places.[1, 66–69]

It was stated in the Introduction that electronic transitions are accompanied by smaller changes in vibrational and rotational energy. Be-

[64] G. N. Lewis and M. Calvin, *Chem. Revs.*, **25**, 273 (1939).

[65] G. E. K. Branch and M. Calvin, "The Theory of Organic Chemistry," Prentice-Hall, New York (1941), pp. 162–168.

[66] W. R. Brode, "Chemical Spectroscopy," John Wiley & Sons, New York (1943), 2nd ed.

[67] T. R. P. Gibb, "Optical Methods of Chemical Analysis," McGraw-Hill Book Co., New York (1942).

[68] G. F. Lothian, "Absorption Spectrophotometry," Hilger and Watts, London (1949).

[69] H. H. Cary and A. O. Beckman, *J. Optical Soc. Am.*, **31**, 682 (1941) (Beckman spectrophotometer).

cause of the many possible vibrational and rotational energy changes that can accompany a given electronic transition, electronic bands are characteristically broad. Furthermore, whatever fine structure a band may exhibit in the vapor phase is largely smeared out in solution be-

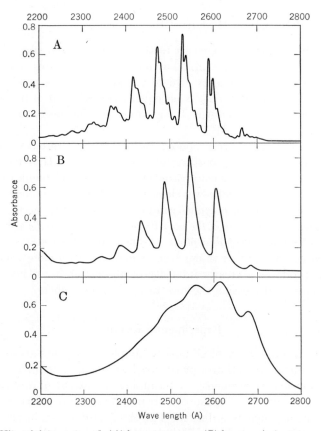

FIG. 5. Ultraviolet spectra of: (*A*) benzene vapor; (*B*) benzene in isoöctane solution; (*C*) α-picoline in isoöctane solution.

cause of two effects. (*a*) The solvent molecules hinder, or prevent completely, the rotation of the solute molecules. (*b*) The stray electrical fields from the solvent molecules perturb the electrical forces within the solute molecules and, therefore, alter their vibrational frequencies to some extent. This smearing out in solution is more pronounced for polar solvents than for non-polar ones. It is illustrated for benzene in Figs. 5*A* and 5*B*. Since the spectrum of benzene is exceptionally complex, Fig. 5*C* is presented as being more nearly typical of organic molecules.

Before summarizing the experimental observations, it may be well to define some terms which are frequently met in the literature on electronic spectra.

*Chromophore.** A covalently unsaturated group fundamentally responsible for electronic absorption.

*Auxochrome.** A saturated group that, when attached directly to a chromophore, alters both the wavelength and the intensity of the absorption maximum. The effect usually, although not always, is one of increasing both. Some typical auxochromes are OH, $NH_2$, $CH_3$, Cl, Br, and S.

*Bathochrome.* A group that causes a shift of absorption bands to longer wavelength.

*Hypsochrome.* A group that causes a shift of absorption bands to shorter wavelength.

*Hyperchrome.* A group that causes an increase in the molecular extinction coefficient.

*Hypochrome.* A group that causes a decrease in the molecular extinction coefficient.

Table II gives the characteristic ultraviolet absorption of a number of chromophore groups. Most of these values have been selected from the much more extensive tables in Braude's excellent review paper.[4] The absorptions are described by giving $\lambda_{max}$, the wavelength at the absorption maximum, and $\epsilon_{max}$, the molecular extinction coefficient at this wavelength. These values are only approximate, since they vary somewhat from compound to compound. It will be noted that the bands listed for some of the single chromophores fall in the vacuum ultraviolet.

The following empirical generalizations can be made concerning electronic spectra. Most of them are illustrated by data in Table II.

*Saturated organic compounds* such as the paraffins and cycloparaffins are transparent in the visible and quartz ultraviolet.

Compounds containing the *single chromophore groups C=C, C=N, or C≡N* also have no absorption maxima in these regions, although at high concentrations a band in the vacuum ultraviolet may become so intense that its shoulder extends up into the quartz range.

*Isolated chromophores.* If two chromophores are separated by two or more saturated bonds (such as —$CH_2$—), their absorptions are approximately additive.

*Conjugated chromophores.* The conjugation of two or more chromophores produces a system with new absorption properties, in which both $\lambda_{max}$ and $\epsilon_{max}$ have increased. This increase continues as long as the conjugated system is lengthened, although the rate of increase diminishes as the number of conjugated chromophores is augmented. When the

* These definitions of chromophore and auxochrome are due to Braude (ref. 4). They do not quite agree with the older definitions (ref. 1, p. 274), but they have the great advantage of being logical and definite.

## TABLE II

CHARACTERISTIC ULTRAVIOLET ABSORPTION OF VARIOUS CHROMOPHORES

| System | Example | $\lambda_{max}(m\mu)$ | $\epsilon_{max}$ |
|---|---|---|---|
| **A. *Single chromophores*** | | | |
| —C=C— | 3-Octene | 185 | 8,000 |
| —C≡C— | Dipropargyl | 202 | ..... |
| | | 245 | ..... |
| —C=N— | (a) Acetoxime | 190 | 5,000 |
| | (b) $(CH_3)_2C=NCH_3$ | 230 | ..... |
| —C≡N | Methyl cyanide | 167 | ..... |
| —C=O | Acetone | 188 | 900 |
| | | 279 | 15 |
| —CO₂— | Acetic acid | 204 | 40 |
| —C=S | (a) Diethylthioncarbonate | 330 | 5 |
| | (b) $(CH_3)_2C=S$ | 400 | ..... |
| —N=N— | $CH_3N=NCH_3$ | 347 | 4.5 |
| —N=O | Nitrosobutane | 300 | 100 |
| | | 665 | 20 |
| —ON=O | Octyl nitrite | 230 | 2,200 |
| | | 370 | 55 |
| —NO₂ | Nitromethane | 270 | 14 |
| —ONO₂ | Ethyl nitrate | 270 | 12 |
| **B. *Two isolated chromophores*** | | | |
| C=C—C—C—C=C | Diallyl | 175 | ~20,000 |
| C=C—C—C—C=O | Allylacetone | 278 | 30 |
| —CO₂—C—CO₂— | Malonic acid | <220 | ..... |
| —CO₂—C—C—CO₂— | Succinic acid | 204 | 100 |
| **C. *Conjugated chromophores*** | | | |
| (C—C)₂ | 1,3 Butadiene | 217 | 20,900 |
| (C=C)₃ | 1,3,5-Hexatriene | 247.5 | 56,000 |
| | | 257.5 | 79,000 |
| | | 267.5 | 68,000 |
| (C=C)₄ | 1,3,5,7-Octatetraene | 268 | ..... |
| | | 278 | ..... |
| | | 290 | ..... |
| | | 304 | ..... |
| (C=C)₅ | Vitamin A | 328 | 51,000 |
| N=C—C=N | Dimethylglyoxime | 226 | 17,000 |
| O=C—C=O | Glyoxal | 195 | 35 |
| | | 280 | 2.5 |
| | | 463 | 3.5 |

## TABLE II

CHARACTERISTIC ULTRAVIOLET ABSORPTION OF VARIOUS CHROMOPHORES (*Continued*)

| System | Example | $\lambda_{max}(m\mu)$ | $\epsilon_{max}$ |
|---|---|---|---|
| | D. *Cumulated chromophores* | | |
| C=C=C | Ethylallene | 170 | 4,000 |
| | | 227 | 50 |
| C=C=O | Diethylketene | 227 | 360 |
| | | 375 | 20 |
| N=C=N | Diethyldicarbodiimide | 230 | 200 |
| | | 270 | 25 |
| | E. *Homocyclic and heterocyclic rings* | | |
| Benzene | | 260 * | 250 |
| Naphthalene | | 275 | 5,600 |
| | | 314 | 320 |
| Anthracene | | 380 | 630 |
| Cyclopentadiene | | 244 | 2,500 |
| Pyrrole | | 240 | 300 |
| Furan | | 250 | 1 |
| Thiophene | | 235 | 4,500 |
| Pyridine | | 250 | 2,000 |
| Quinoline | | 275 | 4,500 |
| | | 311 | 6,300 |
| Isoquinoline | | 262 | 2,300 |
| | | 318 | 3,200 |

* See Fig. 5.

number of conjugated groups reaches five or six, $\lambda_{max}$ approaches the visible region and a yellow color develops.

*Adjacent (cumulated) double bonds.* When two chromophores are directly connected, as in C=C=C or C=C=O, they form a new chromophore whose absorption is generally different from that of either of the originals, or from that of the related conjugated system. They often absorb at slightly longer wavelengths than when the bonds are conjugated, but with much lower intensity.

*Crossed conjugation.* This frequently, but not invariably, gives a lower value for $\lambda_{max}$ than straight conjugation. For example, $\lambda_{max}$ for 1,1-diphenylethylene ($Ph_2>C=CH_2$) is 250 m$\mu$, whereas for *cis*-stilbene (Ph—CH=CH—Ph) it is 280 m$\mu$.

*Isocyclic systems.* The electronic spectra of isocyclic systems resemble those of their acyclic analogs, although sometimes $\lambda_{max}$ increases more than is expected (steroids, triterpenoids).

*Aromatic systems.* The spectra differ markedly from those expected for cyclohexatrienes. They may be regarded as chromophores in their own right.

*Cis-trans isomers.* A *trans* isomer usually has a somewhat higher $\lambda_{max}$ and $\epsilon_{max}$ than the *cis* isomer. They differ more in intensity than in the position of absorption. Some examples are listed. Presumably the

|  | $\lambda_{max}$, m$\mu$ | $\epsilon_{max}$ |
|---|---|---|
| *cis*-Ph—CH=CH—COOH | 264 | 9,500 |
| *trans*-Ph—CH=CH—COOH | 273 | 20,000 |
| *cis*-Ph—CH=CH—Ph | 280 | 13,500 |
| *trans*-Ph—CH=CH—Ph | 295 | 27,000 |
| *cis*-Ph—N=N—Ph | 324 | 15,000 |
|  | 438 | 1,200 |
| *trans*-Ph—N=N—Ph | 319 | 20,000 |
|  | 445 | 300 |

greater linear extension of the *trans* form is responsible for its higher intensity (p. 163). Zechmeister and his co-workers have used the electronic spectra very effectively in studying the *cis-trans* isomerization and the stereochemistry of carotenoids and diphenylpolyenes.[70]

*"Woodward's rules" for dienes and α,β-unsaturated ketones.* These rules provide an excellent example of the type of empirical generalization that can sometimes be made for limited classes of compounds. Woodward has shown that the position of the intense band of dienes and α,β-unsaturated ketones in the 230–250 m$\mu$ region may be correlated with the ex-

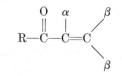

tent of substitution of the carbon-carbon double bond. For *α,β-unsaturated ketones* he gives the following rule.[71]

| Substitution | | Most Probable $\lambda_{max}$, m$\mu$ |
|---|---|---|
| α or β | | 225 |
| αβ or ββ | 1. No exocyclic C=C bond | 235 |
|  | 2. One exocyclic C=C bond | 240 |
| αββ | 1. No exocyclic C=C bond | *ca.* 247 |
|  | 2. One exocyclic C=C bond | 252 |

These values are accurate to about ±5 m$\mu$. Although they are valid only for alcoholic solutions, Woodward gives suitable corrections for other solvents. For *conjugated dienes* the absorption maximum of buta-

[70] L. Zechmeister, *Chem. Revs.*, **34**, 267 (1944).
[71] R. B. Woodward, *J. Am. Chem. Soc.*, **63**, 1123 (1941); **64**, 76 (1942).

diene in hexane ($\lambda_{max}$ = 217 m$\mu$) is used as a reference. To this is added the following increments.[72]

1. Each alkyl substituent or ring residue linked to the diene chromophore increases $\lambda_{max}$ by 5 m$\mu$.

2. Each exocyclic double bond increases $\lambda_{max}$ by 5 m$\mu$. The effect is doubled if the same bond is exocyclic to two rings.

Thus, the absorption maximum for $\Delta^{3,5}$-cholestadiene, whose chromophoric portion is shown, is calculated to be 217 + [3 × 5] (three sub-

stituents) + 5 (one exocyclic double bond) = 237 m$\mu$. The observed value is 234 m$\mu$.[73] Fieser[73] has extended these generalizations, with especial reference to steroids, and gives a good summary of them. Both he and Woodward provide examples of their usefulness in deducing details of structure.

## Applications of Electronic Spectra

Applications will now be considered wherein the electronic spectrum is used: (1) as a characterizing property, (2) in determining structure, (3) to detect steric hindrance, and (4) for quantitative analysis.

**1. As a Characterizing Property.** Because the electronic spectrum is a characteristic property, it lends itself to some useful applications. The following examples are typical.

*Qualitative Identification.* The spectrum is obviously of help in identifying materials. To cite a specific example, Jones has demonstrated that condensed aromatic ring systems can be identified by their electronic spectra.[74] The spectrum does not always provide as subtle a test as one might desire, however, because it is characteristic of the chromophoric system rather than of the complete molecule. Certain parts of a molecule can often be greatly altered without changing the absorption characteristics appreciably.

*Proof of Identity.* Although the ultraviolet spectrum may not be a discriminating test for proving the identity of two substances, at least the two spectra must be identical if the compounds are the same. It is,

[72] R. B. Woodward, *ibid.*, **64**, 72 (1942).

[73] L. F. Fieser and M. Fieser, "Natural Products Related to Phenanthrene," Reinhold Publishing Corp., New York (1949), pp. 184 ff.

[74] R. N. Jones, *J. Am. Chem. Soc.*, **66**, 185 (1944); **67**, 2021 (1945); *Chem. Revs.*, **32**, 1 (1943); **41**, 353 (1947).

therefore, widely used as one piece of evidence in such studies. It was one of many physical properties that was employed in establishing the identity of natural and synthetic benzylpenicillin.[20, 21]

*Determining Purity.* In some cases the ultraviolet spectrum is a very sensitive test of purity. Small amounts of aromatic compounds can readily be detected in hexane or cyclohexane because the latter are transparent in the quartz ultraviolet whereas aromatics absorb at 250–280 m$\mu$. Another interesting example is afforded by the preparation of pure fatty acids. Brode and co-workers [75] were able to measure the amounts of di-, tri-, and tetraene-conjugated acids appearing as impurities in linoleic acid (I). The pure acid possesses no absorption maximum above

$$C_5H_{11}-CH=CH-CH_2-CH=CH-(CH_2)_7-COOH$$
I. Linoleic acid

210 m$\mu$, since it is a system containing only isolated ethylenic bonds and a carboxyl group. On the other hand a fatty acid with two conjugated ethylenic bonds has a maximum at 235 m$\mu$, one with three at 270 m$\mu$, and one with four near 300 m$\mu$ (Table II). It is obviously possible to determine the efficacy of various purification procedures by watching for the disappearance of these bands. Markley describes such an experiment.[76]

*Tracing a Substance.* Miller, Burr, and co-workers have used the ultraviolet spectrum to determine the fate of fats ingested in the body.[77] When eleostearic acid (II) is fed to rats it is rapidly changed to a new

$$C_4H_9-CH=CH-CH=CH-CH=CH-(CH_2)_7-COOH$$
II. Eleostearic acid

acid exhibiting a high absorption at 235 m$\mu$ and a loss of absorption at 270 m$\mu$. Apparently one double bond has been destroyed to give a conjugated diene molecule.

**2. Determination of Molecular Structure.** There are many examples in the literature concerning the use of electronic spectra in determining the structure of organic molecules. Many of these applications depend on comparing the spectrum of the compound in question with the spectra of closely related model compounds. It is sometimes possible to decide between several alternative structures from this evidence. Other applications require a knowledge of the characteristic absorption of various

[75] W. R. Brode, J. W. Patterson, J. B. Brown, and J. Frankel, *Ind. Eng. Chem., Anal. Ed.*, **16**, 77–80 (1944).

[76] K. S. Markley, "Fatty Acids," Interscience Publishers, New York (1947), pp. 151–154.

[77] E. S. Miller and G. O. Burr, *Proc. Soc. Exptl. Biol. Med.*, **36**, 726–729 (1937); E. S. Miller, R. H. Barnes, J. P. Kass, and G. O. Burr, *ibid.*, **41**, 485–489 (1939); G. O. Burr and E. S. Miller, *Chem. Revs.*, **29**, 419–438 (1941).

chromophores. The use of "Woodward's rules" has already been mentioned (p. 168). Two further examples will be described, one involving fatty acids and one vitamins.

*Isomerization of Fatty Acids.* It has been shown spectroscopically that isolated double bonds in fatty acids can be made to shift position to give conjugated double bonds by saponification with potassium hydroxide.[78] Linolenic acid (III) serves as an example. It of course exhibits

$$C_2H_5—CH{=}CH—CH_2—CH{=}CH—CH_2—CH{=}CH—(CH_2)_7—COOH$$
III. Linolenic acid

no absorption maximum above 210 m$\mu$, but saponification results in a product having strong absorption maxima at 230 and 270 m$\mu$. This indicates a conjugated triene system. Kass and Burr have provided confirmation by preparing pseudo-eleostearic acid (IV) by this method

$$C_3H_7—CH{=}CH—CH{=}CH—CH{=}CH—(CH_2)_8—COOH$$
IV. Pseudo-eleostearic acid

and proving its structure by degradative oxidation.[79]

*Structure of Vitamins.* The ultraviolet spectrum was of great importance in the determination and proof of structure of several vitamins, of which vitamins $B_1$[80] and $K_1$[81] are notable examples. The case of vitamin $K_1$ is especially interesting because the spectrum was used in several different ways. This vitamin was isolated from alfalfa as a yellow oil by Dam and Karrer in 1939. They determined the ultraviolet spectrum, which is quite characteristic, and reported $\epsilon_{max}$ to be 280. A few months later Doisy and his co-workers also isolated a yellow oil from alfalfa. The spectrum was identical with that of the other product except that the absorption was more intense. They reported $\epsilon_{max}$ as 385 and concluded from this that the product of Dam and Karrer was only 70% pure. They also pointed out that several properties of the substance, including the spectrum, suggested a quinoid structure. At almost the same time R. N. Jones deduced from the spectrum that vitamin $K_1$ was an $\alpha$-naphthoquinone and, furthermore, was probably a 1,4-naphthoquinone with alkyl substituents at the 2- and 3-positions. At this point Fieser, who had been working for many years on the chemistry of quinones, was able to make a correct guess at the structure and to synthesize the vitamin. One of the pieces of evidence for the identity of the synthetic and the natural product was the ultraviolet spectrum, which agreed with that reported by Doisy's group. Just a few days earlier,

[78] Discussion and references in K. S. Markley, ref. 76, pp. 147–149.
[79] J. P. Kass and G. O. Burr, *J. Am. Chem. Soc.*, **61**, 3292 (1939).
[80] R. R. Williams *et al.*, *ibid.*, **59**, 526 (1937); J. K. Cline *et al.*, *ibid.*, **59**, 530, 1052 (1937).
[81] L. Fieser, *Science*, **91**, 31–36 (1940).

Doisy's group had deduced the structure of the molecule by degradation of the natural product. Thus, in this one problem the ultraviolet spec-

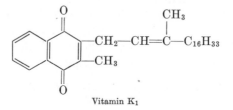

Vitamin K₁

trum was used as a characterizing property, a test of purity, a guide to structure, and a proof of identity.

**3. Detecting Steric Hindrance.** Pickett, Walter, and France [82] first pointed out that the electronic spectrum may sometimes be used to detect restricted rotation. Consider biphenyl (a) as an example. It ap-

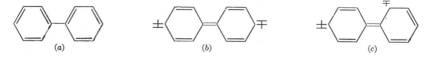

pears that in the ground state the rotation around the carbon-carbon bond is slightly hindered, and that at equilibrium in the vapor phase and in solution one half of the molecule is twisted with respect to the other half because of the mutual repulsion of the *ortho* hydrogen atoms. [83] However, if the hindering barrier is not too high a few of the molecules are nearly coplanar at any time at room temperature because of thermal motion. For these molecules ionic structures like *b* and *c*, with a double bond between the two rings, make important contributions to excited electronic states important in absorption. They give the maximum extension to the conjugated system and should lead to intense absorption at relatively long wavelengths. They require, however, that the two phenyl rings be almost coplanar.* Hence, it may be predicted that biphenyl derivatives having only very slightly hindered rotation will exhibit an intense absorption characteristic of the entire ring system. This absorption will be due to that fraction of the molecules that are nearly coplanar. However, those biphenyl derivatives that have a very highly hindered rotation will have virtually no molecules that are coplanar at any instant. Consequently, they should exhibit absorption approximat-

[82] L. W. Pickett, G. F. Walter, and H. France, *J. Am. Chem. Soc.*, **58**, 2296 (1936).
[83] O. Bastiansen, *Acta Chem. Scand.*, **3**, 408 (1949), and references therein.
* Electronic transitions are so much faster than nuclear motions that the nuclei are essentially stationary during them. Consequently, electronic transitions may occur while biphenyl is approximately coplanar even though this is not a stable configuration.

ing that of the single ring structures (at shorter wavelengths, and less intense per absorbing molecule).

These predictions have been confirmed in many, although not all, instances.[82, 84, 85] For example, Rodebush and co-workers present data demonstrating that biphenyl and a number of its *meta*- and *para*-substituted derivatives have intense absorption near 2600 Å. When two or more methyl groups are substituted in the *ortho* positions, the absorption is weakened enormously because the interference of these *ortho* groups prevents a coplanar configuration.* Similar results are found for acetophenone vs. *ortho*-substituted acetophenones. These authors show that the spectrum affords a qualitative, but not a quantitative, test for restricted rotation. It is somewhat better for determining interference than making a scale model of the molecule, because the present knowledge of van der Waals' radii is not satisfactory. The method is also of advantage where optical resolution cannot be used as a criterion. The optical method requires that each half of the molecule have only one plane of symmetry [86] and so is not applicable to substances such as

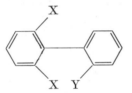

Usually, the introduction of blocking groups shifts the absorption to shorter wavelengths by increasing the energy of the upper state. There are cases where introduction of blocking groups shifts absorption to longer wavelengths. The explanation is that they prevent coplanarity and thus prevent resonance between forms that are important to the ground state. The ground state is thus less stable than it would otherwise be and is, therefore, closer in energy to the upper electronic state (which is presumed to be less affected). Several examples of both types, and many references, may be found in Ferguson's review paper.[87] Brooker and co-workers [88] have given an extensive discussion of the effect of steric hindrance on the color of dye molecules.

[84] M. T. O'Shaughnessy and W. H. Rodebush, *J. Am. Chem. Soc.*, **62**, 2906 (1940).

[85] B. Williamson and W. H. Rodebush, *ibid.*, **63**, 3018 (1941).

* The expected shift to shorter wavelengths has not been observed, however. Wheland has offered an explanation for this (ref. 61, pp. 161–162).

[86] R. L. Shriner, R. Adams, and C. S. Marvel in H. Gilman, "Organic Chemistry," John Wiley & Sons, New York (1943), 2nd ed., Vol. I, pp. 345–346.

[87] L. N. Ferguson, *Chem. Revs.*, **43**, 385–446 (1948).

[88] L. G. S. Brooker, F. L. White, R. H. Sprague, S. G. Dent, Jr., and G. Van Zandt, *ibid.*, **41**, 325 (1947).

**4. Quantitative Analysis.** This application is given only passing mention here, although it is very practical and extensively used. It is based on the Lambert-Beer law and is identical in every respect with quantitative analysis by infrared spectra. Complete discussions may be found in standard textbooks.[1, 66, 67, 68] The method is widely used for analyzing vitamin preparations,[89] various multicomponent mixtures (e.g., benzene, toluene, ethylbenzene, and xylenes), and other systems exhibiting characteristic visible or ultraviolet absorption. The use of electronic spectra in measuring the rate of a reaction is an application of this type. Another example is the measurement of dissociation constants from the change of absorption spectra with $pH$. Most of this work has been done with indicators in the visible range of the spectrum, but the method is equally applicable to ultraviolet spectra. The ionization constants of pyridine and of nicotinic acid (both acidic and basic constants) have been determined in this way by Hughes, Jellinek, and Ambrose.[90] They give references to other work. It is also possible to determine the solubility of a known compound (e.g., benzene in water) by measuring its concentration in a saturated solution. Finally, vapor pressures can in some cases be determined. For instance, the dynamic gas saturation method [91] might be employed, the volatilized material absorbed in some suitable substance, and its weight determined spectrophotometrically.[92]

### Compilations of Data on Visible and Ultraviolet Spectra

1. "Catalog of Ultraviolet Absorption Spectrograms," American Petroleum Institute Research Project 44, Carnegie Institute of Technology, Pittsburgh, Pa.
2. E. P. Carr, M. L. Sherrill, and V. Henri, "International Critical Tables," Vol. 5; W. C. Holmes, *ibid.*, Vol. 7, McGraw-Hill Book Co., New York (1929).
3. Landolt-Bornstein, "Physikalische-chemische Tabellen," Julius Springer, Berlin. Covers the literature up to 1934.
4. V. Henri, in "Tables annuelles de constantes et données numériques," McGraw-Hill Book Co., New York (1910–1936). About 750 pages of data.
5. E. A. Braude, "Ultraviolet Light Absorption and the Structure of Organic Molecules," *Ann. Repts. on Progress Chem.* (*Chem. Soc. London*), **XLII**, 105–130 (1945). Extensive tables on the characteristic absorption of chromophores, effect of auxochromes, etc. Does not give complete spectra.
6. W. R. Brode, "The Absorption Spectra of Vitamins, Hormones, and Enzymes," "Advances in Enzymology," edited by F. F. Nord and C. H. Werkman, Interscience Publishers, New York (1944), Vol. IV, p. 269.

[89] See, for example, "Methods of Vitamin Assay," The Association of Vitamin Chemists, Interscience Publishers, New York (1947), pp. 24, 34, 153, 171, 173.

[90] E. B. Hughes, H. H. G. Jellinek, and B. A. Ambrose, *J. Phys. & Colloid Chem.*, **53**, 410–423 (1949).

[91] F. Daniels, ref. 2, p. 173.

[92] The author is indebted to Dr. R. C. Hirt for pointing out these last two applications.

7. R. A. Morton, "The Application of Absorption Spectra to the Study of Vitamins, Hormones, and Coenzymes," Adam Hilger, London (1942), 2nd ed.
8. F. Ellinger, "Tabulae Biologicae," **12**, 291 (1937); **16**, 265 (1938). W. Junk, Den Haag. Absorption spectra data for natural products—sugars, proteins, etc.
9. R. A. Friedel and M. Orchin, "Ultraviolet Spectra of Aromatic Compounds," John Wiley & Sons, New York (1951). About 600 spectra in loose-leaf form, all on the same scale.

Other compilations are listed by Harrison, Lord, and Loofbourow (ref. 1, p. 423) and by Brode (ref. 66, pp. 239–242).

## COMPARISON OF THE UTILITY OF INFRARED AND ULTRAVIOLET SPECTRA

A brief summary of the relative advantages and disadvantages of infrared and ultraviolet spectra may be of interest.

### Advantages of Infrared Compared to Visible and Ultraviolet Spectra

1. The infrared spectrum is almost invariably richer in bands than the ultraviolet spectrum, and it, therefore, provides more experimental data.

2. The infrared spectrum is much more sensitive to changes in molecular structure.

3. All organic compounds have absorption in the infrared, whereas many are transparent in the visible and ultraviolet and, therefore, cannot be distinguished by their absorption in those regions.

4. Powders and crystalline materials can be used in the infrared without putting them in solution—a practical convenience.

### Advantages of Visible and Ultraviolet Spectra Compared to Infrared Spectra

1. As a result of the transparency of many compounds in the visible and ultraviolet, a variety of solvents is available for studying electronic spectra. These solvents vary in character from non-polar to highly polar. In the infrared, on the other hand, there is no solvent transparent over the entire range 3–15 $\mu$. Furthermore, polar solvents are not suited for general use because their spectra are intense and are rich in bands.

2. The Lambert-Beer law can be applied more fully, for two reasons. (a) Cell thicknesses can be determined with good accuracy in ultraviolet spectroscopy, since they are of the order of 1 cm. This is not usually true for the thin infrared cells, which are only about 0.01 cm. thick. (b) The

ratio of spectral slit width to band width may be made much smaller in ultraviolet than in infrared spectroscopy. As a result the Lambert-Beer law is valid over a greater range of absorbances in ultraviolet work.[93]

3. In favorable cases the method is much more sensitive than infrared spectra. As little as 1 to 10 parts per million of some substances can be detected. On the other hand, this sensitivity may cause difficulty in some cases.

4. The experimental equipment for visible and ultraviolet spectra is more highly perfected than that for infrared. (This advantage is being rapidly overcome, however.)

The reader has doubtless concluded by now that a study of the infrared spectrum is generally more rewarding than one of the ultraviolet. If the author were forced to choose only one of these two tools as an adjunct to studies in organic chemistry, he would unhesitatingly select the infrared. There are, of course, many instances for which ultraviolet data are to be preferred, for example when distinguishing between molecules containing different types of condensed aromatic ring systems, and for many applications in quantitative analysis. Since the solution of a problem in organic structure often requires all the pertinent information that can be obtained, the chemist will often want to have recourse to both types of spectra.

## GENERAL REFERENCES

### General

G. R. Harrison, R. C. Lord, and J. R. Loofbourow, "Practical Spectroscopy," Prentice-Hall, New York (1948), Chapters 11, 14, and 17.

M. G. Mellon, ed., "Analytical Absorption Spectroscopy," John Wiley & Sons, New York (1950). Instrumental details, analytical applications.

W. West, "Spectroscopy and Spectrophotometry," Chapter 21 in A. Weissberger's "Physical Methods of Organic Chemistry," Interscience Publishers, New York (1949), 2nd ed., Vol. I, Part II, pp. 1241–1398.

G. F. Lothian, "Absorption Spectrophotometry," Hilger and Watts, London (1949).

R. E. Burk and O. Grummitt, "Frontiers in Chemistry," Interscience Publishers, New York (1945), Vol. IV, Chapter V, "Application of Absorption Spectra to Chemical Problems," W. R. Brode, pp. 97–122; Chapter VI, "The Infrared Spectrometer and Its Application," R. B. Barnes, pp. 123–147.

### Infrared

H. M. Randall, R. G. Fowler, N. Fuson, and J. R. Dangl, "Infrared Determination of Organic Structures," D. Van Nostrand Co., New York (1949).

R. S. Rasmussen, "Infrared Spectroscopy in Structure Determination and Its Application to Penicillin," in L. Zechmeister's "Progress in the Chemistry of Organic Natural Products," Springer-Verlag, Vienna (1948), pp. 331–386.

[93] See Lothian, ref. 68, pp. 28–31.

R. B. Barnes, R. C. Gore, U. Liddel, and V. Z. Williams, "Infrared Spectroscopy," Reinhold Publishing Corp., New York (1943). Contains an extensive bibliography.

R. B. Barnes, R. C. Gore, R. W. Stafford, and V. Z. Williams, "Qualitative Organic Analysis and Infrared Spectrometry," *Anal. Chem.*, **20**, 402–410 (1948).

V. Z. Williams, "Infrared Instrumentation and Techniques," *Rev. Sci. Instruments*, **19**, 135–178 (1948).

G. Herzberg, "Infrared and Raman Spectra of Polyatomic Molecules," D. Van Nostrand Co., New York (1945). Theory.

G. B. B. M. Sutherland, "Infrared and Raman Spectra," Methuen and Co., London (1935). Theory.

## Ultraviolet

W. R. Brode, "Chemical Spectroscopy," John Wiley & Sons, New York (1943), 2nd ed.

E. A. Braude, "Ultra-Violet Light Absorption and the Structure of Organic Molecules," *Ann. Repts. on Progress Chem. (Chem. Soc. London)*, **XLII**, 105–130 (1945). An excellent review containing many tables of data and an extensive bibliography.

A. Maccoll, "Color and Constitution," *Quart. Revs. (London)*, **1**, 16–58 (1947). A general review, especially good for its comparison of the several theories of light absorption.

L. N. Ferguson, "Relationships between Absorption Spectra and Chemical Constitution of Organic Molecules," *Chem. Revs.*, **43**, 385–446 (1948). A good review with 300 references.

G. N. Lewis and M. Calvin, "The Color of Organic Substances," *Chem. Revs.*, **25**, 273–328 (1939).

"Symposium on Color and the Electronic Spectra of Complex Molecules," *Chem. Revs.*, **41**, 199–419 (1947).

H. Sponer and E. Teller, "Electronic Spectra of Polyatomic Molecules," *Revs. Modern Phys.*, **13**, 75–170 (1941). Theory. Contains an extensive table of spectra and a bibliography for each compound.

J. R. Platt and H. B. Klevens, "Spectroscopy of Organic Molecules in the Vacuum Ultraviolet," *Revs. Modern Phys.*, **16**, 182–223 (1944). A good review of absorption below 2000 Å. Continues the bibliography of the preceding reference.

# CHAPTER 3

## LIPIDS

J. C. Cowan

*Northern Regional Research Laboratory*

H. E. Carter

*University of Illinois*

## CONTENTS

## INTRODUCTION

Most natural food products fall into three large groups: carbohydrates, lipids, and proteins. The lipids consist of esters of the higher fatty acids and related compounds and are characterized by solubility in organic solvents, such as ether, benzene, and chloroform, and by insolubility in water. There is some disagreement as to terminology in this field. The use of lipid(e) as a generic name is now generally accepted,[1] although other terms (fats, lipins, lipoids) have been used. The following classification of the lipids is essentially that proposed by Bloor [1] and is widely employed in the United States.

[1] Bloor, *Chem. Revs.*, **2**, 243 (1925); "Biochemistry of the Fatty Acids," Reinhold Publishing Corp., New York (1943), p. 1.

## Lipids

Simple lipids: esters of the fatty acids with various alcohols.

 1. Fats: esters with glycerol.
 2. Waxes: esters with alcohols other than glycerol.

Compound lipids: esters of fatty acids with alcohols and containing other groups in addition to alcohols and acids.

 1. Phospholipids (phosphatides): esters containing phosphorus and a nitrogenous base.
    Lecithin (phosphatidyl choline).
    Cephalin (phosphatidyl ethanolamine).
    Phosphatidyl serine.
    Acetal phospholipid (plasmalogen).
    Inositol lipids (lipositol, diphosphoinositide).
    Sphingomyelin.
    Cardiolipin.
 2. Phosphatidic acids: phospholipids minus the organic base.
 3. Glycolipids (galactolipids): esters containing carbohydrate, a nitrogenous base, but no phosphorus.
    Cerebrosides.
    Gangliosides.
 4. Sulfolipids: esters containing sulfuric acid.

Derived lipids: substances derived from the preceding groups which have the general properties of lipids, such as fatty acids, alcohols, nitrogenous bases, and hydrocarbons.

The first portion of this chapter will deal with the fats; the remainder, with the phospholipids and related lipids.

## FATS

### J. C. COWAN

## Definition

Natural fats * are mixed glyceryl esters of various saturated and unsaturated, straight-chain, even-carbon acids. Minor exceptions exist, such as the cyclopentyl group in chaulmoogric acid [2] and the branched, odd-carbon chains in the wax of the tubercle bacillus.[3] Fatty acids and glycerol were first isolated from fats by Geoffroy in 1741; additional

---

* The term fat originally referred only to glycerides that are solid at room temperature but now refers to all triglycerides; the terms fat and oil are frequently used interchangeably.

[2] Shriner and Adams, *J. Am. Chem. Soc.*, **47**, 2727 (1925); see Hofmann and Lucas, *ibid.*, **72**, 4328 (1950), for details of a nineteen-carbon acid with a cyclopropane ring.

[3] Anderson and Chargaff, *J. Biol. Chem.*, **85**, 77 (1929); Ginger and Anderson, *ibid.*, **157**, 203 (1945).

investigation was reported by Scheele in 1779.  Subsequently, with a series of publications during the period 1813–1825, Chevreul [4] established the glyceryl-ester nature of fats and the mixed nature of the acids. The mixed distribution of the acids on the glyceryl radical was not established for another three-quarters of a century.[5]

## Origin of Fat

Animal [6] and vegetable [7] fats originate primarily from carbohydrates.* In animals, fats are formed from carbohydrates by a reaction involving a two-carbon radical, presumably acetate, to give even-carbon chains. When labeled carbon is present in the carboxyl group of the acetate radical in fat fed to animals, the labeled carbon appears in both the carboxyl group of the "synthesized" acid and the carbon chain of the alkyl group.  When deuterium is present in the methyl group of the acetate fed, deuterium accumulates in the body fat.[8] Fats from the same variety and species of plants and animals are usually almost identical, but climatic conditions [9] do alter composition.  More unsaturated fats are found in seeds from test plantings of the same variety grown in cooler climates.  With animals, ingested fat can change the composition of body fat.[10]  Table I gives representative compositions of some commercially important fats and shows the effect of climatic conditions and dietary fat on the composition.

In the laboratory, fats are released from their source materials by a variety of methods, including cold and hot pressing and extraction with solvents such as hexane, hot ethanol or 2-propanol, trichloroethylene, benzene, and ether.  The three commonly employed commercial methods are continuous screw pressing, hexane extraction, and cooking or rendering of fat.

**Use.**  Fats are used chiefly for food, for the production of soap, as a source of glycerol, and as protective coatings.  The total world consumption of fats from 1934 to 1938 was estimated to be 23.2 million metric tons annually.  The major fats of commerce of animal origin

[4] Ralston, "Fatty Acids and Their Derivatives," John Wiley & Sons, New York (1948), p. 4.

[5] Guth, *Z. Biol.*, **44**, 78 (1902) [*Chem. Zentr.*, [1] **74**, 133 (1903)].

[6] Wierzuchowski and Ling, *J. Biol. Chem.*, **64**, 697 (1925); Bernhard and Bullet, *Helv. Chim. Acta*, **26**, 1185 (1943).

[7] Burr and Miller, *Botan. Gaz.*, **99**, 773 (1938).

* Liebig first suggested that fats are formed from carbohydrates (1850).

[8] Rittenberg and Bloch, *J. Biol. Chem.*, **160**, 417 (1945).

[9] Cartter and Hopper, "Influence of Variety, Environment and Fertility Level on the Chemical Composition of Soybean Seed," *U. S. Dept. Agr. Tech. Bull.* **787**, 30 (1942).

[10] Ellis and Isbell, *J. Biol. Chem.*, **69**, 239 (1926).

TABLE I

ACID COMPOSITION OF SOME COMMERCIAL FATS

| Fats | Alkanoic 14 | Alkanoic 16 | Alkanoic 18 | Monoenoic 16 | Monoenoic 18 | Dienoic 18 | Trienoic 18 | Hydroxy 18 | Remarks | References |
|---|---|---|---|---|---|---|---|---|---|---|
| | Percentage Composition of Acids / Kind and Carbon-Chain Lengths of Acids | | | | | | | | | |
| Coconut | 18 | 11 | 2 | .. | 8 | Trace | .. | .. | 12-Carbon acid, 45%; 10-Carbon acid, 8% | 11 |
| Palm | 2 | 42 | 6 | 1.8 | 38 | 10 | 1 | .. | | 12 |
| Lard | 2 | 26 | 12 | .. | 59 | 1 | .. | .. | High-carbohydrate diet | 10 |
| Lard | <1 | 14 | 8 | .. | 40 | 38 | .. | .. | Soybeans alone | 13 |
| Beef tallow | | | 50 | .. | 46 | 3.2 | 0.5 | .. | Dienoic acid is linoleic | 14 |
| Butter | 12 | 25 | 9 | 4 | 29 | 4 | .. | .. | 4- to 10-Carbon acids, 9%, and 12-carbon acid, 4% | 15 |
| Castor oil | | 2 | | .. | 7 | 3 | .. | 87 | Hydroxy is ricinoleic acid | 16 |
| Tung | | 4 | | .. | 9 | 10 | 77 | .. | Trienoic acid is α-eleostearic acid | 17 |
| Linseed | | 9 | | .. | 18 | 11 | 58 | .. | Trienoic acid is linolenic acid | 17a |
| Linseed | | 9 | | .. | 17 | 14 | 60 | .. | "Redwing" Variety, Oregon | 17a |
| Linseed | | 10 | | .. | 25 | 22 | 43 | .. | "Redwing" Variety, Nebraska | 17a |
| Soybean | | 15 | | .. | 22 | 53 | 10 | .. | Trienoic acid is linolenic acid | 18 |
| Cottonseed | | 27 | | .. | 19 | 54 | .. | .. | | 18 |
| Shortening | | 33 | | .. | 62 | 5 | From cottonseed oil | From cottonseed oil | Two-stage hydrogenation, "isoöleic" acid, 8% | 19 |
| Margarine | | 27 | | .. | 68 | 5 | From cottonseed oil | From cottonseed oil | Selective hydrogenation, "isoöleic" acid, 21% | 19 |

[11] Longenecker, J. Biol. Chem., 130, 167 (1939).

[12] Hilditch, Meara, and Roels, J. Soc. Chem. Ind., 66, 284 (1947).

[13] Knight, Jordan, and Swern, J. Biol. Chem., 164, 477 (1946).

[14] Hilditch and Longenecker, ibid., 122, 497 (1938).

[15] Kaufmann and Bornhardt, Fette u. Seifen, 45, 444 (1939).

[16] Hilditch and Riley, J. Soc. Chem. Ind., 65, 74 (1946).

[17] Swain, Brice, Nicols, and Riemenschneider, presented at American Oil Chemists' Society, November, 1948.

[17a] Painter and Nesbitt, Oil & Soap, 20, 208 (1943).

[18] Mitchell, Kraybill, and Zschiele, Ind. Eng. Chem., Anal. Ed., 15, 1 (1943).

[19] Bailey, "Industrial Oil and Fat Products," Interscience Publishers, New York (1945), pp. 616, 617.

are tallow, lard, and butter; those of vegetable origin include the oils of cottonseed, coconut, peanut, palm, soybean, castor bean, and flaxseed. Several major changes in fat production and consumption were brought on by World War II, one being an estimated 15% to 20% temporary reduction in the total world usage. Also, the United States became a major exporter of fats rather than a major importer. An increase of approximately 50%, or 1.5 million metric tons, in fat production was achieved in the United States by increased animal slaughter and increased production of soybean oil. The average per capita consumption of fat in the United States in 1948 was 31 kg., which was divided approximately 3 to 2 between edible and industrial uses. This per capita figure does not include fats naturally present in foods, such as fat in meat, flour, and cheese.

## Acids in Fats

The major constituents of fats are acids, which represent approximately 90% of the weight. The chemistry of a particular fat depends primarily on its component acids, and consequently the chemistry of the acids is emphasized in this section of the chapter. The acids may be classified according to their degree and kind of unsaturation: saturated or fatty;* mono- and polyunsaturated, including monoethenoid, polyethenoid, ethynoid, and diethynoid; non-conjugated and conjugated; and according to other functional groups present, such as hydroxyl and carbonyl.

The even-carbon, straight-chain acids containing four to twenty-six carbon atoms have been found in fats. Twelve-, sixteen-, and eighteen-carbon acids are the most important of the saturated series.

The monoölefinic acids have a wide variety of isomers and homologs occurring in natural fat. Straight-chain, even-carbon, monoölefinic acids from ten through twenty-six and including thirty carbon atoms have been reported. Chaulmoogra oil contains acids which have a cyclopentenyl group and have a varying total number of carbon atoms: six, ten, twelve, fourteen, sixteen, or eighteen.[20] Acids containing an eighteen-carbon chain are most widespread and abundant, oleic acid being the most common. It has been estimated that the distribution of acids in worldwide commercial fats is, in percentage: oleic, 34; linoleic, 29; palmitic, 11; lauric, 7; linolenic, 6; myristic, 3; erucic, 3; stearic, 3; and all others, 4.[21]

* "Fatty" originally denoted acids of the saturated series but now is commonly used to refer to all acids of fats. "Fat acid" can be used to designate acids of fats.

[20] Cole and Cardoso, *J. Am. Chem. Soc.*, **61**, 2349 (1939).

[21] Boekenoogen, *Olein, Vetten Oliezadan*, **26**, 143 (1941) [*C. A.*, **37**, 2778 (1943)].

The double bond in the monoölefinic acids is usually between the ninth and tenth carbon atoms. Although other arrangements exist, the group —CH=CH—(CH$_2$)$_7$—CO$_2$H predominates in all the major unsaturated acids of commercial importance except erucic, and occurs in many other mono- and polyunsaturated acids. One monoethynoic acid, tariric or 6-octadecynoic acid,[22] is found in fats.

Di-, tri-, tetra-, penta-, and hexaenoic acids occur in fats, the unsaturation occurring in a variety of ways. Linoleic or *cis*-9-*cis*-12-octadecadienoic acid contains a 1,4-pentadiene group, —CH=CH—CH$_2$— CH=CH—. This methylene separation of double bonds is found in most other non-conjugated, naturally occurring, polyunsaturated acids.[23, 24] In certain marine oils [25] two methylene groups have been found separating double bonds, —CH=CH—CH$_2$—CH$_2$—CH=CH—. A naturally occurring conjugated dienoic acid has been reported, but those of most commercial importance are formed by the dehydration of castor oil.[26] Conjugated trienoic acids such as eleostearic, or 9,11,13-octadecatrienoic acid,[27] and licanic acid [28] are found in natural fats. Other representative functional groups are the conjugated tetraene in parinaric acid,[29] the ketonic group in licanic acid,[30] the conjugated acetylenic group in isanic acid,[31] and the hydroxyl group in ricinoleic acid.[32] Table II gives the systematic names, the principal source, and a distinguishing feature of a number of important and unusual acids present in fats.

Pure acids can be separated from mixtures resulting from saponification or hydrolysis of fats by the following procedures: fractional crystallization,[33] fractional distillation,[34a, b, c] preparation and debromination of polybromides,[35] adsorption chromatography,[36] and crystallization of urea-fatty acid complexes.[37a, b] Fractional distillation of the methyl

[22] Arnaud, *Compt. rend.*, **114**, 79 (1892).

[23] Nunn and Smedley-McLean, *Biochem. J.*, **29**, 2742 (1935).

[24] Erdmann, Bedford, and Raspe, *Ber.*, **42**, 1334 (1909).

[25] Tsujimoto, *Bull. Soc. Chem. Japan*, **3**, 299 (1928).

[26] Priest and von Mikusch, *Ind. Eng. Chem.*, **32**, 1314 (1940).

[27] Boeseken and Ranenswaay, *Rec. trav. chim.*, **44**, 241 (1925).

[28] Farmer and Brown, *Biochem. J.*, **29**, 631 (1935).

[29] Farmer and Sunderland, *J. Chem. Soc.*, 759 (1935).

[30] Brown and Farmer, *ibid.*, 1632 (1935).

[31] Steger and Van Loon, *Rec. trav. chim.*, **59**, 1156 (1940).

[32] Goldsobel, *Ber.*, **27**, 3121 (1894).

[33] Foreman and Brown, *Oil & Soap*, **21**, 183 (1944).

[34] (a) Hilditch, "The Chemical Constitution of Natural Fats," John Wiley & Sons, New York (1947), p. 474; (b) Weitkamp, Smiljanic, and Rothman, *J. Am. Chem. Soc.*, **69**, 1936 (1947); (c) Weitkamp, *J. Am. Oil Chemists' Soc.*, **24**, 236 (1947).

[35] Smith, *Org. Syntheses*, **22**, 75, 82 (1942).

[36] Riemenschneider, Herb, and Nicols, *J. Am. Oil Chemists' Soc.*, **26**, 371 (1949).

[37] (a) Schlenk, *Ann.*, **565**, 204 (1949); (b) Schlenk and Holman, *J. Am. Chem. Soc.*, **72**, 5001 (1950).

## TABLE II

### REPRESENTATIVE ACIDS OF FATS *

| Systematic Name | Common Name | Occurrence | M.P., °C. | Distinguishing Features |
|---|---|---|---|---|
| Dodecanoic | Lauric | Coconut oil | 43.5 | Saturated, 12 carbons |
| Tetradecanoic | Myristic | Nutmeg oil | 54.4 | Saturated, 14 carbons |
| Hexadecanoic | Palmitic | Beef fat; most fats | 62.9 | Saturated, 16 carbons |
| Octadecanoic | Stearic | Beef fat | 69.6 | Saturated, 18 carbons |
| cis-9-Octadecenoic | Oleic | All fats | 14 | Monoölefinic, 18 carbons |
| trans-11-Octadecenoic | Vaccenic | Animal fat | 42.5 | Monoölefinic, 18 carbons |
| cis-13-Docosenoic | Erucic | Rapeseed | 33.5 | Monoölefinic, 22 carbons |
| 9,12-Octadecadienoic | Linoleic | Vegetable oils; corn | −5 | Non-conjugated dienoic, 18 carbons |
| 9,12,15-Octadecatrienoic | Linolenic | Vegetable oils; linseed | −11 | Non-conjugated trienoic, 18 carbons |
| 5,8,11,14-Eicosatetraenoic | Arachidonic | Brain and liver fats | | Non-conjugated tetraenoic, 20 carbons |
| 4,8,12,15,18,21-Tetracosahexaenoic | Nisinic | Sardine oil | | Non-conjugated hexaenoic, 24 carbons |
| 12-Hydroxy-9-octadecenoic | Ricinoleic | Castor beans | 5 | Hydroxyl, 18 carbons |
| 6-Octadecynoic | Tariric | Picramnia | | Acetylenic, 18 carbons |
| 17-Octadecen-9,11- or 9,15-diynoic | Isanic | Isano oil | 39.5 | Conjugated and acetylenic bonds, 18 carbons with terminal double bond |
| 13-Cyclopentenyltridecanoic | Chaulmoogric | Chaulmoogra oil | 71 | Cyclopentenyl group, 18 carbons |
| 9,11,13-Octadecatrienoic | Eleostearic | Tung oil | α49, β72 | Conjugated trienoic, 18 carbons, geometric isomers † |
| 9,11,13,15-Octadecatetraenoic | Parinaric | Parinarium oil | α86, β96 | Conjugated tetranoic, 18 carbons, geometric isomers † |
| 4-Keto-9,11,13-octadecatrienoic | Licanic | Oiticica oil | α75, β100 | Conjugated trienoic with carbonyl group, 18 carbons, geometric isomers † |

* Caproic, caprylic, and capric acids are found in some fats, such as those from sheep and goats. All acids below 12 carbons were omitted to conserve space. † The low-melting form (α) is the natural form but it readily isomerizes with iodine, sulfur, or other catalyst to the high-melting form (β).

esters is preferred for separating acids of the same degree of unsaturation but of different chain lengths. Fractional crystallization from solvents such as acetone, methanol, or petroleum hydrocarbon at 0° to −30°
and crystallization of urea-fatty acid complexes are used to separate saturated and high-melting acids from unsaturated and low-melting acids.
At temperatures of −30° to −70°, solvent crystallization can be used to
prepare concentrated fractions of oleic, linoleic, and linolenic acids. In
crystallization with urea, the higher-melting and usually more saturated
acids predominate in the urea complexes. The complexes of the polyunsaturated acids are very stable to oxidation and serve as a convenient
means for storing these acids in the laboratory.[37b] For the preparation
of pure linoleic and linolenic acids, a combination of solvent fractionation and polybromide debromination is very satisfactory. To obtain
linoleic acid, the unsaturated acids of corn,[38] safflower, or tobacco-seed
oils are suitable raw materials. The saturated acids are readily removed
by crystallization from acetone at −30°. The unsaturated acids are
brominated to give 9,10,12,13-tetrabromostearic acid, m.p. 115° to
115.5°, and the tetrabromo acid is converted to linoleic acid by esterification, debromination with zinc, and saponification.[35] The pure acid,
m.p. −5.2° to −5°, is obtained by repeated fractional crystallization from
a hydrocarbon solvent. Adsorption fractionation on silicic acid in combination with fractional distillation and solvent crystallization has given
pure methyl linoleate, m.p. −35° to −34°, linolenate, m.p. −46.5° to
−45.5°, and arachidonate, I.V. 316.1, theory, 318.8.[36, 39]

**Distribution of the Acids.** Although the component acids are mainly
responsible for the physical and chemical properties of fats, the distribution of these acids on the glyceryl radical also has an effect. Actual
distribution has not yet been fully clarified for most natural fats; two
major theories and modifications thereof are current. The "rule of
even distribution" was proposed by Hilditch and has been primarily de-
fended by him.[40] Simply stated, it means that the acids tend to be distributed equally among the glyceride molecules. An acid will appear
more than once in the same glyceride molecule only when its mole per
cent is greater than 33 and will appear more than twice in the same
glyceride only when the mole per cent is greater than 67. Alternatively,
a postulated "random distribution" of the acids in glyceride molecules is
based on a consideration of the composition of the acids of fat and the
statistical probabilities of the occurrence of individual glycerides.[41] For

[38] Mathews, Brode, and Brown, *J. Am. Chem. Soc.*, **63**, 1064 (1941); Brown and Frankel,
*ibid.*, **60**, 54 (1938).

[39] Herb, Riemenschneider, and Donaldson, *J. Am. Oil Chemists' Soc.*, **28**, 55 (1951).

[40] Hilditch, *ibid.*, **26**, 41 (1949).

[41] Longenecker, *Chem. Revs.*, **29**, 201 (1941); Mattil and Norris, *Science*, **105**, 257 (1947).

example, the amount of any monoacid triglyceride is equal to the cube of the mole fraction of that acid: a fat containing 0.1 mole of stearic acid would contain 0.001 mole of tristearin. If the acids present in a given fat are considered only as saturated or unsaturated, the sum of the amounts of the different glycerides present would be represented by the expression $S^3 + 3S^2U + 3SU^2 + U^3$, where $S$ and $U$ are the mole fractions of the saturated and unsaturated acids, $S^3$ is the amount of trisaturated glycerides, $3S^2U$ is the amount of the disaturated glycerides, etc.

By fractional crystallization from acetone, a procedure useful for both the fats and the acids, the component glycerides of solid or semisolid fats can be estimated. Riemenschneider and co-workers [42] performed a systematic fractionation of lard and tallow from acetone in which the precipitate obtained from each crystallization was recrystallized and the filtrates were combined for a new crystallization according to the scheme in Fig. 1. This scheme shows only one-sixth of the total recrystalliza-

Tallow solution

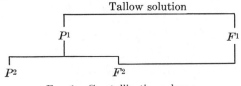

FIG. 1.  Crystallization scheme.

tion procedure. Filtrates $(F_1)$ and $(F_2)$ are combined and treated similarly to the original solution. The component acids (linoleic and other polyunsaturated acids, oleic acid, and saturated acids) of each fraction were determined from the iodine value (I.V.), and by spectrophotometric analysis for polyunsaturated acids. By assuming that not more than two glyceride classes were present in each fraction, a calculation of the glyceride content was made. Table III gives the component acids of the initial tallow and fractions thereof, and Table IV gives the calculated and experimental glyceride content. Neither random nor even distribution fits the experimental glyceride composition, but the actual composition resembles more closely that of random distribution.

One method of testing for random distribution is to determine the changes in physical characteristics effected by interesterification with catalysts such as sodium methoxide and stannous hydroxide.[43] The softening and melting points of soybean and cottonseed oil were substantially altered by interesterification whereas lard and oleo stock (high-

[42] Riemenschneider, Luddy, Swain, and Ault, *Oil & Soap*, **23**, 276 (1946). Figure 1, Table III, and Table IV by courtesy of the publishers.
[43] Norris and Mattil, *ibid.*, **23**, 289 (1946); *J. Am. Oil Chemists' Soc.*, **24**, 274 (1947).

## TABLE III

ACID COMPOSITION OF TALLOW FRACTIONS FROM SYSTEMATIC
ACETONE CRYSTALLIZATION

| | Conditions of Crystallization | | Percentages of Acids | | | |
|---|---|---|---|---|---|---|
| | Temper- ature, °C. | Solvent to Fat Ratio, cc./g. | % of Total | Linoleic * | Oleic | Saturated |
| $P_2$ | 18–19 | 26 to 1 | 19 | 0.38 | 7.35 | 92.3 |
| $P_4$ | 3 | 7.2 to 1 | 38 | 1.70 | 35.3 | 63.0 |
| $P_6$ | −13 | 6 to 1 | 21 | 3.11 | 55.6 | 41.3 |
| $P_8$ | −28 | 17 to 1 | 18 | 3.76 | 62.9 | 32.3 |
| $P_{10}$ | −35 | 79 to 1 | 1.8 | 5.41 | 75.5 | 18.1 |
| $P_{12}$ | −45 | 100 to 1 | 0.9 | 6.91 | 79.9 | 12.6 |
| $F_{11}, F_{12}$ | | | 1.3 | 10.34 | 78.6 | 3.4 |
| Initial tallow | | | 100 | 2.33 | 41.4 | 55.5 |

* Total of linoleic, linolenic, and arachidonic acids.

grade inedible tallow from low-temperature wet rendering of fresh internal fat of beef carcasses) were essentially unchanged. These observations are consistent with the theory of random distribution for animal fats, and they support previous work with acetone fractionation indicating an even distribution for vegetable fats.

## TABLE IV

GLYCERIDE COMPOSITION OF TALLOW IN MOLE PER CENT

| | Class of Glycerides | | | |
|---|---|---|---|---|
| | Tri- saturated | Di- saturated | Mono- saturated | Triun- saturated |
| Calculated from analysis of fractions | 15.0 | 46.0 | 36.9 | 2.2 |
| Calculated for random distribution | 19.4 | 42.3 | 30.8 | 7.5 |
| Calculated for even distribution | .... | 55.5 | 43.7 | ... |

Studies of the fractionation of soybean oil by acetone crystallization [44]

[44] (a) Golumbic, Martin, and Daubert, *Oil & Soap*, **23**, 187 (1946); (b) Hilditch, Meara, and Holmberg, *J. Am. Oil Chemists'* Soc., **24**, 321 (1947).

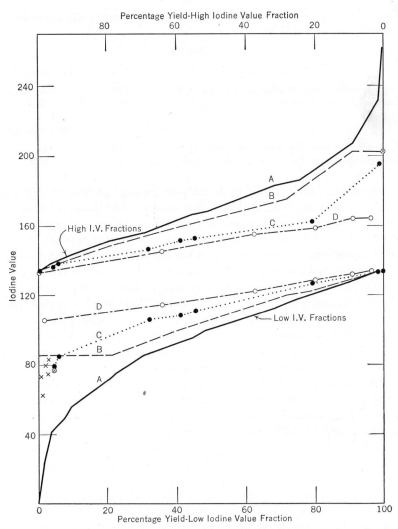

FIG. 2.   Distribution of acids in soybean oil: random distribution, $A$; even distribution, $B$; experimental by Daubert,[44a] $C$, ● ; experimental by Hilditch,[44b] $D$, ○; countercurrent distribution, $x$; adsorption analyses,[45] ⊗.

and by countercurrent distribution and adsorption analysis [45] indicate that this fat is not distributed in a true even pattern but approaches random distribution.   Figure 2 shows the expected distribution for even and random patterns as well as fractions obtained from procedures just mentioned.   The pertinent acid compositions of the high- and low-iodine-

[45] Dutton, Lancaster, and Brekke, *ibid.*, **27**, 25 (1950).

value fractions from adsorption analysis and acetone crystallizations are summarized in Table V.

### TABLE V

| Fractions from Soybean Oil | I.V. | Linolenic Acid |
|---|---|---|
| Highest iodine value (by adsorption analyses) [45] | 202 | 38.43 |
| High iodine value (by adsorption analyses) [45] | 195 | 35.3 |
| | | Saturated Acids |
| Lowest iodine value (by adsorption analyses) [45] | 78 | >33 |
| Lowest iodine value (by acetone crystallization) [44a] | 79 | 56.2 |

Apparently, neither pure even nor pure random patterns of distribution exist in many fats. Hilditch has modified the theory of even distribution until, in many cases, it approaches the random pattern. A modification of his theory proposes that unsaturated fats are synthesized to conform to the even pattern but are subsequently hydrogenated in a random fashion to upset the even rule and to result in the observed anomalies. On the other hand, advocates of the random pattern have found it necessary to devise "partial random" patterns [46] to explain their results. It is probable that actual distribution lies somewhere between the extremes of pure even and pure random patterns. Application of improved techniques is needed before a complete understanding of the distribution of the acids in fats is attained.

**Polymorphism.** Many fats, their acids, and their acid derivatives crystallize in two or more polymorphic forms. These forms are distinguished by variation in characteristics such as melting point and heat of fusion and by differences in their x-ray diffraction patterns. The acids crystallize with the long axes of the hydrocarbon chains parallel; the terminal groups become associated to form planes. X-ray diffraction patterns reflect this arrangement in the so-called short spacings which are determined by the cross-sectional arrangement of the chains and in the long spacings which are integral multiples of the distance between the planes of the terminal groups. These patterns show short and long spacings which are characteristic of the structure of three crystalline forms, usually designated as $\alpha$, $\beta'$, and $\beta$. Figure 3 [47] illustrates the cross-sectional arrangements of the chain axes which give rise to the short spacings that predominate in many fatty molecules. With most $\beta'$- and $\beta$-forms the long axes are tilted from the perpendicular. In the $\alpha$-form the long axes are perpendicular to the terminal-group plane. The long spacings for simple (one-acid) triglycerides are approximately twice

[46] Doerschuk and Daubert, *ibid.*, **25**, 425 (1948).
[47] Lutton, *ibid.*, **27**, 276 (1950). Figures 3 and 4 by courtesy of the publishers.

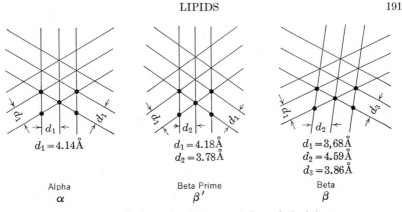

$d_1 = 4.14\text{Å}$

$d_1 = 4.18\text{Å}$
$d_2 = 3.78\text{Å}$

$d_1 = 3.68\text{Å}$
$d_2 = 4.59\text{Å}$
$d_3 = 3.86\text{Å}$

Alpha
$\alpha$

Beta Prime
$\beta'$

Beta
$\beta$

FIG. 3.   Cross-sectional structures (speculative).*

the chain length.   Many fatty compounds exhibit a double-chain-length structure, which is depicted for tristearin as the reversed-tuning-fork arrangement in Fig. 4.   No attempt is made to show tilting of the long-chain axes.

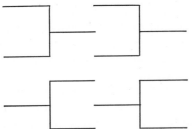

FIG. 4.   Reversed tuning-fork arrangement of triglycerides.

Tristearin exhibits the polymorphism characteristic of saturated triglycerides.   By rapidly cooling liquid tristearin, the $\alpha$- or low-melting form can be obtained.   The $\alpha$-form melts at 54° and rearranges to a $\beta'$-form which melts at 64° with subsequent rearrangement to the stable $\beta$-form which melts at 73.1°.[48]   The $\beta$-form can be readily obtained by crystallization.   The x-ray patterns of the three forms are illustrated in Fig. 5.   The $\alpha$-form has the greatest long spacing, 50.6 Å, suggesting long-chain axes perpendicular to the terminal-group planes.   The $\beta'$- and $\beta$-forms have long spacings of 46.8 Å and 45.2 Å, respectively, indicating tilted axes.   However, the $\alpha$-form of triolein has a comparatively short long spacing, which suggests that it may have tilted axes.[49]   The nomenclature and the reasons for its use, based on the length of the short

* Courtesy of Dr. E. S. Lutton, Procter & Gamble Co.
[48] Lutton, *J. Am. Chem. Soc.*, **67**, 524 (1945).   Figure 5 by courtesy of the publishers.
[49] Ferguson and Lutton, *ibid.*, **69**, 1445 (1947).

spacings, can be found in Lutton's publication.[48]  This nomenclature differs from that used by Malkin.[50]

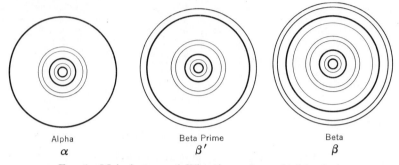

| Alpha | Beta Prime | Beta |
|:---:|:---:|:---:|
| $\alpha$ | $\beta'$ | $\beta$ |

FIG. 5.   Main features of diffraction pattern of tristearin.*

**Chemical Reactivity.**   The reactions of the acids of fats are characterized usually by independent behavior of the carboxyl group and the double bonds or other functional groups present in the chain.   An exception is in the fusion of oleic acid in molten alkali to give palmitic acid.[51]   An isomerization to 2-octadecenoic acid probably occurs first, followed by cleavage to the sixteen-carbon acid.   For the most part, the unsaturated linkages present in the acid radicals exhibit properties similar to those shown by unsaturated hydrocarbons.   With most of the unsaturation present in the middle of a long chain, steric effects are important.   9,11,13-Octadecatrienoic (eleostearic) acid was long considered to be a dienoic acid because usual treatment with bromine gave only a tetrabromo derivative.   The conjugated acids are more reactive than are similar non-conjugated acids.   However, the 1,4-pentadiene arrangement in many polyunsaturated acids is much more reactive than two isolated double bonds.   Linoleic acid, which has this active allylic arrangement, reacts with hydrogen six to seven times as fast as 9,15-octadecadienoic acid (isolinoleic).[52]   The carboxyl group extends the number of suitable solvents, and the high molecular weight of the fats and their acid derivatives permits high temperatures in liquid-phase reactions.   Fats and some derivatives are not generally used as the gaseous phase in reactions, although fatty acids are employed in vapor-phase reactions.   The discussion of the chemical properties of fats is divided into two parts: reactions of the unsaturated chain, and reactions of the carboxyl group.

[50] Clarkson and Malkin, *J. Chem. Soc.*, 666 (1934).
* Courtesy of Dr. E. S. Lutton, Procter and Gamble Co.
[51] Varrentrapp, *Ann.*, **35**, 196 (1840).
[52] Bailey and Fisher, *Oil & Soap*, **23**, 14 (1946).

**Oxidation and Autoxidation.** Chemical oxidation of fat is similar to oxidation of hydrocarbons. Ozone [24, 53] and neutral potassium permanganate in acetone [54] have been used extensively to cleave double bonds to determine their positions in the chain. Chromic acid will also cleave the chain at the double bonds, and this reaction with oleic acid is the basis for the commercial production of azelaic acid.[55] Peracids [56] and cold alkaline permanganate give epoxy and dihydroxy acids. The actual identity and interrelationships of many of the primary uncleaved oxidative products have been disputed. The disputes are understandable when one considers the number of inversions that occur when interconversions are effected.

Since oleic acid (I), Fig. 6, is converted by epoxidation or by oxidation with cold permanganate to two different 9,10-dihydroxystearic acids, inversion must occur. Wittcoff has shown that this inversion occurs during hydrolysis of the oxirane ring and not during oxidation with alkaline permanganate.[57] Permanganate gives the normal oxidative products: the *erythro* form (III) from the *cis* acid, oleic (I); and the *threo* form (IV) from the *trans* acid, elaidic (II).

The interrelationships of the various primary oxidation products of *cis*- and *trans*-9-octadecenoic acids are shown in Fig. 6.[58] Permanganate and peracids give *cis* addition, but hypohalites give *trans* addition. Inversions occur upon dilute alkaline hydrolysis and upon opening of the oxirane ring in V and VI with dry hydrogen chloride. Inversion also occurs upon closing of the oxirane ring with concentrated alkali and upon conversion of the 9,10-dihydroxystearic acids to mixtures of 9,10(10,9)-chlorohydroxystearic acids (VII and VIII).

Epoxidized oils have been prepared by the action of peracids,[59] with considerable interaction between polyunsaturated acids to give polymeric products. Peracids react more readily with double bonds having a high electron density, such as that in oleic acid, than with terminal or $\alpha,\beta$-double bonds.[60] Analysis for saturated acids [61] and glycerides [62] is often made by oxidative procedures.

[53] Harries and Thieme, *Ber.*, **39**, 3728 (1906).

[54] Armstrong and Hilditch, *J. Soc. Chem. Ind.*, **44**, 43 (1925).

[55] Myers and Sprang, U. S. pat. 2,369,108 (1945) [*C. A.*, **39**, 3952 (1945)]; Fitzpatrick and Myers, U. S. pat. 2,450,858 (1948) [*C. A.*, **43**, 884 (1949)].

[56] King, *J. Chem. Soc.*, 37 (1943).

[57] Wittcoff, Moe, and Iwen, *J. Am. Chem. Soc.*, **70**, 742 (1948).

[58] Swern, *ibid.*, **70**, 1235 (1948). Figure 6 by courtesy of the publishers.

[59] Findley, Swern, and Scanlan, *ibid.*, **67**, 412 (1945).

[60] Swern, *ibid.*, **69**, 1692 (1947).

[61] Bertram, *Z. Untersuch. Lebensm.*, **55**, 179 (1928).

[62] Hilditch and Lea, *J. Chem. Soc.*, 3106 (1927).

Autoxidation of fats, the absorption of oxygen and subsequent reactions, has been the subject of extensive theoretical and practical studies. Many edible fats absorb oxygen to give oxidative cleavage products assumed to be responsible for rancidity and off-flavor, and "drying" * oils

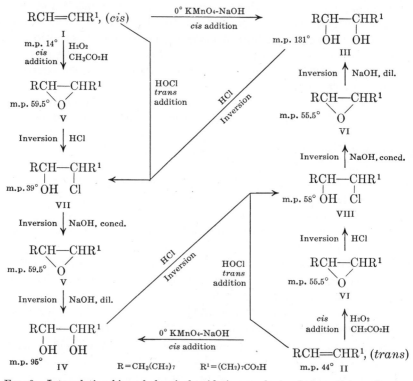

FIG. 6.   Interrelationships of chemical oxidation products of *cis*- and *trans*-9-octadecenoic acids.

in paints and varnishes absorb oxygen to give cross-linked polymeric films. The reaction is characterized, first, by an induction period which involves the destruction of antioxidants and the appearance of small amounts of hydroperoxides; second, by an autocatalytic period in which hydroperoxides rise to a maximum, initial setting of drying-oil films occurring, and rancid or off-flavors appearing in most edible oils; and third, by a concluding period in which further oxidation occurs, leading to in-

* Drying does not refer to loss of water, although this does occur.  It refers to the conversion of a film of fat from a liquid to a polymer.

creased rancidity and destruction of peroxides in edible fats, and to peroxide destruction in and hardening of drying oils.

Antioxidants are substances that protect fat from oxidation during the induction period.  This protection may occur through reaction of the antioxidant with hydroperoxides or other active molecules initially formed, thus stopping the chain reaction.  The isolation of $\alpha$-tocopheroxide (IX$a$), Fig. 7, from the oxidation of $\alpha$-tocopherol (IX) in the presence of ferric chloride and 2,2'-bipyridyl, appears to support this theory.[63]

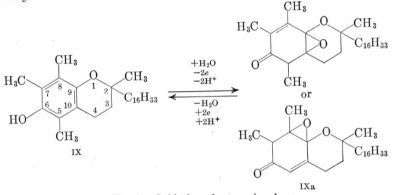

FIG. 7.  Oxidation of $\alpha$-tocopherol.

Other antioxidants include gallic acid and its esters, hydroquinone and ascorbic acid and their derivatives, and nordihydroguaiaretic acid.  Most naturally occurring or synthetic antioxidants in fats are $o$- or $p$-di- or polyphenolic compounds or other compounds having a similar electronic configuration.[64]  When both an antioxidant such as tocopherol and an acid such as citric are present in a fat, the stability is increased to a greater extent than could be predicted on the basis of the effect of either alone; i.e., there is a synergistic effect.  Such acidic substances when present alone do not greatly increase the oxidative stability of a fat.  A major portion of the activity of synergists appears to be due to inactivation of metallic prooxidants.[65]  Citric and other polycarboxylic acids and polyhydric alcohols reduce the effect of traces of metallic impurities.[66]  These acidic "synergists" may react with oxidized forms (quinones) of the antioxidants to give quinol complexes (phosphorylated quinones), as shown in Fig. 8, which interrupt the chain reaction by

[63] Boyer, *J. Am. Chem. Soc.*, **73**, 733 (1951).   Figure 7 by courtesy of the publishers.
[64] Mattil, *Oil & Soap*, **22**, 1 (1945).
[65] Riemenschneider, *Trans. Am. Assoc. Cereal Chemists*, **5**, 50 (1947).
[66] Dutton, Schwab, Moser, and Cowan, *J. Am. Oil Chemists' Soc.*, **25**, 385 (1948).

inactivation of activated fat molecules such as XI, Fig. 9, or XVIII, Fig. 11.[67]

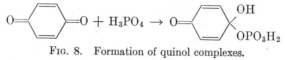

FIG. 8.  Formation of quinol complexes.

The formation of hydroperoxides from the autoxidation of fat derivatives was first established by Farmer and Sutton,[68] who isolated hydroperoxides from methyl oleate after autoxidation at 35° under ultraviolet light.  The reaction appears to proceed by a free-radical mechanism, with hydroperoxide groups appearing on the tenth > eleventh > eighth > ninth carbon atoms with the apparent order of preference as indicated.[69]  All the isomeric hydroperoxides from methyl oleate may arise from the formation of free radicals in the presence of oxygen and ultraviolet light as shown in Fig. 9.

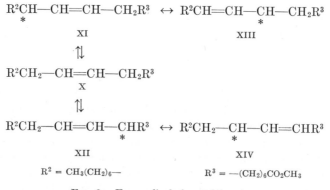

FIG. 9.   Free radicals from oleic ester.

The initial free radicals are presumably formed by abstracting one hydrogen from the active methylene group adjacent to the double bond.  The radicals XI and XII could undergo 1-3 shifts to form two new free radicals, XIII and XIV.  Addition of oxygen to these free radicals to give new free radicals such as XV, Fig. 10, and subsequent formation of the hydroperoxide by abstracting hydrogen from another oleate molecule, would give the hydroperoxide (XVI).  These reactions may account for the autocatalytic effects in autoxidation.  The structure of the hydroperoxides formed would correspond to XI, XII, XIII, and XIV.

[67] Calkins, J. Am. Chem. Soc., **69**, 384 (1947).  Figure 11 by courtesy of the publishers.
[68] Farmer and Sutton, J. Chem. Soc., 119 (1943).
[69] Ross, Gebhart, and Gerecht, J. Am. Chem. Soc., **71**, 282 (1949).

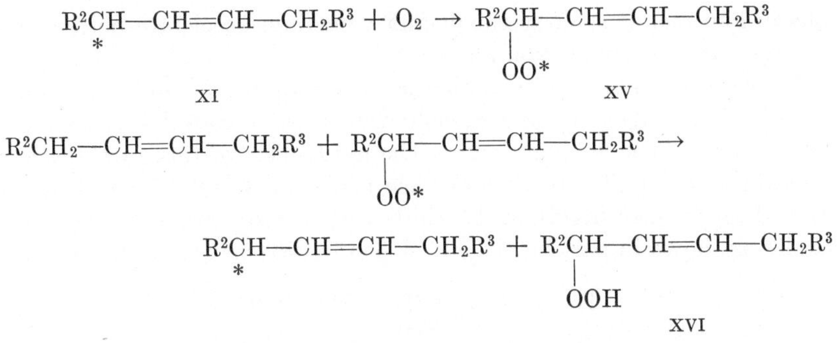

$$R^2CH—CH\!\!=\!\!CH—CH_2R^3 + O_2 \rightarrow R^2CH—CH\!\!=\!\!CH—CH_2R^3$$

$$\underset{*}{\quad} \qquad\qquad\qquad\qquad\qquad \underset{OO*}{\overset{|}{\phantom{O}}}$$

XI                                                          XV

$$R^2CH_2—CH\!\!=\!\!CH—CH_2R^3 + R^2CH—CH\!\!=\!\!CH—CH_2R^3 \rightarrow$$

$$\underset{OO*}{\overset{|}{\phantom{O}}}$$

$$R^2CH—CH\!\!=\!\!CH—CH_2R^3 + R^2CH—CH\!\!=\!\!CH—CH_2R^3$$

$$\underset{*}{\quad} \qquad\qquad\qquad\qquad\qquad \underset{OOH}{\overset{|}{\phantom{O}}}$$

XVI

FIG. 10.   Hydroperoxide formation and chain propagation.

These hydroperoxides are reasonably stable and can be isolated from autoxidation mixtures by fractional molecular distillation,[68] fractional crystallization from acetone at −80°,[70] and countercurrent distribution between two immiscible solvents.[71]  They are odorless, mobile liquids which do not decompose at 0°, decompose slowly at 25° when exposed to daylight and air, and decompose rapidly at 120° or higher.  At 150°, decomposition is complete in 15 minutes.  When the hydroperoxide from methyl oleate is reacted with oleic acid at 90°, 9,10-epoxystearic acid, m.p. 59.5°, and dihydroxystearic acid, m.p. 95.5°, are formed.[72]

After the autocatalytic period in which the amount of peroxide rises to high levels, decomposition and polymerization reactions become predominant.  Termination reactions are probably effected by the mutual destruction of chain carriers such as XI and XV to give dimeric products.  Oleic acid is reported to give dihydroxystearic acid, unsaturated keto acids, and di- and polymeric keto acids.[73]  Further oxidation and cleavage of fats lead to saturated aldehydes and acids, as would be expected from cleavage at the double bond, as well as to products containing at least one less carbon atom.  Unsaturated aldehydes such as 2,4-decadienal,[74] maleic dialdehyde,[75] 2-heptenal[76] from soybean oil, and 2-octenal and 2,4-decadienal from cottonseed oil[77] have been reported as cleavage products of autoxidation.  Metals such as lead, aluminum, and barium accelerate the autocatalytic phase of the oxidation of methyl oleate; metals such as zinc and thallium accelerate the decomposition

[70] Swift, Dollear, and O'Connor, *Oil & Soap*, **23**, 355 (1946).

[71] Fugger, Zilch, Cannon, and Dutton, *J. Am. Chem. Soc.*, **73**, 2861 (1951).

[72] Swift and Dollear, *J. Am. Oil Chemists' Soc.*, **25**, 52 (1948).

[73] Ellis, *Biochem. J.*, **46**, 129 (1950).

[74] Stapf and Daubert, *J. Am. Oil Chemists' Soc.*, **27**, 374 (1950).

[75] Schepartz and Daubert, *ibid.*, **27**, 367 (1950).

[76] Martin, Schepartz, and Daubert, *ibid.*, **25**, 113 (1948).

[77] Swift, O'Connor, Brown, and Dollear, *ibid.*, **26**, 297 (1949).

phase; and metals such as cobalt and vanadium accelerate both auto-catalytic and decomposition phases.[78]

Linoleic acid undergoes a similar autoxidation at 35° under exposure to ultraviolet light to give monohydroperoxides containing approximately 70% diene conjugation.[79] The mechanism of this autoxidation appears to be similar to that of oleic acid and its esters, i.e., a free-radical mechanism involving 1,3-shifts with the formation of hydroperoxides as shown in part in Fig. 11. Upon hydrogenation, only two dif-

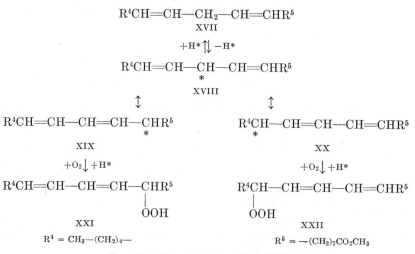

FIG. 11. Autoxidation of linoleic ester.

ferent hydroxystearic acids are isolated, the 9- and 13-hydroxystearic acids expected from hydrogenation of the two hydroperoxides XXI and XXII.[80] During the early stages of autoxidation, the formation of hydroperoxides quantitatively parallels the formation of dienoic conjugation. Consequently, it is entirely possible that XXI and XXII are the only monohydroperoxides obtained and that no hydroperoxide derived from XVIII is formed. Calculations of bond and resonance energies indicate that XIX and XX are much more stable than XVIII.[81, 82]

If carotene is present in a solution containing lipoxidase and linoleic acid, the carotene is rapidly destroyed by oxygen. In the absence of either lipoxidase or linoleic acid (or other polyunsaturated acids), the carotene is destroyed much more slowly.

[78] Skellon, J. Chem. Soc., 2020 (1950).
[79] Bolland and Koch, ibid., 445 (1945).
[80] Bergström, Arkiv. Kemi, Mineral. Geol., 21A, No. 15, 1 (1945); Nature, 156, 717 (1945).
[81] Bolland and Gee, Trans. Faraday Soc., 42, 244 (1946).
[82] Bergström and Holman, Nature, 161, 55 (1948).

Although decomposition and polymerization become the predominant reactions occurring after the maximum in peroxide value is reached, the monohydroperoxide begins to disappear from solutions before this maximum occurs.  In aqueous solutions of sodium linoleate, two moles of oxygen are absorbed per mole of acid without polymerization and with almost complete destruction of conjugation.  The monomeric hydroperoxide may have the structure XXIII, but data are not conclusive.[83] A similar derivative from methyl linoleate has been postulated.[84]

$$CH_3(CH_2)_4CH\!-\!CH\!=\!CH\!-\!CH\!-\!CH(CH_2)_7CO_2CH_3$$
$$\underset{}{O\!-\!\!-\!\!-\!\!-\!\!-\!\!-\!\!-\!\!-\!\!-\!O} \quad OOH$$

XXIII

Linolenic acid and its esters autoxidize with the development of dienoic conjugation closely paralleling the development of peroxides in the early stages of oxidation.  Triene conjugation appears later in the autoxidation and apparently results from a second reaction, possibly of oxygen with the initial peroxide.  The first oxidative product, which is stable under the very mild conditions of 4°, darkness, and absorption of over 0.1 mole of oxygen per mole of ester, is not monomeric but dimeric.  This dimeric product, which disappears on more vigorous oxidation, contains a peroxide group, presumably a hydroperoxide; two conjugated double bonds; and two unconjugated double bonds, as shown by reaction with hydrogen, ultraviolet absorption, and peroxide determinations.  However, the molecular weight of 497 instead of 602 for a dimeric peroxide indicates that cleavage occurs.[85]  It is evident that autoxidative reactions of linolenic acid are more complex than those of oleic and linoleic acids and esters.

Conjugated acids react with oxygen somewhat differently from nonconjugated acids.  Eleostearic acid and its esters absorb oxygen readily with the destruction of the conjugated triene and with an increase in diene conjugation.[86]  Dimeric products containing one and two moles of oxygen per mole of original ester are isolated.[86, 87]  Presumably the oxygen adds to one of the end double bonds, at the ninth or thirteenth carbon atom, to give a diradical, XXIV.

$$R^6CH\!=\!CH\!-\!CH\!=\!CH\!-\!CH\!-\!CHR^1$$
$$* \quad \underset{}{|}$$
$$O\!-\!O*$$

$$R^6 = CH_3\!-\!(CH_2)_3\!-\!\quad R^1 = -\!(CH_2)_7CO_2H$$

XXIV

[83] Bergström, Blomstrand, and Laurell, *Acta Chem. Scand.*, **4**, 245 (1950).
[84] Lundberg, Chipault, and Hendrickson, *J. Am. Oil Chemists' Soc.*, **26**, 109 (1949).
[85] Fugger, Cannon, Zilch, and Dutton, *ibid.*, **28**, 285 (1951).
[86] Brauer and Steadman, *J. Am. Chem. Soc.*, **66**, 563 (1944).
[87] Allen and Kummerow, *J. Am. Oil Chemists' Soc.*, **28**, 101 (1951).

If 1,3-shifts of the carbon free radical occurred, the 1,2-, 1,4-, and 1,6-positions could react further. On hydrogenation of the fractionally crystallized products from autoxidized methyl eleostearate, at least three different isomeric methyl dihydroxystearates are isolated. Only one of these stearates contains hydroxyl groups attached to adjacent carbons. Polymeric peroxides having a structural unit similar to XXIV linked at the free-radical carbons may result from a reaction of XXIV with a double bond of another monomeric molecule, addition of oxygen to this newly formed diradical, and repetition of the reaction until termination of the chain results. Methyl eleostearate reaches maximum viscosity at an absorption of one mole of oxygen per mole of ester, which would agree with the postulated reactions.[88] Methyl linoleate reaches a maximum viscosity after absorbing two to three moles of oxygen, which is an additional difference between the two types of esters.

Although studies on autoxidation have clarified our understanding of the initial reactions, the polymerization or "drying" reactions are still a subject of speculation. Films of drying oils set shortly before the maximum in peroxide content is reached.[89] Thereafter the peroxides and conjugation [90] gradually disappear, but appreciable amounts of both still remain after 100 hours. During hardening of the films, a loss in weight occurs. The cleavage products appear similar to those encountered in edible oils. Volatile acids, aldehydes, water, and carbon dioxide are the main products formed. Metallic salts such as those of lead, manganese, and cobalt are catalysts or driers. Current theories concerning the oxidative polymeric reactions include the formation of dimeric and polymeric peroxides which may decompose to give polyethers [91] and substituted dioxanes,[92] and the formation of unsaturated ketones which can undergo Diels-Alder reactions with a conjugated diene.[93]

**Polymerization.** Heat-polymerization reactions of polyunsaturated non-conjugated esters in oils such as linseed and soybean have been clarified by Wheeler.[94] Linoleic ester isomerizes to conjugated isomers; the conjugated ester then reacts with the non-conjugated ester to give a dimeric product (XXV) similar in structure to that obtained from 1,4-pentadiene.[95]

---

[88] Triebs, *Ber.*, **75**, 331 (1942).
[89] Overholt and Elm, *Ind. Eng. Chem.*, **33**, 658 (1941).
[90] Hendrickson, Cox, and Konen, *J. Am. Oil Chemists' Soc.*, **25**, 73 (1948).
[91] Farmer, *J. Oil & Colour Chemists' Assoc.*, **31**, 393 (1948).
[92] Triebs, *Ber.*, **75**, 1164 (1942).
[93] Powers, *Ind. Eng. Chem.*, **41**, 304 (1949).
[94] Paschke and Wheeler, *J. Am. Oil Chemists' Soc.*, **26**, 278 (1949).
[95] Ahmad and Farmer, *J. Chem. Soc.*, 1176 (1940).

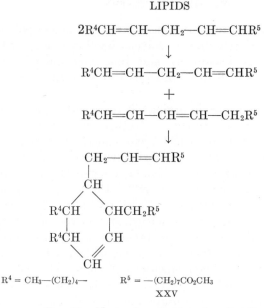

$$2R^4CH{=}CH{-}CH_2{-}CH{=}CHR^5$$

$$\downarrow$$

$$R^4CH{=}CH{-}CH_2{-}CH{=}CHR^5$$

$$+$$

$$R^4CH{=}CH{-}CH{=}CH{-}CH_2R^5$$

$$\downarrow$$

$R^4 = CH_3{-}(CH_2)_4{-}$     $R^5 = {-}(CH_2)_7CO_2CH_3$

XXV

Fig. 12. Heat polymerization of methyl linoleate.

The dimeric products formed react with other conjugated or non-conjugated isomers to give trimeric products.[96] Trimeric products are predominant when boron trifluoride is used as a catalyst.[97] Linolenic and eleostearic acids, and presumably other polyunsaturated acids having more than two double bonds, give dimeric and trimeric products of greater density than similar products from dienoic acids, indicating that the trienoic products are bicyclic [98] or tricyclic.[99] Conjugated acids and esters such as eleostearic probably form dimers and trimers by a modified Diels-Alder reaction between the conjugated system of one molecule and an activated double bond of the other, in a manner similar to that of alloöcimene [100] and sorbic esters.[101] Alloöcimene and methyl eleostearate [102] give cyclic monomers as well as dimers and trimers, and it appears likely that any triene with all bonds conjugated would behave similarly. Glycerides containing a high percentage of polyunsaturated acids increase rapidly in viscosity when heated at 290° to 300°. The polymer length and amount of branching increase with the duration of

[96] Bradley and Johnston, *Ind. Eng. Chem.*, **33**, 86 (1941).

[97] Cowan *et al.*, *ibid.*, **41**, 1647 (1949).

[98] Bradley and Johnston, *ibid.*, **32**, 802 (1940).

[99] Ault, Cowan, Kass, and Jackson, *ibid.*, **34**, 1120 (1942).

[100] Fugitt and Hawkins, *J. Am. Chem. Soc.*, **67**, 242 (1945); **69**, 319 (1947).

[101] Farmer and Morrison-Jones, *J. Chem. Soc.*, 1339 (1940).

[102] Rossmann, *Fettchem. Umschau*, **40**, 117 (1933); Sunderland, *J. Oil & Colour Chemists' Assoc.*, **28**, 137 (1945).

heating: dimers, trimers, tetramers, pentamers, and higher polymers of glycerides have been separated by solvent fractionation.[103] At 300°, isano oil polymerizes explosively and tung and linseed oil form cross-linked polymers in 8 to 12 minutes and 8 to 12 hours, respectively.

The polyunsaturated acids in drying oils react with a variety of materials such as butadiene, styrene, and other vinyl compounds,[104–106] phenolic resins,[107] cyclopentadiene,[108] and maleic anhydride.[109] The 1,4-pentadiene radical of non-conjugated polyunsaturated acids retards vinyl and diene polymerization and should be removed from soaps used in this type of emulsion polymerization.[110a] However, conjugated oils such as tung oil can be copolymerized with styrene.[105, 106] If non-conjugated oils are conjugated or polymerized, styrene can be polymerized in solutions containing the oils. The products in the polymerized oils are low-molecular-weight polymers of styrene with only a few units derived from the oil.[106, 110b] Polymerizations of vinyl and allyl esters of stearic, oleic, linoleic, and 10,12-octadecadienoic acids show that the vinyl groups react with the unsaturation in the acid chain.[110c] This reaction creates new free radicals which probably react by radical combination, thereby robbing the reaction either of initiating radicals or of propagating polymer chains. The 1,4- and 1,3-diene systems in the linoleate and 10,12-octadecadienoate are more reactive with free radicals and consequently are stronger modifiers of vinyl polymerization than the double bond in the oleate.

Maleic anhydride reacts with conjugated fats in a Diels-Alder type of addition. This reaction has been used to measure conjugation in oils, but it is not so good for this purpose as spectrophotometric analysis.[18] Maleic anhydride can be used to determine the *cis-trans* isomerism in conjugated acids. For example, α-eleostearic acid adds maleic anhydride at carbons 11 and 14 whereas β-eleostearic acid adds at carbons 9 and 12. This difference in addition products indicates *trans* configurations at carbon 13 for the α-acid and at carbon 9 for the β-acid.[111] 1,3-Pentadiene behaves similarly, the *trans* form undergoing a

[103] Bernstein, *J. Phys. & Colloid Chem.*, **52**, 613 (1948).

[104] Powers, *Ind. Eng. Chem.*, **38**, 837 (1946).

[105] Hewitt and Armitage, *J. Oil & Colour Chemists' Assoc.*, **29**, 109 (1946).

[106] Brunner and Tucker, *Research*, **2**, 42 (1949).

[107] Charlton and Perrins, *J. Oil & Colour Chemists' Assoc.*, **30**, 185 (1947).

[108] Gerhart, U. S. pat. 2,387,895 (1945) [*C. A.*, **40**, 496 (1946)]; U. S. pat. 2,392,732 (1945) [*C. A.*, **40**, 2693 (1946)].

[109] Clocker, U. S. pat. 2,188,882 (1940) [*C. A.*, **34**, 3845 (1940)].

[110] (a) Ault *et al.*, *J. Am. Oil Chemists' Soc.*, **26**, 700 (1949); (b) Dyer and Maxwell, *ibid.*, **26**, 649 (1949); (c) Harrison and Wheeler, *J. Am. Chem. Soc.*, **73**, 839 (1951).

[111] Morrell and Samuels, *J. Chem. Soc.*, 2251 (1932).

Diels-Alder addition with maleic anhydride [112] whereas the *cis* form does not.

Maleic anhydride will react also with non-conjugated mono- and poly-unsaturated acids.[109, 113] Methyl oleate and maleic anhydride form four isomers when heated at 200°. The reaction resembles that of oxygen with this ester at 35°. Maleic anhydride is attached at carbons 8, 9, 10, and 11.[114] The structures of these products are similar to formula XXVI, and the mode of formation may be similar to that of the formation of hydroperoxides.[115]

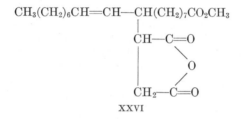

XXVI

Methyl linoleate and maleic anhydride give more complex products. A small amount of a monomeric adduct is formed which appears to be a Diels-Alder addition product of one mole of maleic anhydride with an isomerized (conjugated) methyl octadecadienoate. The predominant adduct is polymeric and contains a multiple number of maleic anhydride and methyl linoleate units. One isolated product indicates the presence of three maleic anhydride and two methyl linoleate units.[116]

**Isomerization.** Both geometric and position isomerism are encountered in unsaturated fatty acids. Most of the unsaturated acids of fats occur naturally as the *cis* forms including the most important non-conjugated unsaturated acids, oleic, linoleic, and linolenic. Vaccenic, eleostearic, and other natural polyunsaturated conjugated acids are exceptions, but most of the natural conjugated acids (conjugation of double bonds with one another and not with the carboxyl group) contain some *cis* configuration. Most of the rules that apply to isomeric forms of other organic compounds hold also for fat acids. *Trans* isomers melt at a higher temperature than *cis* isomers, are less soluble, react more slowly, and have different x-ray patterns and infrared absorption spectra, etc. Table VI summarizes some of the properties of some isomeric octadecenoic acids.

[112] Craig, *J. Am. Chem. Soc.*, **65**, 1006 (1943).
[113] Bickford, Krauczunas, and Wheeler, *Oil & Soap*, **19**, 23 (1942).
[114] Bickford, Fisher, Kyame, and Swift, *J. Am. Oil Chemists' Soc.*, **25**, 254 (1948).
[115] Ross, Gebhart, and Gerecht, *J. Am. Chem. Soc.*, **68**, 1373 (1946).
[116] Teeter, Geerts, and Cowan, *J. Am. Oil Chemists' Soc.*, **25**, 158 (1948).

## TABLE VI

### Properties of Isomeric Octadecenoic Acids

| Acid | M.P., °C. | Extinction Coefficient at 10.36 $\mu$ [117] | Autoxidation with Catalyst * [118] |
|---|---|---|---|
| cis-9-Octadecenoic | 13 | 0.133 † | 475 ‡ |
| trans-9-Octadecenoic | 44.5 | 0.552 | 25 |
| cis-6-Octadecenoic | 33–34 | 0.129 | ... |
| trans-6-Octadecenoic | 54 | 0.56 | ... |

* Milliliters of $O_2$ adsorbed in 300 minutes in the presence of hemin.

† Carbon disulfide used as a solvent.

‡ Linoleic acid, a frequent impurity in preparations of oleic acid, accelerates the oxidation of oleic acid and thus may account in part for this comparatively high value.

*Cis* isomers can be readily converted to *trans* isomers by a variety of catalysts such as sulfur, selenium, halogens (particularly iodine), oxides of sulfur and nitrogen, and nickel hydrogenation catalysts.[119] Selenium [117, 120] is probably the most convenient of these catalysts; oleic acid or ester can be heated to 150° to 200° in the presence of 0.1% to 0.3% of this element to give an equilibrium mixture containing 67% of the elaidic isomer. Certain of these catalysts will also effect position isomerization; for example, oleic acid on being heated with nickel catalysts gives *trans* isomers of 8- and 10-octadecenoic acids.[121]

Isomerization of the polyunsaturated acids is considerably more complex than that of the monoölefinic acids. *Cis* and *trans* configurations at each double bond, and the relative positions of the double bonds in the chain, account for this complexity. Chemists have long sought methods of converting non-conjugated fats to conjugated fats, which are preferred materials for protective coatings. Alkali, nickel on carbon black, sulfur dioxide, and iodine compounds are catalysts for inducing conjugation.[119] The conjugated fats are more reactive and dry more quickly than the corresponding non-conjugated fats. The tabulated data show the differences in autoxidation rates between some conjugated and non-conjugated trienoic acids, as well as the accelerating effect of the carboxyl group.[122]

[117] Swern, Knight, Shreve, and Heether, *ibid.*, **27**, 17 (1950).

[118] Kuhn and Meyer, *Z. physiol. Chem.*, **185**, 204 (1929).

[119] Cowan, *Ind. Eng. Chem.*, **41**, 294 (1949).

[120] Bertram, U. S. pat. 2,165,530 (1939) [*C. A.*, **33**, 8433 (1939)].

[121] Bauer and Krallis, *Chem. Umschau Gebiete, Fette, Öle, Wachse u. Harze*, **38**, 201 (1931); *Fettchem. Umschau*, **41**, 194 (1934).

[122] Meyer, Burr, and Kass, *Oil & Soap*, **18**, 107 (1941). Table reprinted by courtesy of the publishers.

|  | Mole $O_2$/mole |
|---|---|
|  | acid/100 minutes |
| Acid | at 40° |
| α-Eleostearic acid | 2.68 |
| Linolenic acid | 0.52 |
| Ethyl linolenate | 0.24 |

The well-known shift of $\beta,\gamma$- to $\alpha,\beta$-unsaturated acids with alkali was extended by Moore [123] to dienoic and trienoic acids containing a 1,4-pentadiene system, such as linoleic and linolenic acids, wherein the shifts involve only the double bonds and not the carboxyl groups. Treatment with excess alkali in boiling ethanol for several days, or better in boiling ethylene glycol [124] for 1 hour, shifts double bonds in linolenic acid from their non-conjugated positions to conjugated positions. Acids containing both dienoic and trienoic conjugation are formed from linolenic acid, and conjugated dienoic acids are formed from linoleic acid. Another procedure for obtaining a conjugated dienoic acid is the dehydration of ricinoleic acid. For some time the various isomers formed from these reactions did not appear to agree with the expected products. Most of the anomalies of these reactions have been clarified, and two rules concerning the shifting of bonds in polyunsaturated acids have been formulated.[125] These rules follow.

When the double bond involved in the shift is *trans*, the new bond formed can assume either the *cis* or the *trans* configuration. When the double bond involved in the shift is *cis*, the new bond formed assumes predominantly the *trans* configuration. The reactions and interrelationships of linoleic acid and some of its isomeric forms are shown in the schematic diagram in Fig. 13. When *cis*-9,*cis*-12-octadecadienoic acid (XVII) is heated with alkali at 200°, two isomers are formed in predominant and approximately equal amounts, the *trans*-10,*cis*-12-acid (XXVII) and the *cis*-9,*trans*-11-acid (XXVIII). When these two acids are treated with $I_2$ in the presence of sunlight, the *cis* bonds are rearranged to *trans* bonds to give the *trans*-10,*trans*-12-acid (XXIX) and the *trans*-9,*trans*-11-acid (XXX), respectively. These same acids were first isolated by reactions on ricinoleic acid (XXXIII). von Mikusch's acid (XXIX) is formed by alkali isomerization of dehydrated ricinoleic acid,[126] and it is probable that alkali isomerizes XXXI to give XXIX. Mangold's acid (XXX) is readily obtained from the mixture of acids

[123] Moore, *Biochem. J.*, **31**, 138 (1937).

[124] Kass and Burr, *J. Am. Chem. Soc.*, **61**, 3292 (1939).

[125] Nicols, Herb, and Riemenschneider, *ibid.*, **73**, 247 (1951). Figure 13 and Table VII by courtesy of the publishers.

[126] von Mikusch, *ibid.*, **64**, 1580 (1942).

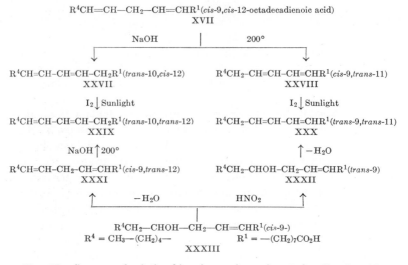

Fig. 13. Source and relationship of some isomeric octadecadienoic acids.

formed from the dehydration of ricinelaidic acid (XXXII).[127] The melting points and specific extinction coefficients of these conjugated octadecadienoic acids are shown in Table VII. In addition, *trans*-9,*trans*-

### TABLE VII

Properties of Conjugated Octadecadienoic Acids

| Position and Isomerism of Double Bonds | M.P., °C. | Specific Extinction Coefficient * and Wavelength |
|---|---|---|
| XXVII, *trans*-10,*cis*-12 | 22–23 | 95 at 233 m$\mu$ |
| XXVIII, *cis*-9,*trans*-11 | −6 to 3 (impure) | 87 at 233 m$\mu$ |
| XXIX, *trans*-10,*trans*-12 | 57 | 115 at 231 m$\mu$ |
| XXX, *trans*-9,*trans*-11 | 54 | 115 at 231 m$\mu$ |
| Mixture of XXIX and XXX | 44–46 | 115 at 231 m$\mu$ |

* $\alpha = E_{1\,cm.}^{0.1\%}$.

12-octadecadienoic acid, m.p. 29°, a product which would be expected from the dehydration of ricinelaidic acid, has been prepared by the selenium isomerization of methyl linoleate.[128]

By the rules formulated from studies on the isomerization of linoleic acid, the expected reaction products from isomerization of linolenic acid can be predicted. The 9 and 15 double bonds will shift to give *trans*-

[127] Mangold, *Monatsh.*, **15**, 309 (1894).
[128] Kass and Burr, *J. Am. Chem. Soc.*, **61**, 1062 (1939).

10,*cis*-12,*trans*-15-octadecatrienoic acid, and the double bond at position 12 will move to the 11 or 13 position to give *cis*-9,*trans*-11,*cis*-15- or *cis*-9,*trans*-13,*cis*-15-octadecatrienoic acids. An acid identified as *trans*-10,*trans*-12,*trans*-14-octadecatrienoic acid, m.p. 79°, has been isolated,[124] and the ultraviolet absorption spectrum of alkali isomerized linolenic acid indicates the presence of a considerable amount of dienoic conjugation.[18, 129] However, the alkali isomerization of linolenic acid needs further clarification.

Another method for conjugating the double bonds in the 1,4-pentadiene radical is treatment with active-halogen compounds such as *tert*-butyl hypochlorite[130] or N-bromosuccinimide.[131] These reactions introduce a reactive halogen into the acid chain, Fig. 14.

$$C_4H_9OCl + XVII \rightarrow R^4CH{=}CH{-}CH{=}CH{-}CHR^1 + C_4H_9OH$$
$$\underset{Cl}{|}$$

FIG. 14.    Shifting of double bonds by active-halogen compounds.

**Hydrogenation.** Adkins and Shriner in Vol. I, Chapter 9, of this Treatise have presented basic information on catalytic hydrogenation of organic molecules. They describe the preparation of the various forms of platinum, palladium, nickel, and copper chromite which are the only catalysts used extensively either in laboratory research or in commercial production of fats. Only nickel and copper chromite are used industrially for large-scale catalytic hydrogenation of fats and fat derivatives. These two catalysts are affected adversely by "poisons" present in fats; such poisons may be removed by alkali refining and bleaching.

Hydrogenation of the hydrocarbon portion of the fat molecule or derivative proceeds readily at 25° to 250° and 5 to 60 pounds-per-square-inch pressure with nickel catalysts to give partially or fully saturated derivatives. Complete or nearly complete saturation, as measured by the iodine value, is readily achieved at the higher temperatures of 200–250°. Oleic esters are readily hydrogenated with nickel catalysts to give stearic esters, although isomerization may occur without hydrogenation.[121] Hydrogenation of linoleic, linolenic, and other polyunsaturated esters is frequently more complex than saturation of simple double bonds.

Methyl linolenate on hydrogenation at 180° with nickel-kieselguhr catalyst gives 9,15- and 10,14-octadecadienoic esters, indicating that the

[129] Brice and Swain, *J. Optical Soc. Am.*, **35**, 532 (1945).
[130] Teeter, Bachmann, Bell, and Cowan, *Ind. Eng. Chem.*, **41**, 849 (1949).
[131] Bergström and Hansson, *Acta Chem. Scand.*, **4**, 435 (1950).

12-double bond is most easily hydrogenated.[132] The 8,14- as well as the
9,15- and 10,14-isomers can be isolated by a low-temperature fractional
crystallization of methyl linolenate hydrogenated at room temperature
and atmospheric pressure, using palladium black on barium sulfate as
the catalyst. All three isomers have a strong infrared absorption at
10.3 $\mu$, indicating the presence of at least one *trans* double bond.[133]
Methyl eleostearate is reported to give vaccenic acid as well as intermediate conjugated dienoic derivatives.[134] Linoleic acid gives various so-
called isoöleic acids which are both position and *trans* isomers of oleic
acid. For example, linoleic acid yields 8- and 10-octadecenoic acids on
hydrogenation, and oleic acid is reported to give similar products.[135]

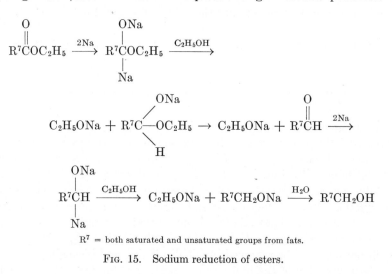

$R^7$ = both saturated and unsaturated groups from fats.

FIG. 15. Sodium reduction of esters.

These isomeric products are formed under conditions of selective hydrogenation, i.e., high temperatures (135° to 200°) and low pressures (10
pounds per square inch or less). Selective hydrogenation refers to the
preferential absorption of hydrogen by the more unsaturated acids present in a mixture. Experimentally, it is found that esters of polyunsaturated acids containing 1,4-pentadiene structures absorb hydrogen 20 to
40 times as fast as monoölefinic acids. Relative reactivities of some
unsaturated esters toward catalytic hydrogenation as expressed in whole
numbers are: oleic, 1; isomeric octadecenoic acids, 1; isomeric "linoleic"
acids containing 9,15-octadecadienoic acid, 3; linoleic, 20; linolenic, 40.[52]

[132] Van der Veen, *Chem. Umschau Gebiete Fette, Öle, Wachse u. Harze*, **38**, 89 (1931).
[133] Rebello and Daubert, *J. Am. Oil Chemists' Soc.*, **28**, 183 (1951).
[134] Boeseken and Krimpen, *Proc. Acad. Sci. Amsterdam*, **31**, 238 (1928).
[135] Hilditch and Vidyarthi, *Proc. Roy. Soc. (London)*, **A122**, 552, 563 (1929).

Copper chromite at temperatures of 200° to 300° under 100 to 300 atm. of hydrogen converts fats to glycerol and fatty alcohols.[136] Zinc chromite will hydrogenate oleic acid to oleyl alcohol in 68% yield and to stearyl alcohol.[137] Sodium and ethanol will also effect reduction to the corresponding unsaturated alcohols when esters of oleic, linoleic, and linolenic acids are used. The mechanism of this reaction is shown in Fig. 15.[138]

**Other Reactions of the Alkyl Chain.** All halogens add to oleic acid, but low temperatures are necessary with fluorine and chlorine to decrease substitution reactions. Bromine and oleic acid give 9,10-dibromostearic acid, m.p. 28.5° to 29°, whereas elaidic acid and bromine give an isomer, m.p. 29° to 30°. Treatment with zinc and hydrogen chloride regenerates the starting acids, and consequently any inversion must necessarily occur twice.[139]

To polyunsaturated non-conjugated acids, addition of bromine occurs stepwise. Linoleic acid gives 12,13-dibromo-9-octadecenoic acid [140] and then 9,10,12,13-tetrabromostearic acid. The polybromides from linoleic and linolenic acids are stable compounds which can be readily isolated and which serve as intermediates in the purification of the acids.[35] Linoleic acid gives two isomeric tetrabromides, one a solid, m.p. 114° to 115°, and the other a liquid. The solid form is regenerated to linoleic acid, but treatment of the liquid form does·not give complete conversion to linoleic acid.[141] Impurities such as monobromoöctadecenoic acid are present in the product from the last reaction.[142] Eleostearic acids add three molecules of bromine, each additional molecule adding with increasing difficulty. The tetrabromide is 9,10,13,14-tetrabromo-11-octadecenoic acid.[143] By prolonged treatment of this tetrabromide with bromine, the hexabromide is formed.[144] Steric effects are even more powerful with acetylenic acids, since 9-octadecynoic acid adds only one molecule of bromine.

Hydrogen halides add much less readily than halogens, the ease of addition being in the order HI > HBr > HCl > HF, whereas the halogens follow the reverse order $F_2$ > $Cl_2$ > $Br_2$ > $I_2$. Addition of halogen acid to oleic acid has been reported to give mixtures of 9- and 10-halo acids.[145]

[136] Adkins and Folkers, *J. Am. Chem. Soc.*, **53**, 1095 (1931).
[137] Komori, *J. Soc. Chem. Ind. Japan*, **42**, Suppl. binding, 46 (1939).
[138] Hansley, *Ind. Eng. Chem.*, **39**, 55 (1947). (Reprinted by permission.)
[139] Nicolet, *J. Am. Chem. Soc.*, **43**, 2122 (1921).
[140] Toyama and Tsuchiya, *J. Soc. Chem. Ind. Japan*, **38**, Suppl. binding, 36 (1935).
[141] Riemenschneider, Wheeler, and Sando, *J. Biol. Chem.*, **127**, 391 (1939).
[142] Kummerow and Green, *J. Am. Oil Chemists' Soc.*, **24**, 196 (1947).
[143] Kametaka, *J. Chem. Soc.*, **83**, 1042 (1903).
[144] van Loon, *Rec. trav. chim.*, **50**, 32 (1931).
[145] Piotrowski, *Ber.*, **23**, 2531 (1890).

Addition to $\alpha,\beta$-unsaturated acids, the mode of addition to terminal double bonds, and the influence of peroxides are discussed elsewhere in this Treatise.

Other addition reactions include those of hypochlorous acid to give chlorohydroxy compounds,[146] sulfuric acid to give sulfates,[147] chlorosulfonic acid to give chlorosulfonates,[148] aromatic hydrocarbons and aluminum chloride to give products such as phenyl- and xylyl-stearic acid,[149] nitrosyl chloride to give chloronitroso derivatives,[150] mercuric acetate in methanol to give acetoxymercurimethoxy derivatives,[151] and thiocyanogen to give dithiocyanates.[152] With all except the symmetrical additives, mixed derivatives are obtained and some apparent shifting of the double bond occurs under drastic conditions. Thiocyanogen, in contrast to bromine, adds first to the double bond closer to the carboxyl group. Linoleic acid reacts with slightly more than one mole and linolenic acid with slightly more than two moles of thiocyanogen.[153] Although both bromine and thiocyanogen have been used for determining the amounts of polyunsaturated acids, alkali isomerization followed by spectrophotometric analysis is more suitable for most determinations. Iodine monochloride and iodine monobromide are used extensively for determination of total unsaturation, except in conjugated fats;[154] a modified procedure has been applied to conjugated fats. Hydrogenation is suitable for determination of unsaturation in fats containing both conjugated and non-conjugated double bonds.

Alkali cleavage of ricinoleic acid gives a variety of products, depending on reaction conditions. Figure 16 shows the main products of this reaction and the proposed mechanism.[155] The reaction has four different stages including isomerization, cleavage, hydrogen exchange, and dehydrogenation. First it is assumed that the double bond in ricinoleic acid shifts from position 9 to position 10. Water cleaves the 12-hydroxy-10-octadecenoic acid to give methyl hexyl ketone (XXXIVa) and 10-hydroxydecanoic acid (XXXIVb). No additional reaction occurs at 200°.

[146] Atherton and Hilditch, *J. Chem. Soc.*, 204 (1943).

[147] Schaeffer, Roe, Dixon, and Ault, *J. Am. Chem. Soc.*, **66**, 1924 (1944).

[148] Bauer and Stockhausen, *J. prakt. Chem.*, **130**, 35 (1931). Disputed by Pomeranz, *Seifensieder-Ztg.*, **59**, 3, 79 (1932).

[149] Stirton *et al.*, *J. Am. Oil Chemists' Soc.*, **25**, 365 (1948).

[150] Kaufmann and Rover, *Fette u. Seifen*, **47**, 103 (1940).

[151] Ralston, Christensen, and Josh, *Oil & Soap*, **14**, 5 (1937).

[152] Kaufmann, *Analyst*, **51**, 264 (1926).

[153] Mathews, Brode, and Brown, *Oil & Soap*, **18**, 182 (1941).

[154] Wijs, *J. Soc. Chem. Ind. (London)*, **17**, 699 (1898). For analytical procedures see Mehlenbacher, "Official and Tentative Methods," American Oil Chemists' Society, Chicago, Ill., 1946. Revised annually.

[155] Hargreaves and Owens, *J. Chem. Soc.*, 753 (1947). Figure 16 by courtesy of the publishers.

Hydrogen exchange between XXXIV*a* and XXXIV*b* occurs at 250° to give 2-octanol and sebacic semialdehyde. The latter is oxidized at this temperature to sebacic acid.

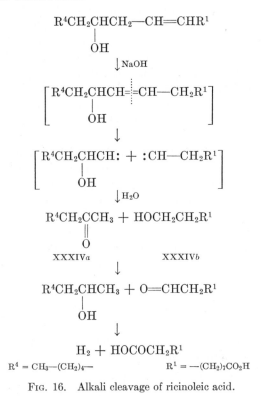

$$R^4 = CH_3—(CH_2)_4—  \qquad  R^1 = —(CH_2)_7CO_2H$$

Fig. 16. Alkali cleavage of ricinoleic acid.

Pyrolysis of ricinoleic acid leads to the formation of a mixture of heptanal and 10-undecenoic acid.[155a]

$$R^4CH_2—CH—CH_2CH=CHR^1 \rightarrow R^4CH_2CHO + CH_2=CHCH_2R^1$$
$$\underset{OH}{|}$$

**Reactions of the Carboxyl Group.** The carboxyl group in fatty acids undergoes the reactions normally expected. A few of the more important reactions will be reviewed.

Acids are obtained from fat by any one of several processes. Saponification with potassium hydroxide-methanol is well suited for laboratory work,[35] whereas aqueous hydrolysis at high temperature and pressure is frequently employed for continuous commercial conversion of fats to

[155a] Vernon and Ross, *J. Am. Chem. Soc.*, **58**, 2430 (1936).

acids and glycerol.[156]   Twitchell's reagent, a product obtained by sulfonating a reaction product of fatty acid and aromatic hydrocarbon, was formerly used, and new Twitchell reagents from petroleum products are still used industrially for batch cleavage of fat.[157]   Glycerides undergo alcoholysis with mono- and polyhydric alcohols, acidolysis with organic acids, and interesterification with other esters.[158]   Catalysts accelerate these reactions, but they occur to some extent at elevated temperatures without added catalysts.   Examples include the conversion of glycerides to methyl esters using sodium hydroxide [159] as a catalyst, acidolysis of a saturated triglyceride with oleic acid in the presence of a small amount of water,[160] and interesterification between glycerides using sodium methoxide [161] as a catalyst.

Reaction of fatty acids in the liquid phase with ammonia leads at 200° to the formation of amides and at 300° to the formation of nitriles. Stearamide when heated at a temperature of 300° disproportionates to give a mixture of stearonitrile and stearic acid.[162, 163]   The reactions involved may be expressed by the following equilibria.

$$R^7CO_2H + NH_3 \rightleftarrows R^7CO_2NH_4 \underset{+H_2O}{\overset{-H_2O}{\rightleftarrows}} R^7CONH_2 \underset{+H_2O}{\overset{-H_2O}{\rightleftarrows}} R^7CN$$

$R^7$ = both saturated and unsaturated groups from fats.

Commercially the conversion of fatty acids to the corresponding nitriles is accomplished by a combination of liquid-phase and vapor-phase catalytic processes.[163a]

Nitriles are converted to higher aliphatic primary and secondary amines by catalytic hydrogenation.

$$R^7C\equiv N + 2H_2 \rightarrow R^7CH_2NH_2$$

$$2R^7C\equiv N + 4H_2 \rightarrow (R^7CH_2)_2NH + NH_3$$

Quaternary ammonium salts are produced by reaction of these amines with alkylating agents such as methyl chloride.

$$R^7CH_2NH_2 + 3CH_3Cl + 2NaOH \rightarrow [R^7CH_2N(CH_3)_3]Cl + 2NaCl + 2H_2O$$

Both amine salts and quaternary ammonium salts are cationic surface-active agents and are employed as antiseptics, flotation agents, and emulsifiers.

[156] Barnebey and Brown, *J. Am. Oil Chemists' Soc.*, **25**, 95 (1948).
[157] Twitchell, *J. Am. Chem. Soc.*, **22**, 22 (1900).
[158] Cowan, *J. Am. Oil Chemists' Soc.*, **27**, 492 (1950).
[159] Wright *et al.*, *Oil & Soap*, **21**, 145 (1944).
[160] Eckey, U. S. pat. 2,378,005 (1945) [*C. A.*, **39**, 4505 (1945)].
[161] Eckey, *Ind. Eng. Chem.*, **40**, 1183 (1948).
[162] Ralston, Hoerr, and Pool, *J. Org. Chem.*, **8**, 473 (1943).
[163] Ralston, Harwood, and Pool, *J. Am. Chem. Soc.*, **59**, 986 (1937).
[163a] Kenyon, Stingley, and Young, *Ind. Eng. Chem.*, **42**, 202 (1950).

Acid chlorides are derived from the fatty acids by treatment with the usual reagents, phosphorus trichloride, phosphorus pentachloride, or thionyl chloride. Acid chlorides are used commercially in the production of detergents.[163b]

$$3R^7COH + PCl_3 \rightarrow 3R^7C\text{---}Cl + H_3PO_3$$
$$\quad\;\; \overset{\|}{O} \qquad\qquad\qquad \overset{\|}{O}$$

Sodium hydride at elevated temperatures effects the acetoacetic ester synthesis on the esters of fatty acids. Both saturated and unsaturated esters undergo the reaction, and linoleic esters are reported to give superior products for drying oils.[164] Sodium effects the acyloin condensation to give hydroxy ketones.[165] Saturated acids give dialkyl ketones when heated with iron.[166] Alkyl aryl ketones are prepared by Friedel-Crafts or Grignard reactions.[166a] When either saturated or unsaturated acids react with acetic anhydride, ketenes are formed.[167]

### Synthetic Glycerides

The many methods of synthesis of the acids in fats are not discussed here, and the student is referred to the general references at the end of the chapter. Synthesis of triglycerides of individual acids or of glycerides having a random arrangement of mixed acids presents no unusual difficulties. Direct esterification under diminished pressure, reaction of acid chlorides with glycerol in the presence of a tertiary amine, and glycerolysis of methyl esters are all satisfactory methods.

Mono-, di-, or triglycerides of definite rather than random structure are more difficult to prepare, because 1,2-acyl glycerides rearrange under acidic or alkaline conditions to give 1,3-acyl glycerides.

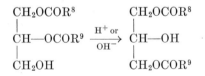

Fischer and co-workers were the first to show this migration [168] by proving the non-identity of the triglycerides XXXVI and XXXVII.

[163b] Kastens and Aya, *ibid.*, **42**, 1626 (1950).
[164] Hansley and Rogers, U. S. pat. 2,361,027 (1944) [*C. A.*, **39**, 2212 (1945)].
[165] Hansley, *J. Am. Chem. Soc.*, **57**, 2303 (1935).
[166] Easterfield and Taylor, *J. Chem. Soc.*, **99**, 2298 (1911).
[166a] Ralston and Christensen, *Ind. Eng. Chem.*, **29**, 194 (1937).
[167] Sorenson, U. S. pat. 2,513,825 (1950) [*C. A.*, **44**, 8678 (1950)].
[168] Fischer, *Ber.*, **53B**, 1621 (1920).

If no migration occurred, these glycerides would be identical; $R^8$ and $R^9$ represent different, saturated, straight-chain alkyl groups. Fairbourne [169] and others have extended Fischer's work with 1,2-acetonyl

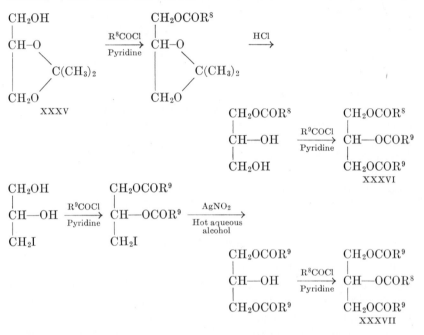

glycerol (XXXV) to clarify many erroneously reported syntheses of glycerides and to describe some properties of the products.

2-Acyl glycerides or unsymmetrical diglycerides can be prepared only by the use of protecting groups on the 1- or 1- and 3-positions of glycerol. Migration of both aromatic and aliphatic acyl groups from the 2- to the 1-position occurs with facility in a short time in the presence of 0.1 $N$ HCl or $NH_4OH$, and 0.0067 $N$ HCl or 0.013 $N$ $NH_4OH$ causes the migration of aliphatic acyl groups.[170] 2-Acyl glycerides (XXXIX) can be prepared from the dtrityl ether of glycerol (XXXVIII).[171, 172]

$$
\begin{array}{ccccc}
CH_2OC(C_6H_5)_3 & & CH_2OC(C_6H_5)_3 & & CH_2OH \\
| & & | & & | \\
CH{-}OH & \xrightarrow[\text{Pyridine}]{R^8COCl} & CH{-}OCOR^8 & \xrightarrow[\text{Pd}]{H_2} & CH{-}OCOR^8 \\
| & & | & & | \\
CH_2OC(C_6H_5)_3 & & CH_2OC(C_6H_5)_3 & & CH_2OH \\
\text{XXXVIII} & & & & \text{XXXIX}
\end{array}
$$

[169] Fairbourne, *J. Chem. Soc.*, 369 (1930).
[170] Daubert and King, *J. Am. Chem. Soc.*, **60**, 3003 (1938).
[171] Verkade, *Fette u. Seifen*, **45**, 457 (1938).
[172] Daubert, *J. Am. Chem. Soc.*, **62**, 1713 (1940).

1,3-Benzylidene glycerol can be used in an analogous manner.[173]   Unsymmetrical diglycerides (XLI) can be prepared from the $\alpha$-trityl ether or 1-glyceryl benzyl carbonate (XL) [173, 174] by a similar acylation and reduction.

$$CH_2—O—CO—OCH_2C_6H_5$$
$$|$$
$$CH—OH \qquad \xrightarrow[\text{Pyridine}]{R^8COCl}$$
$$|$$
$$CH_2OH$$
$$\text{XL}$$

$$CH_2—O—CO—OCH_2C_6H_5 \qquad CH_2OH$$
$$| \qquad\qquad\qquad\qquad\qquad\qquad |$$
$$CH—OCOR^8 \qquad\qquad \xrightarrow[\text{Pd}]{H_2} \quad CH—OCOR^8$$
$$| \qquad\qquad\qquad\qquad\qquad\qquad |$$
$$CH_2OCOR^8 \qquad\qquad\qquad\qquad CH_2OCOR^8$$
$$\text{XLI}$$

Although unsymmetrical triglycerides have an asymmetric carbon atom, no optical activity traceable to this asymmetry in the higher aliphatic derivatives is found.[175]   Optically active monoglycerides prepared by the conversion of $d$-acetonyl glycerol with an acid chloride give optically inactive triglycerides on further treatment with different acid chlorides.   When an aromatic acid chloride is used, the optical activity is retained.[176]

## Minor Constituents

A variety of substances in addition to the triglycerides are found in simple lipids.   These include waxes, compound lipids such as phospholipids, and derived lipids such as sterols, hydrocarbons, and alcohols.

Although waxes are usually found as minor constituents in many simple lipids, they may occur as major constituents.   Among the more important waxes are carnauba, which is obtained from the leaves of a Brazilian palm, *Copernicia cerifera;* spermaceti, from the head oil of a sperm whale; insect waxes, such as beeswax; and lanolin, from wool grease.   Carnauba wax contains straight-chain primary alcohols such as octacosanol, $C_{28}H_{57}OH$; triacontanol, $C_{30}H_{61}OH$; and dotriacontanol, $C_{32}H_{65}OH$.[177]   Presumably, these alcohols are present as esters of eicosanoic acid, $C_{19}H_{39}CO_2H$, and other acids of longer chain length.   Spermaceti

[173] Bergmann and Carter, *Z. physiol. Chem.*, **191**, 211 (1930).

[174] Daubert and King, *J. Am. Chem. Soc.*, **61**, 3328 (1939).   For review, see Daubert and King, *Chem. Revs.*, **29**, 269 (1941).

[175] Fischer and Baer, *Chem. Revs.*, **29**, 287 (1941).

[176] Baer and Fischer, *J. Biol. Chem.*, **128**, 475 (1939).

[177] Koonce and Brown, *Oil & Soap*, **21**, 67, 231 (1944).

contains cetyl esters of lauric and myristic acids,[178] and lanolin contains cholesterol, cholesteryl esters, and free acids. In addition to straight-chain, even-carbon acids containing 10 to 26 carbon atoms, lanolin contains two series of branched-chain acids, the *iso* series containing an even number of carbon atoms, XLII, where $n$ equals 3 to 11 inclusive, and the *anteiso* series containing an odd number of carbon atoms, XLIII, where $n$ equals 2 to 13 inclusive.[179]

$$CH_3CH(CH_2)_{2n}CO_2H \qquad\qquad CH_3CH_2CH(CH_2)_{2n}CO_2H$$
$$|\qquad\qquad\qquad\qquad\qquad\qquad |$$
$$CH_3 \qquad\qquad\qquad\qquad\qquad\qquad CH_3$$

XLII                                        XLIII

The sterols comprise mainly cholesterol in animal fats, sitosterol and stigmasterol in vegetable fats, and ergosterol in yeast fats. The amount of sterol varies from 0.1% or less for beef tallow to as high as 7.6% for halibut-liver oil.[180]

Vegetable fats contain appreciable amounts of tocopherols, which occur in four types: α-, β-, γ-, and δ-forms, differing in the number and position of the methyl groups on the aromatic ring of IX. They are believed to be 5,7,8-trimethyltocol, 5,8-dimethyltocol, 7,8-dimethyltocol, and 8-methyltocol, respectively.[181] α-, γ-, and δ-Tocopherols are all found in soybean oil, but wheat-germ oil is apparently one of a few oils to contain β-tocopherol. Wheat-germ oil is an excellent source of α-tocopherol or vitamin E.

Among the many phenolic derivatives present in fats are sesamin[182] and gossypol.[183]

Hydrocarbons such as squalene, $C_{30}H_{50}$ (XLIV), which contains six

XLIV

isoprene units, are present in many fats.[184] A definite relationship appears to exist between squalene and vitamin A, since fish-liver oils, which

[178] Hilditch and Lovern, *J. Soc. Chem. Ind.*, **48**, 359T (1929).

[179] Weitkamp, *J. Am. Chem. Soc.*, **67**, 447 (1945).

[180] Kaufmann, *Fette u. Seifen*, **48**, 53 (1941).

[181] Stern, Robeson, Weisler, and Baxter, *J. Am. Chem. Soc.*, **69**, 869 (1947); Emerson and Smith, *ibid.*, **62**, 1869 (1940); Karrer, Fritzsche, Ringier, and Salomon, *Helv. Chim. Acta*, **21**, 820 (1938).

[182] Bruchhausen and Gerhard, *Ber.*, **72**, 830 (1939).

[183] For a review of the structure of gossypol, see Bailey, "Cottonseed and Cottonseed Products," Interscience Publishers, New York (1948), pp. 239–262.

[184] Schmitt, *Ann.*, **547**, 115 (1941).

contain large amounts of either one, seldom contain much of the other. The related carotene pigments are present in many vegetable fats.

## PHOSPHOLIPIDS

### H. E. CARTER

The phospholipids are widely distributed in both plant and animal tissues, constituting an essential structural element of cells. Certain tissues (brain, spinal cord, liver, spleen, lung, egg yolk, and seeds of plants) contain unusually large quantities of lipids and have been used in preparative work. The nervous system is unique in its high content of both phospholipids and cerebrosides (35% of the dry weight). Cerebrosides occur in minute quantities in other tissues but are always prepared from brain or spinal cord. Soybean oil, corn oil, and linseed oil phospholipids are readily available commercially. These materials contain lecithin, cephalin, inositol lipids, and other substances. Egg yolk is a convenient starting material for the preparation of lecithin.[1]

### Isolation Methods

The preparation of crude phospholipid fractions from brain and soybean phospholipid will be outlined here, and the further purification of these fractions will be discussed under the individual components.

Certain of the difficulties inherent in the separation of phospholipid mixtures are readily apparent from a brief consideration of their structures.

The presence of both polar and non-polar groups renders these substances potent emulsifying agents. Since they are also amphoteric in nature, it is not surprising that the phospholipids tend to carry along a variety of organic and inorganic materials. Thus, many otherwise insoluble substances will dissolve in organic solvents containing phospholipids. On the other hand, when phospholipids are precipitated from solution, they carry down by adsorption or intermolecular salt formation a variety of otherwise soluble substances. Most phospholipids autoxidize rapidly, a reaction that is accelerated by the presence of traces of iron and copper salts, which tend to accumulate in phospholipid fractions. The glycerolipids are hydrolyzed readily by either acidic or basic reagents since both the fatty acid ester linkages and the phosphate ester bonds are labile. They are also cleaved rapidly by certain enzymes. It is therefore important that in preparative work fresh tissue be used and

[1] Levene and Rolf, *J. Biol. Chem.*, **46**, 193 (1921).

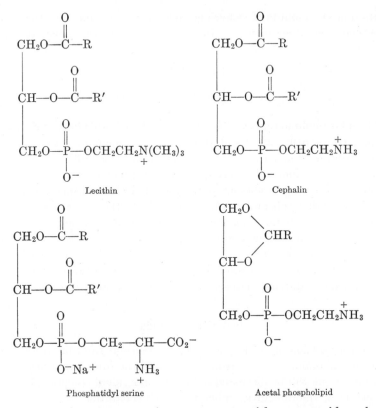

Lecithin

Cephalin

Phosphatidyl serine

Acetal phospholipid

that prolonged exposure to air or treatment with strong acids or bases be avoided.

**Brain.** The fresh tissue is first dried in order to avoid the formation of intractable emulsions in subsequent extractions with organic solvents. Dehydration with solvents is preferable, and acetone has several advantages for this purpose.[2] It removes neutral fats, sterols, and waxes but has little ability to dissolve phospholipids. Furthermore, acetone has the unique property of converting phospholipids (or tissues containing them) into friable powders which are readily filtered and handled.

The dry, fat-free tissue is then extracted with an appropriate solvent. Ether or petroleum ether[2] removes the glycerophosphatides and leaves most of the sphingolipids (cerebrosides and sphingomyelin) in the residue. Subsequent extraction of the residue with hot ethanol[2] gives a crude mixture of the sphingolipids (so-called "protagon"). Chloroform, chloroform-methanol, and ether-ethanol have been employed to remove both the phospholipids and the sphingolipids in one operation.

[2] Carter, Haines, Ledyard, and Norris, *ibid.*, **169**, 77 (1947).

In many tissues the phospholipids are at least in part combined with proteins in lipoprotein complexes. Certain of these, such as thromboplastin, are fairly stable, whereas others are readily disrupted. As a result, preliminary treatment of a tissue with ethanol may increase the amount of phospholipid extractable with ether. Folch [3] isolated from brain a chloroform-soluble lipid-protein complex for which he proposed the term "proteolipide."

The ether-soluble material is further fractionated by treatment of the ether solution with ethanol. Lecithin remains in solution, and material precipitates which was originally thought to be pure cephalin. It is now recognized [4] that the so-called "cephalin" is actually a complex mixture containing cephalin (phosphatidyl ethanolamine *), phosphatidyl serine, and inositol lipid. Folch [5] developed a method for separating the cephalin fraction into these three components by fractional precipitation from a chloroform solution with methanol. Diphosphoinositide is least soluble, phosphatidyl serine next, and cephalin most soluble.

**Soybean.** Crude soybean phospholipid is obtained commercially as a by-product in the preparation of soybean oil. In the solvent-extraction process, which is now widely used, the beans are cracked and flaked by being passed through heavy rollers, and the flakes are then extracted with hexane. When the hexane is evaporated the residual oil deposits a viscous gum ("sludge") containing a high percentage of phospholipid. Treatment of the oil with steam "hydrates" out additional phospholipid ("foots"). Extraction of these materials with acetone removes adhering oil, giving a light brown powder sold as "soybean lecithin." This material is separated into lecithin and cephalin fractions by the ethanol-ether procedure.

This cephalin fraction differs from that of brain in that it contains no phosphatidyl serine [6] but has a high content of inositol lipid [6,7] and contains sitosteryl glucoside.[8] By repeated precipitations from ether and chloroform, Woolley [9] prepared a material, "lipositol," which he thought to be homogeneous. More recent studies [6-8] have shown the presence of at least two inositol lipids in soybean. A crude inositol lipid fraction

---

[3] Folch, *Federation Proc.*, **9**, 171 (1950).

[4] Folch, *J. Biol. Chem.*, **146**, 35 (1942).

* Since the term "cephalin" was long applied to the ethanol-insoluble lipid mixture, the suggestion has been made that it be replaced by "phosphatidyl ethanolamine" (ref. 4) when referring to the specific substance. In this chapter "cephalin" will be used for the specific compound and "cephalin fraction" for the ethanol-insoluble mixture.

[5] Folch, *ibid.*, **177**, 497 (1949).

[6] Scholfield, Dutton, Tanner, and Cowan, *J. Am. Oil Chemists' Soc.*, **25**, 368 (1948).

[7] Carter, Celmer, McCormick, Nyman, and Saunders, *Federation Proc.*, **8**, 190 (1949).

[8] Carter and Celmer, unpublished data.

[9] Woolley, *J. Biol. Chem.*, **147**, 581 (1943).

is conveniently prepared by extracting soybean phospholipid with glacial acetic acid, which removes lecithin and cephalin but leaves most of the inositol lipid in the residue.[7] It should be emphasized that these separations are not clean cut and must be repeated several times. Mutual solubility effects play a pronounced role, and many substances such as glucose,[10] stachyose,[8] urea,[11] and even sodium chloride,[11] are soluble in ether or petroleum ether solutions of phospholipids. Cerebrosides and sphingomyelin, although almost ether-insoluble, are present in the ether extracts of brain tissue. It should also be noted that the precipitation techniques generally employed in phospholipid work have certain inherent disadvantages. The precipitates are usually amorphous and tend to adsorb contaminating materials. Intermolecular salt formation may result in the precipitation of otherwise soluble substances. As a result cephalin, although readily soluble in ethanol when pure, is a component of the fraction precipitated from ether by ethanol. The introduction of solvent-solvent fractionation offers promise for the elimination of some of these difficulties.

### Lecithin

Vauquelin [12] is generally recognized as the first investigator to isolate a phosphorus-containing lipid. He prepared crude lecithin from brain in 1812. Gobley [13] obtained a similar material from egg yolk and named it lecithin (Greek, *lekitos* = egg yolk). Lecithin was first obtained in a relatively pure form by Diakonow [14] in 1868.

**Preparation.** The crude ethanol-soluble lecithin fraction described in the previous section provides the usual starting material for the preparation of lecithin. Purification is usually achieved by the method of Levene and Rolf,[15] based on the observation that lecithin gives a crystalline ether-insoluble cadmium chloride complex. (Cephalin gives an ether-soluble complex.) Pangborn [16] has modified the procedure by introducing a purification step involving distribution of the cadmium chloride complex between 80% ethanol and petroleum ether. The purified complex gives a clear solution in chloroform from which the free lecithin is regenerated by treatment with anhydrous methanolic ammonia. Further work is needed on the composition and properties of the lecithin-cadmium chloride complex.

[10] Mayer, *Biochem. Z.*, **1**, 81 (1906).
[11] Christensen, *J. Biol. Chem.*, **129**, 531 (1939).
[12] Vauquelin, *Ann. chim.*, [1] **81**, 37 (1812).
[13] Gobley, *J. pharm. chim.*, [3] **11**, 409 (1847); **12**, 1 (1847).
[14] Diakonow, *Zentr. med. Wiss.*, vi, 2 (1868).
[15] Levene and Rolf, *J. Biol. Chem.*, **72**, 587 (1927).
[16] Pangborn, *ibid.*, **137**, 545 (1941).

Lecithin may also be purified by chromatography.[17]   When a petroleum ether solution of phospholipids is passed over a column of magnesium oxide, all the components are adsorbed.   The choline-containing compounds (lecithin and sphingomyelin) are eluted with methanol.

**Structure.**  Lecithin on mild hydrolysis yields two moles of fatty acid, one of choline, and one of glycerophosphoric acid.   The last compound is a mixture of the α- and β-forms.*   This suggests the possibility that leci-

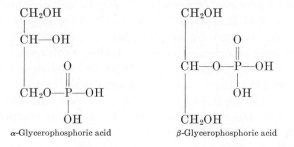

α-Glycerophosphoric acid          β-Glycerophosphoric acid

thin itself exists as a mixture of the α- and β-isomers shown in the formulas, and there are actually reports in the literature of the separation of the two forms.[18]   However, the homogeneity of these materials seems

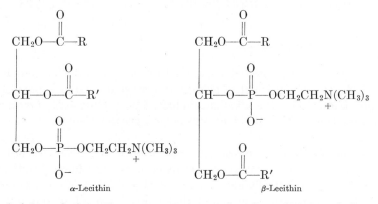

α-Lecithin                  β-Lecithin

doubtful, and the only strong argument for the existence of the two forms is the isolation of the two glycerophosphoric acids on hydrolysis.

This evidence would have no significance if it could be shown that α-glycerophosphoric acid is converted to the β-form under the usual hydrolysis conditions.   Therefore, extensive studies have been made of the

---

[17] Taurog, Enteman, Fries, and Chaikoff, *ibid.*, **155**, 19 (1944).

* The two isomers can be separated on the basis of the fact that barium β-glycerophosphate gives an insoluble double salt with barium nitrate whereas the α-form does not [Karrer and Salomon, *Helv. Chim. Acta*, **9**, 3 (1926)].

[18] Rae, *Biochem. J.*, **28**, 152 (1934); Suzuki and Yokayama, *Proc. Imp. Acad.* (*Tokyo*), **6**, 341 (1930).

behavior of the glycerophosphoric acids (GPA) on treatment with acid and alkali. Both isomers are highly resistant to hydrolysis, especially by alkali. (Anderson and de Suto-Nagy [19] employed 10% sulfuric acid in a sealed tube at 160° for complete hydrolysis.) However, strong acids [20,21] catalyze a reversible interconversion of $\alpha$- and $\beta$-glycerophosphoric acid (the equilibrium mixture contains about 75% of the $\alpha$- and 25% of the $\beta$-form). Strong alkali [20] also causes a reversible reaction which favors $\beta$-glycerophosphoric acid. Weak alkali does not cause $\alpha,\beta$-isomerization, and Burmaster [21] reaffirmed the presence of both forms in lecithin and cephalin, by showing that each yielded a mixture of $\alpha$- and $\beta$-glycerophosphoric acid on mild alkaline hydrolysis. This situation has now been clarified by the observations of Baer and Kates,[22] who discovered that isomerization does occur in the hydrolysis of $\alpha$-glycerylphosphorylcholine (GPC) under very mild conditions *with either acid or alkali*. With L-$\alpha$-glycerylphosphorylcholine as the starting material

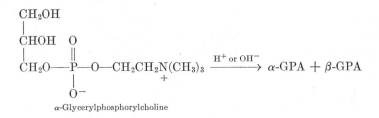

$\alpha$-Glycerylphosphorylcholine

the final product consisted of a mixture of L-$\alpha$- and $\beta$-glycerophosphoric acids. The product of acid hydrolysis contained 91% of $\alpha$-glycerophosphoric acid; the alkaline product, 44%. Obviously, racemization would accompany the interconversion, since the $\beta$-isomer is optically inactive.

Presumably these same reactions may occur in the hydrolysis of lecithins and cephalins. Since the naturally occurring lecithins are optically active and yield optically active $\alpha$-glycerophosphoric acid on enzymatic hydrolysis, there can be no doubt that most, if not all, of the natural lecithins (and cephalins) exist in the $\alpha$-form. Whether any $\beta$-forms occur in nature is doubtful, since there is little or no evidence for their existence.

Levorotatory glycerophosphoric acid ((−)-GPA) has long been known as a product of the enzymatic hydrolysis of lecithins. More recently levorotatory $\alpha$-glycerylphosphorylcholine ((−)-GPC) has been isolated

[19] Anderson and de Suto-Nagy, *J. Biol. Chem.*, **171**, 761 (1947).
[20] Folch, *ibid.*, **146**, 31 (1942).
[21] Burmaster, *ibid.*, **165**, 565 (1946).
[22] Baer and Kates, *ibid.*, **175**, 79 (1948).

from autolysates of pancreas.[23]   The configuration of these compounds has now been established by Baer and co-workers.[24]   In assigning configurations to asymmetrically substituted derivatives of glycerol Baer and Fischer [25] logically chose to relate them to the glyceraldehydes to which they would be oxidized (with no migration of the acyl group). Thus a monosubstituted glycerol giving D-glyceraldehyde on oxidation is assigned the D-configuration, and vice versa.

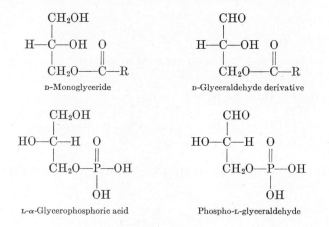

D-Monoglyceride        D-Glyceraldehyde derivative

L-α-Glycerophosphoric acid      Phospho-L-glyceraldehyde

Baer and co-workers synthesized L-α-glycerophosphoric acid and L-α-glycerylphosphorylcholine from acetone-D-glyceraldehyde as shown in the following equations.   The change from the D- to the L-series results from the fact that the reference carbon atom is reversed in the conversion of acetone-D-glycerol to L-α-glycerophosphoric acid.

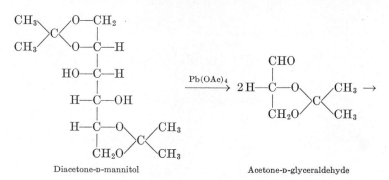

Diacetone-D-mannitol          Acetone-D-glyceraldehyde

[23] Schmidt, Hershman, and Thannhauser, *ibid.*, **161,** 523 (1945).

[24] Baer and Fischer, *ibid.*, **128,** 491 (1939); Baer and Kates, *J. Am. Chem. Soc.*, **70,** 1394 (1948).

[25] Baer and Fischer, *J. Biol. Chem.*, **128,** 475 (1939).

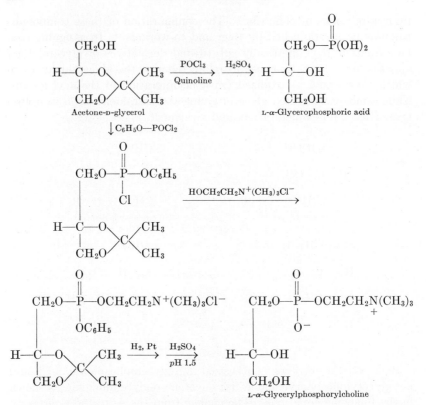

The synthetic products were identical with the natural ones in every respect. Therefore, these syntheses establish the fact that natural

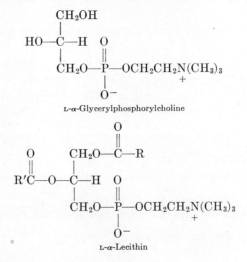

L-α-Glycerylphosphorylcholine

L-α-Lecithin

$\alpha$-glycerophosphoric acid and $\alpha$-glycerylphosphorylcholine possess the the L-configuration. Thus, lecithin and its hydrolysis products have the L-configuration.

**Fatty Acids.** The idea that lecithin always contains one saturated and one unsaturated acid has been proved erroneous. Some plant lecithins contain two unsaturated fatty acids, and a saturated "hydrolecithin" containing two molecules of palmitic acid (L-$\alpha$-dipalmitoyl lecithin) has been obtained from *Cysticercus* larvae,[26] from lung,[27] and from brain and spleen.[28] Sinclair[29] found that the rat-liver phospholipids contained 33% of saturated fatty acid, the muscle 27%, and the kidney 26%. Beef-liver phospholipids contain oleic, linoleic, arachidonic, palmitic, and stearic acids.[30] Soybean lecithin, purified through the cadmium chloride complex,[31] contains palmitic acid (15%), stearic acid (6.3%), oleic acid (13%), linoleic acid (63%), and linolenic acid (2%). The high proportion of unsaturated fatty acids in lecithin renders it particularly susceptible to autoxidation.

**Ionic Structure.** Lecithin has been formulated as a non-ionic substance and as an "endo" salt.[32] The latter structure involves the ex-

$$
\begin{array}{c}
\quad\quad\quad\quad\quad\quad O \\
\quad\quad\quad\quad\quad\quad \| \\
\quad\quad O \quad\quad CH_2OC\text{---}R \\
\quad\quad \| \quad\quad\quad | \\
R'C\text{---}O\text{---}CH \quad\quad O \\
\quad\quad\quad\quad\quad | \quad\quad\quad \| \\
\quad\quad\quad\quad CH_2O\text{---}P\text{---}OCH_2CH_2N(CH_3)_3 \\
\quad\quad\quad\quad\quad\quad | \quad\quad\quad\quad\quad\quad + \\
\quad\quad\quad\quad\quad\quad O^-
\end{array}
$$

pansion of the valence shell of the nitrogen atom to ten, which is not in accord with modern concepts. More recent studies have supported the "zwitterion" or dipolar ion structure first proposed by Jukes.[33]

In view of the strongly acidic nature of the phosphate group and the basic strength of the quaternary nitrogen atom, it might be expected that the isoelectric point of lecithin would be close to $pH$ 7. Chain and Kemp[34] calculated the value to be 7.5. Actually the experimental values

[26] Lesuk and Anderson, *ibid.*, **139**, 457 (1941).

[27] Thannhauser, Benotti, and Boncoddo, *ibid.*, **166**, 669 (1946).

[28] Thannhauser and Boncoddo, *ibid.*, **172**, 135 (1948).

[29] Sinclair, *ibid.*, **111**, 261 (1935).

[30] Snider and Bloor, *ibid.*, **99**, 555 (1933).

[31] Thornton, Johnson, and Ewan, *Oil & Soap*, **21**, 85 (1944).

[32] Grün and Limpächer, *Ber.*, **60**, 147 (1927).

[33] Jukes, *J. Biol. Chem.*, **107**, 783 (1934).

[34] Chain and Kemp, *Biochem. J.*, **28**, 2052 (1934).

vary from 1.75 to 6.7.[35] Certain of these discrepancies were due to the study of lecithin contaminated with fatty acid and/or with cephalin. More careful workers using fresh, purified lecithin obtained values of about 6.7.[34,36] This figure may be low, since even under the mild conditions of titration fatty acid is liberated from pure lecithin. In any event, the isoelectric point of lecithin must lie near neutrality. Since it is the salt of a strong acid and a strong base, it has little buffering capacity at physiological $p$H ranges.[37]

**Properties.** Highly purified samples of lecithin are clear, waxy, highly hygroscopic solids, which autoxidize so rapidly that they turn yellow or brown in a few minutes on exposure to air. Lecithin softens to an oil at about 60°, browns and begins to decompose at 110°. It is soluble in the ordinary organic solvents (ethanol, ether, hexane, benzene, acetic acid) with the exception of methyl acetate and acetone. The last solvent is particularly useful in precipitating lecithin from solution. In the author's experience, lecithin and other phospholipids can be preserved under acetone better than in the dry state.

Lecithin finds many commercial uses because of its emulsifying properties.[38] Actually, pure lecithin is not highly surface-active, but in combination with carbohydrate or protein it acquires remarkable emulsifying properties.[39] (Commercial lecithin always contains carbohydrate.[40]) Lecithin promotes an oil-in-water type of emulsion.[41]

In contact with water lecithin forms oily, threadlike, twisting, cylindrical growths called myelin forms. These are liquid crystals.[42]

Lecithin is usually a highly unsaturated substance having an iodine number of 100 or above. It reacts readily with oxygen, and also with hydrolytic agents. The choline-phosphate linkage is cleaved under relatively mild conditions by either acid or alkali. Cleavage of choline [43] occurs at an appreciable rate, even in neutral alcohol at 60–70°. Aqueous acids or alkalies will hydrolyze lecithin to fatty acids, choline, and glycerophosphoric acid; the hydrolysis is complete in 6 hours at 37° with 1 $N$ potassium hydroxide.

Lecithin is also hydrolyzed rapidly by enzymes, of which four types are known.[44]

[35] Bull, *Cold Spring Harbor Symposia Quant. Biol.*, **8**, 63 (1940).
[36] Bull and Frampton, *J. Am. Chem. Soc.*, **58**, 594 (1936).
[37] Fabish, *Biochem. Z.*, **242**, 121 (1931).
[38] Hilty, *J. Am. Oil Chemists' Soc.*, **25**, 186 (1948).
[39] Sell, Olsen, and Kremers, *Ind. Eng. Chem.*, **27**, 1222 (1935).
[40] Horvath, *Ind. Eng. Chem., News Ed.*, **13**, 89 (1935).
[41] Seifriz, *Am. J. Physiol.*, **66**, 124 (1923).
[42] Steiger, *Mikrokosmos*, **35**, 54 (1941).
[43] Paal, *Biochem. Z.*, **211**, 244 (1929).
[44] Belfanti, Contardi, and Ercoli, *Ergeb. Enzymforsch.*, **5**, 213 (1936).

**Lecithinase A.** This enzyme was first detected in cobra venom and has since been obtained from other snake venoms [45] and from animal tissues [46] (liver, muscle, brain, pancreas). It selectively hydrolyzes one fatty acid from the lecithin molecule, usually an unsaturated acid.[47] The product, lysolecithin, is a crystalline solid (soluble in chloroform, insoluble in ether), which has an optical activity of $-2.6°$ (chloroform). Lysolecithin is a powerful hemolytic agent and has been assumed to be responsible, at least in part, for the toxic effects of certain snake venoms. However, Gronchi [48] has questioned this view. Lecithinase A is active also on cephalin but not on acetal lipids, sphingomyelin, or cerebrosides.

**Lecithinase B** is present in rice bran [49] and in various animal tissues [49] including the pancreas. It converts either lecithin or lysolecithin to $\alpha$-glycerylphosphorylcholine and is responsible for the production of L-$\alpha$-glycerylphosphorylcholine by autolyzing pancreas.

**Lecithinase C** has been found in carrots [50] and in cabbage leaves.[51] It will cleave choline from lecithin, giving phosphatidic acids, which are soluble in ether and acetone and slightly soluble in water. Phosphatidic acids had been isolated earlier from several plant sources.[52] It now seems

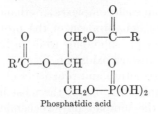

Phosphatidic acid

likely that they are not present as such but are formed by the action of lecithinase C during the processing.

**Lecithinase D** is found as a component of certain bacterial toxins.[53] It cleaves phosphorylcholine from lecithin, giving a diglyceride, but does not attack lysolecithin or glycerylphosphorylcholine.[54] It also splits phosphorylcholine from sphingomyelin.

[45] King and Dolan, *Biochem. J.*, **27**, 403 (1933); Slotta and Fraenkel-Conrat, *Ber.*, **71B**, 1076 (1938).

[46] Belfanti and Arnaudi, *Boll. sez. ital., soc. intern. microbiol.*, **4**, 399 (1932); Francioli, *Fermentforschung*, **14**, 241 (1934).

[47] Fairbairn, *J. Biol. Chem.*, **157**, 633 (1945).

[48] Gronchi, *Sperimentale*, **90**, 262 (1936).

[49] Contardi and Ercoli, *Arch. sci. biol.* (*Italy*), **21**, 1 (1935); *Biochem. Z.*, **261**, 275 (1932).

[50] Hanahan and Chaikoff, *J. Biol. Chem.*, **169**, 699 (1947).

[51] Hanahan and Chaikoff, *ibid.*, **172**, 191 (1948).

[52] Tristam, *Biochem. J.*, **36**, 400 (1942).

[53] MacFarlane and Knight, *ibid.*, **35**, 884 (1941).

[54] MacFarlane, *ibid.*, **42**, 587 (1948).

Lecithins give the usual reactions of unsaturated acids (addition of halogens, reduction, etc.). Catalytic reduction gives "hydrolecithins." These substances are white, crystalline, non-hygroscopic powders which are soluble in ethanol and insoluble in acetone and ether. They no longer autoxidize and can be kept indefinitely. These substances have similar properties to those of the saturated dipalmitoyl lecithin isolated from lung.[27]

The ability of lecithin to form complexes with a wide variety of substances (carbohydrates, proteins, inorganic salts) has been mentioned previously. The tendency of lecithin to pick up copper and iron salts [55] may be partly responsible for the rapidity with which it reacts with oxygen. Proteins form complexes with lecithin which are soluble in chloroform.[56] It seems likely that in the animal body many of the compound lipids exist and exert their physiological functions in the form of lipoproteins. Thromboplastin, a component of the blood-clotting mechanism, is a lipoprotein, and the $\beta$-globulin fraction of blood is a water-soluble lipoprotein containing 40–60% of lipids (phospholipids and cholesterol). Over half the lipids of egg yolk are bound to protein, as lipovitellin and lipovitellenin.[57] Ether extracts only a small proportion of the lipid from such complexes; [57] ethanol removes much more, probably as a result of denaturation of the protein component. It is interesting to note that phospholipids while in lipoprotein combination are much more stable toward oxidation.

Elucidation of the structure and properties of the lipid-carbohydrate and lipid-protein complexes is one of the most important problems involved in a study of the complex physicochemical structures of protoplasm.

**Synthesis.** Several approaches have been made to the synthesis of lecithin or hydrolecithin. In several the possibility of $\alpha,\beta$-migrations was not excluded, and the products often had physical properties not comparable to those of the naturally occurring materials. Baer and Kates [58] finally succeeded in developing a reliable procedure for synthesizing L-, D-, and DL-$\alpha$-lecithins. Acetone-D-glycerol was converted to the benzyl ether, and this was acylated to the diglyceride. Reduction of the benzyl ether over palladium yielded the D-diglyceride, which was converted into L-$\alpha$-dipalmitoyl lecithin as shown.* The product was a crystalline solid, identical in all its properties (solubility, optical activity,

[55] Thunberg, *Skand. Arch. Physiol.*, **33**, 228 (1916).
[56] Parsons, *Biochem. J.*, **22**, 2, 800 (1928).
[57] Fevold and Lausten, *Arch. Biochem.*, **11**, 1 (1946).
[58] Baer and Kates, *J. Am. Chem. Soc.*, **72**, 942 (1950).
* D-Diglyceride gives L-lecithin since the reference carbon is reversed in this reaction.

etc.) with the natural product.   L-α-Distearoyl and other lecithins were prepared by the same procedure.

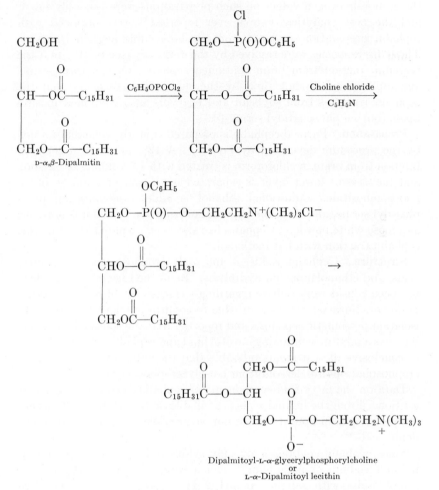

Dipalmitoyl-L-α-glycerylphosphorylcholine
or
L-α-Dipalmitoyl lecithin

## Cephalin

Thudichum (1884) isolated cephalin (Greek, *kephale* = head) from brain and reported that it yielded on hydrolysis fatty acids, glycerophosphoric acid, and a nitrogenous base other than choline.   In 1913 Baumann [59] identified the base as ethanolamine (colamine) and indicated that it could be determined by the Van Slyke procedure.   Al-

[59] Baumann, *Biochem. Z.*, **54**, 30 (1913).

though cephalin was long believed to be the sole component of the alcohol-insoluble phospholipid fraction, it was finally recognized that the carbon-hydrogen values on such preparations were generally low,[60] and the best analytical figures ever reported [61] were obtained with cephalin preparations isolated from alcohol-soluble lecithin fractions. These discrepancies were resolved by the discovery (see p. 219) that the cephalin fraction from brain contained cephalin, phosphatidyl serine, and diphosphoinositide,[4, 5] and by the subsequent discovery that the cephalin fractions from soybean and egg yolk also contained inositol lipids (but no phosphatidyl serine).[62]

**Preparation.** Purified cephalin is prepared from the cephalin fraction by the procedure developed by Folch.[4, 5] A 12% solution of cephalin fraction from brain in chloroform is treated with 1.5 volumes of ethanol, and the viscous lower layer is separated for use in preparation of diphosphoinositide. Additional ethanol is added, precipitating phosphatidyl serine, and from the supernatant solution cephalin is obtained as a loose white powder. Cephalin has also been prepared by extracting cephalin fraction with hot methanol.[63]

**Structure.** Cephalin yields $\alpha$- and $\beta$-glycerophosphoric acids, fatty acids, and ethanolamine on hydrolysis. As in the case of lecithin there has been considerable debate regarding the existence of $\alpha$- and $\beta$-forms. However, Burmaster [21, 64] was unable to confirm previous reports of the isolation of isomeric cephalins and reported that the so-called "$\beta$-cephalin" was a mixture containing inositol lipid and cephalin. In the absence of conclusive data it seems probable that the naturally occurring glycerophosphatides are derived from L-$\alpha$-glycerophosphoric acid.

Data on the fatty acid components of cephalin must be viewed with caution. From the limited reports available on reasonably well-purified samples, cephalin appears to contain stearic, oleic, linoleic, and arachidonic acids.[35]

Since cephalin contains a strongly acidic and a weakly basic group, it binds sodium or potassium [65] over a wide $pH$ range and forms insoluble salts with salmine at $pH$ 2–11.[66] At neutrality, therefore, cephalin probably should be represented by a mixture of the two ionic species shown below. The isoelectric point is low but has not been determined on purified cephalin.

[60] Gray, *J. Biol. Chem.*, **136**, 167 (1940).
[61] Levene and West, *ibid.*, **35**, 285 (1918); Rudy and Page, *Z. physiol. Chem.*, **193**, 251 (1930).
[62] Chargaff, Ziff, and Rittenberg, *J. Biol. Chem.*, **144**, 343 (1942).
[63] Maltaner, *J. Am. Chem. Soc.*, **53**, 4019 (1931).
[64] Burmaster, *J. Biol. Chem.*, **165**, 577 (1946).
[65] Christensen and Hastings, *ibid.*, **136**, 387 (1940).
[66] Chargaff, *ibid.*, **125**, 661 (1938).

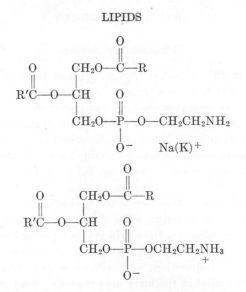

**Properties.**   Cephalin is a white hygroscopic powder which darkens slowly on exposure to air.   It is soluble in methanol, ethanol, and glacial acetic acid.   It is soluble in moist ether but not very soluble in dry ether.[67]   Folch's cephalin preparation had an iodine number of 78.

Data on the hydrolysis of pure cephalin are very scanty.   There is some evidence that the ethanolamine-phosphate linkage is more stable than the choline-phosphate linkage.   With barium hydroxide cephalin yields only 19% of glycerophosphoric acid under conditions which cleave lecithin to the extent of 90%.   Lecithin is hydrolyzed to glycerophosphoric acid by boiling with 6 $N$ hydrochloric acid for 30 minutes, whereas 2 hours of refluxing with 4 $N$ hydrochloric acid is required to liberate ethanolamine from cephalin.[5]

Cephalin, like lecithin, hydrates to give myelin forms.   It also tends to solubilize a variety of organic and inorganic substances (sugars, sodium chloride, glycogen) in ether.[68]   It forms an ether-soluble cadmium chloride complex.[16]

Lysocephalin is obtained by the action of lecithinase A on cephalin. Lysocephalin is a white, crystalline solid which is insoluble in ether.   It has no hemolytic properties.   Lecithinase C does not attack cephalin.[54]

Cephalin has some thromboplastic activity and is a component of the much more active lipoprotein thromboplastin.

**Synthesis.**   The synthesis of $\beta$-cephalins has been reported by Rose [69] and by Hunter, Roberts, and Kester.[70]

[67] Parnas, *Biochem. Z.*, **22**, 411 (1909).

[68] Frank, *ibid.*, **50**, 273 (1913).

[69] Rose, *J. Am. Chem. Soc.*, **69**, 1384 (1947).

[70] Hunter, Roberts, and Kester, *ibid.*, **70**, 3244 (1948)

## Phosphatidyl Serine

MacArthur in 1914 reported that amino acid nitrogen accounted for more than 20% of the total nitrogen of brain cephalin.[71]  It was almost 30 years later that several workers almost simultaneously suggested the presence of an amino acid in brain lipids [72] and actually isolated L-serine from lipid hydrolysates.[73]  Folch then succeeded in isolating and characterizing a homogeneous serine-containing lipid, phosphatidyl serine, from the cephalin fraction of brain by the procedure described in the previous section.[4, 5, 74]

**Structure.**  In phosphatidyl serine the phosphate must be attached to the $\beta$-hydroxyl group of serine, since the $\alpha$-amino and carboxyl groups are free.  The presence of a free carboxyl and a substituted phosphoric acid makes phosphatidyl serine a strongly acidic substance, which exists in brain as the mixed sodium and potassium salt.  Stearic and oleic acids account for most of the fatty acid content.  On the basis of these data the structure shown has been assigned to phosphatidyl serine.

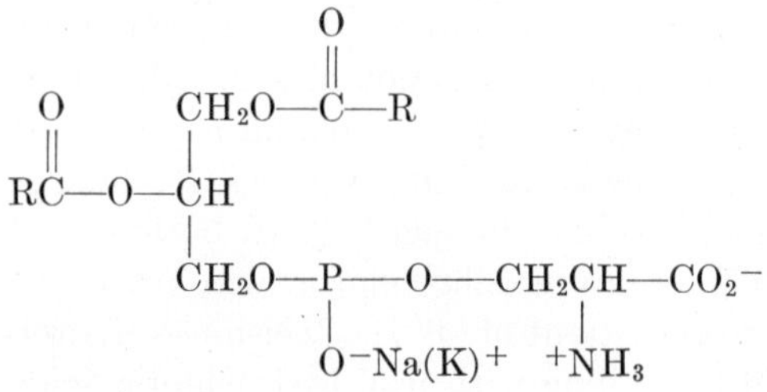

$$
\begin{array}{c}
\phantom{xxxxxxxxxxxxx} \overset{\displaystyle O}{\overset{\|}{} } \\[2pt]
\overset{\displaystyle O}{\overset{\|}{}} \qquad CH_2O\!-\!C\!-\!R \\[4pt]
RC\!-\!O\!-\!CH \\[4pt]
CH_2O\!-\!P\!-\!O\!-\!CH_2CH\!-\!CO_2{}^- \\[4pt]
\qquad \underset{O^-Na(K)^+}{|} \quad \underset{{}^+NH_3}{|}
\end{array}
$$

**Properties.**  Since phosphatidyl serine has less unsaturation (iodine number = 33–40) than lecithin or cephalin, it is more stable toward autoxidation and can be obtained as a white powder which darkens only slowly on standing.  Phosphatidyl serine is insoluble in methanol and ethanol and soluble in ether, hexane, and chloroform.  The neutral salt forms a stable emulsion in water from which the free acid is precipitated with 0.1 $N$ hydrochloric acid.

[71] MacArthur, *ibid.*, **36**, 2397 (1914).
[72] Folch and Schneider, *J. Biol. Chem.*, **137**, 51 (1941); Chargaff, Ziff, and Rittenberg, *ibid.*, **138**, 439 (1941).
[73] Folch, *ibid.*, **139**, 973 (1941); Chargaff and Ziff, *ibid.*, **140**, 927 (1941).
[74] Folch, *ibid.*, **174**, 439 (1948).

## Acetal Phospholipid (Plasmalogen)

In the course of studies on the staining of tissues, Feulgen and Voit [75] observed a substance which gave a color with the fuchsin aldehyde reagent. Treatment of the tissue with mercuric chloride intensified the color. These observations led to the discovery of an acetal phospholipid (plasmalogen) in several tissues (muscle,[76, 77] brain [78]) which liberates a mixture of fatty aldehydes (plasmal) on treatment with mercuric chloride. Purified acetal phospholipid has been prepared from the ether-soluble lipids of muscle [77] and brain [78, 79] by treatment with alkali, which saponifies other glycerophosphatides but leaves the acetal lipid intact.

**Structure.** Cleavage of purified material with mercuric chloride liberates the aldehyde component, and from the residue α-glycerylphosphorylethanolamine [77, 79] is obtained as a crystalline compound (m.p. 86–87°). On this basis acetal phospholipids may be assigned the structure shown. The aldehyde component of acetal phospholipid consists

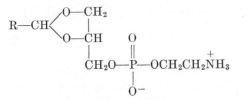

mainly of palmitic and stearic aldehydes,[78] but an unsaturated component (probably oleic aldehyde) has also been reported.[80]

**Properties.** The purified acetal phospholipids crystallize from ethanol as long needles which soften at about 80° and decompose above 150°. They are soluble in chloroform, methanol, and warm ethanol, but insoluble in ether, hexane, or benzene. Prolonged alkaline hydrolysis cleaves ethanolamine and gives plasmalogenic acids.[77]

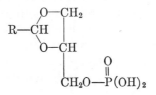

[75] Feulgen and Voit, *Arch. ges. Physiol.* (*Pflügers*), **206**, 389 (1924).

[76] Feulgen, Imhaüser, and Behrens, *Z. physiol. Chem.*, **180**, 161 (1929).

[77] Feulgen and Bersin, *ibid.*, **260**, 217 (1939).

[78] Klenk and Schumann, *ibid.*, **281**, 25 (1944).

[79] Thannhauser, Boncoddo, and Schmidt, *Federation Proc.*, **9**, 238 (1950).

[80] Klenk, *Z. physiol. Chem.*, **282**, 18 (1945).

## Cardiolipin

In 1922 Kolmer [81] reported a new antigen for complement fixation tests of syphilis, consisting of an extract of heart muscle to which lecithin and cholesterol had been added. Subsequently, Pangborn [82] separated the serologically active component as the barium and sodium salt of a phospholipid which contained no nitrogen. On mild alkaline hydrolysis it yielded a mixture of unsaturated acids (oleic and linoleic), glycerol, glycerophosphate, and glyceryltriglycerophosphate. These products suggest that cardiolipin is a complex phosphatidic acid whose non-fatty-acid skeleton might be represented as shown.

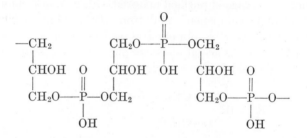

Cardiolipin exists naturally as the sodium salt, which is readily soluble in ether, petroleum ether, chloroform, and benzene; moderately soluble in methanol; and slightly soluble in acetone. It disperses to a cloudy solution in water. The free acid has an apparent molecular weight of 726, is optically active, and has an iodine number of 119.

### INOSITOL LIPIDS

The presence of inositol in the lipids of tubercle bacilli was discovered by Anderson [83] in 1930. Subsequently, inositol lipids were reported in soybean,[84] brain,[85] liver,[86] egg yolk, and other sources. Most of these substances have not been obtained in a pure state, and none has been completely characterized. The inositol lipids from brain (diphosphoinositide) and soybean have received the most attention.

[81] Kolmer, *Am. J. Syphilis*, **6**, 82 (1922).
[82] Pangborn, *J. Biol. Chem.*, **143**, 247 (1942); **153**, 343 (1944); **157**, 691 (1945); **161**, 71 (1945); **168**, 351 (1947).
[83] Anderson, *J. Am. Chem. Soc.*, **52**, 1607 (1930); Anderson and Roberts, *ibid.*, **52**, 5023 (1930).
[84] Klenk and Sakai, *Z. physiol. Chem.*, **258**, 33 (1939).
[85] Folch and Woolley, *J. Biol. Chem.*, **142**, 963 (1942).
[86] Macpherson and Lucas, *Federation Proc.*, **6**, 273 (1947).

## Diphosphoinositide

The cephalin fraction from brain is separated into three components by precipitation from a chloroform solution with ethanol.[5]  The least-soluble fraction is a crude inositol lipid preparation which is purified by an extensive series of reprecipitations and finally by dialysis to remove inorganic phosphate.[87]  The final product is a mixed calcium-magnesium salt of an acidic lipid.  The salt is a white powder which is insoluble in water and in most organic solvents with the exception of moist chloroform.  The free acid is water-soluble.  On complete hydrolysis diphosphoinositide yields glycerol, fatty acid, and inositol in approximately molecular equivalent proportions.  Mild acid hydrolysis gives an inositol diphosphate which was established by periodate oxidation to have the phosphate groups in the *meta*-position.

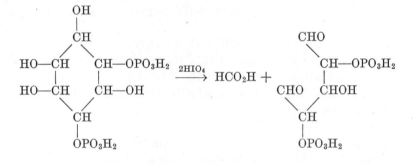

## Inositol Lipids of Soybean (Lipositol)

Woolley [9] isolated an inositol lipid (lipositol) from soybean phosphatide by the chloroform-ethanol precipitation procedure.  The product was a creamy powder which darkened only slowly on exposure to air.  It contained inositol (16%), galactose, fatty acids, tartaric acid, phosphoric acid, ethanolamine, and potassium.  Subsequently, Scholfield *et al.*[6] and Carter *et al.*[7,8] separated the inositol lipid of soybean into two fractions by distribution between hexane and methanol.  The hexane fraction contained carbohydrate and glycerol, whereas the methanol fraction was devoid of carbohydrate.  Much further work remains to be done on the isolation and characterization of the inositol lipids of plant and animal tissues.

[87] Folch, *J. Biol. Chem.*, **177**, 505 (1949).

## SPHINGOLIPIDS

The term sphingolipid [2] is used as a generic name to describe a group of substances—sphingomyelin, cerebrosides, and gangliosides—derived from the organic base sphingosine. The sphingolipids occur in unusually high amounts in the white matter of nerve cells (brain, spinal cord, etc.) and in low concentration in other tissues (lung, kidney, liver, spleen, adrenals, blood). A related substance, *fungus cerebrin*, is found in mushrooms,[88] yeast,[89] and molds.[90]

### Cerebrosides

Thudichum first isolated and characterized the cerebrosides phrenosin and kerasin from brain tissue.[91] In 1925–1926 Klenk [92] isolated a third cerebroside, nervone, and obtained evidence for a fourth, oxynervone.[93] These substances differ only in the fatty-acid component, as indicated.

Kerasin: lignoceric acid $(CH_3(CH_2)_{22}CO_2H)$.

Phrenosin: cerebronic acid $(CH_3(CH_2)_{21}CHOH—CO_2H)$.

Nervone: nervonic acid $(CH_3(CH_2)_7CH{=}CH—(CH_2)_{13}CO_2H)$.

Oxynervone: oxynervonic acid $(CH_3(CH_2)_7CH{=}CH(CH_2)_{12}CH-OH—CO_2H)$.

More recently, Klenk has shown [94] that pure phosphorus-free cerebrosides contain in addition to the above acids small amounts of palmitic, stearic, and hexacosanoic acid. However, phrenosin and kerasin are the major components of the cerebrosides of brain and together with nervone constitute the only individual cerebrosides that have been isolated in a pure condition.

**Preparation.** The crude cerebroside fraction (p. 218) from brain contains traces of sphingomyelin and other phospholipids. These can be removed by treatment of an ammoniacal methanolic solution with zinc hydroxide, which precipitates the phosphatides, or by passing a pyridine solution of the crude cerebroside over an alumina column, which adsorbs the phosphatides.[94] Phrenosin and kerasin are obtained by fractionat-

[88] Zellner, *Monatsh.*, **32**, 133 (1911).

[89] Reindel, Weickmann, Picard, Luber, and Turula, *Ann.*, **544**, 116 (1940).

[90] Bohonos and Peterson, *J. Biol. Chem.*, **149**, 295 (1943).

[91] Thudichum, "Die chemische Konstitution des Gehirns des Menschen und der Tiere," Franz Pietzeker, Tübingen (1901).

[92] Klenk, *Z. physiol. Chem.*, **145**, 244 (1925).

[93] Klenk, *ibid.*, **157**, 291 (1926).

[94] Klenk and Leupold, *ibid.*, **281**, 208 (1944).

ing the cerebroside mixture from chloroform-methanol [94, 95] or from aqueous acetone.[96]

**Structure.** Hydrolysis of cerebrosides with methanolic sulfuric acid yields fatty acids (esters), methyl galactoside, and a mixture of bases containing sphingosine and its degradation products (O-methyl ethers, anhydrosphingosine). Triacetylsphingosine is readily obtained from the mixture and is a useful derivative for the isolation and purification of sphingosine.[97, 98] Klenk, Levene, and others characterized sphingosine as a dihydroxyaminoöctadecene. The location of the substituent groups was established by periodate-oxidation studies.[99] Dihydrosphingosine (prepared by catalytic reduction of sphingosine) reacts with two moles of periodate to give ammonia, formaldehyde, formic acid, and palmitaldehyde. N-Benzoyldihydrosphingosine fails to react with periodate. These results can be explained only as shown.

$$CH_3(CH_2)_{14}CH-CH-CH_2 \xrightarrow{2HIO_4}$$
$$\qquad\qquad\quad | \quad\ \ | \quad\ \ |$$
$$\qquad\qquad\quad OH \ \ NH_2 \ OH$$

$$CH_3(CH_2)_{14}CHO + HCO_2H + H_2CO + NH_3$$

$$CH_3(CH_2)_{14}CH-CH-CH_2OH \xrightarrow{HIO_4} \text{no reaction}$$
$$\qquad\qquad\ | \quad\ \ |$$
$$\qquad\qquad\ OH \ \ NH$$
$$\qquad\qquad\qquad\quad |$$
$$\qquad\qquad\qquad\quad CO$$
$$\qquad\qquad\qquad\quad |$$
$$\qquad\qquad\qquad\quad C_6H_5$$

Previous studies on the oxidation of sphingosine had shown the double bond to be in the 4,5-position. Sphingosine, therefore, has the following formula.

$$CH_3(CH_2)_{12}CH{=}CH-CH-CH-CH_2$$
$$\qquad\qquad\qquad\qquad | \quad\ \ | \quad\ \ |$$
$$\qquad\qquad\qquad\qquad OH \ \ NH_2 \ OH$$

Since cerebrosides have no free amino group, the fatty-acid component must be attached by an amide linkage.* The point of attachment of

[95] Loening and Tierfelder, *ibid.*, **68**, 464 (1910).
[96] Rosenheim, *Biochem. J.*, **8**, 110 (1914).
[97] Klenk and Diebold, *Z. physiol. Chem.*, **198**, 25 (1931).
[98] Carter, Norris, Glick, Phillips, and Harris, *J. Biol. Chem.*, **170**, 269 (1947).
[99] Carter, Glick, Norris, and Phillips, *ibid.*, **170**, 285 (1947).

* The term ceramide has been proposed for amides of sphingosine [Reichel and Thannhauser, *J. Biol. Chem.*, **135**, 15 (1940)]. A ceramide, lignocerylsphingosine, occurs as such in liver [Fränkel and Bielschowsky, *Z. physiol. Chem.*, **213**, 58 (1932)] and in spleen [Tropp and Wiedersheim, *ibid.*, **222**, 39 (1933)].

galactose has not been completely established. However, work of Carter *et al.*[100] on the catalytic reduction of sphingosine derivatives indicates that it is attached to the primary alcohol group. Reduction of triacetylsphingosine with platinum causes hydrogenolysis of the allylic carbon-oxygen bond, giving diacetylsphingine, which is easily characterized.

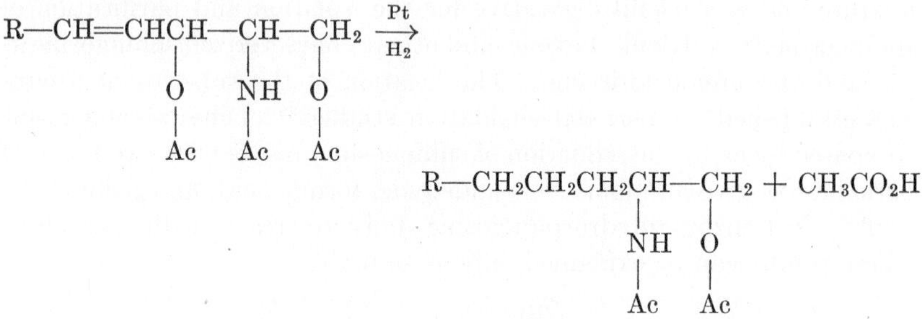

$$
\begin{array}{c}
\text{R—CH=CHCH—CH—CH}_2 \xrightarrow[\text{H}_2]{\text{Pt}} \\
\quad\quad\quad | \quad\quad | \quad\quad | \\
\quad\quad\quad \text{O} \quad \text{NH} \quad \text{O} \\
\quad\quad\quad | \quad\quad | \quad\quad | \\
\quad\quad\quad \text{Ac} \quad \text{Ac} \quad \text{Ac}
\end{array}
$$

$$
\begin{array}{c}
\text{R—CH}_2\text{CH}_2\text{CH}_2\text{CH—CH}_2 + \text{CH}_3\text{CO}_2\text{H} \\
\quad\quad\quad\quad\quad\quad\quad | \quad\quad | \\
\quad\quad\quad\quad\quad\quad\quad \text{NH} \quad \text{O} \\
\quad\quad\quad\quad\quad\quad\quad | \quad\quad | \\
\quad\quad\quad\quad\quad\quad\quad \text{Ac} \quad \text{Ac}
\end{array}
$$

Under the same conditions hexaacetylphrenosin gives acetic acid but no reducing sugar. Methanolysis of the reduction product gives sphingine. These results are best explained by the following reactions.

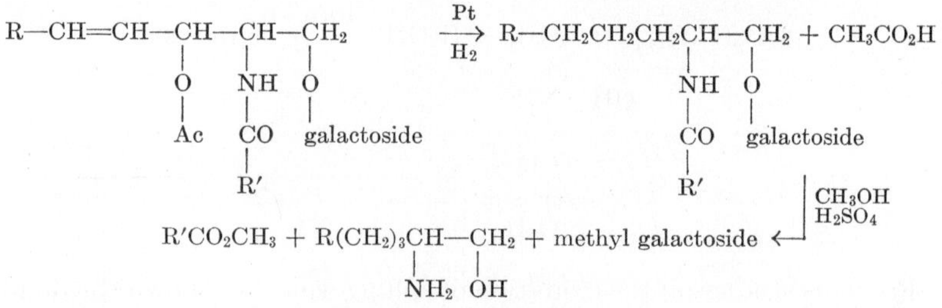

$$
\begin{array}{c}
\text{R—CH=CH—CH—CH—CH}_2 \xrightarrow[\text{H}_2]{\text{Pt}} \text{R—CH}_2\text{CH}_2\text{CH}_2\text{CH—CH}_2 + \text{CH}_3\text{CO}_2\text{H} \\
\quad\quad\quad | \quad\quad | \quad\quad | \quad\quad\quad\quad\quad\quad\quad\quad\quad\quad | \quad\quad | \\
\quad\quad\quad \text{O} \quad \text{NH} \quad \text{O} \quad\quad\quad\quad\quad\quad\quad\quad\quad \text{NH} \quad \text{O} \\
\quad\quad\quad | \quad\quad | \quad\quad | \quad\quad\quad\quad\quad\quad\quad\quad\quad\quad | \quad\quad | \\
\quad\quad\quad \text{Ac} \quad \text{CO} \quad \text{galactoside} \quad\quad\quad\quad\quad \text{CO} \quad \text{galactoside} \\
\quad\quad\quad\quad\quad | \quad\quad\quad\quad\quad\quad\quad\quad\quad\quad\quad\quad\quad | \\
\quad\quad\quad\quad\quad \text{R}' \quad\quad\quad\quad\quad\quad\quad\quad\quad\quad\quad\quad\quad\quad \text{R}'
\end{array}
$$

$$
\text{R}'\text{CO}_2\text{CH}_3 + \text{R(CH}_2)_3\text{CH—CH}_2 + \text{methyl galactoside} \xleftarrow[\text{H}_2\text{SO}_4]{\text{CH}_3\text{OH}}
$$
$$
\quad\quad\quad\quad\quad\quad\quad | \quad\quad | \\
\quad\quad\quad\quad\quad\quad\quad \text{NH}_2 \quad \text{OH}
$$

Oxidation of N-benzoylsphingine gives benzoyl-α-aminostearic acid,[100] further confirming the structure assigned. These results indicate that cerebrosides have the following general structure.

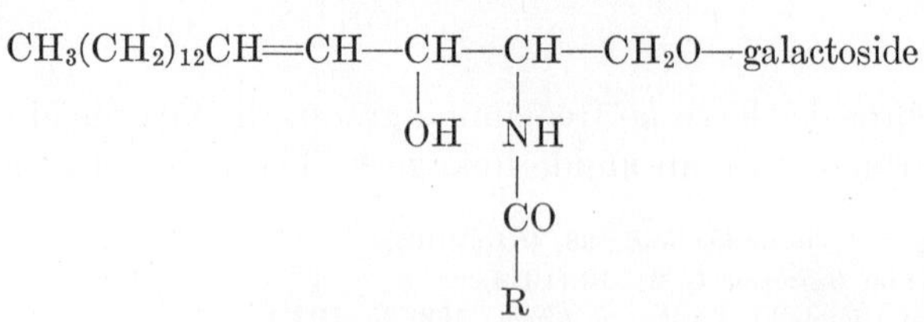

$$
\begin{array}{c}
\text{CH}_3(\text{CH}_2)_{12}\text{CH=CH—CH—CH—CH}_2\text{O—galactoside} \\
\quad\quad\quad\quad\quad\quad\quad\quad\quad | \quad\quad | \\
\quad\quad\quad\quad\quad\quad\quad\quad\quad \text{OH} \quad \text{NH} \\
\quad\quad\quad\quad\quad\quad\quad\quad\quad\quad\quad\quad | \\
\quad\quad\quad\quad\quad\quad\quad\quad\quad\quad\quad\quad \text{CO} \\
\quad\quad\quad\quad\quad\quad\quad\quad\quad\quad\quad\quad | \\
\quad\quad\quad\quad\quad\quad\quad\quad\quad\quad\quad\quad \text{R}
\end{array}
$$

In addition to compounds of this type, cerebrosides and sphingomyelin containing dihydrosphingosine also occur in nature. Although galactose is the carbohydrate found in cerebrosides from normal individuals, the

[100] Carter, Greenwood, and Humiston, *Federation Proc.*, **9,** 159 (1950).

cerebrosides which accumulate in the spleen in Gaucher's disease sometimes contain glucose instead.[101]

**Properties.** In marked contrast to the more highly unsaturated lecithins and cephalins, the cerebrosides are relatively stable toward autoxidation and are readily obtained as white crystalline powders which can
be kept almost indefinitely. The cerebrosides are almost insoluble in
ether and petroleum ether but are soluble in pyridine and in hot ethanol
or hot acetic acid. They are not soluble in water but on warming with
water they hydrate and swell, giving strongly anisotropic "myelin
forms." On heating, the cerebrosides pass through an anisotropic liquid-
crystalline phase to an isotropic liquid.[102] Phrenosin is completely converted to liquid crystals at 130°, and the second transition ("clearing
point") occurs at 212–215°. Kerasin has a clearing point of 185–187°;
nervone, of 180°. The cerebrosides also pass through a liquid-crystalline
phase on separating from a cooled pyridine solution. When viewed
through a polarizing microscope between crossed Nicol prisms, the
liquid crystals of phrenosin and kerasin show characteristic differences
which form the basis of the "selenite plate test" for distinguishing the
two substances.[96]

Cerebrosides give reactions characteristic of the double-bond and
alcoholic groups (addition of bromine, formation of acyl derivatives,
etc.). They are hydrolyzed by aqueous or alcoholic acids to sphingosine,
fatty acid (or ester), and galactose (or alkyl galactoside). Aqueous acid
has the disadvantage that the galactose formed condenses with sphingosine. Drastic alkaline hydrolysis cleaves the amide linkage, giving
galactosidosphingosine (psychosine).[103] Psychosine is difficult to obtain
in a pure state and has not been well characterized.

## Sphingomyelin

In 1884 Thudichum [91] discovered a new phosphatide which differed
from lecithin and cephalin in that it was ether-insoluble, contained no
glycerol, and had a nitrogen:phosphorus ratio of 2:1. The term di-
aminophosphatide was introduced to describe compounds of this type.
Sphingomyelin occurs in abundance in nervous tissue and in lower concentration in adrenals,[104] kidneys, liver, egg yolk,[105] and blood.[106]

[101] Halliday, Deuel, Tragerman, and Ward, *J. Biol. Chem.*, **132**, 171 (1940); Klenk and
Rennkamp, *Z. physiol. Chem.*, **272**, 280 (1942).
[102] Rosenheim, *Biochem. J.*, **8**, 121 (1914).
[103] Klenk, *Z. physiol. Chem.*, **153**, 74 (1926); Klenk and Harle, *ibid.*, **178**, 221 (1928).
[104] Rosenheim and Tebb, *J. Physiol.*, **38**, liv (1909).
[105] Levene, *J. Biol. Chem.*, **24**, 69 (1916).
[106] Sinclair, *ibid.*, **174**, 343 (1948).

**Preparation.** Crude sphingomyelin is readily obtained from nervous tissue by a variety of procedures. Extraction of dried brain with hot ethanol (either before [107] or after [2] removal of glyceryl lipids with ether) gives a mixture of sphingolipids (protagon) which can be fractionated from pyridine [108] (cerebrosides soluble, sphingomyelins insoluble), glacial acetic acid [2] (cerebrosides insoluble in the cold, sphingomyelins soluble), or chloroform-methanol [109] (sphingomyelin more soluble than cerebroside). Despite the low solubility in ether and acetone, cerebrosides and sphingomyelins are removed from tissues by continuous extraction (several days) with these solvents.[109–111] The cerebrosides are usually concentrated in the earlier fractions under these conditions. Complete removal of cerebroside is more difficult but may be accomplished by passing a solution of the crude materials in petroleum ether-methanol over an alumina column.[112] The cerebroside-free sphingomyelin is recrystallized from chloroform-ethanol or chloroform-pyridine.

If lung is used as starting material, the cerebroside problem is less acute, but in this case ether-insoluble "hydrolecithin" contaminates the sphingomyelin fraction.[111] It may be removed by treatment with sodium ethoxide solution [112] (which causes transesterification of the lecithin) or by the action of aqueous alkali.[111] The alkali hydrolyzes the choline-phosphate linkage in lecithin but not in sphingomyelin, which is surprisingly resistant to the action of alkali.

**Structure.** Complete hydrolysis of sphingomyelin yields sphingosine, choline, a fatty acid, and phosphoric acid. Since sphingomyelin is a neutral substance and contains no free amino group, the following structure seems well established except for the point of attachment of the

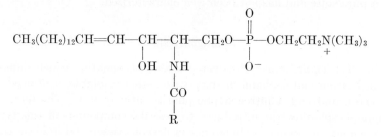

phosphate group. The dipolar ion (zwitterion) structure is supported by the fact that sphingomyelin does not bind sodium or potassium and

[107] Levene, *ibid.*, **18**, 453 (1914).
[108] Rosenheim and Tebb, *J. Physiol.*, **38**, li (1909); **41**, i (1910–1911).
[109] Merz, *Z. physiol. Chem.*, **193**, 59 (1930).
[110] Klenk, *ibid.*, **166**, 268 (1927).
[111] Thannhauser, Benotti, and Boncoddo, *J. Biol. Chem.*, **166**, 677 (1946).
[112] Klenk and Rennkamp, *Z. physiol. Chem.*, **267**, 145 (1940).

has no buffer capacity over the $p$H range 3–11.[65]  The isoelectric point of sphingomyelin is approximately $p$H 7.[34]

Several fatty acids have been found in sphingomyelin.  Material from brain contains stearic, lignoceric, and nervonic acids,[109] whereas that from lung [113] and spleen [111] contains only palmitic and lignoceric.

Dihydrosphingosine has been found in sphingomyelin as well as in cerebroside.[113]

**Properties.**  Sphingomyelin is a white crystalline substance which is relatively stable in air and light, since it contains little unsaturation (iodine number = $ca.$ 30).  Sphingomyelin is non-hygroscopic but swells in water to give emulsions and "myelin forms."  It is easily soluble in benzene, glacial acetic acid, and warm ethanol but is not soluble in cold pyridine.  Sphingomyelin from lung melts at 209° and has an optical activity of +6.25°.  Material from brain is very similar.

Sphingomyelin gives a complex with cadmium acetate which is almost insoluble in ethanol and has been used in purification.[112]  It also gives an acetone-insoluble product with Reinecke acid, which has been used for analytical purposes.[114]  (Choline gives an acetone-soluble Reineckate.[115])

### DISORDERS OF LIPID METABOLISM

A group of clinical conditions has been described involving the accumulation of excessive quantities of lipids in brain, spleen, liver, lung, and other organs.[116]  Niemann-Pick disease, Tay-Sachs disease (amaurotic idiocy), and Gaucher's disease have been studied in some detail.  In Niemann-Pick disease there is a marked increase in the sphingomyelin content of liver, spleen, brain, and other organs.[117]  The glyceryl phospholipids remain in the normal range, and the cerebroside content of the brain decreases somewhat.  The characteristic alteration of Tay-Sachs disease is the presence in the brain of a high content of a substance giving cerebroside tests but containing, in addition, an aminohydroxy acid, neuraminic acid.[118]  Klenk proposed the name "ganglioside" [119] for this type of substance.  The gangliosides are present in normal brain and spleen in very low concentrations.[120, 121]  However, in Tay-Sachs disease

---

[113] Thannhauser and Boncoddo, *J. Biol. Chem.*, **172**, 141 (1948).

[114] Thannhauser, Benotti, and Reinstein, *ibid.*, **129**, 709 (1939).

[115] Beattie, *Biochem. J.*, **30**, 1554 (1936).

[116] Sperry, *J. Mt. Sinai Hosp., N. Y.*, **9**, 799 (1942); Thannhauser and Schmidt, *Physiol. Rev.*, **26**, 275 (1946).

[117] Klenk, *Z. physiol. Chem.*, **229**, 151 (1934); Chargaff, *J. Biol. Chem.*, **130**, 503 (1939).

[118] Klenk, *Z. physiol. Chem.*, **235**, 24 (1935).

[119] Klenk and Schumann, *Ber.*, **75B**, 1632 (1942).

[120] Klenk, *ibid.*, **273**, 76 (1942).

[121] Klenk and Rennkamp, *ibid.*, **273**, 253 (1942).

they may occur to the extent of 8% of the dry weight and are also present in moderately increased concentration in the brain in Niemann-Pick disease. The gangliosides have not been fully characterized. On hydrolysis they yield sphingosine, fatty acid, neuraminic acid, and a mixture of galactose and glucose.[120, 121]

In Gaucher's disease the most striking abnormality is the high content of cerebroside in liver and spleen. (Liver normally contains little or no cerebroside.) Furthermore, the kerasinlike cerebroside which is deposited often contains glucose instead of galactose.[101] Little is known about the origin of these metabolic disorders.

## GENERAL REFERENCES

Bailey, "Industrial Oil and Fat Products," Interscience Publishers, New York (1951), 2nd ed.

Bailey, "Cottonseed and Cottonseed Products," Interscience Publishers, New York (1948).

Bloor, "Biochemistry of Fatty Acids," Reinhold Publishing Corp., New York (1943).

Bull, "The Biochemistry of the Lipids," John Wiley & Sons, New York (1937).

Folch-Pi and Sperry, "Chemistry of Lipids," *Ann. Rev. Biochem.*, **17**, 147 (1948).

Hefter-Schonfeld, "Chemie und Technologie der Fette," Julius Springer, Vienna (1936), Vol. I.

Hilditch, "The Chemical Constitution of Natural Fats," John Wiley & Sons, New York (1947), 2nd ed.

Kunze, "Lecithin," Rosenmeier and Dr. Saenger K-Co., Berlin (1941); J. W. Edwards, lithoprinted by Edwards Bros., Ann Arbor, Mich. (1945).

MacLean and Smedley-MacLean, "Lecithin and Allied Substances," Longmans, Green & Co., London (1927).

Markley, "Fatty Acids," Interscience Publishers, New York (1947).

Markley, "Soybeans and Soybean Products," Interscience Publishers, New York (1950), Vols. I and II.

Ralston, "Fatty Acids and Their Derivatives," John Wiley & Sons, New York (1948).

Thierfelder and Klenk, "Die Chemie der Cerebroside und Phosphatide," Julius Springer, Berlin (1930).

Warth, "Chemistry and Technology of Waxes," Reinhold Publishing Corp., New York (1947).

Wittcoff, "The Phosphatides," Reinhold Publishing Corp., New York (1951).

Working and Andrews, "Structure of Phospholipids," *Chem. Revs.*, **29**, 245 (1941).

# CHAPTER 4

## ORGANIC DYES

### H. W. Grimmel

*Metro Dyestuff Corporation, West Warwick, R. I.*

### CONTENTS

## INTRODUCTION

Organic dyes, according to a broadly accepted definition, are colored organic compounds having the ability to impart their color to materials to be dyed in an aqueous medium. Thus, one speaks of dyes with "affinity" for animal, vegetable, or synthetic fibers, for paper, wood, etc. This affinity may be general or selective.

Developments of the last decades have shown that, if this classification were allowed to set the boundaries of the realm of dyes, a great part of what we know to be dyes in a broader sense of the word would have to be excluded. The use of pigments in the dyeing of plastics, of alcohol-soluble dyes for coloring lacquers, and of pigment colors for the dyeing of rubber furnishes abundant evidence that the above definition should be broadened. Thus, in order to include all types of dyes and their uses, this survey will deal with organic colorants in general, the dyes which are applied from an aqueous medium forming a subdivision of the total.

Most of the dyes in use today differ radically in their chemical constitution from the natural dyes used 100 years ago, notwithstanding the fact that some of the natural dyes, like alizarin or indigo, are now produced from coal-tar derivatives on a large scale and no sharp line of separation exists between coal-tar and natural dyes.

A survey of organic dyes, to be complete, should cover not only the dyes and their chemistry but also the equally large field of intermediates required to prepare the dyes. The chemistry of the intermediates encompasses almost every type of reaction with which the organic chemist is familiar as well as numerous synthetic methods not generally encountered. Such a survey would be of great interest and value to the organic chemist, but limitations of time and space prevent its inclusion in this volume.

The discussion to follow is a survey of dyes, primarily those known to have been used commercially. It represents only a small percentage of the total, but the important chemical types are illustrated. The methods of synthesis starting with intermediates common to the dye industry are indicated, as are the more important properties of the dyes, so that the reader can gain a general idea of the chemistry involved and also of the effect of structure and substituents on shade and fastness.

A word of explanation regarding the relatively small percentage of references to recent literature is in order. Fundamental research on new dyes is constantly in progress in the industry, and the results are represented in thousands of patents issued in the last decade alone. Many new dyes have also come on the market, but as their structures are generally not published it is impossible to determine whether dyes disclosed in recent patents are actually of commercial interest. Much new and interesting chemistry is disclosed in these patents, but in a field of this magnitude some limitations must be set and it is more important to acquaint the reader first with information on dyes which are, or have been, of commercial interest. This phase alone will certainly be of value to the average organic chemist and will provide him with an adequate background for study both of the patent literature and of the intermediates.

## Color and Constitution

**General Concepts.** The color of a substance is determined by its selective absorption of light. When white light strikes a chemical compound, a part of the light is reflected, a part absorbed, and a part is transmitted. This last part lacks those portions of the incident light that have been absorbed or reflected, and their absence will reveal itself spectroanalytically in absorption bands. Since the reflected light, in most cases, has a different composition from the incident light, selective absorption of certain wavelengths of the spectrum has occurred. This phenomenon is not limited to the visible part of the spectrum but takes place in the same manner in the ultraviolet and infrared wavelengths. Whenever selective absorption occurs in the visible part of the spectrum, the eye will perceive the change as appearance of colors complementary to the colors represented by the absorbed wavelengths.

Since white light confers different colors on different chemical compounds, it is clear that the reason for this must be found in the different chemical constitution of these bodies. Color is, therefore, a function of the chemical constitution of the molecule.

It is essential to keep in mind that the color as it appears to the human eye is only a special case of the general feature of the absorption of electromagnetic waves. White light is composed of waves of different length and is corpuscular in nature. The light corpuscles are called photons, and their motion is governed by the electromagnetic field. Light represents electromagnetic energy.

The atoms of a molecule vibrate rapidly with respect to each other.

In addition, the whole molecule rotates. The electronic structure of the molecule in its unexcited state remains unaffected by either motion, but absorption of light may vary the amplitude of the vibrations of the atoms or the speed of the molecular rotation. These changes are called electronic, vibrational, or rotational excitation. If the absorption of visible or ultraviolet light results in only one electronic excitation, such an absorption is confined to a single wavelength. Usually, simultaneous changes in both the vibrational and rotational state of the molecule are responsible for the broad nature of absorption spectra, since each electronic state can be represented by a large number of vibrational and rotational states and a transition between two electronic states does not merely indicate a single change in energy. When absorption occurs in the ultraviolet part of the spectrum, no color, of course, is evident to the eye, but the electrons of the molecules affected exist in a state of excitation. The absorbing molecule has been raised to a higher level of energy. With progressive structural changes in molecules designed to decrease this excitation the absorption bands enter the visible part of the spectrum. Thus, by the introduction of certain atoms or groups of atoms into a molecule, a colorless compound may be changed into a colored one and the first visible absorption will be observable in the violet region of the spectrum with yellow as the visible color discernible to the eye. If the constraints on the electrons in the molecules are progressively reduced through further changes the absorption bands will be shifted successively towards regions of longer wavelengths with the visible color changing from yellow through orange, red, violet, and blue to green.

If the shift is carried further, absorption bands existing up to now in the ultraviolet will shift into the visible violet with the result that again a yellow visible to the eye will appear. This is known as the theory of the yellow of the second order [1] and has been observed in the group of tetraphenylethane dyes.[2]

The shift of the absorption from violet towards red or the change from visible greenish yellow to green is called bathochromic; the reverse, hypsochromic.[3]

It has been shown that the number of double bonds, especially conjugated double bonds, in a dyestuff molecule, is of fundamental importance, whereas the nature of the atoms attached to the double bonds is of only secondary influence. Organic dyes are to an overwhelming degree derivatives of isocyclic or heterocyclic aromatic rings. The intro-

[1] Piccard, *Ber.*, **46**, 1843 (1913).
[2] Wizinger, *Ber.*, **60**, 1377 (1927).
[3] Schütze, *Z. physik. Chem.*, **9**, 109 (1892).

duction of substituents and the proximity of the substituents to the chromophoric group exert a marked influence on the absorption of the molecule.

**Early Theories.** The first theory regarding the relation between constitution and color was set forth in 1876 by Witt,[4] after Graebe and Liebermann [5] had already published their observation that all colored organic compounds became colorless on reduction and that therefore unsaturation was a characteristic of the absorption phenomenon. According to Witt's views, every dye contains at least one group belonging to a class of unsaturated radicals which he called chromophores. The most important chromophores are the following:

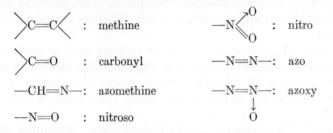

| | | | |
|---|---|---|---|
| $>C{=}C<$ | : methine | $-N{<}^O_O$ | : nitro |
| $>C{=}O$ | : carbonyl | $-N{=}N-$ | : azo |
| $-CH{=}N-$ | : azomethine | $-N{=}N-$ | : azoxy |
| $-N{=}O$ | : nitroso | | |

The molecule containing a chromophore is called a chromogene. A chromogene may be colored but does not yet represent a dye. To achieve this a further introduction of salt-forming groups, "auxochromes," into the molecule is required. Hydroxy and amino, sulfonic and carboxylic acid radicals are examples of auxochromes. In spite of the inadequacies of this theory, in having to rely on different chromophoric groups for the many dyestuff classes, it has served well to bring order out of chaos, and the classification it affords has been widely accepted.

There have been many efforts to enlarge upon Witt's ideas and to formulate new approaches. In 1888 Nietzki added the quinonoid group to the list of chromophores and Armstrong developed a quinonoid theory of color,[6] supported in 1900 by E. and O. Fischer. Kauffmann [7] rejected a sharp dividing line between auxochromes or chromophores, and his ideas were strengthened by the work of Willstätter and Piccard which brought forth the theory of meriquinoid-haloquinoid isomerism with isorropesis (recurring creation and breakage of linkages). Tautomerism and isomerism in the creation of colored compounds were stressed by Baly (1904) and Hantzsch (1906), respectively.[8]

Witt, *Ber.*, **9**, 522 (1876).

[5] Graebe and Liebermann, *Ber.*, **1**, 106 (1868).

[6] Armstrong, *Proc. Chem. Soc.*, 27 (1888).

[7] Kauffmann, *Ber.*, **39**, 1959, 2722 (1906); **40**, 843, 2338 (1907); **41**, 4413 (1908).

[8] Hantzsch and Gorke, *Ber.*, **39**, 1073 (1906).

Partly on the basis of work done by Pfeiffer in 1910–1916, Dilthey published in 1924 his conception of a new theory concerning chromophores which subsequently was augmented by Wizinger's ideas on new auxochromes.[9] Whereas, according to the then existing theories, chromophores were represented by a plurality of doubly bonded unsaturated groups, the theory of Dilthey and Wizinger postulates the existence of coördinatively unsaturated single atoms, there being no color without the presence of such a chromophore. For the production of deep and intensive color, however, the chromophore must be charged positively or negatively, or, expressed differently, the transformation of a coördinated unsaturated atom (the chromophore) into the ionic state results in a great intensification of the light absorption. This electrical charge is introduced by the auxochrome, of which Wizinger distinguishes three kinds.

1. *Positive Auxochromes.* These are radicals such as methoxy, hydroxy, amino, dimethylamino, and anilino which favor the electropositive state and intensify the color in positive ions having a coördinatively unsaturated central atom, where their effect is also bathochromic.

2. *Negative Auxochromes or Antiauxochromes.* Examples of such groups are nitroso, nitro, carbonyl, cyano, sulfonyl, and azo. These radicals favor the electronegative state and intensify the color of negative ions containing a coördinatively unsaturated central atom. Their effect is likewise bathochromic.

3. *Amphoteric Auxochromes.* Such auxochromes are, for example, aryl and vinyl radicals, which favor ionization toward either the positive or negative and act bathochromic in either positive or negative ions having a coördinatively unsaturated central atom. Dilthey's proposal that the constitution of pararosaniline be expressed as in formula I with an asterisk indicating the coördinatively unsaturated central carbon atom is shown.

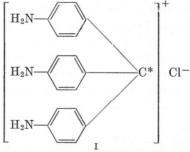

I

[9] Dilthey, *Ber.*, **53**, 261 (1920); **55**, 1275 (1922); *J. prakt. Chem.*, **2**, 109, 273 (1925); Wizinger, *Z. angew. Chem.*, **39**, 564 (1926); **40**, 503, 675, 937 (1927); **42**, 668 (1929); *Ber.*, **60**, 1377 (1927); Dilthey and Wizinger, *J. prakt. Chem.*, **2**, 118, 321 (1928).

The theories discussed so far are based mainly on the structural characteristics associated with color. As a bridge to the modern concepts of resonance as related to color, Stieglitz's publications [10] have to be cited. Stieglitz maintains that color is produced by oscillation of electrons involved in an intramolecular oxidation-reduction process. A dye contains both oxidizing and reducing groups (chromophores and auxochromes) and a conjugated system connecting both serves as a means of communication.

**The Application of Resonance to Color Theory.** The modern interpretation of the auxochrome and chromophore is based largely on the work of Bury,[11] Lewis,[12] Schwarzenbach,[13] Pauling,[14] Ingold,[15] and Adams and Rothstein.[15a] Baeyer[15b] had suggested that the color of the triphenylmethane dyes was due to the oscillation of an atom in the molecule. Doebner's Violet, for example, was considered to be in a state of oscillation between the two forms $A$ and $B$.

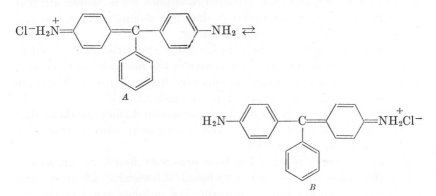

With the realization of the distinction between electrovalent and covalent bonds it became evident that the oscillation was purely structural, and that the change from one form to the other involved movement of electrons and not movement of atoms. It is apparent that the structures $A'$ and $B'$ are ions which differ only in the distribution of the

[10] Stieglitz, *Proc. Natl. Acad. Sci. U. S.*, **9**, 303 (1923); *J. Franklin Inst.*, **200**, 35 (1925).

[11] Bury, *J. Am. Chem. Soc.*, **57**, 2115 (1935).

[12] Lewis *et al.*, *ibid.*, **38**, 762 (1916); **61**, 1886 (1939); **62**, 2973, 3529 (1940); **63**, 3005, 3232 (1941); **64**, 1774, 2801, 2808 (1942); **65**, 520, 1144, 1150, 2102, 2107, 2419 (1943); **66**, 1579, 2100 (1944); **67**, 770, 994, 1232 (1945); *Chem. Revs.*, **25**, 273 (1939).

[13] Schwarzenbach *et al.*, *Helv. Chim. Acta*, **20**, 490, 498, 627, 654, 1253, 1591 (1937).

[14] Pauling, *Proc. Natl. Acad. Sci. U. S.*, **25**, 577 (1939).

[15] Ingold, *J. Chem. Soc.*, 1310 (1926); Heisenberg, *Z. Physik*, **39**, 499 (1926); Heitler and London, *ibid.*, **44**, 438 (1927); Pauling, "The Nature of the Chemical Bond," Cornell University Press, Ithaca, N. Y. (1939).

[15a] Adams and Rothstein, *J. Am. Chem. Soc.*, **36**, 1472 (1914).

[15b] Baeyer, *Ann.*, **354**, 152 (1907).

electron charge. Since both electronic structures correspond to the same energy, neither structure alone can be considered to represent the normal state of the molecule, which, instead, is represented essentially

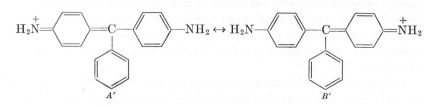

by an average of both. It can be demonstrated, also, that there will exist another combination of structures which represents an excited state of the molecule.

The molecule is described, therefore, as resonating between these pairs of structures, since the principal conditions for resonance are that the structures should correspond to the same atomic arrangement and to the same number of unpaired electrons.

In the normal state, the negative ion ($Cl^-$) associated with $A'$ and $B'$ may be considered to be near the center of the molecule, so that these pairs of structures have large and opposing dipole moments. Hence, in its normal state and its excited state, the molecule will have a zero dipole moment. It can be shown by quantum-mechanical methods that under these circumstances the electronic transition between resonating structures results in deep color.

As a consequence of what has been presented above, the division of groups into chromophore and auxochrome is somewhat arbitrary since the function of these groups is to modify the molecule so as to introduce the possibility of resonance. Nitrogen and oxygen atoms are important in dyes in order to introduce large dipole moments.

As a further elaboration of this theory, Wheland [16] has indicated that the ion of Crystal Violet presumably possesses the structures II, III, and IV, although structures like V, VI, and VII must be involved. Actually, if these latter structures were not possible, resonance could be of only minor importance since resonance cannot occur between structures which differ widely in the positions of the electrons. Furthermore, ions II, III, and IV would have practically identical energy, and the light absorption occurring during a transition of one form into another would, therefore, be at a tremendously longer wavelength than that actually observed. With structures like V, VI, and VII these difficulties are removed. The successive transitions, for example, of II to V, V to VI,

[16] Wheland, "The Theory of Resonance," John Wiley & Sons, New York (1944).

and VI to VII, etc., leading eventually to III and IV, would involve
energy changes resulting in light absorption in the visible spectrum.

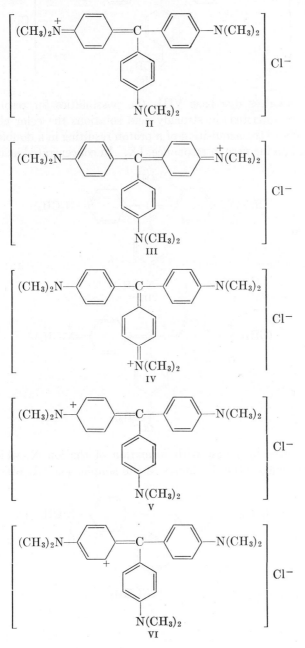

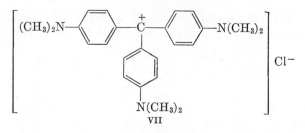

$$\text{VII}$$

In the colorless dye base VIII, the possibilities for resonance are much more restricted; in strongly acid solutions the color changes to green, owing to the acquisition of a proton resulting in a double positive charge and an increase in resonance, IX. In concentrated acid solution

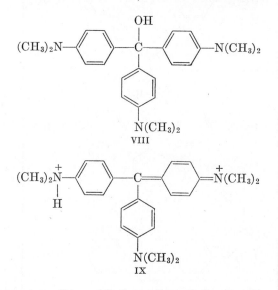

$$\text{VIII}$$

$$\text{IX}$$

the color turns to yellow with formation of the ion X, which in its resonance configuration is similar to the simpler ion XI, which is also yellow.

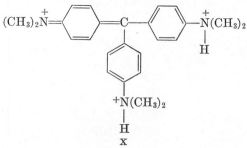

$$\text{X}$$

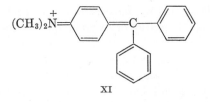

XI

The concept of resonance in its relation to dye structures has been extensively explored and certain restrictions on its general applicability have been noted by Lewis.[17] For a detailed review the reader is referred to the relevant chapters of the literature.[17] Many more ideas and refinements of existing theories have been suggested by others.[18]

The development of the technical dye industry has largely taken place along certain rules based on a vast background of experimentation, using scientific methods to a very high degree. The dye chemist has learned to predict with fair accuracy changes of color to be expected from a change in the structure of a dye molecule. This advancement of his art, however, has been more or less empirical and cannot claim to have been guided by physical theories.

## Classification of Dyes

A dye is defined according to either the type of chemical compound it represents or the method of application for which it is principally useful. The chemist is primarily interested in the chemical classification which will be used in the succeeding pages, but a proper understanding of dyes in general can come only with a suitable knowledge of the terms used to classify them according to their dyeing properties. A very brief definition of each of the more important types is, therefore, in order.

**Basic and Acid Dyes.** As their names imply, these dyes contain either basic or acidic groups and for dyeing from an aqueous solution are rendered soluble by salt formation.

**Direct Dyes.** Direct dyes, usually acid dyes, have affinity for cotton from a neutral solution, generally in the presence of an electrolyte such as sodium chloride or sodium sulfate.

**Developed Dyes.** Developed dyes are capable of undergoing reactions on the fiber to produce less soluble dyes having improved fastness to washing. Thus, the dye is applied to the fiber and then, depending on

[17] Lewis and Calvin, *Chem. Revs.*, **25**, 273 (1939); Wheland, "The Theory of Resonance," John Wiley & Sons, New York (1944); Remick, "Electronic Interpretations of Organic Chemistry," John Wiley & Sons, New York (1949), 2nd ed.

[18] Schwarzenbach *et al.*, *Helv. Chim. Acta*, **20**, 490, 627, 654, 1591 (1937); Bury, *J. Am. Chem. Soc.*, **57**, 2115 (1935); Arndt *et al.*, *Ber.*, **57**, 1903 (1924); **63**, 587, 2963 (1930).

its structure, is developed by diazotization and reaction with a coupling component such as β-naphthol or resorcinol, or by coupling with a diazo compound, or by condensation with formaldehyde.

**Vat Dyes.** Vat dyes are compounds capable of reduction to a soluble "leuco" form which has affinity for the fiber and is readily reoxidized on the fiber to the original dye. The term leuco is used for the reduced form, but it should be noted that it is usually highly colored. Although not universally fast, these dyes as a class offer the best all-around fastness, especially to light and washing.

**Sulfur Dyes.** Like vat dyes, sulfur dyes can be reduced to soluble leuco forms which can be reoxidized on the fiber. They differ from vat dyes in that they always contain sulfur and the reduction requires sodium sulfide whereas sodium hydrosulfite is used for vat dyes.

**Pigments.** Pigments are water-insoluble dyes which are applied to a multitude of materials by various means. They involve a very large class, both organic and inorganic, and will be dealt with in this survey only to a limited extent as they represent organic colorants which are related chemically to the various types of dyes to be considered.

**Mordant Dyes.** Mordant dyes are capable of combining with various metals to form metal complexes of different types. Since a variety of chemical types are useful for this purpose, a brief review is in order before taking up the various chemical classes of dyes. Additional references will be made within certain classes to dyes of this type.

A great number of dyes when treated with metal oxides or metal salts show the valuable property of forming metal complexes. The dye proper may be treated in solution or suspension with the metal salt, in which case metallized dyes result with which fibers may be dyed or the metal complex may be formed on the fiber. In the latter case, the following procedures may be used. (1) The fiber is first treated with a metal salt and the formation of the metal lake is effected in the dyeing operation; (2) the dyeing is carried out in the presence of the metal salt; and (3) the dye is applied to the fiber as usual and the dyeing is then treated with a solution of the metal salt.

The constitutional requirements for such dyes have been thoroughly investigated. Whereas Liebermann,[19] von Kostanecki,[20] Erdmann,[21] Nietzki and others postulated empirical rules, Werner was able to elucidate the basic principles.[22] He showed that mordant dyes are

[19] Liebermann, *Ber.*, **20**, 3146 (1887).
[20] von Kostanecki, *Ber.*, **22**, 1347 (1889).
[21] Erdmann, *Ann.*, **247**, 358 (1888).
[22] Werner, *Ber.*, **41**, 1062 (1908).

characterized by the possession of a salt-forming group and a group which can form a coördinated compound with a metallic atom in such relative positions that an internal complex salt can be produced. Such complexes are formed with ease when the conditions for the formation of heterocyclic five- or six-membered rings are present. Baudish, Morgan,[23] and Drew [24] have furnished proofs for this postulate in many cases. The formulas below indicate the main types of compounds which have been used for formation of metal complexes. The position of the metal (M) is merely indicated since the exact composition of a metal complex is dependent on the particular compound and conditions used. There is still much to be learned about metalized dyes, and to present specific formulas which have been postulated in the literature would give the reader an erroneous impression unless accompanied by considerable discussion, which space does not permit.

1. Alizarines:

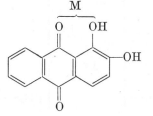

2. o-Hydroxycarbonyl-, o-hydroxynitroso-, and o-hydroxyazo- dyes of the general types:

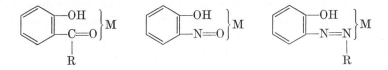

3. Salicylates:

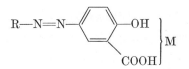

[23] Morgan and Smith, *J. Soc. Dyers Colourists*, **41**, 233 (1925).

[24] Chattaway and Drew, *J. Chem. Soc.*, 198 (1938); Drew and Fairbairn, *ibid.*, 823 (1939); Drew and Dunton, *ibid.*, 1064 (1940).

4. *o*-Amino-*o'*-hydroxyazo dyes and *o,o'*-dihydroxyazo dyes. (*a*) No oxidation:

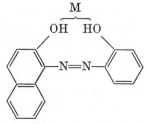

(*b*) With oxidation (in this case a specific example is given to illustrate the change involved; the dye used is Diamond Black PV):

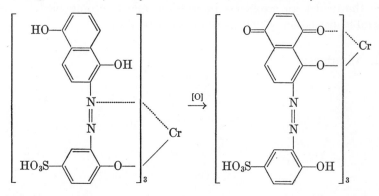

The ratio of metal to organic dye is not fixed, and several distinct stages of this ratio have been found.[25]

Chemically, dyes are classified as nitroso, nitro, and azo dyes, di- and triarylmethanes, quinoneimines, methines, acridines, sulfur dyes, quinones, chromones, and porphyrazines (tetrazaporphins). The meaning of these terms is immediately apparent to the organic chemist, and it is this classification which will be used in this survey.

## NITROSO AND NITRO DYES

### Nitroso Dyes

The nitrosophenols obtained by action of nitrous acid on phenolic compounds can be considered in their tautomeric form as quinoneoximes.

[25] Morgan *et al.*, *ibid.*, 1731 (1924); Elkins and Hunter, *ibid.*, 1598 (1935); 1346 (1938); Pfeiffer *et al.*, *J. prakt. Chem.*, **149**, 217 (1937); Drew *et al.*, *J. Chem. Soc.*, 292 (1938); 823 (1939); Crossley, *Am. Dyestuff Reptr.*, **27**, 124 (1938); Beech and Drew, *J. Chem. Soc.*, 603, 608, 1064 (1940); Pfeiffer, *Angew. Chem.*, **53**, 93 (1940); *Ber.*, **74**, 935 (1941); Handler and Smith, *J. Am. Chem. Soc.*, **63**, 1371 (1941).

They are identical with the products resulting from the action of hydroxylamine on benzoquinones.[26]

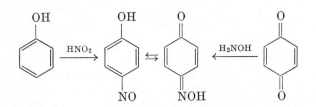

In some cases both tautomeric forms have been isolated.[27]   It seems reasonable to assume that the quinone-monoxime ion is stabilized by resonance hybridization.   Nitroso dyes are represented mostly by compounds with the nitroso and hydroxyl groups *ortho* to each other since the value of these dyes rests in their ability to form metal complexes, a faculty absent in the *p*-nitrosophenol compounds.   Nitroso compounds of amines have no value as dyes but are used as important intermediates.

The technical value of the class of nitroso dyes is small, and their use as mordant dyes for wool and cotton is limited.   The colors obtained with iron salts are green; those from cobalt, chromium, and nickel are brown.   The best feature of nitroso dyes is their good light-fastness.

The most important dye of this type is the iron complex from 1-nitroso-2-naphthol.   It is used as a pigment for the coloring of rubber and wallpaper, and in the printing trade (Pigment Green B or Gambine Y).[28] The corresponding dye from 2-naphthol-6-sulfonic acid, Naphthol Green B,[29] finds limited application for the dyeing of wool.   The use of dinitrosoresorcinol on mordanted cotton for the formation of Solid Green O is today only of historical interest.

The light-fast blue iron complexes of compounds such as XII are of recent development [30] and merit attention as pigments either *per se* or formed on the fiber.

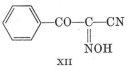

XII

[26] Goldschmidt, *Ber.*, **17**, 213, 801 (1884).

[27] Taylor and Baker, in Sidgwick, "The Organic Chemistry of Nitrogen," Clarendon Press, Oxford (1942), p. 222.

[28] Koehler, Ger. pat. 25,469 (1883); Morgan and Smith, *J. Soc. Dyers Colourists*, **41**, 233 (1925).

[29] Hoffmann, U. S. pat. 316,036 (1885).

[30] Schmidt, U. S. pat. 2,264,334 (1941) [*C. A.*, **36**, 1560 (1942)].

## Nitro Dyes

Dyes containing the nitro group as sole chromophore represent one of the oldest classes of coal-tar dyes; their importance, however, is on the wane. Introduction of the nitro group into the benzene nucleus shifts the absorption to the visible part of the spectrum. Specifically, only those compounds carrying the —$NO_2$ group *ortho* to a phenolic hydroxyl or amine may be considered to be dyes. According to Witt, the —$NO_2$ group represents the chromophore; compounds of this class according to Dilthey-Wizinger owe their coloristic properties to the presence of coördinatively unsaturated oxygen or nitrogen.

Synthesis of these dyes is generally effected by one of the following methods: (1) nitration according to standard procedures; (2) condensation of nitrochloroaryl compounds with arylamines, e.g. SRA Golden Yellow XII (XIII) and Amido Yellow E (XVII); (3) linkage of nitroarylamines with formaldehyde, e.g. Lithol Yellow 2G (XVI). The dyes of this class range from greenish yellow to yellowish brown. They may be used as pigments or as dyes for acetate silk, wool, or leather, depending on the substituents. Specific examples are shown.

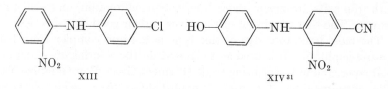

XIII                              XIV[31]

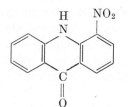

XV   Celanthrene Fast Yellow

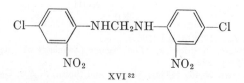

XVI[32]

[31] Ritter, U. S. pat. 2,200,343 (1940) [*C. A.*, **34**, 6097 (1940)].

[32] Badische Anilin- und Sodafabrik, Ger. pat. 220,630 (1909) [*C. A.*, **4**, 2209 (1910)].

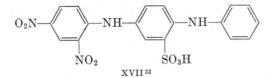

XVII [33]

Lithol Yellow 2G (XVI), a yellow pigment of good light-fastness, is the condensation product of 4-chloro-2-nitroaniline with formaldehyde. Amido Yellow E (XVII), obtained from 2,4-dinitrochlorobenzene and 4-aminodiphenylaminesulfonic acid, on the other hand, represents an orange acid dye, useful for the dyeing of wool and leather and having very good light-fastness and good level dyeing properties. Older dyes of this series like Naphthol Yellow S [34] (2,4-dinitro-1-naphthol-7-sulfonic acid) have all but disappeared from the textile dyeing field, owing to their poor fastness properties. Naphthol Yellow S has only a limited use as a lake color and for food dyeing purposes.

## AZO DYES

The azo dyes are the largest class of organic dyestuffs. No natural dyes contain this chromophore. The chromophoric azo group, —N=N—, is always connected on one side with an aromatic or heterocyclic nucleus; on the other it may be linked to an unsaturated molecule of the carbocyclic, heterocyclic, or aliphatic type. This possibility of connecting an almost unlimited number of different molecules by way of the azo bridges is the reason for the great number of representatives of this group.

Azo dyes are formed by a number of reactions, the most important of which are listed.

1. The coupling reaction [35,36] which consists of the action of a diazonium compound upon phenols, amines, or other compounds containing active methylene groups, for example

$$C_6H_5\overset{+}{\underset{\underset{N}{\parallel}{N}}{N}}Cl^- + C_6H_5ONa \rightarrow C_6H_5N=NC_6H_4OH + NaCl$$

The use of other coupling components and the effect of substituents and coupling conditions will be discussed later. The mechanism of the

[33] Schmidlin, U. S. pat. 1,059,571 (1913) [C. A., 7, 2122 (1913)].

[34] Caro, U. S. pat. 225,108 (1880); Levinstein, U. S. pat. 289,543 (1883).

[35] Hodgson and Marsden, J. Soc. Dyers Colourists, 60, 16 (1944); Hodgson and Norris, ibid., 65, 226 (1949).

[36] Griess et al., Z. Chem., 9, 132 (1866); Ann., 154, 211 (1870); Kekule, Z. Chem., 9, 688 (1866); Ber., 3, 234 (1870); Kimmich, Ber., 8, 1026 (1875).

reaction has been studied extensively by Dilthey, Karrer, Meyer, Hodgson,[37] and others.

2. The action of quinones or quinoneimines on phenylhydrazines and the closely related reaction of nitroso compounds with amines.

$$O{=}C_6H_4{=}O + H_2NNHC_6H_5 \rightarrow HOC_6H_4N{=}NC_6H_5 + H_2O$$

$$C_6H_5N{=}O + H_2NC_6H_5 \rightarrow C_6H_5N{=}NC_6H_5 + H_2O$$

3. The oxidation of amino and hydrazo compounds.

$$2C_6H_5NH_2 \rightarrow C_6H_5N{=}NC_6H_5$$

$$C_6H_5NHNHC_6H_5 \rightarrow C_6H_5N{=}NC_6H_5$$

4. The reduction of nitro compounds.

$$2C_6H_5NO_2 \rightarrow C_6H_5\overset{\overset{\textstyle O}{\uparrow}}{N}{=}NC_6H_5 \rightarrow C_6H_5N{=}NC_6H_5$$

## General Concepts

The hue * of an azo dye is influenced by the number of chromophores, the character and the position of auxochromes, the size of the molecule, and other factors such as the presence, number, and position of sulfonic acid or carboxylic acid groups. All these substituents affect also the ease of preparation of the dye and the conditions most suitable. A brief consideration of the types of intermediates which can be used will serve to illustrate this.

**Intermediates.** Practically all carbocyclic aromatic amines and many heterocyclic amines are capable of diazotization but the ease of diazotization varies with the basicity of the amine. Thus, the introduction of negative substituents such as nitro and sulfonic acid groups, and even halogens, reduces the basicity to a point where the amine salt is hydrolyzed at least partially in dilute acid and diazotization is incomplete. Complete and rapid diazotization is obtained only by increasing the acid strength sufficiently to give a stable salt. With a compound such as 2,4-dinitroaniline, the best results are obtained only in concentrated sulfuric acid with a solution of nitrosylsulfuric acid, this being prepared first by the addition of sodium nitrite to sulfuric acid.

[37] Dilthey and Blankenberg, *J. prakt. Chem.*, **142**, 182 (1935); Meyer and Lenhardt, *Ann.*, **398**, 74 (1913); Hodgson, *J. Soc. Dyers Colourists*, **58**, 228 (1942); Hauser and Breslow, *J. Am. Chem. Soc.*, **63**, 418 (1941); Wistar and Bartlett, *ibid.*, **63**, 413 (1941); Dimroth, *Ber.*, **41**, 4012 (1908); von Auwers, *Ber.*, **47**, 1286 (1914); Karrer, *Ber.*, **48**, 1398 (1915).

* Hue is not synonymous with color, or rather color perception. Hue is one of the attributes; saturation and brightness are the others.

In other cases, the amine salt is stable but too insoluble for rapid reaction and the inverse method may be used or it may be necessary again to use concentrated sulfuric acid or even organic solvents. Diazotization in organic solvents with compounds such as amyl nitrite has been used often, but mostly in laboratory work with amines very difficult to diazotize or in isolating an anhydrous diazonium compound. For a more complete discussion of this subject the reader is referred to Saunders.[38]

The introduction of negative substituents has the beneficial effect of increasing the activity of the diazonium compound in the coupling reaction. Thus, 2,4-dinitrobenzenediazonium chloride is one of the most active diazo compounds, and benzenediazonium chloride and its alkyl and alkoxy derivatives are markedly less reactive. Care must be exercised, however, that too high a $p$H is not used in working with negatively substituted diazo compounds since these compounds are readily converted to antidiazotates which do not undergo the coupling reaction.

As far as the coupling components are concerned, aromatic hydroxy compounds are by far the most common and undergo coupling readily unless negatively substituted. Polyhydroxy compounds are generally not suitable if oxidation to a quinone is possible since this reaction generally takes place more readily with simultaneous reduction of the diazo compound. Thus, resorcinol is one of the most active coupling components, reacting readily with two, and even three, moles of diazo compound, but catechol and hydroquinone are never used commercially for this purpose.

Alkoxy compounds and ethers of hydroquinone will couple under special conditions with the more active diazo compounds,[39] but these reactions are of theoretical interest only.

In the alicyclic and aliphatic series there are many compounds which contain active methylene groups and will couple readily. Examples are β-diketones and related compounds of the type $RCOCH_2X$ and $RNH-COCH_2X$, where X is a negative group such as $-COOH$, $-COOR$, $-CONHR$, $-CN$, $-SO_3H$, $-SO_2R$, or $-NO_2$. The nitro group has such a strong activating effect that even the nitroparaffins are soluble in aqueous alkali and will couple with diazo compounds.

Heterocyclic coupling components, which do not have active methylene groups in the true sense of the term but which still couple, are

[38] Saunders, "The Aromatic Diazo Compounds and Their Technical Applications," Longmans, Green & Co., New York (1949).

[39] Meyer et al., Ann., **398**, 74 (1913); Ber., **47**, 1714 (1914); von Auwers and Michaelis, Ber., **47**, 1275 (1914); **48**, 1716 (1915); Dilthey and Blankenberg, J. prakt. Chem., **142**, 188 (1935); Jambuserwala and Mason, J. Soc. Dyers Colourists, **46**, 339 (1930).

compounds such as pyrrole, methylindole, and indazole. Finally, even certain hydrocarbons will couple under special conditions with very active diazo compounds.[40]

Aromatic amines, primary, secondary, and tertiary, will couple readily in many cases. With the primary and secondary amines it is usually necessary to operate at an acidic pH in order to prevent formation of diazoamino compounds.[41] The weaker the base, the lower must be the pH, since the negative substituents both deactivate the ring and cause hydrolysis of the amine salt, thereby leaving the amino group free for reaction. Amines such as 2,5-dichloroaniline and p-nitroaniline form diazoamino compounds so readily that special conditions (high acid concentration and excess nitrous acid) must be used to prevent diazoamino formation during the diazotization reaction. Thus, amines of this type are practically useless for reaction with a diazo compound to form an aminoazo compound. Differences of this type may be illustrated as shown.

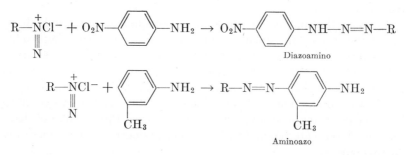

Diazoamino formation is often prevented by use of the so-called *omega* acid, formed by reaction of the amine with sodium bisulfite and formaldehyde in aqueous solution. After the coupling is complete the *omega* acid is readily hydrolyzed:

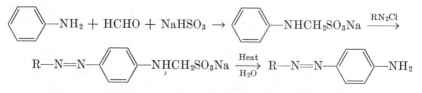

As with dihydroxy compounds, diamines are not useful if they are readily oxidized, viz., o- or p-diamines, but m-phenylenediamine is a

[40] Thiele, *Ber.*, **33**, 668 (1900); Sues, *Ann.*, **556**, 65, 85 (1944); Meyer, *Ber.*, **52**, 1468 (1919); Meyer and Tochtermann, *Ber.*, **54**, 2283 (1921); Smith and Pade, *J. Am. Chem. Soc.*, **56**, 2169 (1934); Fieser and Campbell, *ibid.*, **60**, 1142 (1938).

[41] Rosenhauser, *Ber.*, **61**, 392 (1928); **63**, 1056 (1930); **64**, 1438 (1931); Earl, *Ber.*, **63**, 1666 (1930); Meyer, *Ber.*, **54**, 2267 (1921).

very reactive and useful coupling component. Efforts to counteract this oxidation tendency in *o*- and *p*-diamino and dihydroxy compounds have been reported.[42]

Acylated amines in general do not react with diazo compounds.[43] An exception is found in the thiophene series, where Hurd[44] has shown that 2-acetylaminothiophene will couple in the 5-position to give an azo dye.

**General Rules for the Coupling Reaction.** In the benzene series coupling always takes place in the position *para* to the amino or hydroxyl group, if not otherwise substituted, in which event the *o*-position is taken. Replacement of substituents such as sulfo and carbonyl groups in *o*- or *p*-positions by the azo group is possible.[45]

β-Naphthols and β-naphthylamines couple in the α-position only. If this place is occupied, either no coupling takes place or the substituent is eliminated as in the case of 2-naphthol-1-sulfonic acid.

α-Naphthols and α-naphthylamines couple predominantly in the *p*-position, but under certain conditions preponderately in the *o*-position. If the *p*-position is occupied, coupling takes place exclusively in the *o*-position. α-Naphthol will couple with two moles of diazo compound to give a disazo dye.

When dealing with aminonaphthol compounds capable of coupling twice, the amino group will direct the position of the azo group in acid medium and the hydroxyl group will exert its influence in alkaline solution.

**Structure of Azo Compounds.** As indicated above, the action of a quinone on a phenylhydrazine gives an azo compound. This compound is identical with the product obtained from benzenediazonium chloride and the corresponding phenol; e.g., α-napthoquinone and phenylhydrazine give the same product as α-naphthol and benzenediazonium chloride.[46] In spite of considerable work by various investigators,[47] opinion is still divided as to whether the azo structure (XVIIIa) or the hydrazone structure (XVIIIb) is correct.

XVIIIa                    XVIIIb

[42] Anilin u. Extrakt-Fabriken, Ger. pat. 224,024 (1909) [*C. A.*, **4**, 3304 (1910)].

[43] König, *Ber.*, **54**, 981 (1921).

[44] Hurd and Priestley, *J. Am. Chem. Soc.*, **69**, 859 (1947).

[45] Grandmougin and Freimann, *J. prakt. Chem.*, **78**, 384 (1908).

[46] Zincke and Bindewald, *Ber.*, **17**, 3026 (1884); cf. Kekule and Hidegh, *Ber.*, **3**, 234 (1870); Kimich, *Ber.*, **8**, 1027 (1875).

[47] von Auwers, *Ber.*, **28**, 2888 (1895); **34**, 4256 (1901); **39**, 3160 (1906); *Ann.*, **360**, 11 (1908); Lindemann, *Ann.*, **431**, 270 (1923); Jacobsen, *Ber.*, **36**, 4093 (1903); Hantzsch, *Ber.*, **32**, 590, 3089 (1899).

The bulk of the evidence favors the hydrazone structure in the case of the o-hydroxyazo compounds. Undoubtedly both forms exist, and the nature of the substituents will affect the equilibrium position.[48] This was also indicated earlier by the work of Lauer,[49] who demonstrated that certain p-hydroxyazo compounds would condense with cyclopentadiene in a typical Diels-Alder reaction.

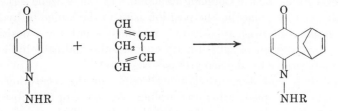

However, at least two nitro groups were necessary in the R radical before the reaction would take place.

In the series of aminoazo dyes two possible tautomeric forms can be postulated. The free bases are known only in one form, to which the

azo structure is ascribed.[49a] In the course of investigations concerning the salts of aminoazo compounds, Thiele [50] was able to isolate two hydrochloride salts of different colors. Hantzsch and others [51] extended this investigation and on the basis of spectroscopic differences the existence of both forms in the p-series seems to be established. The status of both the hydroxyazo and aminoazo compounds has been reviewed briefly by Hurd.[52]

**Classification.** A strict scientific classification of azo dyes is extremely difficult; proposals in this line have been advanced by Bucherer, von Bülow, Pauli, and Winther. The generally accepted principle is based on the number of azo bridges contained in the molecule. Thus one distinguishes between monoazo, disazo, trisazo, and polyazo dyes in general. Specifically, the following main groups may be considered.

[48] Fierz-David et al., Helv. Chim. Acta, 29, 1718 (1946).

[49] Lauer and Miller, J. Am. Chem. Soc., 57, 520 (1935).

[49a] Meyer, Ber., 21, 12 (1888).

[50] Thiele, Ber., 36, 3965 (1903).

[51] Hantzsch and Hilscher, Ber., 41, 1171 (1908); Hantzsch, Ber., 41, 2435 (1908); 42, 2129 (1909); 46, 1537 (1913); 52, 520 (1919); Hantzsch and Burawoy, Ber., 63, 1760 (1930); Hewitt, Ber., 41, 1986 (1908); Kehrmann, Ber., 50, 856 (1917); Vorländer, Ber., 56, 1229 (1923).

[52] See pp. 671–675 in Vol. I of this Treatise.

1. Monoazo dyes.

$$D \rightarrow C \quad (D = \text{diazo compound, } C = \text{coupler})$$

2. Disazo dyes.  (*a*) Primary:

$$D \rightarrow C \leftarrow D' \quad \text{or} \quad C \leftarrow D \rightarrow C'$$

A coupling component capable of being coupled twice may react with two molecules of a diazo compound or an aromatic diamine capable of tetrazotization may be coupled to two moles of a coupler.  D and D' in the equations above as well as C and C' may represent the same or different compounds.

(*b*) Secondary:

$$D \rightarrow C \rightarrow C'$$

This class comprises those dyes where a diazo compound D is coupled with a primary arylamine of such a structure that the resulting aminoazo dye, D → C, can be diazotized and coupled with C'.

3. Trisazo dyes.

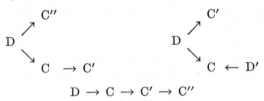

$$D \rightarrow C \rightarrow C' \rightarrow C''$$

The schemes above suggest three different kinds of trisazo dyes.  In the same way other azo dyes with still more azo linkages can be built up to form tetrakis-, pentakis-, etc., azo dyes.  It is customary to group these dyes with more than three azo bridges under the name of polyazo dyes.

In a specific discussion of the different classes only a very few important prototypes can be considered as representatives of a multitude of technical dyes numbering several thousand.

## Monoazo Dyes

The group of monoazo dyes used on a technical scale is very large and is being applied in many divergent fields.  The fastness properties range all the way from poor to excellent, and the dyes are used for all kinds of fibers and articles.  In a way somewhat outdated today, they may be classified coloristically into basic and acidic azoic dyes and pigments.

## Basic Dyes

The simplest and oldest prototype of the basic dyes is aminoazobenzene (XIXa). It is not satisfactory for the dyeing of fibers since it sublimes readily, but it is still being applied today for the coloring of lacquers, waxes, and acetate silk. It is used not so much for the production of golden yellow shades when acetate silk is dyed directly as for its property of being able to be diazotized on the fiber and developed with suitable "developers" like 2-hydroxy-3-naphthoic acid and phloroglucinol to form deep black shades. Homologs of aminoazobenzene [53] and other monoazo dyes carrying naphthalene nuclei (XIXb) are used for the same purpose.

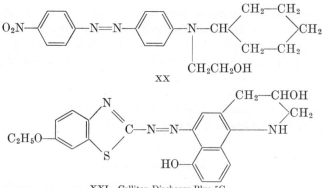

XIXa                                    XIXb

Good light-fastness is claimed for certain diphenylamineazo dyes,[54] and other shades than yellow are obtainable by appropriate substitutions ($NO_2$, Cl, Br, $CH_3$) in both the diazo and coupling nuclei. Red dyes are available from structures like XX,[55] and still deeper shades may be obtained by the choice of heterocyclic ring systems (XXI),[56] where shades from yellow to green on acetate silk are available.

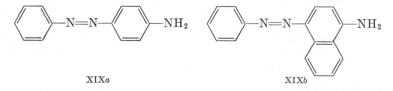

XX

XXI   Celliton Discharge Blue 5G

[53] Jones and Kilby, U. S. pat. 1,850,155 (1932) [C. A., **26**, 2875 (1932)]; Stenger and Miller, U. S. pat. 2,057,455 (1936) [C. A., **30**, 8636 (1936)].

[54] Krzikalla and Garbsch, U. S. pat. 2,069,743 (1937) [C. A., **31**, 2443 (1937)].

[55] Krzikalla and Garbsch, U. S. pat. 2,092,398 (1937) [C. A., **31**, 8208 (1937)]; Baumann, U. S. pat. 2,118,661 (1938) [C. A., **32**, 5637 (1938)].

[56] Helberger and Taube, U. S. pat. 2,149,051 (1939) [C. A., **33**, 4433 (1939)].

The action of diazobenzene ions on *m*-phenylenediamine yields *Chrysoidine*, XXII, a dye containing a second amino group in the coupler:

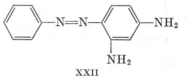

XXII

This dye and its homologs from toluidine and *m*-toluenediamine, owing to their low cost, are still used extensively for the dyeing of leather, paper, and jute. Their fastness is only moderate.

## Azo Pigments

The monoazo dyes obtained through the coupling of diazo compounds with couplers of a phenolic character yield shades varying from yellow to green and, when capable of forming metal complex compounds, even to black. They are very numerous and when free of solubilizing groups like —COOH or —SO₃H are used for the coloring of oils, waxes, lacquers, gasoline, and plastics and for the dyeing of acetate silk or for the formation of very fast azoic dyes on the fiber. The use of pigments of this class for the printing and paint industry is considerable.[56a]

The following few examples may serve as illustrations. *Hansa Yellow G*, XXIII,[57] the coupling product of diazotized *o*-nitraniline on acetoacetanilide, is used together with its homologs extensively in the graphic art, wallpaper, and paint industries. The use of aromatic phenols as couplers usually leads to yellow or orange dyes of high solubility in solvents or oils and therefore unsuitable for the paint trade. An increase in molecular weight through the use of β-naphthol as coupler decreases this solubility to a certain extent, as in *Sudan Orange R* (XXIV), the azo dye from diazobenzene and β-naphthol. When this dye is further "loaded" with nitro groups as in *Lithol Fast Orange RN* (XXV),[58] its solubility in oil has been suppressed to such an extent that it can be used as a pigment dye in the graphic art and paint industries, where, owing to its good light-fastness and its low cost, it is in high favor.

[56a] For a detailed discussion of azo pigments, see, for example, Glassman, *J. Oils & Colour Chemists' Assoc.*, **33**, 191 (1950).

[57] Wagner, U. S. pat. 1,082,719 (1913) [*C. A.*, **8**, 825 (1914)].

[58] Lauch, U. S. pat. 912,138 (1909) [*C. A.*, **3**, 1091 (1909)].

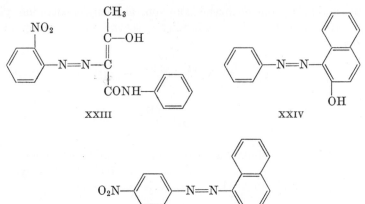

XXIII              XXIV

XXV

## Azoic Dyes

*General.*  This class represents those water-insoluble azo pigments which are formed on the fiber. The first important product to be used in this manner was Para Red, the combination of diazotized $p$-nitro-aniline and $\beta$-naphthol, which is sold either as the finished dye, to be used as a pigment in the printing, lacquer, and wallpaper industries, or in the form of its components for the production of the dye on the fiber. In the latter case, cotton is impregnated with an alkaline solution of $\beta$-naphthol and, after drying, the color is "developed" with a solution of diazotized $p$-nitroaniline.  Neither Para Red nor $\beta$-naphthol as such has affinity for the fiber, and so the dyeing created by the Para Red process adheres only mechanically to the fiber and has a tendency to rub off.

This defect prompted extensive research to obtain products of better fastness and resulted in a large group of naphthols (coupling components) and fast bases (diazo components), proper combination of which will give any desired shade. As some of these shades are defective in one or more fastness properties, others are too expensive, and still others lack adequate brightness, considerable research is still in progress.

*Naphthols.*  The solution to the poor fastness of dyeings of Para Red and related compounds came with the discovery that arylides (XXVI) of 2-hydroxy-3-naphthoic acid have affinity for cotton from alkaline solution and the dyes derived from them have markedly improved fastness to washing and rubbing. This led to the long line of naphthols which are all named as derivatives of the simplest prototype, the anilide, which was called Naphthol AS. Obviously, many combinations are possible, and of these quite a large number are used commercially to obtain the optimum combination of shade and fastness properties.[59] A few that are used extensively are indicated.

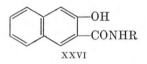

XXVI

Naphthol AS:    R = phenyl
Naphthol AS-D:    R = o-methylphenyl [60]
Naphthol AS-RL:    R = p-methoxyphenyl [61]
Naphthol AS-BS:    R = m-nitrophenyl [61]
Naphthol AS-TR:    R = 2-methyl-4-chlorophenyl [61]
Naphthol AS-SW:    R = β-naphthyl [61]

It is possible to obtain only a limited range of shades with naphthols of this type. Thus, in general, aniline and chlorinated anilines will give orange shades; anisidines and chlorinated toluidines and anisidines give reds; dianisidine and a few special types give blues; and the intermediate Bordeaux and violet shades may be obtained with a few specific combinations. However, to obtain yellows, greens, browns, and blacks, it becomes necessary to go to different types of compounds.

The yellows are obtained using active methylene type compounds; the only ones of importance are acylacetanilides. The most important yellow naphthol is still Naphthol AS-G (XXVII).[61]

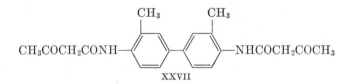

XXVII

Later research directed toward improving the shade and fastness led to a number of special types, of which Naphthol AS-L3G (XXVIII) [62] and Naphthol AS-L4G (XXIX) [63] are examples.

[59] Mehta and Thosar, *J. Soc. Dyers Colourists*, **56**, 160 (1940); Bhat *et al.*, *ibid.*, **56**, 166 (1940); **58**, 155, 203 (1942).

[60] Wagner, U. S. pat. Re. 17,364 (1929) [*C. A.*, **23**, 4080 (1929)].

[61] Konrad, U. S. pat. 1,723,183 (1929) [*C. A.*, **23**, 4578 (1929)]; Woetzel and Lint, U. S. pat. 1,727,920 (1929) [*C. A.*, **23**, 5326 (1929)].

[62] Henle and Kracker, U. S. pat. 1,971,409 (1934) [*C. A.*, **28**, 6574 (1934)].

[63] Schrader and Zerweck, U. S. pat. 2,093,214 (1937) [*C. A.*, **31**, 8216 (1937)].

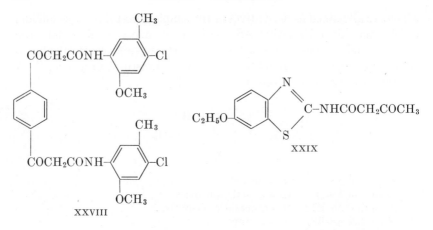

XXVIII

XXIX

Naphthols of the acylacetanilide type are always prepared by the reaction of an ethyl acylacetate with the amine, the ethyl alcohol which is liberated generally being removed by distillation as it is formed. Thus, the required intermediate for Naphthol AS-L3G is terephthalyl-acetic ester, which is prepared in the usual way from terephthalyl chloride and ethyl acetoacetate.

The 2-amino-6-ethoxybenzothiazole required for Naphthol AS-L4G may be prepared by ring closure of 4-ethoxyphenylthiourea with bromine or in one step from *p*-phenetidine, sodium thiocyanate, and bromine in a solvent such as acetic acid.

Brown to black shades have been obtained from carbazole and benzocarbazole derivatives, Naphthols AS-LB (XXX) [64] and AS-SR (XXXI*a*) [65] being examples.

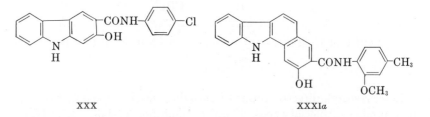

XXX                              XXXI*a*

The only naphthol that has been found to give a green shade of suitable brightness and fastness to be used commercially is Naphthol AS-GR (XXXI*b*).[66] The best shade and fastness are obtained with Fast Blue BB base (2,5-diethoxy-4-benzoylaminoaniline), but even this

[64] Schmelzer *et al.*, U. S. pat. 1,819,127 (1931) [*C. A.*, **25**, 5678 (1931)].
[65] Ballauf and Hefner, U. S. pat. 1,867,106 (1932) [*C. A.*, **26**, 4610 (1932)].
[66] Gassner and Meiser, U. S. pat. 1,960,375 (1934) [*C. A.*, **28**, 4607 (1934)].

combination leaves much to be desired and the usage of this naphthol is relatively small.

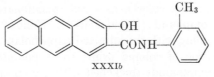

XXXI*b*

Theoretically any diazo compound may be used for the "development" of dyes on the fiber. In practice certain restrictions are observed. Since one of the main advantages of the azoic dyes is their fastness to washing, no solubilizing groups like carboxylic and sulfonic acid radicals are permitted. Experience has shown that only specific combinations of certain naphthols with specific diazo compounds yield the fastest combinations. Examples are shown.

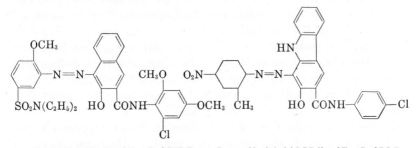

*Red:* Naphthol AS-ITR [67] and Fast Red ITR Base (3-amino-4-methoxybenzenesulfondiethyl-amide) [67]    *Brown:* Naphthol AS-LB [68] and Fast Red RL Base (2-methyl-4-nitroaniline) [68]

*Fast Bases and Stabilized Diazo Compounds.* The diazo compounds are available to the textile dyeing and printing trades either in the form of the amines for diazotization by the user or as ready-made and stabilized diazo salts (Fast Color Salts), stabilization being effected by forming heavy metal double salts (Zn, Sn, Cd, etc.) or salts with aromatic or aliphatic sulfonic acids [69] or complex salts with $HBF_4$,[70] fluorosulfonic acid,[71] etc.

For the printing trade only mechanical mixtures of naphthols with diazo compounds in special forms are offered. Since the printing pastes

[67] Neelmeier and Lamberz, U. S. pat. 1,976,187 (1934) [*C. A.*, **28**, 7546 (1934)].

[68] Muth, U. S. pat. 1,940,059 (1933) [*C. A.*, **28**, 1541 (1934)].

[69] Montmollin and Bonhote, U. S. pat. 1,629,906 (1927) [*C. A.*, **21**, 2388 (1927)]; Keller and Schnitzpahn, U. S. pat. 1,717,453 (1929) [*C. A.*, **23**, 4081 (1929)]; Schmidt, U. S. pat. 1,840,333 (1932) [*C. A.*, **26**, 1619 (1932)]; Guenther and Lange, U. S. pat. 1,572,715 (1926) [*C. A.*, **20**, 1243 (1926)].

[70] Hentrich and Tietze, U. S. pat. 1,813,621 (1931) [*C. A.*, **25**, 5298 (1931)].

[71] Hentrich *et al.*, U. S. pat. 1,847,513 (1932) [*C. A.*, **26**, 2469 (1932)].

are alkaline, such diazos have to be in a form stable at the $p$H of their application. They are presented, therefore, either in the form of their isodiazotates (Rapidfast colors), as antidiazosulfonates (Rapidazoles), or as diazoamino compounds (Rapidogens *). None of these compounds are capable of coupling with the admixed naphtholate *per se*.

For the production of colored prints the goods are printed with a solution of these compounds thickened with a gum and the prints are "developed" by contact with acid (formic, acetic) vapors which bring about the regeneration of the latent diazo and immediate coupling with the admixed naphtholate.

Only a limited number of isodiazotates [72] are stable enough under the conditions of usage to be applicable technically: dichloroanilines, chloronitroanilines, and nitroanilines; but even this limited selection does not answer modern requirements of stability in the print pastes. Rapidazoles are more stable in this respect. They contain the diazo compounds in the form of the non-coupling antidiazosulfonates [73] or diazosulfites.[74] By the action of light or higher temperatures the true coupling diazo compound is regenerated. Application of Rapidazoles has been more or less restricted to blue or black shades obtainable from $p$-phenylenediamine derivatives like 4-amino-4'-methoxydiphenylamine, which in the form of its antidiazosulfonate and in mixture with Naphthol AS represents the fast Rapidazole Blue I B.[75]

The most successful form of application of diazo compounds in azoic work has been with diazoamino compounds. They are stable and offer a complete range of shades of very good brightness and fastness. As a rule they represent combinations of diazo compounds from strong bases with stabilizing amines of weakly basic character of such a nature that upon cleavage with acid only the original diazo results. Most of the stabilizing amines carry solubilizing groups: $-SO_3H$, $-COOH$, $-SO_2NH_2$, or a plurality of $-OH$ groups. They may be aliphatic, such as $CH_3NHCH_2COOH$ (sarcosin) [76] or $CH_3NHCH_2CH_2SO_3H$

---

* These are the original types first offered in Germany by I. G. Farbenindustrie A.-G. and in the United States by General Aniline. Other trade names are Pharmasols (Pharma Chemical Co.), Diagens (du Pont), and Calconyls (American Cyanamid Co., Calco Division).

[72] Laska and Zitscher, U. S. pat. 1,505,568 (1924) [*C. A.*, **19**, 182 (1925)]; Zitscher, U. S. pat. 1,608,284 (1926) [*C. A.*, **21**, 328 (1927)]; Fischer and Freund, U. S. pat. 1,951,571 (1934) [*C. A.*, **28**, 3593 (1934)].

[73] Fischer, *Ann.*, **190**, 73 (1878); Hantzsch, *Ber.*, **27**, 1715, 1726 (1894).

[74] Claus, *J. prakt. Chem.*, **50**, 239 (1894); Hodgson, *J. Chem. Soc.*, 470 (1942).

[75] Zitscher and Seidenfaden, U. S. pat. 1,897,410 (1933) [*C. A.*, **27**, 2824 (1933)]; U. S. pat. 1,909,851 (1933) [*C. A.*, **27**, 4092 (1933)]; U. S. pat. 1,920,542 (1933) [*C. A.*, **27**, 4936 (1933)]; U. S. pat. 1,959,995 (1934) [*C. A.*, **28**, 4607 (1934)].

[76] Glietenberg *et al.*, U. S. pat. 1,882,560 (1932) [*C. A.*, **27**, 849 (1933)].

(methyltaurine),[77] or aromatic (N-ethylsulfoanthranilic acid),[78] or heterocyclic (Prolin).[79]  Other stabilizers proposed in the patent literature and used to some extent technically are amino sugars, guanidine derivatives, sodium cyanamide,[80] and cyanamidecarboxylic acid.[80]  Examples of combinations of this type are shown.

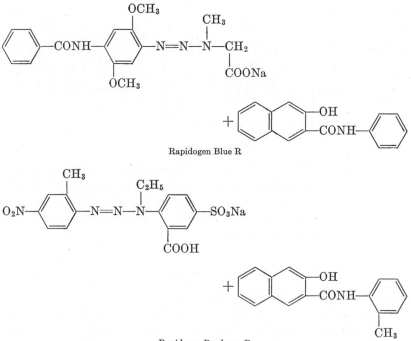

Rapidogen Blue R

Rapidogen Bordeaux R

With the exception of the alcohol- or oil-soluble types which are less suitable for dyeing of acetate silk, no other monoazo dyes free from solubilizing groups like —COOH or —SO$_3$H have affinity for commercial fibers.  However, those monoazo dyes which contain hydroxy or amino group in $o,o'$-positions to the azo bridge can be converted into their

[77] Neelmeier and Glietenberg, U. S. pat. 1,879,424 (1932) [C. A., 27, 1199 (1933)].

[78] Hentrich et al., U. S. pat. 1,858,623 (1932) [C. A., 26, 3805 (1932)]; Ossenbeck and Tietze, U. S. pat. 1,867,088 (1932) [C. A., 26, 4612 (1932)]; Hentrich et al., U. S. pat. 1,871,850 (1932) [C. A., 26, 5967 (1932)]; U. S. pat. 1,874,524 (1932) [C. A., 26, 5967 (1932)]; Glietenberg et al., U. S. pat. 1,882,560 (1932) [C. A., 27, 849 (1933)]; U. S. pat. 1,882,562 (1932) [C. A., 27, 851 (1933)].

[79] Markush, U. S. pat. 1,982,681 (1934) [C. A., 29, 558 (1935)].

[80] Taube, U. S. pat. 2,054,397 (1936) [C. A., 30, 7867 (1936)]; Taube and Tietze, U. S. pat. 2,049,674 (1936) [C. A., 30, 6574 (1936)].

metal complexes, which will dye animal or nylon fibers in very fast
shades.[81]

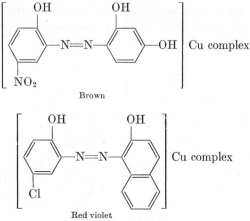

Brown

Cu complex

Red violet

The same dyes may also be used as pigments in the printing or lacquer
industry. The metalization of the underlying azo dyes can be carried
out in aqueous or alcoholic media or in formamide by treatment with
organic or inorganic metal salts. Copper, chromium, and cobalt are
used preferentially as the metals.

### Acid Dyes

The acid monoazo dyes, i.e., those containing carboxylic or sulfonic
acid groups, find their use mainly in the field of wool dyeing and the
manufacture of color lakes. They have undergone a gradual historical
development from dyes with no particular fastness to dyes that rate
very high in this respect. All shades are represented, and a few types
will be discussed below.

*Acid Wool Colors.* The coupling product of diazometanilic acid and
diphenylamine was prepared in 1879 and is one of the oldest yellow dyes
for wool and paper. Still older is *Orange II*, the azo dye from diazo-
sulfanilic acid and β-naphthol. It has been known since 1876, and its
use has shifted from the dyeing of wool to the dyeing of paper and the
production of color lakes for wallpaper. *Ponceau 2R*,[82] the azo dye from
diazo-2,4-xylidine and R salt, yields bright but rather fugitive shades on
wool. It is used today more for color lake work, where the fastness of
the lakes obtained is more acceptable. *Sulfon Acid Blue RA*,[83] prepared

[81] Kvalnes and Carson, U. S. pat. 2,374,106 (1945) [*C. A.*, **40**, 218 (1946)].
[82] Baum, U. S. pat. 210,233 (1878).
[83] Ulrich, U. S. pat. 611,664 (1898).

in 1893, was one of the first blue monoazo dyes. Its constitution is shown by XXXII.

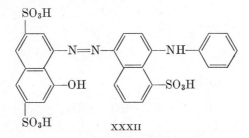

XXXII

Increased molecular size of dyes within a given class contributes generally to a somewhat better fastness to washing at the cost of levelness * of the dyeings. *Flavazin L* (XXXIII) [84] is very deficient in wash fastness of wool dyeings, but *Polar Yellow 5G* (XXXIV) [85] excels in this respect.

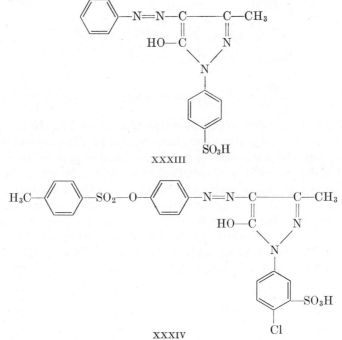

XXXIII

XXXIV

* When dyeing textile piece goods with a mixture of dyes it is essential that these dyes be compatible with each other and dye the fiber to the same degree at varying $pH$ and temperature conditions. Dyes that fulfill these conditions are called "level dyes."

[84] Möllenhoff, *Ber.*, **25**, 1941 (1892).
[85] Richard, U. S. pat. 1,067,881 (1913) [*C. A.*, **7**, 3031 (1913)].

Further examples of modern wool dyes combining good all-around fastness are shown.

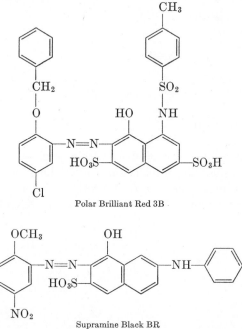

Polar Brilliant Red 3B

Supramine Black BR

*Lakes.* Many water-soluble monoazo dyes are used for the production of lakes for the wallpaper, paint, lacquer, and printing industries. For this purpose the water-soluble dye is precipitated as a water-insoluble color lake by the addition of metal salts (Al, Ba, Ca, Sr, etc.). Although the "pigments" (dyes without —$SO_3H$ or —COOH groups) are not water-soluble either, they nevertheless, especially in the realm of monoazo dyes with lower molecular weight, exhibit very often a more or less pronounced tendency to bleed in oil or to sublime. This defect, as a rule, is absent with dyes like Lithol Red R (XXXV), Lithosol Red 2B (XXXVI), and Tartrazine (XXXVII), or similar ones, when used as metal lakes.

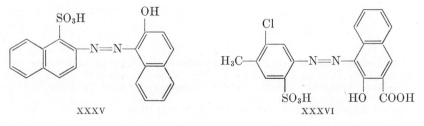

XXXV                                    XXXVI

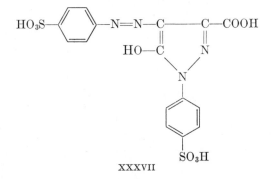

XXXVII

*Metalizable Types.* The number of metalized dyes in the series of acid monoazo dyes is vast. The good all-around fastness of this group has stimulated continuous research. The free acids are applied primarily on wool and leather; salts with organic amines are used for the coloring of spirit lacquers. Originally, the shades obtainable with these dyes, extending from yellow to black, were rather dull, but considerable improvements have been made in this direction. The metal complexes are produced by the action of metal salts like chromium fluoride or alkali bichromates on the dyed goods in a dye bath, or the complex of the dye is formed previous to the dyeing operation by treating the dye proper in an aqueous or organic medium with the metalizing agents, mostly chromium, copper, or cobalt salts. The complex metalized dye is then applied to the fiber.

Several distinct types are known and in use. (*a*) Dyes that are metalized on the fiber because their metal complexes are too insoluble for normal dyeing operations.

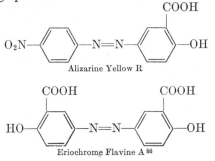

Alizarine Yellow R

Eriochrome Flavine A [86]

(*b*) Dyes that cannot form a metal complex without the simultaneous or prior use of oxidizing agents (like chromic acid) whereby, in some cases, *o,o'*-dihydroxyazo dyes are formed,

[86] Mettler, U. S. pat. 1,157,169 (1915) [*C. A.*, **9**, 3366 (1915)].

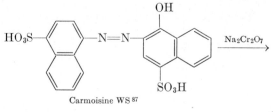

OH

Carmoisine WS [87]

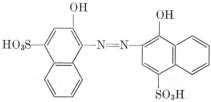

or in other cases quinonoid structures result.

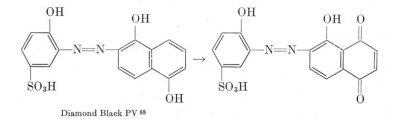

Diamond Black PV [88]

(c) Dyes that can be used either way.

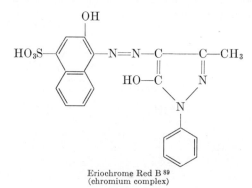

Eriochrome Red B [89]
(chromium complex)

---

[87] Rosenhauer *et al., Ber.*, **62**, 2717 (1929).

[88] Kahn, U. S. pat. 722,715 (1903); Morgan *et al., J. Chem. Soc.*, 645 (1915); 1126 (1919); 704 (1921); 160 (1922); 1731 (1924); *J. Soc. Dyers Colourists*, **37**, 43 (1921); **41**, 233 (1925).

[89] Sandmeyer, U. S. pat. 793,743 (1905); Hagenbach, U. S. pat. 808,919 (1906).

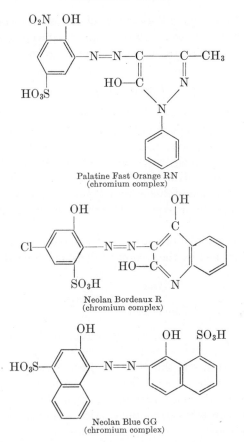

Palatine Fast Orange RN
(chromium complex)

Neolan Bordeaux R
(chromium complex)

Neolan Blue GG
(chromium complex)

The structure of these chromium complexes has not been established with certainty, and different forms containing different ratios of chromium to dye are known. Usually the most useful complex has a chromium/dye ratio of 1:1. For maximum stability two metalizable groups are needed, one on each side of the azo linkage and *ortho* to this linkage, and at least one of these groups should be hydroxyl. The other group, if not hydroxyl, is usually amino, carboxyl, or an enolic hydroxyl as in the pyrazolones above. Groups such as alkoxy or chloro, which are converted to hydroxyl under special metalization conditions, are also used.

## DISAZO DYES

All monoazo dyes discussed above, with the exception of the typical color lakes and pigments, dye wool. Their affinity for vegetable fibers is negligible. The disazo dyes to be dealt with now form the bridge to those dyes which, though still dyeing wool, are mainly characterized by their property to dye cotton directly from an aqueous dye bath. This feature is partly a function of increased molecular size, partly of constitution.

### Primary Types

One of the oldest basic azo dyes is formed by the action of sodium nitrite (two moles) on a mineral acid solution of m-phenylenediamine (three moles), whereby one mole of the diamine is tetrazotized and couples with the remaining two moles to form Bismarck Brown.[90]

Shades of a more reddish brown may be obtained from substituted diamines like 2,4-diaminotoluene and 2,4-diaminoanisole. Such dyes are used for the dyeing of paper and leather, and in the printing trade. Their fastness is poor.

The action of two moles of a diazo compound on a central "coupling" molecule is exemplified by the resorcinol dyes, of which Resorcin Brown is an example.

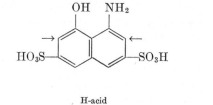

2,4-Xylidine $\searrow$
$\rightarrow$ Resorcinol
Sulfanilic acid $\nearrow$

These dyes of various hues, mostly orange to brown, are now used principally for the dyeing of chrome-tanned leather, seldom for wool.

Of greater importance in this class are those dyes that feature as their middle component naphthalene derivatives. Some of the more common aminonaphtholsulfonic acids and dihydroxynaphthalenesulfonic acids have the valuable property of coupling twice, as indicated by the arrows in the formulas below.

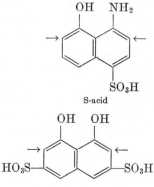

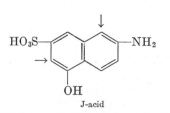

H-acid        S-acid

J-acid        Chromotrope acid

[90] Griess, *Ber.*, **11**, 627 (1878).

The most important prototype of the wool colors in this class is Buffalo Black NB (XXXVIII).[91]

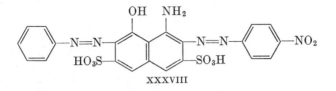

XXXVIII

Variation of the diazo compounds produces a great number of dyes ranging from blue to black and green.

*Direct Dyes.* By further varying the center component and substituting J-acid derivatives or other "substantive" components the character of the dye is changed to one with affinity for cotton.

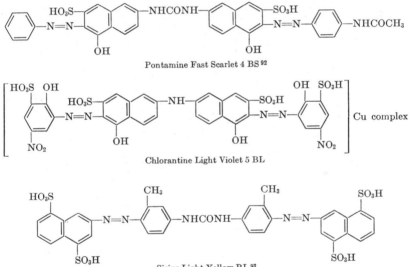

Pontamine Fast Scarlet 4 BS [92]

Chlorantine Light Violet 5 BL

Sirius Light Yellow RL [93]

*Substantivity.* Experience has shown that certain configurations and specific intermediates confer upon dyes affinity for cotton. These are primarily:

(a) *Benzidine* and its *o*-derivatives. 2,2'-Substituted derivatives have no affinity unless they form part of a ring system. Therefore, 2,2'-dichlorobenzidine confers no affinity, while dyes derived from

[91] Hoffmann, U. S. pat. 480,326 (1892).
[92] Israel and Kothe, U. S. pat. 663,498 (1900).
[93] Günther and Hesse, U. S. pat. 935,016 (1908) [*C. A.*, **4**, 116 (1910)].

diaminocarbazole (**XXXIX**) or benzidinesulfone (**XL**) yield substantive dyes.

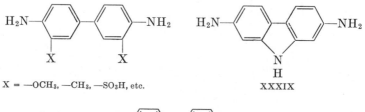

X = —OCH₃, —CH₃, —SO₃H, etc.

XXXIX

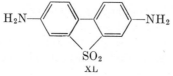

XL

(b) *Dehydrothiotoluidine* and derivatives:

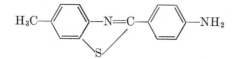

(c) *J-acid* and derivatives:

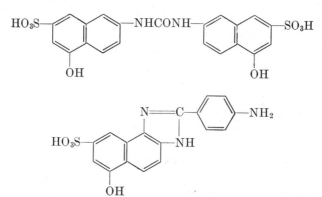

(d) *1,5-Diaminonaphthalene:*

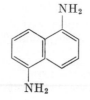

(e) Two arylamines linked together in the p-position by —CH=CH—, —NHCONH—, —NH—, or —N=N—.    Examples of compounds
$$—N\underset{\underset{O}{\downarrow}}{=}N—$$

utilizing this principle are:

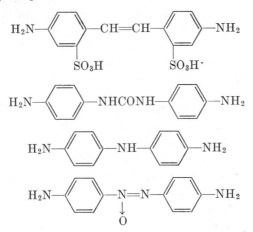

(f) Repeated use of the p-aminobenzoyl radical:

Benzidine and Related Types.    Another group of primary disazo dyes is based on the use of an aryl-*para*-diamine.    The simplest prototype of such dyes is represented by "Violet Black" (XLI), obtained by diazoti-

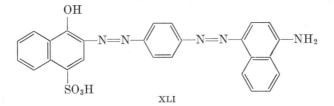

XLI

zation of p-aminoacetanilide, coupling with 4-naphthol-1-sulfonic acid, saponification, and subsequent coupling of the diazotized intermediate compound with α-naphthylamine.    The overwhelming majority of the dyes of this class, however, are based on the use of benzidine and its homologs.    Although both amino groups are diazotized simultaneously and monodiazobenzidine can be obtained only in a circuitous way,[94] the

[94] Täuber, *Ber.*, **27**, 2627 (1894).

diazo groups of the tetrazobenzidine show a distinct difference in their speed of coupling. Extensive use of this feature is made in the synthesis of asymmetrical dyes. The shades of these are governed by the substituents in the benzidine nucleus as well as by the nature of the couplers. There is a progressive bathochromic effect when substituting tolidine and dianisidine for benzidine, while shades from yellow to black are obtainable from couplers like salicylic acid, β-naphthylaminesulfonic acid, α-naphthylaminesulfonic acid, α-naphthol- and β-naphtholsulfonic acids, aminonaphtholsulfonic and, finally, peri-aminonaphtholsulfonic acids.

According to modern standards, none of the straight benzidine dyes are featured by good light-fastness. Their easy application, however, secured for them a dominant role for decades. Recent developments, and especially the synthesis of metalized dyes in this series, have reduced this handicap. Another drawback of the benzidine dyes is their poor wash-fastness. Efforts to correct this defect have been successful only to a certain degree. A few examples of this type of dye are shown. (B = benzidine; D = dianisidine.)

B ⟨ Salicylic acid / Salicylic acid          Chrysamine G (yellow)

B ⟨ 4-Naphthylamine-1-sulfonic acid / 4-Naphthylamine-1-sulfonic acid          Congo Red

D ⟨ 8-Amino-1-naphthol-5,7-disulfonic acid / 8-Amino-1-naphthol-5,7-disulfonic acid          Chicago Blue 6B

B ⟨ Salicylic acid / 7-Amino-1-naphthol-3-sulfonic acid (coupled acid)          Diamine Fast Red FC

B ⟨ Salicylic acid / 7-Amino-1-naphthol-3-sulfonic acid (coupled alkaline)          Diamine Brown M

The moderate light-fastness of these and similar dyes is the reason for their decreasing importance. Based on the observation that after-treatment of dyeings with solutions of chromium or copper salts improves their light-fastness, several new promising developments in this field have taken place. There are available complex copper salts of dianisidine dyes, the dyeings of which show excellent light-fastness. For example, the copper complex salt of the above-mentioned Chicago Blue 6B is Pontamine Fast Blue 6 GL.[95] It has been established that during the metalization the methyl groups of the dianisidine split off. Although the light-fastness is visibly improved, there is little improvement in wash-fastness. The introduction of —COOH groups, however, in strategic positions of a dye and metalization of the latter on the fiber are beneficial in this respect. Dyes of this class are largely based on benzidine-3,3'-dicarboxylic acid and the corresponding diglycolic acid.

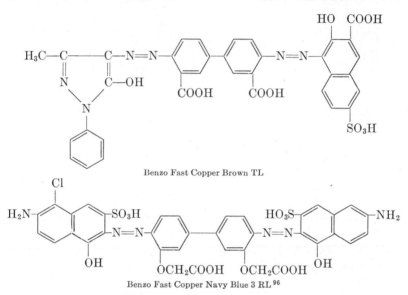

Benzo Fast Copper Brown TL

Benzo Fast Copper Navy Blue 3 RL [96]

In all probability the better fastness of these dyes to washing is due to heavy metal complex and salt formation, which results in a much less soluble dye.

Developed Types. Before these developments, attempts were made to improve the wash-fastness of direct azo dyes by other means. It was reasoned that a dye of larger molecular size with the same number of solubilizing groups would possess less solubility and therefore should have better wash-fastness. This was accomplished by treating fibers dyed with certain dyes capable of either being (a) coupled again on the fiber with a diazo compound free from solubilizing groups (para dyes); (b) capable of being diazotized on the fiber and coupled with β-naphthol or other couplers (diazo dyes); or (c) capable of condensation with formal-

[95] Mendoza, U. S. pat. 2,036,159 (1936) [C. A., **30**, 3654 (1936)].

[96] Taube and Bayer, U. S. pat. 2,158,843 (1939) [C. A., **33**, 7124 (1939)].

dehyde. Though the fastness to washing was indeed improved, the light-fastness was not changed materially. Examples of these three types are shown.

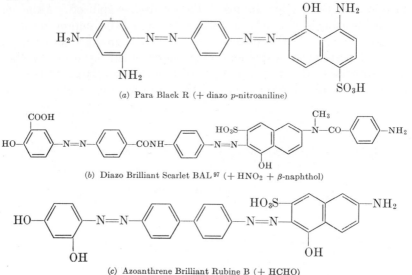

(a) Para Black R (+ diazo p-nitroaniline)

(b) Diazo Brilliant Scarlet BAL [97] (+ HNO₂ + β-naphthol)

(c) Azoanthrene Brilliant Rubine B (+ HCHO)

**Stilbene Dyes.** By the action of concentrated sodium hydroxide on p-nitrotoluene-o-sulfonic acid, yellow to orange dyes are obtained of good substantivity and fairly good fastness on cotton. Through researches of Green [98] they have been recognized as derivatives of azoxy-azodistilbenetetrasulfonic acid (XLII).

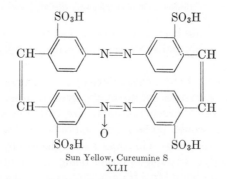

Sun Yellow, Curcumine S
XLII

By further oxidation of this dye greener shades are obtained; reducing agents favor the formation of disazo dyes of redder shade.

[97] Roos, U. S. pat. 2,061,104 (1936) [*C. A.*, **31**, 873 (1937)].
[98] Green *et al.*, *J. Chem. Soc.*, 1424 (1904); 1610 (1906); 2076 (1907); 1712 (1908); cf. Schultz, *Ber.*, **19**, 3234 (1886).

## *Secondary Types*

Dyes of this type are used mostly for the dyeing of wool, their affinity for the cotton fiber normally not being satisfactory. Their dyeings on the fiber are usually faster than those of monoazo dyes of the same shade. The fastness to washing and fulling is usually good. It is interesting to note that the color shifts from orange to black as benzene nuclei are replaced with naphthalene nuclei.

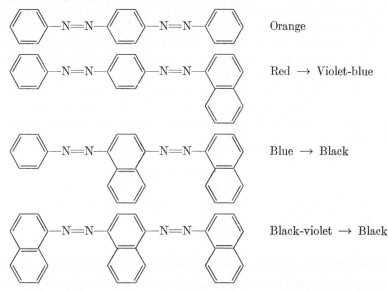

A few examples of acid and chrome wool dyes belonging to this class are

4-Aminoazobenzene-4'-sulfonic acid → Salicylic acid: Calcochrome Orange GR

Aminoazotoluene → 4-Naphthol-1-sulfonic acid:   Cloth Red B

*p*-Aminosalicylic acid → α-Naphthylamine → 1-Naphthol-5-sulfonic acid: Diamond Black F

1-Naphthylamine-3,6-disulfonic acid → α-Naphthylamine → α-Naphthylamine: Naphthylamine Black D

The selection of very substantive substituents leads to dyes having affinity for cotton.

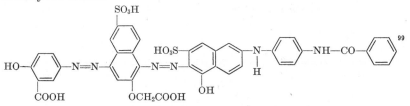

[99] Delfs and Bayer, U. S. pat. 2,125,625 (1938) [*C. A.*, **32**, 7739 (1938)].

## Trisazo and Polyazo Dyes

### General

The higher-molecular-weight azo dyes containing three or more azo bridges can be obtained in a number of different ways as outlined on p. 266. They are dyes with affinity for the vegetable fiber, and their fastness to light ranges from moderate to excellent. This fastness is not a function of the number of azo groups but of constitution. In general, benzidine derivatives are definitely less fast to light than polyazo dyes based on secondary disazo dyes in which the progressive couplings take place in the p-position. The importance of this group of dyes lies in the field of blue, green, and black hues.

Certain disazo dyes with diazotizable amino groups may be diazotized and "developed" on the fiber to trisazo dyes. The same procedure, of course, can be applied to create tetrakis and pentakis azo dyes on the fiber as in

$$
B \left\langle \begin{array}{l} \nearrow \text{ 8-Amino-1-naphthol-3,6-disulfonic acid} \\ \searrow \text{ 7-Amino-1-naphthol-3-sulfonic acid} \end{array} \right.
$$

Diazo Black BHN

$$
B \left\langle \begin{array}{l} \nearrow \text{ }\alpha\text{-Naphthylamine } \rightarrow \text{ 8-Amino-1-naphthol-3,6-disulfonic acid} \\ \searrow \text{ 8-Amino-1-naphthol-3,6-disulfonic acid} \end{array} \right.
$$

Diazo Blue Black RS

Tetrazotization of goods dyed with these dyestuffs and coupling with m-phenylenediamine in the dye bath yield shades of fairly good fastness to washing even though the light-fastness remains moderate.

Quite a few trisazo dyes of the benzidine type are in use which, in spite of their moderate light-fastness, but owing to their other properties and low cost have retained a high degree of popularity in the trade.

$$
B \left\langle \begin{array}{l} \nearrow \text{ Phenol} \\ \searrow \text{ 8-Amino-1-naphthol-3,6-disulfonic acid } \leftarrow p\text{-Nitraniline} \end{array} \right.
$$

Pontamine Green BXN

$$
B \left\langle \begin{array}{l} \nearrow \text{ 8-Amino-1-naphthol-3,6-disulfonic acid } \leftarrow \text{ Aniline} \\ \searrow \text{ }m\text{-Phenylenediamine} \end{array} \right.
$$

Direct Deep Black EA

$$
B \left\langle \begin{array}{l} \nearrow \text{ Salicylic acid} \\ \searrow \text{ }m\text{-Phenylenediamine } \leftarrow \text{ 7-Amino-1-naphthol-3,6-disulfonic acid} \end{array} \right.
$$

$$
\uparrow
$$

Naphthionic acid

Trisulfon Brown B

When the benzidine linkage is replaced by other aryl *para*-diamines, somewhat faster dyes are obtainable, such as

*m*-Phenylenediamine ← *p*-Phenylenediamine
            ↘
        8-Amino-1-naphthol-3,6-disulfonic acid
            ↗
*m*-Phenylenediamine ← *p*-Phenylenediamine
      Columbia Fast Black G

made by coupling of diazotized *p*-nitroaniline twice on H-acid, reduction of the nitro groups with sodium sulfide, rediazotization, and coupling with *m*-phenylenediamine.

Even better light-fastness is obtainable by building up secondary disazo dyes as shown in the following examples.

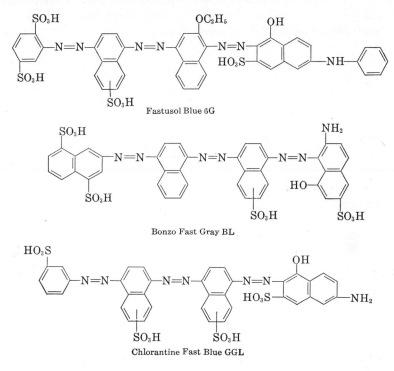

Fastusol Blue 6G

Bonzo Fast Gray BL

Chlorantine Fast Blue GGL

## Dischargeable Types

One of the main advantages of azo dyes over other dyes is their property of cleaving easily into more or less colorless fragmentary intermediates when treated with proper reducing agents. The textile printing industry makes extensive use of this feature by printing patterns on dyed goods with such reducing agents as sodium hydrosulfite or sodium sulfoxylate. By steaming such prints the natural white color of the undyed textile material reappears through the destruction of the azo dye on the printed pattern. Unfortunately, not all azo dyes cleave into colorless components, especially in alkaline printing pastes. Recent work has concerned itself with the creation of polyazo dyes which will discharge white.[100] The results of this work have established that to discharge white a dye must cleave readily to give products which are white and preferably not substantive. Secondly, it is generally true that substituents such as hydroxyl and primary and secondary amino groups favor the formation of such cleavage products, whereas sulfonic and carboxylic acid radicals, alkyl, aryl, halogen, methoxy, and tertiary amino radicals have a negative influence in this direction. To illustrate, Chrysophenine G (XLIII) discharges poorly in alkaline medium and Brilliant Yellow (XLIV) gives excellent results.

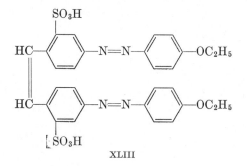

XLIII

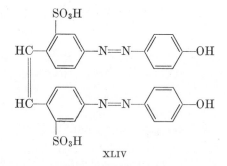

XLIV

[100] Roos, U. S. pat. 2,200,040 (1940) [*C. A.*, **34**, 6092 (1940)]; U. S. pat. 2,196,028 (1940) [*C. A.*, **34**, 5290 (1940)]; U. S. pat. 2,192,153 (1940) [*C. A.*, **34**, 4584 (1940)]; U. S. pat. 2,172,712 (1939) [*C. A.*, **34**, 634 (1940)]; U. S. pat. 2,149,073 (1938) [*C. A.*, **33**, 4432 (1939)]; U. S. pat. 2,129,964 (1938) [*C. A.*, **32**, 9513 (1938)]; U. S. pat. 2,127,986 (1938) [*C. A.*, **32**, 8152 (1938)]; Blumberger, U. S. pat. 2,128,537 (1938) [*C. A.*, **32**, 8792 (1938)].

The use of highly substantive components like

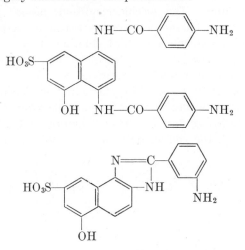

and

cannot be expected to yield dyes of satisfactory dischargeability.  An example of a good discharge dye is Diazo Brilliant Scarlet 3B Extra (XLV).

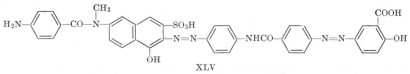

XLV

## Triazine Types

The use of a urea grouping to link together two aminoazo dyes has already been illustrated (e.g., Sirius Light Yellow RL, p. 283).  Such dyes are prepared by the reaction of phosgene with two moles of an aminoazo dye.  Unsymmetrical dyes of this type have also been prepared, but the results have not been completely satisfactory because the second chlorine in the phosgene molecule reacts as readily as the first and mixtures are obtained.  This difficulty was avoided and simultaneously new types of dyes were made available when it was discovered that cyanuric chloride (2,4,6-trichloro-1,3,5-triazine) could be reacted with aminoazo dyes and, moreover, that the dyes obtained were substantive to cotton.

Cyanuric chloride offers the distinct advantage that replacement of each successive chlorine becomes increasingly difficult.  Thus, the first chlorine atom is reactive even in the cold, the second only at room temperature and above, and the third usually requires refluxing in aqueous solution or in some cases even anhydrous conditions at much higher temperatures. The specific conditions needed vary with the nature of the amine, but in any event increasingly vigorous conditions are needed for the second and third chlorine atoms. Generally, the third chlorine is replaced by a simple radical such as anilino but a third chromophore can be introduced if desired.

Obviously numerous possibilities exist, and evidence of the many compounds which have been made is found in the patent literature. One of the more interesting combinations is Chlorantine Fast Green BL [101a] (XLVI), in which the combination of blue and yellow chromophores results in a green.

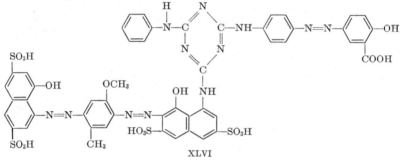

XLVI

More recently [101b] the use of an anthraquinone residue to provide the blue unit has been disclosed and is claimed to give dyes of improved shades and fastness properties. A dye of this type is illustrated.

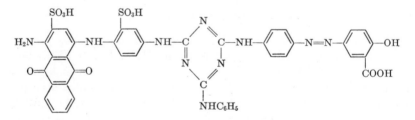

### DIARYL AND TRIARYLMETHANE DYES

This large group of dyes may be subdivided into (1) diarylmethanes and (2) triarylmethanes, which, in turn, may be grouped into (a) diaminotriarylmethanes, (b) triaminotriarylmethanes, (c) hydroxy-triarylmethanes, and (d) derivatives of the triarylcarbinolcarboxylic acids.

---

[101] (a) Fritzsche et al., U. S. pat. 1,667,312 (1928) [C. A., **22**, 2065 (1928)]. (b) Kaiser, U. S. pat. 2,391,164 (1945) [C. A., **40**, 2995 (1946)].

The first coal-tar dyes discovered belong to this group, which excels in bright and powerful shades; unfortunately, most of these beautiful hues are paired with poor fastness to light and washing. The basic members are used predominantly for the dyeing of silk and mordanted cotton in the textile field, and the sulfonated dyes are applied for the dyeing of wool. Further uses for both classes are in the paper and color lake industry.

## Diarylmethanes

Only a few dyes of technical value belong to this class. They are made either by fusion of $p,p'$-tetraalkyldiaminobenzophenones with ammonium chloride and zinc chloride or by heating $p,p'$-tetraalkyldiaminodiphenylmethanes with sulfur, ammonium chloride, and common salt in an ammonia atmosphere. In the latter case the thioketone represents an intermediate state. The dye Auramine O (XLVII) is a

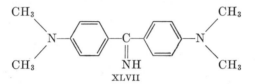

XLVII

powerful basic yellow dye used extensively for the dyeing of paper. Homologs from monomethyl-$o$-toluidine have been prepared but have met with no technical acceptance. Controversies regarding the constitution of auramine as formulated by Graebe (XLVII) or Stock (quinoneimine) have been resolved by Semper [102] and Grandmougin [103] in favor of Graebe's original formula.

## Triarylmethanes

**Structure.** The action of benzaldehyde on dimethylaniline in the presence of zinc chloride leads to a colorless compound, "Leucomalachite Green" (XLVIII). This leuco compound may be oxidized to the color-

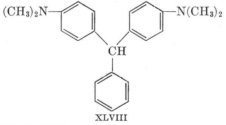

XLVIII

[102] Semper, *Ann.*, **381**, 234 (1911).
[103] Grandmougin and Favre-Ambrumyan, *Ber.*, **47**, 2127 (1914).

less "carbinol" (XLIX), the hydroxy group in which is so stable toward metals that heating with sodium metal to 185° is required to obtain the alcoholate.  The carbinol can be easily reduced, but resists esterification

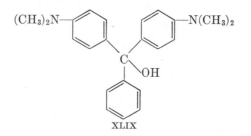

XLIX

by acetic anhydride or methylation by methyl chloride.  The action of acid changes the carbinol into the dye proper, and the composition of the dye shows that in this change the hydroxyl group of the carbinol is replaced by the acid anion.  This change is not instantaneous as with the formation of a salt, but slow.  Evidently the carbinol behaves like a pseudobase.

Numerous suggestions have been advanced regarding the formulation of the cation.  The older quinone theory as originated by Armstrong and enlarged by Nietzki proposed formula L.

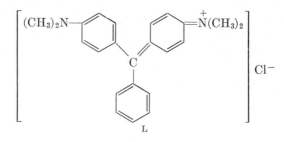

L

While there are no triphenylmethane dyes based on *meta*-amines (in analogy with the lack of *meta*-quinones) and conductivity measurements carried out by Hantzsch and Osswald [104] lend support to the quinone formula as pictured above, the intense color value of the salts cannot be similarly explained.  A $N/50,000$ solution of Malachite Green has about the same depth of color as a $N/1$ solution of copper sulfate, while a $N/50$ solution of quinone has that of a $N/1$ potassium chromate solution.  Clearly the quinone or quinonimine structure *per se* cannot give rise to the great color intensity of the dyes.  Georgievics [105] considered the unsaturated condition of the whole molecule to be responsible for the color, and not the presence of a quinonoidal structure.  Will-

[104] Hantzsch and Osswald, *Ber.*, **33**, 278 (1900).
[105] Georgievics, *Chem. Ztg.*, **44**, 41 (1920).

stätter,[106] on the strength of investigations dealing with quinoneimines, was of the opinion that a meriquinoid state produced the intense color of the triarylmethanes.    Other authors sought the primary cause in oscillation between the quinonoid and benzene rings of the dye molecule, and still other investigations have been undertaken to prove that the state of the central methane carbon atom is decisive.    The line of this development is marked by publications of v. Baeyer,[107] Werner, Pfeiffer,[108] Hantzsch,[109] Kehrmann, and Dilthey.    In the light of the resonance theory, the two extreme resonance configurations of Malachite Green may be written as shown.

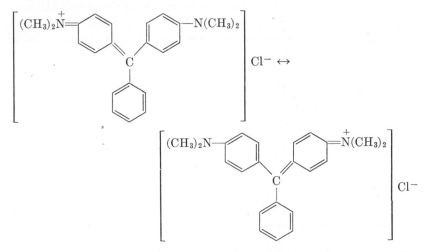

In sulfonated triarylmethane dyes the sulfonic acid groups can be neutralized with alkali without diminishing the color value.    There is also the possibility of formation of an inner salt between the sulfonic acid radical and the dye cation, either within the same molecule or between two molecules.

The triarylmethanes, as a rule, carry very much the same substituents as the azo dyes.    It is advantageous to classify them accordingly. There are variously substituted primary, secondary, and tertiary amino groups, and hydroxyl and acyloxy groups.    Solubility and acid character is imparted by such substituents as sulfonic and carboxylic radicals; the use of the salicylic grouping in addition confers mordant dyeing properties.    Triarylmethane dyes carrying a substituent (Cl, $SO_3H$, $CH_3$, etc.) *ortho* to the central carbon atom show increased fastness to alkali.

[106] Willstätter and Piccard, *Ber.*, **41**, 1462 (1908).

[107] v. Baeyer, *Ann.*, **354**, 152 (1907).

[108] Stobbe and Haertel, *Ann.*, **370**, 99 (1910); Pfeiffer, *Ann.*, **376**, 285 (1910); **383**, 92 (1911); **404**, 1 (1914); **412**, 253 (1917).

[109] Hantzsch, *Ber.*, **52**, 509 (1919).

The nuclei linked together through the central carbon atom may be of the benzene, naphthalene, or heterocyclic series.

As a rule triarylmethane dyes have poor light-fastness. There are, however, exceptions to this rule, and certain configurations will increase the light-fastness of their dyeings to that of the average azo dye.

The typical color scale of the triarylmethanes extends from red through violet to green and blue.

**Preparation.**   Triarylmethane dyes can be made in many ways, the most important of which are sketched below.

1. By condensation of aryl compounds with diphenylmethane derivatives such as tetramethyldiaminobenzophenone (Michler's ketone), the corresponding chloride, hydrol, or even the methane itself.   The use of the hydrol leads to the production of a leuco compound which must be oxidized to the dye.

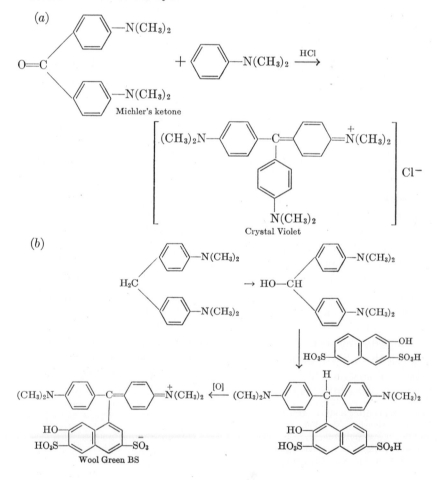

(*c*)

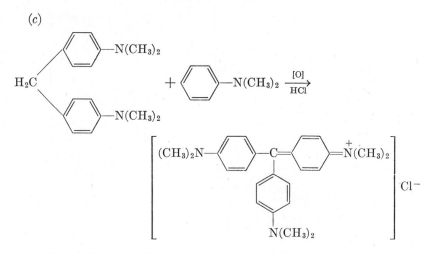

2. The oxidative condensation of three aryl nuclei, one of which must have an aliphatic side chain to furnish the central carbon. This is the

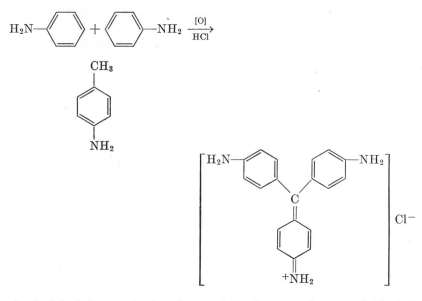

classical fuchsine synthesis, also used in the manufacture of Methyl Violet.

3. By condensation of aryl aldehydes, or toluene derivatives chlorinated in the side chain, with arylamines or phenols. When using benzotrichloride compounds the dyes are formed directly, whereas the use of benzalchlorides or benzaldehydes leads to the formation of leuco compounds requiring further oxidation to the dye.

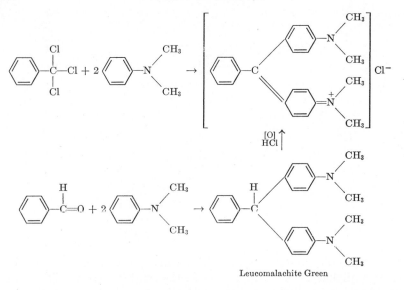

Leucomalachite Green

There are other methods which, however, have not gained technical importance, e.g., the action of carbon tetrachloride on arylamines or phenols in the presence of aluminum chloride or the condensation of the sodium ketyl of Michler's ketone with chlorobenzene.

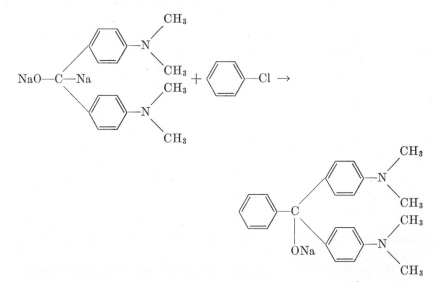

Attempts have been made to impart the generally better fastness of azo dyes to triphenylmethanes by diazotizing aminotriphenylmethanes and coupling them with suitable azo couplers. The dyes obtained, however, lose the brilliant hue of the triphenylmethanes without gaining appreciably in fastness. They have practically disappeared from the market.

## Diaminotriarylmethanes

**Basic Dyes.** This class is generally obtained by condensation of benzaldehydes with arylamines. The prototype of this series, Doebner's Violet (LI), obtained from aniline and benzotrichloride has never

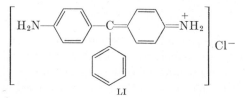

LI

attained great technical importance. Substitution of the amino hydrogens in this dye with alkyl or aryl substituents leads to green dyes, and the tetramethylated compound, Malachite Green, prepared by condensation of benzaldehyde with dimethylaniline and oxidation of the leuco compound formed with lead peroxide, has attained great technical use. It possesses a pure green shade which is somewhat bluer than the corresponding dye obtained from diethylaniline. Of far greater importance, however, is nuclear substitution in the position *ortho* to the central carbon. The shade turns to blue-green and blue and at the same time the poor fastness to alkali shown by Malachite Green is very much improved. This is a very important factor.

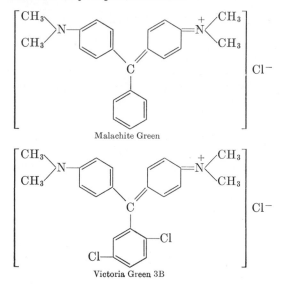

Malachite Green

Victoria Green 3B

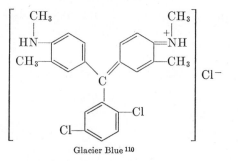

Glacier Blue [110]

All the dyes of this group have great tinctorial power. As basic dyes they will dye silk, jute, paper, straw, wood, and lacquers. For the dyeing of wool the corresponding sulfonic acids are preferred.

**Acid Dyes.** The link between the basic and typical acid dyes is furnished by dyes carrying —COOH groups. Condensation of tetramethyldiaminobenzohydrol and benzoic acid with subsequent oxidation will yield Chrome Green (LII), a dye usable for cotton printing on a chrome mordant. Similar dyes are obtained from salicylic acid and β-hydroxynaphthoic acid. Their value is limited.

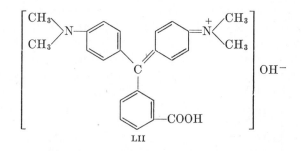

LII

The acid dyes carrying sulfonic acid groups are more important. Satisfactory solubility of triphenylmethane dyes for dyeing purposes is obtained only by the introduction of two sulfonic groups into the molecule. Since Malachite Green can be sulfonated only once, in the benzaldehyde nucleus,[111] a second benzene nucleus and sulfonation position has to be provided by condensation compounds like ethylbenzylaniline and dibenzylaniline, as such or in the form of their sulfonic acids.

Dyes of the acid Malachite Green series are: Light Green SF,[112] trisulfonic acid of the condensation product of benzaldehyde with ethyl-

[110] Schmidt and Bachelut, U. S. pat. 525,627 (1894); Gnehm and Bänziger, *Ber.*, **29**, 875 (1896).

[111] Mayer, "Chemie der organischen Farbstoffe," Springer, Berlin (1924), p. 87.

[112] Friedländer, *Ber.*, **22**, 588 (1889).

benzylaniline; Guinea Green BA, condensation product of benzaldehyde with ethylbenzylanilinesulfonic acid.

They yield bright colors which possess poor fastness. A definite step toward faster dyes was the recognition that a sulfonic group *ortho* to the central carbon would impart better fastness, even to a considerably higher degree than the presence of substituents like —Cl or —CH₃. This effect of substitution on the fastness to alkali is illustrated in the dyes below, Neptune Blue BRA (LVI) being the best, Malachite Green (LIII) the worst, and Setoglaucin O (LIV) and Erioviridin B (LV) being intermediate in fastness.

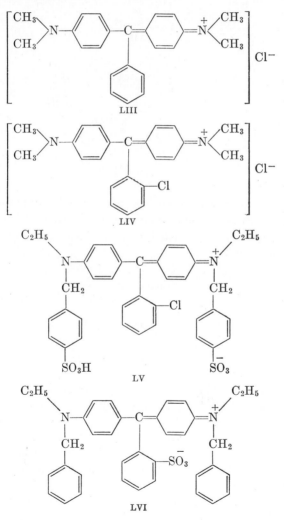

By the introduction of the *o*-sulfonic acid group, the shade of the dye is changed towards the bluer side of the visible spectrum. The more important dyes of this group are Patent Blue V (LVII) and Xylene Blue AS (LVIII).

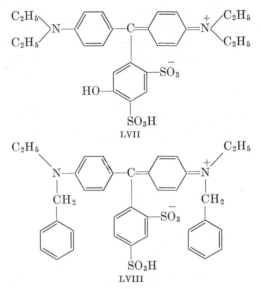

LVII

LVIII

Replacement of the aryl nucleus carrying the sulfonic group by naphthalene derivatives, as in Naphthalene Green V (LIX), also leads to alkali-fast dyes even though the sulfonic acid groups are not *ortho* to the central carbon.

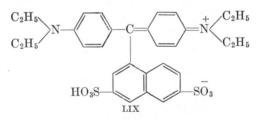

LIX

None of these dyes have satisfactory fastness to light but their use is still widespread since in combination dyeings with faster dyes their properties are often materially enhanced.

Efforts have been made dating back to the 1930's to improve the general properties of the triarylmethane dyes by various means. It is claimed in numerous patents [113] that the use of longer aliphatic chains

[113] Boeger and Meissner, U. S. pat. 1,876,842 (1932) [*C. A.*, **27**, 195 (1933)]; Francke, U. S. pat. 1,938,014 (1933) [*C. A.*, **28**, 1198 (1934)]; Boeger and Oswald, U. S. pat. 1,959,-

increases the strength of these dyes; for example, dye LX is claimed to be twice as strong as LXI.

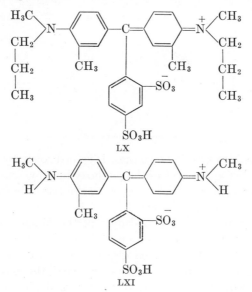

LX

LXI

Of interest also are proposals to utilize indole nuclei.[114]  It has been shown that dyes containing such a structure exhibit fastness comparable to that of the better average azo dyes.

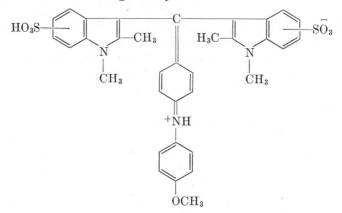

455 (1934) [C. A., 28, 4606 (1934)]; Wahl et al., U. S. pat. 2,003,407 (1935) [C. A., 29, 4951 (1935)]; Wolff et al., U. S. pat. 2,192,188 (1939) [C. A., 34, 4585 (1940)]; Boeger and Meissner, Ger. pat. 490,377 (1927) [C. A., 24, 2302 (1930)].

[114] Wolff, U. S. pat. 2,032,033 (1936) [C. A., 30, 2767 (1936)]; Muehlbauer and Neemann, U. S. pat. 2,154,926 (1939) [C. A., 33, 5672 (1939)]; Wolff and Heim, U. S. pat. 2,198,298 (1940) [C. A., 34, 5670 (1940)]; Wolff and Beniers, U. S. pat. 2,202,037 (1940) [C. A., 34, 6825 (1940)].

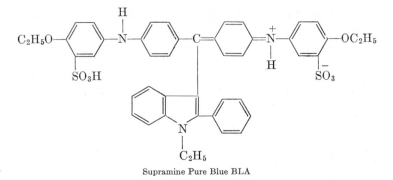

Supramine Pure Blue BLA

Whether the increased light-fastness is gained solely by the use of the indole radical or the presence of the p-ethoxydiphenylamine grouping is, however, open to discussion, inasmuch as the latter grouping is known to enhance light-fastness in other dyes.

A unique use to which the acid dyes of the Malachite Green series have been put is their application for antihalation layers on the back of photographic films. These green gelatin layers absorb light reflected from the back of the film. After the exposure of the film their purpose has been fulfilled, and their easy discoloration in the alkaline fixation bath recommends them highly for this purpose.

### Triaminotriarylmethanes

**Basic Dyes.** Fuchsine, the oldest triphenylmethane dye, is prepared by three principal methods: (a) oxidation of a mixture of aniline, o-toluidine, and p-toluidine with arsenic acid; (b) oxidation of the same mixture with nitrobenzene; (c) formation of diaminodiphenylmethane from aniline and formaldehyde and oxidation of this base in the presence of aniline with nitrobenzene, hydrogen chloride, and ferrous chloride. Methods (a) and (b) will yield a methyltriaminotriphenylcarbinol; method (c) leads to an unmethylated product. Since, however, in the "methyl-fuchsine" the methyl group is in the m-position to the central

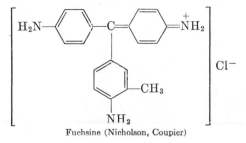

Fuchsine (Nicholson, Coupier)

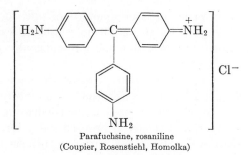

Parafuchsine, rosaniline
(Coupier, Rosenstiehl, Homolka)

carbon, it exerts hardly any influence on the shade and the dye in its coloristic properties is very close to the unmethylated product.

Both variations are still being used today for a variety of purposes under a great many names (Magenta, Cerise, Brilliant Fuchsine, Diamond Fuchsine, etc.). Application of this basic dye with the hue of the flower of the fuchsia plant extends to the dyeing of silk, wool, and paper, and to a host of other, minor fields.

The alkylated fuchsines, penta- and hexamethyl-rosanilines, Methyl and Crystal Violet, respectively, are, however, used to a much greater extent.

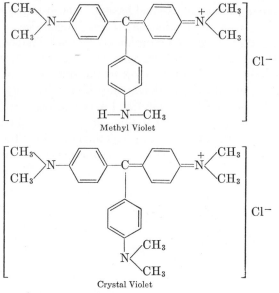

Methyl Violet

Crystal Violet

Neither of these dyes is made by alkylation of rosaniline, but by different methods starting with dimethylaniline. Methyl Violet is commonly produced by exposing dimethylaniline, either in aqueous solution or in the presence of large amounts of salt, to the oxidizing action of air with copper sulfate or phenol acting as catalysts. The central carbon evidently stems from the formaldehyde cleaved out of the dimethylaniline.

Crystal Violet, on the other hand, is made from phosgene and dimethylaniline, Michler's ketone being formed as an intermediate. Frequently phosphorus oxychloride is used as the condensing agent. Both are very powerful dyes, and though little used today for the dyeing of textiles, their consumption for other purposes such as the dyeing of paper or for hectographic inks, duplicating papers, typewriter ribbons, and stamp pads is large.

It was noted above that methylation of rosaniline resulted in a deepening of the shade from a bright bluish red (rosaniline) to a violet (Crystal Violet). Later it was found that the introduction of aryl groups had an even greater effect. Thus, reddish to greenish blue shades of very pure hue may be obtained by successive substitution of the amino hydrogens with phenyl radicals. These basic blues are known as rosaniline blues or spirit blues and are used to a limited extent for the dyeing of spirit lacquers.

**Acid Dyes.** Disulfonated rosaniline, Acid Magenta O, is as sensitive to alkali as the unsulfonated dye and has the same absorption spectrum; evidently little or no sulfonation has taken place *ortho* to the central carbon (cf. p. 304). It is used occasionally where brilliance of hue is of prime importance and no consideration need be given to fastness.

There are two main classes of dyes in the sulfonated polyalkyl-rosanilines, those substituted in the amino groups by alkyl or aralkyl groups and those where both alkyl and aryl residues are represented. The first group yields pure violet to blue-violet shades; the latter, blues of varying hues. In their fastness to alkali they follow the same rules discussed above under the diaminotriarylmethanes as shown by the examples.

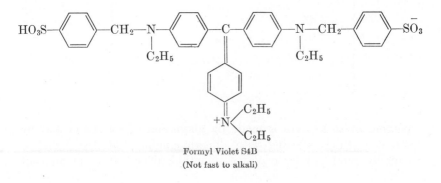

Formyl Violet S4B
(Not fast to alkali)

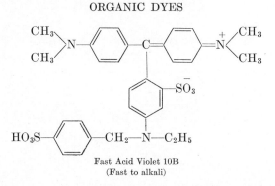

Fast Acid Violet 10B
(Fast to alkali)

Many variations in the substituents were tried, e.g., the use of longer chain aliphatics, but no improvement in the fastness to light was obtained until fairly recently. These later developments were based on the observation made earlier that the introduction of the p-alkoxydiphenylamine grouping has a beneficial effect, for example Brilliant Indocyanine 6B (LXII).[115] In the more recent work the diphenylamine nucleus has

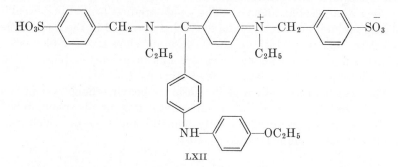

LXII

been retained but the kind and number of the substituents have been varied considerably as illustrated.[116-120]

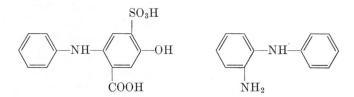

[115] Polikier and Boeger, U. S. pat. 1,731,637 (1929) [*C. A.*, **24**, 246 (1930)]; Wahl *et al.*, U. S. pat. 2,003,407 (1935) [*C. A.*, **29**, 4951 (1935)].

[116] Eckert and Schilling, U. S. pat. 2,183,237 (1939) [*C. A.*, **34**, 2611 (1940)].

[117] Wahl *et al.*, U. S. pat. 2,039,571 (1936) [*C. A.*, **30**, 4335 (1936)].

[118] Wolff and Werner, U. S. pat. 2,072,539 (1937) [*C. A.*, **31**, 3298 (1937)].

[119] Wolff and Werner, U. S. pat. 2,091,463 (1937) [*C. A.*, **31**, 7665 (1937)].

[120] Musher, U. S. pat. 2,199,577 (1940) [*C. A.*, **34**, 6089 (1940)].

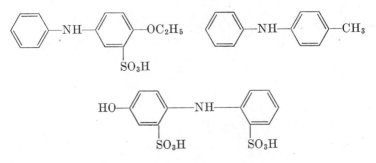

The improvements in light-fastness claimed for such dyes put them on a par with an average wool azo dye.

Strangely enough, the di- or tri-phenylated rosanilines do not show any increase in light-fastness over the rosanilines. The sulfonated derivatives represent acid dyes of very pure blue hue which have been used for the dyeing of wool, silk, paper, and color lakes. Alkali Blue, the sodium salt of the monosulfonic acid, when dyed on wool or silk is applied in a peculiar manner. The goods are first heated in a weakly alkaline solution of the dye, the dye being absorbed in the form of the colorless alkali salt which on acidification develops into the blue color. Higher sulfonated rosaniline blues are known as cotton blues, water blues, ink blues, and under a score of other names.

The poor fastness to light of the basic triphenylmethane dyes in lake work is greatly improved when phosphotungstic or phosphomolybdic acids are used to produce brilliantly colored complex lakes. Such lakes are known as Fanal or Helmerco colors.

### Hydroxytriarylmethanes

The hydroxy derivatives of triphenylcarbinol are called rosolic acids, aurines, or corallines. They are yellow in the form of their free acids, and their salts are red. Synthesis is effected by treatment of phenols with dehydrating agents, preferably in concentrated sulfuric acid, and in the presence of a compound such as formaldehyde, benzaldehyde, or oxalic acid which is capable of yielding the central carbon atom which is required. Oxidation of the resulting methane derivative is effected generally with nitrosylsulfuric acid. The shades of the dyes are red; those of their chrome complexes when the salicylic grouping is used in their structure, violet to blue-green. The simple prototype aurine, tris-($p$-hydroxyphenyl)carbinol, has never attained any importance. The dyes based on salicylic acid are used to a fair degree for wool dyeing and printing. Examples are shown.

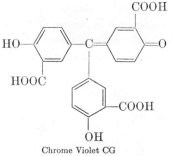

Chrome Violet CG
From HCHO + salicylic acid

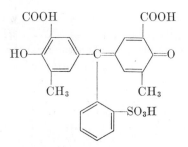

Eriochrome Cyanine R
From benzaldehyde-*o*-sulfonic acid and
cresotinic acid

The light-fastness of these dyes, even in the form of their chrome lakes, is only moderate. Efforts to improve this fastness are evident in patent disclosures like the following compound.[121]

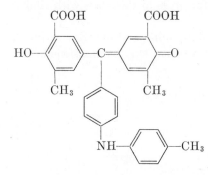

This chapter may be continued with a short discussion of phenol-phthalein, the reaction product between phthalic anhydride and two moles of phenol in the presence of dehydrating agents. Colorless in acid or neutral solution (LXIII), it turns deep carmine red when rendered alkaline (LXIV). With very concentrated alkali, discoloration again

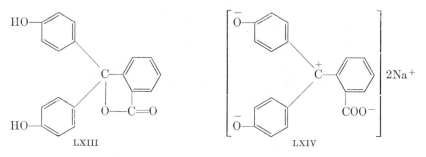

LXIII                                                    LXIV

[121] Francke and Moehrke, U. S. pat. 1,747,541 (1930) [*C. A.*, **24**, 1748 (1930)].

takes place (LXV), while very strong acids form intense orange-red addition compounds (LXVI). The formulas may serve as an explanation of these phenomena in the light of the theory of Dilthey-Witzinger. The dye's importance lies in the indicator field of $pH$ 8.2–10.

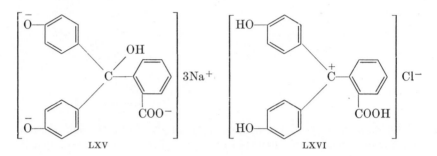

LXV                              LXVI

There are quite a few dyes in this class with similar constitutions and properties.[122]

As an example of an amino hydroxytriphenylmethane, the green dye of the following constitution may be mentioned.[123]

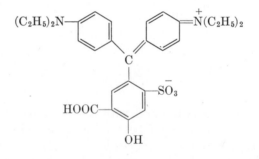

### Xanthenes

The xanthenes belong to the class of di- and tri-arylmethane dyes in that they are cyclic analogs in which two of the aryl nuclei are joined together by an oxygen atom. All are derivatives of xanthene, but none are made from xanthene. This class of dyes is made up of the pyronines (derivatives of diarylmethanes) and phthaleins (derivatives of triarylmethanes). The phthaleins contain a carboxy group in an o-position of at least one of the aryl radicals since they are prepared from phthalic acid.

[122] Clark and Lubs, *J. Am. Chem. Soc.*, **40**, 1443 (1918).
[123] Wolff and Frank, U. S. pat. 2,198,468 (1940) [*C. A.*, **34**, 6089 (1940)].

**Pyronines.** As indicated above, these dyes are derivatives of xanthene (LXVII), the oxygen bridge between the two aryl nuclei generally being formed by the loss of water between two hydroxyl groups in the *o*-position to the methane carbon atom. Thus, the condensation of two

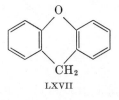

LXVII

moles of *m*-dimethylaminophenol with formaldehyde results in a leuco compound (LXVIII) which on oxidation in the presence of acid is transformed into the red dye Pyronine G (LXIX).[124]

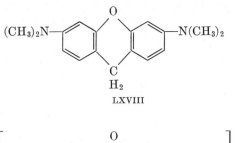

LXVIII

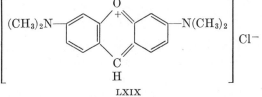

LXIX

This dye is soluble in water with intense red color and yellow fluorescence. It dyes very like fuchsine, but is fast to alkali and its structure usually is not formulated as *p*-quinoid like Malachite Green but *o*-quinoid. Both the methane carbon and the oxygen are to be considered coördinate unsaturated and coördination centers. The oxonium formula is able to account for the alkali-fastness of the dye; not so the ammonium formula. The importance of this dye lies more in the theoretical field than in its practical application. Substitution of cyano on the methene

[124] Möhlau and Koch, *Ber.*, **27**, 2896 (1894).

carbon, incidently, has a strong bathochromic effect; the resulting dye yields on mordanted cotton a greenish blue color.[125]

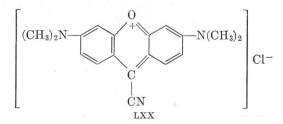

LXX

**Phthaleins.** By the simple process of melting together phthalic anhydride, alkyl-*m*-aminophenols, and zinc chloride (170°), aryl-substituted pyronines are formed. These basic dyes excel by their brilliant red shades on silk and are also used for printing on cotton and for the dyeing of straw, paper, and color lakes. Their light-fastness is not too good, although their wash-fastness is acceptable. The most commonly used are Rhodamine B (LXXI) and its ethyl ester Rhodamine 6G.

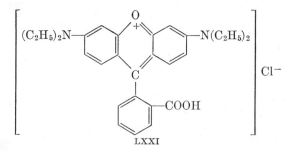

LXXI

By the use of arylaminophenols it is possible to obtain arylated Rhodamines. They unfortunately are too insoluble for practical purposes to be used in the form of their salts and have to be applied in the form of their sulfonic acid derivatives, e.g., Violamine R (LXXII).

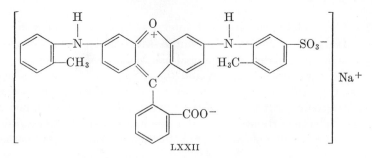

LXXII

[125] Ehrlich and Benda, *Ber.*, **46**, 1931 (1913); von Braun and Aust, *Ber.*, **49**, 989 (1916).

These acid dyes are considerably faster to light than the basic Rhodamines and are used for the dyeing of brilliant shades on silk and wool. A few other dyes of the Rhodamine class are made by condensation with succinic anhydride or benzaldehydedisulfonic acid instead of phthalic anhydride. Their shades are similar, and their dyeing properties do not differ appreciably.

Research in this field has given increased attention to substituents in the phthalic anhydride nucleus.[126, 127] This trend is demonstrated by the two dyes sketched, the first of which, Chromoxane Brilliant Red 3B (LXXIII), finds use as a bright metal complex in textile dyeing and in other fields.

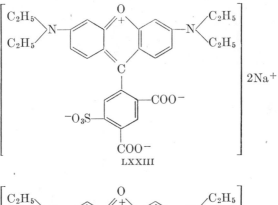

LXXIII

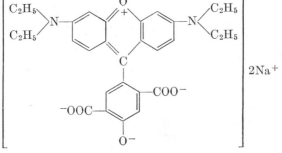

The light-fastness of such dyes is definitely better than that of dyeings obtainable from Rhodamines, while the brilliant hue of the latter is hardly impaired.

Rhodamines in which one of the amino groups has been replaced by hydroxyl are called Rhodoles. They are sensitive to alkali and have never attained any importance. However, the fully hydroxylated com-

[126] Eckert and Schilling, U. S. pat. 2,242,572 (1941) [C. A., 35, 5715 (1941)].
[127] Eckert and Schilling, U. S. pat. 2,153,059 (1939) [C. A., 33, 5199 (1939)].

pounds are worthy of attention. They are formed by the action of phthalic anhydride on resorcinol, and their prototype is fluorescein (LXXIV).[128]

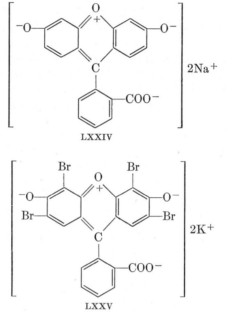

LXXIV

LXXV

This dye is rarely used for the dyeing of textiles but is well known by the strong fluorescence of its sodium salt in water which is still discernible at the dilution of 1 part in 40,000,000. The introduction of halogen into fluorescein leads to interesting dyes. The tetrabromo compound Eosin (LXXV), easily prepared by bromination of the dye in alcohol suspension, dyes silk and wool a yellowish bright red with a strong fluorescence on smooth fibers. The light-fastness is low, but the dinitrodibromo derivative, Eosin BN, is somewhat better in this respect. Its foremost use is in the printing and cosmetic industries (lipsticks). The shade is shifted to a bluish red in the tetraiodo derivative (Erythrosin Extra) and even further to the short-wave end of the spectrum in those dyes containing halogens in the phthalic acid residue (Rose Bengale, Eosin 10B). Their main use is not so much in the field of dyeing textiles or paper but as sensitizers for orthochromatic emulsions.

Dyes of this type containing more than two hydroxyl groups are also known. Thus, the action of phthalic anhydride on pyrogallol results in the formation of Gallein (LXXVI).[129]

[128] Baeyer, *Ber.*, **4**, 558, 662 (1871).
[129] Baeyer, *Ber.*, **4**, 457, 555, 663 (1871).

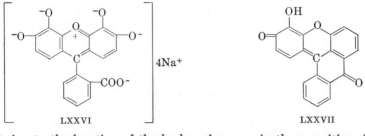

LXXVI                                              LXXVII

Owing to the location of the hydroxyl groups in the *o*-position, it is capable of forming metal complexes and the violet dyeings obtained on chrome-mordanted wool or cotton enjoy very good fastness. These are surpassed, however, by the olive green shades obtained with Coerulein (LXXVII).[129] This dye is obtained from Gallein by treatment with concentrated sulfuric acid at 200°. The resulting compound is a substituted anthraquinone rather than a xanthene since on distillation with zinc dust it yields phenylanthracene. Its close relationship to Anthracene Brown, Anthragallol (see p. 344), is obvious.

### QUINONEIMINE DYES

The dyes of this class can be traced to two basic compounds discovered by Willstätter.[130] Both are practically colorless but yield colored de-

Quinone monoimine     HN=⟨ ⟩=O

Quinone diimine     HN=⟨ ⟩=NH

rivatives when the hydrogen atom of the amino group is replaced by hydroxy- or amino-substituted aryl radicals. Following Grandmougin's suggestion, they are called indophenols (LXXVIII), indoanilines (LXXIX), and indamines (LXXX).

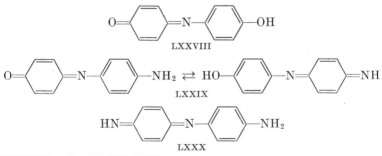

LXXVIII

LXXIX

LXXX

[130] Willstätter, *Ber.*, **37**, 1494 (1904).

All three compounds are very sensitive toward mineral acids and for this reason have found only limited application in the textile dyeing field. They serve, however, as starting materials for valuable dyes when the two benzene nuclei are linked together in the *o,o'*-position with respect to nitrogen by an oxygen, sulfur, or nitrogen atom. Thus, dyes are obtained having the following basic structures.

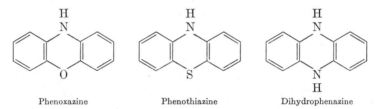

Phenoxazine          Phenothiazine          Dihydrophenazine

They are named oxazine, thiazine, and azine dyes and represent most of the indamines and indophenols manufactured by industry.

## Indophenols, Indoanilines, and Indamines

Indophenols, obtained by oxidation of a mixture of *p*-aminophenol and phenol or by the condensation of *p*-nitrosophenol with a phenol, have never attained technical importance. Indoanilines, accessible through the condensation of *p*-aminodimethylaniline with phenol, are of somewhat greater interest. On reduction they are converted into leuco compounds which can be readily transformed into the coloring matter by oxidation. A dye once used technically in the textile field is the condensation product from *p*-nitrosodimethylaniline and α-naphthol, Indophenol Blue (LXXXI). Although the dye itself exhibits no affinity

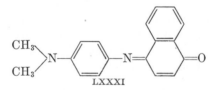

for cotton, its leuco compound shows a definite phenolic character, is substantive to cotton, and can be reoxidized to the dye on the fiber. Its sensitivity to acid, however, has prevented its technical acceptance.

Yet in certain applications such as the dyeing of spirit lacquer or acetate silk this feature is not so important, and the indophenol from *p*-aminodimethylaniline and acetyl-*o*-aminophenol (Celliton Blue B) has been used.

**Color Photography.** The indophenols have found a new and very important use in color photography, which is based to an overwhelming degree on the formation of indophenols in the film. There are several ways to accomplish this, but only one will be considered here. The basic principle is the incorporation of certain couplers (compounds which will react with $p$-aminodimethylaniline to form an anil) into the silver halide-gelatin emulsion of a multilayer film. There will be a "yellow coupler" in the layer sensitized for this color, a cyan coupler for another layer. Care has to be taken that each coupler acts only in the layer in which the respective dye is desired. The migration of couplers into neighboring layers is avoided by the attachment of long aliphatic chains to the couplers or in other ways. When such a film, after exposure, is developed with, for example, $p$-aminodimethylaniline, there is produced at the place of the exposed silver halide a dye to the extent of one mole of dye for four moles of silver. Evidently, the exposed silver halide acts as the oxidizing agent for the dye produced *in situ*. The exact mechanism of the dye formation is still under dispute,[131] but the total equation may be represented as shown.

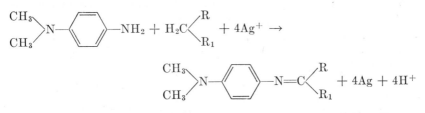

The silver image is subsequently removed by a bleaching process (ferricyanide) and the silver-free color picture finally obtained.

An essential condition of this process is that with one and the same developer the principal colors must be obtained through indophenol or indamine formation. The patent literature abounds with proposals for such couplers. The following may be mentioned, classified according to the colors desired.

*Red:* Pyrazolones, substituted in all conceivable ways; nitriles like malononitrile, $p$-nitrobenzylcyanide, $p$-bromobenzoylacetonitrile, and $\alpha$-naphthoylacetonitrile,

*Cyan:* Phenols and naphthols, in general, such as 1-hydroxy-2-naphthoic acid, hydroxyazaphenanthrenes, and 1-naphtholsulfonamides.

*Yellow:* Ketomethylene compounds like acetoacetic ester, cyanoacetic ester, $p$-nitrobenzoylacetic ester, and acetoacetanilides.

Thus the use of indoanilines is no longer restricted, as it was formerly, to the secondary role of intermediates for azine and sulfur dyes even though this latter application is still the most important and will be dealt with further under these dyes.

[131] Tull, *Brit. J. Phot.*, **85**, 627, 647 (1938); **86**, 115 (1939) [*C. A.*, **33**, 5303, 9163 (1939)].

Indamines, the reaction products of the condensation of $p$-diamines with an arylamine, are of no technical importance as such. Their value, likewise, lies in their role as intermediates in the synthesis of the azines, thiazines, and oxazines.

## Oxazines

**Structure, General Properties.** The oxazines may be considered quinoneimines in which two aryl nuclei are linked together by oxygen.

Extended discussions [132] whether the oxazines are better represented by a $p$-quinoid or $o$-quinoid form have brought no decision. It appears from the available material that both forms are in existence, this compromise view being based on a comparison of absorption spectra and of the colors of solutions of oxazines with solutions of compounds of unquestioned constitution. The dye salts have been termed oxammonium salts since there are present in the cation both coördinate unsaturated nitrogen and oxygen.

The oxazine dyes can be reduced to colorless leuco compounds which by reoxidation even with air are transformed into the original dyes. Coloristically they comprise basic, acid, and direct dyes.

**Preparation.** There are numerous methods of synthesis, the most important of which are: (1) the reaction of aminohydroxy compounds ($o$- or $m$-aminophenols) with suitable phenols; and (2) the condensation of nitroso compounds (for instance, $p$-nitrosodialkylanilines) with phenols. For the production of dioxazines, the condensation of quinones (toluquinone, chloranil) with amines and ring closure by oxidation or other means has attained importance.

In the dyes of this class the basic oxazine nucleus always contains amino groups, primary or substituted, hydroxy groups, or a combination of both. The acid dyes contain one or more sulfonic groups. Other groups such as alkyl, halogen, and carboxyl are often present and have minor effects on shade and/or fastness.

The oldest representative of this class is Meldola's Blue (LXXXII),[133] named after its inventor. It is prepared from $\beta$-naphthol and $p$-nitrosodimethylaniline. It has rather satisfactory fastness and is still used in a limited way for tannin mordanted cotton dyeing or printing and for leather.

Capri Blue (LXXXIII), a bright basic blue of rather good fastness

[132] Kehrmann, *Ber.*, **32**, 2601 (1899); Fierz and Koechlin, *Helv. Chim. Acta*, **1**, 210 (1917).
[133] Meldola, *Ber.*, **12**, 2065 (1879).

to light, is obtained from $p$-nitrosodimethylaniline and diethyl-$m$-amino-cresol.

Replacement of the dialkylamino groups by hydroxyl is accomplished by condensation of nitrosoresorcinol with resorcinol and subsequent bromination to give Iris Blue (LXXXIV), a reddish blue with green fluorescence. The dye LXXXV [134] is an example of a simple dioxazine.

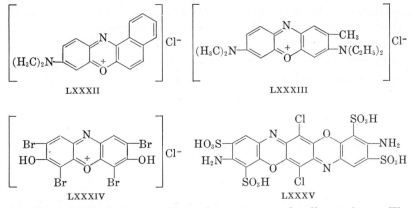

LXXXII                    LXXXIII

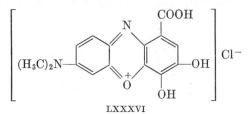

LXXXIV                    LXXXV

**Gallic Acid Derivatives.** These dyes are named gallocyanines. The prototype of this group is LXXXVI, obtained by condensation of gallic acid with $p$-nitrosodimethylaniline, and closely related are Gallamine Blue, from gallamic acid, and Prune, the methyl ester of gallocyanine.

LXXXVI

Also interesting are the dyes obtained by condensation of gallocyanine or Gallamine Blue with naphtholsulfonic acids or resorcinol. Condensation takes place in the 2-position of the gallocyanine with elimination of water to give, for example, with resorcinol the dye LXXXVII.

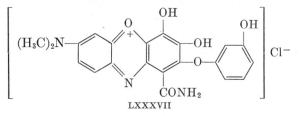

LXXXVII

[134] Greune *et al.*, U. S. pat. 2,139,119 (1938) [*C. A.*, **33**, 2347 (1939)].

They are called phenocyanines or gallazines and dye in greenish blue shades. The gallocyanine dyes are fully equal to the triarylmethane dyes in brilliance of hue but they have far better fastness properties. Their main application is for printing on textiles with metal or tannin mordants. The light-fastness is very good.

With few exceptions the gallocyanines may be brominated or chlorinated directly, yielding bluer and somewhat faster shades. Direct sulfonation is usually possible only with the leuco compounds, and the anilides are somewhat more suited for this treatment. They find use in printing and dyeing of chrome mordanted wool. A typical example is Delphine Blue B (LXXXVIII).

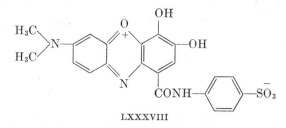

LXXXVIII

In view of the foregoing, it is rather surprising to observe that Alizarine Green (LXXXIX),[135] obtained by condensation of β-naphthoquinonesulfonic acid with 1-amino-2-naphthol-4-sulfonic acid in alkaline solution, is a yellowish green chrome wool dye of only moderate fastness to light.

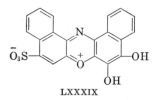

LXXXIX

**Dioxazines.** Of fairly recent origin are the dioxazine dyes, which because of their brilliance and excellent fastness to light have met with great interest. Their synthesis consists usually of the condensation of a quinone with two moles of an arylamine with subsequent ring closure to form the dioxazine nucleus. Their prototypes are old,[136] but the discovery of the more valuable dyes of this type is of fairly recent origin.

---

[135] Reverdin and de la Harpe, *Ber.*, **25**, 1400 (1892); **26**, 1279 (1893).
[136] Maag and Joerg, U. S. pat. 1,065,063 (1913) [*C. A.*, **7**, 2689 (1913)].

A score of patents trace the development of this group.[137]  The shades of the sulfonated dyes range from red to green, the red being definitely less fast to light than the blues or greens.   The sulfonated bases are usually applied in the direct dyeing of vegetable fibers and the unsulfonated bases are being recommended for the dyeing of plastics, etc. The following examples illustrate this series.

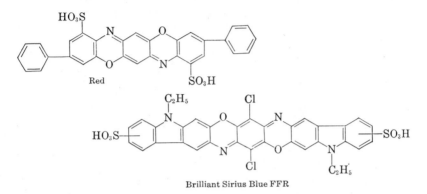

Brilliant Sirius Blue FFR

The best dyes of this group show excellent light-fastness which, however, is tempered by a moderate fastness to acids and alkalies.   They have not been used to a great extent in this country but were used in Europe where fastness to light rather than washing was important.


## Acridines

Acridine dyes are derivatives of acridine and may be considered as di- or tri-phenylmethane dyes substituted by nitrogen in the same way as the xanthene dyes are looked upon as oxygen compounds of the same group.   They are much more basic though, as shown by the easy oxidation of their leuco bases with oxygen of the air and their resistance toward reduction to the leuco compounds.   Their relation to pyridine and quinoline is obvious.

The hues of the acridine dyes range from greenish yellow to reddish brown.   They are used in the dyeing and printing of silk and mordanted cotton and especially for the dyeing of leather.   Unfortunately, their fastness to light is poor.   A favored synthesis consists of the condensation

[137] U. S. pats. 2,016,013; 2,016,504; 2,020,651; 2,024,525; 2,026,092; 2,026,093 (1935); 2,066,915; 2,077,863; 2,077,887; 2,082,344; 2,086,871; 2,092,387; 2,092,399 (1937); 2,130,-016; 2,115,311; 2,115,508; 2,134,505; 2,139,119; 2,139,617 (1938); 2,143,598 (1939); 2,187,-853 (1940); 2,233,940 (1941); 2,278,260; 2,288,522; 2,336,520; 2,336,521; 2,355,496–7 (1942).

of an aldehyde with two moles of a *m*-diamine in the presence of mineral acid.   When using benzaldehyde, phenylacridines result.

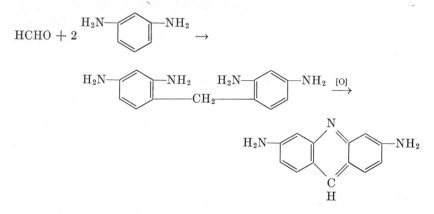

Only a few dyes of this type have achieved technical importance, e.g., Acridine Yellow G (XC) [138] and Flavophosphine GO (XCI).

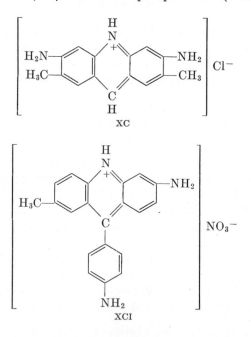

Many acridine dyes show pronounced physiological activity.   In particular, 3,6-diaminoacridinium salts have been recommended for pharma-

[138] Ullmann *et al.*, *Ber.*, **33**, 915 (1900); **34**, 4308 (1901).

ceutical purposes, Trypaflavin and Septacrol being outstanding representatives. Other derivatives, like Rivanol and Atabrine (XCII), also
have attained prominence.

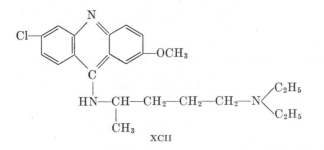

XCII

## Methines

**Natural Products.** The dyes of this class are of various kinds. Common to them is the presence of the chromophore $\geq\!\!C\!\!=\!\!C\!\!<$. Starting
with the dyes that owe their dye character solely to the presence of the
ethylene double bond, one must consider first a number of natural dyes
which are remarkable not so much because of their dyeing properties,
which are negligible, but for their physiological importance. A number
of eminent names [139] are connected with the investigation of these dyes
which, following a proposal of Kuhn and Winterstein (1928), are called
Polyene dyes. They can be discussed here only in a very brief and
selective manner.

Olefins of the lower order are colorless substances. They acquire
color when at least 5–6 double bonds are linked together in uninterrupted
conjugation. Diphenylbutadiene (XCIII) and octatrienoic acid (XCIV)
are colorless; diphenylhexatriene and decatetraenoic acid are yellow.

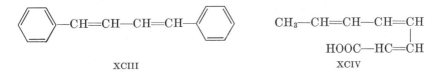

XCIII                              XCIV

Since isoprene, 2-methylbutadiene, forms the basis for many naturally
occurring products, it is not surprising that some natural polymethine
dyes consist of a plurality of isoprene units in which the terminal points
of the long conjugated chain are stabilized either with terpene rings or

[139] Mayer, "Chemie der organischen Farbstoffe," Springer, Berlin (1935), Vol. 2, Chapter 1.

with methyl or carboxyl groups. A few of the dyes of the *carotenoids* are listed.

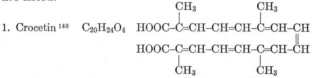

1. Crocetin [140]   $C_{20}H_{24}O_4$

2. Bixin [141]    $C_{25}H_{30}O_4$    A monomethylester with two additional vinyl groups between the carboxyl and the first isoprene unit of the Crocetin structure

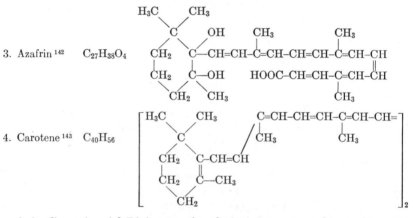

3. Azafrin [142]   $C_{27}H_{38}O_4$

4. Carotene [143]   $C_{40}H_{56}$

Only Crocetin and Bixin are of technical interest as dyes. Crocetin is contained in the form of the glucoside crocin in the safran flower and has been used for the dyeing of textiles and foodstuffs. Bixin is the dyeing principle of the "Orlean" dye and is a substantive dye.

The great importance of the carotenoids lies in their relation to vitamin A. The living organism is capable of breaking down carotene to vitamin A, a process which has been duplicated *in vitro*.[144]

Curcumin is the coloring matter of the root of *Curcuma tinctoria*. Its constitution has been ascertained [145] as shown.

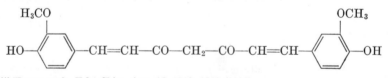

[140] Karrer *et al.*, *Helv. Chim. Acta*, **15**, 1218, 1399 (1932).

[141] Heiduschka and Panzer, *Ber.*, **60**, 546, 1525 (1927); Kuhn and Winterstein, *Ber.*, **65**, 646, 1873 (1932).

[142] Kuhn *et al.*, *Ber.*, **64**, 333 (1931); **65**, 1873 (1932); **66**, 883 (1933).

[143] Karrer *et al.*, *Helv. Chim. Acta*, **16**, 975 (1933).

[144] Olcott and McCann, *J. Biol. Chem.*, **94**, 185 (1931).

[145] Milobedzka *et al.*, *Ber.*, **43**, 2163 (1910); **51**, 1347 (1918).

It is a direct dye for cotton, silk, and wool, but owing to its lack of fastness to alkali is used only as an indicator.

**Synthetic Products.** Turning to the field of synthetic methine dyes, we face a fountainhead of dyes, the development of which has been very active in the last decades and the shades of which cover the whole visible spectrum and beyond. Only a comparatively small number of dyes have been recommended for textile dyeing purposes, but many more are suitable and valuable as photographic sensitizers or desensitizers. The fastness of these dyes shows great variations.

*Basic Dyes.* The condensation products of alkylated *p*-aminobenzaldehydes, or the corresponding benzylidene compounds, with compounds containing an active hydrogen atom lead to dyes ranging from yellow to violet,[146] e.g., Celliton Fast Yellow 7G (XCV) and the orange dye XCVI.

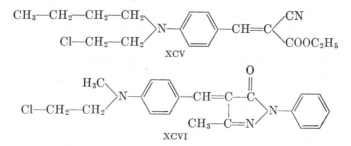

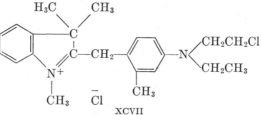

These bright basic dyes show extremely good fastness to light in the yellow hues when dyed on cellulose acetate but diminishing fastness in the orange and red hues. Deeper shades are attainable by the use of heterocyclic compounds, Astrazon Red 6B (XCVII)[147] being a typical example.

These bright basic dyes show extremely good fastness to light in the yellow hues when dyed on cellulose acetate but diminishing fastness in the orange and red hues. Deeper shades are attainable by the use of heterocyclic compounds, Astrazon Red 6B (XCVII) [147] being a typical example.

This red dye is synthesized from 1,3,3-trimethyl-2-methyleneindoline and N-(2-chloroethyl)-N-ethyl-4-amino-2-methylbenzaldehyde.

---

[146] Wahl, U. S. pat. 2,043,081 (1936) [*C. A.*, **30**, 5050 (1936)]; Mueller and Berres, U. S. pat. 2,179,895 (1939) [*C. A.*, **34**, 1861 (1940)]; U. S. pat. 2,206,108 (1940) [*C. A.*, **34**, 7617 (1940)].

[147] Winter and Roh, U. S. pat. 2,164,793 (1939) [*C. A.*, **33**, 8419 (1939)].

*Quinoline Yellow.* By condensation of impure quinoline containing quinaldine with phthalic anhydride, Traub in 1883 [148] obtained a yellow pigment the constitution of which was later clarified [149] and which we know today to be quinophthalone (XCVIII).

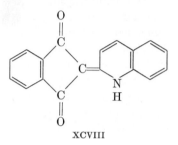

XCVIII

On treatment with fuming sulfuric acid a very bright greenish yellow dye is obtained, Quinoline Yellow, a mixture of mono- and di-sulfonic acids, which dyes wool and silk but has only a moderate fastness to light. Use of chloroquinaldine [150] results in a dye of somewhat improved fastness.

*Cyanines, Use in Color Photography.* Greater importance is attached to dyes of this class which are useful as sensitizers in the photographic field and which are grouped together under the generic name of cyanines.[151]

Vogel in 1873 was the first to observe that the addition of a dye to a silver bromide emulsion confers sensitivity to that part of the spectrum absorbed by the dye. The conclusion followed that by proper selection of dyes the normal sensitivity of an emulsion might be increased for certain desired colors. Not all dyes possess sensitizing action, and many give rise to undesired side effects. It is in the class of cyanine dyes that the best sensitizers have been found. The cyanine dyes contain the system

$$>\!N\!-\!(C\!=\!C)_n\!-\!C\!=\!\overset{+}{N}\!< \;\leftrightarrow\; >\!\overset{+}{N}\!=\!C\!-\!(C\!=\!C)_n\!-\!N\!<$$

In the cyanine dyes the two nitrogens must be members of heterocyclic ring systems in which the conjugated chain linking them extends

[148] Traub, *Ber.*, **16**, 298 (1883).

[149] Jacobsen and Reimer, *Ber.*, **16**, 2603 (1883); Eibner and Hofmann, *Ber.*, **37**, 3023 (1904); Eibner and Löbering, *Ber.*, **39**, 2447 (1906); Eibner and Lange, *Ann.*, **315**, 345 (1901); Eibner, *Chem. Ztg.*, **28**, 1206 (1904).

[150] Bayer and Co., Ger. pat. 204,255 (1907) [*C. A.*, **3**, 843 (1909)]; Brit. pat. 28,266 (1908).

[151] Mees, "The Theory of Photographic Process," Macmillan, New York (1942).

through a part of each heterocyclic ring. The most important heterocycles employed in the synthesis of cyanine dyes are 2- and 4-quinoline,
thiazoline, thiazole, benzothiazole, benzoselenazole, and naphthothia-
zoles. It is, furthermore, essential that the nitrogens be linked by an
odd number of carbon atoms. Lengthening of the chain shifts absorption and sensitization toward the longer wavelengths. Both symmetrical
and unsymmetrical cyanines are known.

Synthesis of these dyes is effected in a number of ways by condensation reactions, the details of which transgress the scope of this chapter.
High purity is essential for their proper performance. A few basic types
are shown.

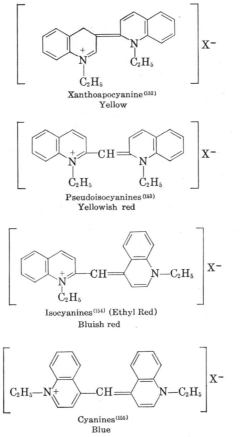

Xanthoapocyanine [152]
Yellow

Pseudoisocyanines [153]
Yellowish red

Isocyanines [154] (Ethyl Red)
Bluish red

Cyanines [155]
Blue

[152] Mills and Ordish, *J. Chem. Soc.*, 81 (1928).
[153] Scheibe, *Ber.*, **54**, 786 (1921).
[154] Fischer, *J. prakt. Chem.*, **98**, 204 (1918).
[155] König and Treichel, *ibid.*, **102**, 63 (1921).

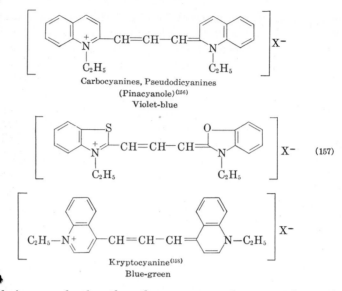

Carbocyanines, Pseudodicyanines
(Pinacyanole)[156]
Violet-blue

(157)

Kryptocyanine[158]
Blue-green

The chain may be lengthened to tetra- and pentacarbocyanines. Furthermore, it may be substituted by alkyl, keto, or alkylated heterocycles as in Neocyanine (XCIX).[159]

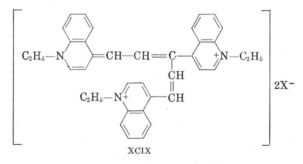

XCIX

Only a few prominent types of the multitude of combinations are mentioned here. Their value lies solely in the photographic field. Very few of the long-chain methine dyes have sufficient fastness to light and acid to make them suitable for textile dyeing purposes. For example, the condensation product of two moles of tetramethylindoline with

[156] Wise et al., Ind. Eng. Chem., **11**, 460 (1919); Mills and Hamer, J. Chem. Soc., 1550 (1920); Braunholtz, ibid., 169 (1922).

[157] Piggott and Rodd, U. S. pat. 2,071,898-9 (1937) [C. A., **31**, 2534 (1937)].

[158] Adams and Haller, J. Am. Chem. Soc., **42**, 2661 (1920).

[159] Dundon, J. Optical Soc. Am., **12**, 397 (1926); Hamer, J. Chem. Soc., 1472 (1928); Brooker et al., J. Optical Soc. Am., **23**, 216 (1933); König, Z. wiss. Phot., **34**, 15 (1935) [Chem. Zentr., **106**, I, 3752 (1935)].

ethyl orthoformate in acetic anhydride gives Astraphloxin FF Extra (C),[160] a very bright red dye used both as a sensitizer and as a textile dyestuff. Similar dyes are described in the patent literature.[161]

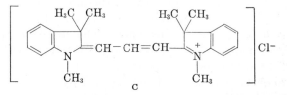

C

**Azomethine Dyes.** Azomethine dyes, containing the chromophore —CH=N—, are of only limited interest for dyeing purposes. The condensation products of aromatic aldehydes and arylamines cleave easily under the influence of mineral acids unless the azomethine group is a member of a heterocyclic nucleus as in the thiazoles. However, if the azomethine link can be stabilized by ring formation as in a metal complex, a dye of suitable stability is obtained. Only a limited number of such dyes have been used. An example is Perlon Fast Yellow RS (CI), the chromium complex of the condensation product of 3,5-dichloro-salicylaldehyde and 2-aminophenol-4-sulfonamide. Similar dyes for color lake purposes are recommended elsewhere.[162]

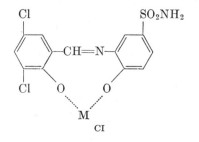

CI

## Thiazines

The thiazines, in analogy to the oxazines, may be considered to be derivatives of quinoneimines in which both aromatic rings are connected by sulfur.

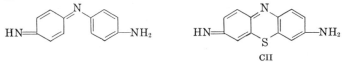

CII

[160] König, U. S. pat. 1,524,791 (1925) [*C. A.*, **19**, 1058 (1925)]; *Ber.*, **57**, 685 (1924).

[161] Wahl, U. S. pat. 1,863,679 (1932) [*C. A.*, **26**, 4480 (1932)]; Schmidt, U. S. pat. 1,910,-478-9 (1933) [*C. A.*, **27**, 4091 (1933)].

[162] Schmidt and Wahl, U. S. pat. 2,116,913 (1938) [*C. A.*, **32**, 5225 (1938)].

The decision whether to regard these dyes as *o*- or *p*-quinoids leans more towards the *p*-structure, although there are well-supported reasons for either form. The absorption spectra definitely favor the *p*-quinoid structure. Sulfur present in a ring structure shows less tendency to change into the thionium form, i.e., to become the cationic coördination center, than oxygen in the oxazines. The dyeing character of the thiazines, therefore, is dominated by the ammonium cation with two coördinate unsaturated nitrogen atoms.

The prototype of this group and the first dye made in this series is Lauth's Violet (CII). It was obtained by oxidation of *p*-phenylene-diamine in dilute aqueous solution with ferric chloride in the presence of hydrogen sulfide, but it never attained importance. Its tetramethyl derivative, however, Methylene Blue (CIII), is still an important dye used for the printing of tannin-mordanted cotton, wool, and silk, and for the dyeing of paper, straw, and leather. Its synthesis by Bernthsen consists of oxidation of a mixture of *p*-aminodimethylaniline and di-methylaniline with bichromate in the presence of sodium thiosulfate and zinc chloride.

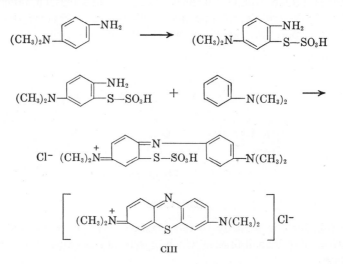

There are other, similar basic dyes of this type derived from mono-ethyl-*o*-toluidine and related compounds, none of which, however, have prevailed technically.

Of limited interest are acid thiazines such as Gallothionin (CIV), made by the oxidation of the mercaptan from dimethyl-*p*-phenylenedi-amine and gallic acid, which dyes bluish violet shades on chrome-mordanted wool. Other examples are the Brilliant Alizarine Blues (CV)

obtained by the condensation of *p*-nitrosodialkylanilines with β-naph-
tholquinonesulfonic acids in the presence of sodium thiosulfate.

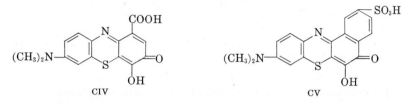

CIV                                    CV

The light-fastness of their metal complexes on the fiber is good. There
have not been any interesting developments in the recent past in this
direction.

## Azines

This important group of dyes is based on two prototypes, Phenazine
(CVI) and the N-substituted Phenazine (CVII).

CVI                                    CVII

Both these types may be substituted in many ways, but in no event
will dyes result when both azine nitrogens have been substituted. It
has been shown by Kehrmann and Nietzki in long controversies with
Fischer and Hepp,[163] who favored the *p*-quinonoid structure, that azines
are *o*-quinonoids.[164] Agreement exists that the basic atoms in the molecule form the center of the inner sphere of the coördination formula
binding the electropositive part of an acid radical in a coördinate way,
while the negative ion enters the outer sphere.

Coloristically the azines are used as basic and acid dyes with hues
ranging from red to blue and black. They are synthesized by a score
of methods, the most important of which are shown.

(*a*) Reaction of *o*-aryldiamines and *o*-arylquinones.

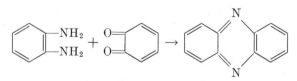

[163] Fischer and Hepp, *Ber.*, **23**, 2788 (1890).

[164] Kehrmann, *Ber.*, **29**, 2316 (1896); Nietzki, *Ber.*, **29**, 2771 (1896); Kehrmann and
Schaposchnikoff, *Ber.*, **30**, 1565, 2620 (1897); **33**, 395 (1900).

(b) Oxidative condensation of an aromatic o-diamine with a *para*-substituted phenol.

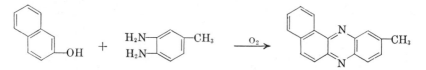

(c) Condensation of o-aminoazo compounds with β-naphthols.

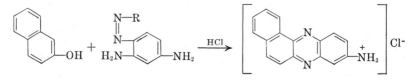

(d) Oxidation of a p-diamine with two moles of a monoamine or one mole of a m-diamine.

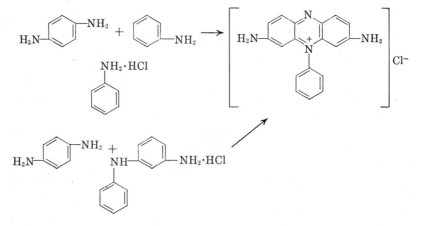

The amino groups in diaminoazines are diazotizable. It should be noted, however, that there is a significant difference in the ease of diazotizability between them, the first being diazotized very readily in dilute acids, the second responding only in concentrated acids. Both will couple with azo couplers to form azo dyes.

**Phenazines.** The monoaminophenazines are known as eurhodines, and they may be obtained, for instance, by the action of an o-diamine on the azo dye phenylazo-α-naphthylamine. They are very weak dyes and without technical value. The bases are yellow; the salts, red.

On treatment with hydrochloric acid they are converted into the hydroxy derivatives with loss of ammonia, the so-called eurhodoles,

which may be obtained also by the condensation of hydroxynaphtho-
quinones with *o*-phenylenediamines. The latter possess a feebly basic
and acid character and are of no technical importance.

In the series of the diaminophenazines, mention may be made of
Toluylene Red, obtained from dimethyl-*p*-phenylenediamine and *m*-tolu-
ylenediamine by way of the indamine. The indamine on heating with
water yields the azine.

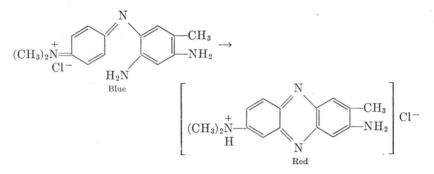

Blue

Red

*N-Phenylphenazines.* The monoaminophenylphenazonium compounds
have not attained technical importance. The diamino derivatives, however, also known as safranines, are of great technical value, especially
Tolusafranine, the synthesis of which is usually effected by oxidation of
one mole of *p*-toluylenediamine and one mole of *o*-toluidine with alkaline
dichromate to the corresponding indamine, which in the presence of
one mole of aniline forms the Safranine, indicated by a change in color
from blue or green to red. Instead of aniline, any other primary arylamine may be used. The technical Safranine represents a mixture of
several homologs of which the following dye is the main component.

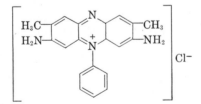

The monobasic salt is red. Substitution by alkoxy groups shifts the
hue toward the yellow, by alkyl and aryl groups toward the blue, side
of the spectrum. Reduction yields a leuco compound which can be
reoxidized readily to the dye and dyes on mordanted cotton with a good
fastness to washing but poor fastness to light. Its main use is for the
dyeing of paper.

The unsubstituted Phenosafranine (diaminophenylphenazonium chloride) is not used for dyeing purposes but has found application as a photographic desensitizer.

By diazotization of Safranine and coupling with various couplers, basic azo dyes (Janus dyes)[165] of moderate fastness and limited technical value are produced.

1. Rosindulines, Indulines. Rosindulines are the aminophenylnaphthazonium dyes, two of which are illustrated.

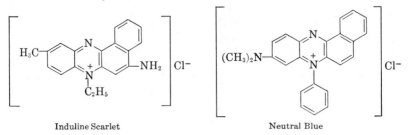

Induline Scarlet       Neutral Blue

Their technical value is small. Aryl-substituted Safranines, on the other hand, are fairly important. The first synthetic coal-tar dye, Mauveine (Perkin, 1856), admittedly has only historical interest. Other

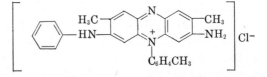

derivatives, however, like the indulines, are used industrially on a large scale. These represent highly arylated safranines and are obtained by condensation of aminoazobenzene, aniline, and aniline hydrochloride at 180°. They yield shades from reddish to greenish blues, depending on the degree of arylation. The dyes in the form of their dye bases are soluble in hydrocarbons; the hydrochloride salts are soluble in ethanol; a low and high degree of phenylation in these dyes may be represented as follows.

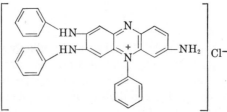

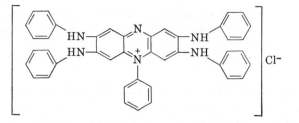

The use of the basic indulines for calico printing has decreased to insignificant amounts, their main use being as intermediates for the sulfonated indulines.

2. Nigrosines. Nigrosines are bluish-blackish indulines which are obtained either by addition of nitroaryl compounds to a regular induline melt or by the reaction of nitrobenzene, aniline, and ferric chloride at 170–200°. Marketed in very large amounts because of their low cost, they are used in the form of their free bases or hydrochloride salts for the coloring of waxes, ink pads, typewriter ribbons, spirit lacquers, and, above all, plastics. They serve further as intermediates for the sulfonated nigrosines. Their exact constitution is unknown, but it is suspected that it is closely related to products grouped together under the generic name Aniline Blacks. These last dyes are created on the textile fiber, mostly cotton, by the oxidation of aniline or its homologs with varying oxidizing agents—sodium chlorate, dichromate, etc.—in the presence of catalysts like copper or vanadium compounds. The course of the reaction is very much dependent on the reaction conditions. *p*-Aminodiphenylamine probably is one of the primary products. Willstätter [166] and Green [167] have contributed materially to our present knowledge of the constitution of these dyes, which in their finished form represent a mixture, the main component of which is an arylazonium dye of probably the following structure.

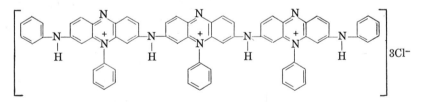

It has been suggested that indamines with eight aniline nuclei form intermediate stages which have been named Emeraldine and Nigraniline and which form greenish salts. These *p*-quinoid compounds are thought

[166] Willstätter and Cramer, *Ber.*, **44**, 2162 (1911).
[167] Green and Johnson, *Ber.*, **46**, 3769 (1913).

to be responsible for the diasgreeable "greening" of faulty Aniline Blacks on the fiber; it is significant that the o-quinonoid dye as shown above does not show this defect. Aniline Black is fast to light and soaping and will stand a light chlorine bleach. It is one of the most important black dyes.

Taken as a whole, there have not been any new developments in the field of the basic azine dyes for some time. It appears that the efforts visible in the patent literature are directed somewhat more toward azines carrying sulfonic groups.

3. Sulfonated Phenazines. The sulfonated derivatives of phenazines or phenylphenazonium chlorides have never been developed to technical significance with the exception of the sulfonated indulines or nigrosines. It was by treating induline bases with concentrated sulfuric acid that Coupier introduced this easy way of solubilizing water-insoluble compounds. These sulfonated products of varying degrees of sulfonation have been used extensively for the dyeing of silk, leather, paper, etc. Similarly sulfonated nigrosines have found wide application in the dyeing of leather, paper, and to a smaller degree for a number of specialties, like shoe polishes. In comparison with other water-soluble dyes, their solubility in aqueous solution is very high, up to 35%, versus a normal solubility requirement of 2–5% for azo dyes. In spite of their moderate fastness, the water-soluble nigrosines may be expected to keep their market owing to their very low price. No material progress is discernible in recent times in this direction.

In the field of the rosindulines considerable and persistent efforts toward improvements are evident in the patent literature. This group of azines dates back to 1890, when it was shown that sulfonated aryl-naphthylrosindulines yield rather bright and fast blue dyes for wool, e.g., Milling Blue (CVIII).[168]

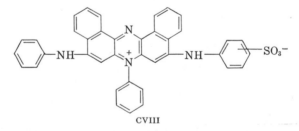

CVIII

Further progress was made by using condensation reactions involving chiefly phenyl-β-naphthylamine or 6,8-dianilinonaphthalenesulfonic acid on the one side and p-phenylenediamine derivatives on the other.

[168] Fischer and Hepp, *Ann.*, **262**, 238 (1891); **272**, 306 (1893).

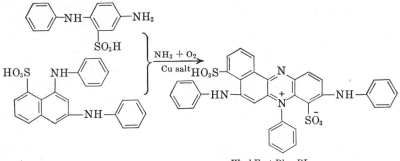

Wool Fast Blue BL

Dyes of this kind show very good light- and wash-fastness, which is even further enhanced in the Novazol acid blues, an example of which is shown.

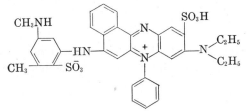

The patent literature lists many variations of the types mentioned above, such as the employment of *p*-methoxydiphenylamines,[169] which, as has already been pointed out for the triarylmethane dyes and violamines, have a beneficial effect on the light-fastness. This theme is pursued further with numerous variations in a number of patents.[170] Metalization of properly constituted azine dyes with the aim of increased light- and wash-fastness is another development.[171] For example, the following dye is capable of metal complex formation, presumably at the salicylic

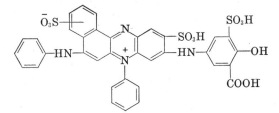

[169] Neelmeier and Nocken, U. S. pat. 1,686,026 (1928) [*C. A.*, **22**, 4833 (1928)].

[170] Nocken and Neelmeier, U. S. pat. 2,001,975 (1935) [*C. A.*, **29**, 4598 (1935)]; Huber and Vogt, U. S. pat. 2,068,056 (1937) [*C. A.*, **31**, 1631 (1937)]; Huber, U. S. pat. 2,178,793 (1939) [*C. A.*, **34**, 1496 (1940)].

[171] Höfchen and Huber, U. S. pat. 2,232,067 (1941) [*C. A.*, **35**, 3453 (1941)].

acid grouping. The hues of such dyes are violet, but metalization changes their shade. The chrome lake of the dye shown is described as a very clear and fast blue especially suited for the chrome printing of cotton goods.

It has been mentioned earlier that the azine dyes may be reduced to their leuco compounds and are easily reoxidized. None of the dyes discussed before, however, exhibits the property of a vat dye, i.e., to dye in the form of its leuco compound on the fiber. There are vat dyes in the anthraquinone series which contain the azine structure in their molecule, and these will be discussed later. The bridge to these dyes is furnished by naphthazines of the following type.

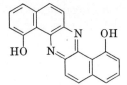

On chlorination of such dihydroxydinaphthazine compounds to a degree that at least six chlorine atoms enter the molecule, red vat dyes of excellent fastness are produced.

## QUINONES

The chromophoric principle common to all quinones is the combination of the ethylene double bond, $>C=C<$, and the carbonyl group, $>C=O$. Dyes are derived from the simple benzoquinones and naphthoquinones and from more complex ring systems—anthraquinones, etc. In each case the dye character is based on the grouping

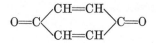

The necessary auxochromes may be hydroxyl or amino groups, and, wherever these are *ortho* or *para* to one of the carbonyl groups, conditions exist for the formation of complex metal salts. Dyes containing sulfonic acid groups have the characteristics of acid dyes for wool. Higher-molecular-weight quinones are represented by the vat dyes.

### Benzoquinones

Quite a few benzoquinones occur in nature, the great majority in molds, fungi, and mushrooms. Certain of these have been found to possess biological activity and have been identified with the active principles of long-known drugs. The simplest known is the yellow 2,6-dimethoxyquinone isolated from *Adonis vernalis* L. by Karrer in 1930. Another dye isolated from a fungus of the Polyporaceae family was isolated as far back as 1877 and identified by methods of degradation and synthesis [172] as polyporic acid (CIX).

The dye of the common poisonous mushroom or fly agaric, *Amanita muscaria* L., likewise belongs to this class. Its constitution has been established by Kögl,[173] who assigned formula CX to it. The structures of a number of other dyes of this group have been elucidated.

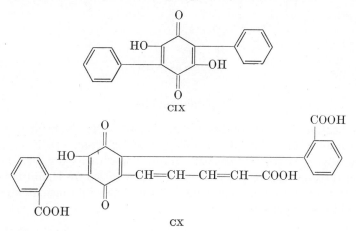

CIX

CX

Technical dyes of this type are represented by Helindon Yellow CG, the condensation product of *p*-chloroaniline and benzoquinone, and Helindon Khaki CR, the corresponding chloranil condensation product. The anilino-hydroquinone, representing an intermediate stage, is oxidized to the quinone by oxygen.

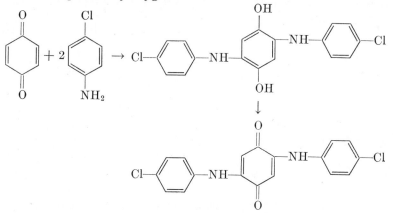

[172] Schildneck and Adams, *J. Am. Chem. Soc.*, **53**, 2373 (1931).
[173] Kögl and Erxleben, *Ann.*, **479**, 11 (1930).

These latter dyes are vat dyes of very good fastness with the additional advantage of requiring a minimum of alkali for vatting and, therefore, being usable for wool dyeing. Upon heating of such dyes with sulfur, ring formation occurs as shown by Herz and the thionation product of Helindon Yellow CG has been shown to have the following constitution.

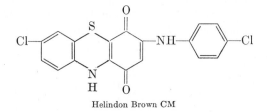

Helindon Brown CM

## Naphthoquinones

On heating 1,5- or 1,8-dinitronaphthalene with oleum and sulfur, Roussin in 1861 obtained a compound which Bohn (1887) explored technically. The reaction mechanism is still open to dispute even though the finished product, naphthazarine, was recognized by Dimroth as the 5,8-dihydroxy-1,4-naphthoquinone. The probable intermediates are indicated in the equations.

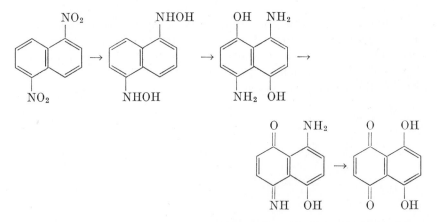

The slightly soluble naphthazarine is used technically in the form of its bisulfite addition product, Alizarin Black S. Its black chromium lake is very fast. Condensation of naphthazarine with phenol yields Alizarin Dark Green W.

Juglon, 5-hydroxy-1,4-naphthoquinone, is a natural dye belonging to this class and obtained from the shells of unripe walnuts. It is reddish yellow but when moist turns into blackish brown compounds. An isomer of Juglon is the dyeing principle of henna leaves, called Lawson, 2-hydroxy-1,4-naphthoquinone. Lapachol and Lomatiol are contained in several tropical woods and seeds and are derived from Lawson by the entrance of unsaturated side chains in the 3-position. Several similar dyes have found their way into the dyeing practice, e.g., Alkannin, which at one time was very popular as a violet dye on mordanted cotton and silk. It is recommended as an indicator and as a reagent for magnesium.

## Anthraquinones

The anthraquinone dyes are represented by hydroxyanthraquinones, alizarin and its derivatives, aminoanthraquinones, mixed hydroxyaminoanthraquinones, and the sulfonic acid derivatives of these dyes. Their occurrence in nature is very frequent.

**Anthraquinone Chemistry.** It might be advantageous at this point to consider some of the rules governing substitution in the anthraquinone nucleus. Keeping in mind that there are two benzene nuclei present in which two vicinal hydrogen atoms have been replaced by negative groups, —CO—, these carbonyl groups may be expected to direct substituents into either the $\alpha$- or $\beta$-positions. Preference for one or the other position will depend on the reaction conditions. The nitro group enters preferentially into the $\alpha$-, the sulfonic group into the $\beta$-position unless mercuric salts are present, in which case $\alpha$-substituted derivatives are obtained. Acid substituents in the $\alpha$-position are very labile, their replacement by amino, alkylamino, arylamino, alkoxy, aryloxy, chlorine, bromine, cyano, hydroxy, or mercapto being easily effected. The same exchange is much more difficult with $\beta$-substituted derivatives. An alkali fusion, which in the case of benzenesulfonic acids will yield the corresponding phenols, yields with $\beta$-anthraquinonesulfonic acids having a free $\alpha$-position di- and polyhydroxyanthraquinones. In order to obtain the monohydroxyanthraquinone aqueous calcium hydroxide is employed.

A plurality of hydroxy groups may be introduced into $\alpha$-hydroxyanthraquinones by heating with oleum or by oxidation with manganese dioxide and sulfuric acid. Similarly, dinitroanthraquinones, when heated with oleum and sulfur or with sulfur sesquioxide, yield polyhydroxyanthraquinones. When using concentrated sulfuric acid in the presence of boric acid, hexahydroxyanthraquinone is obtained.

**Hydroxyanthraquinones.** By far the most important anthraquinone dye of this series is alizarin (CXI). It was obtained originally from the root of the madder plant, in which it is contained as a glucoside, and its constitution was established in 1868 by Graebe and Liebermann, who also synthesized it. The technical manufacture comprises the fusion of anthraquinone-2-sulfonic acid with caustic soda in the presence of an oxidizing agent like potassium chlorate or nitrate. The complex

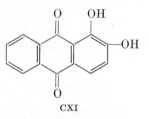

CXI

aluminum lake (red), the violet iron complex, and the brownish violet to blue chromium complex are coloristically important. The dyeing of the famous Turkey Red on cotton has been done since antiquity in the presence of oil mordants, prepared originally from rancid olive oil, today from sulfonated castor oil. The experience that calcium-containing water is required for a good dyeing has suggested the presence of a mixed calcium-aluminum lake in the scarlet red dyeings.

Sulfonation of alizarin leads to the 3-sulfonic acid, the sodium salt of which, Alizarin Red S, is used as a mordant dye for wool with chromium or aluminum salts.

No other dihydroxyanthraquinones have been of interest as dyes, the 1,4-isomer, quinizarin, being valuable only as an intermediate.

There are two trihydroxyanthraquinones of technical interest as dyes, the 1,2,4- and 1,2,3-trihydroxy derivatives called Purpurin and Anthragallol, respectively. The former is a companion of alizarin in the madder root, from which it may be isolated. It is produced technically by the oxidation of alizarin with manganese dioxide or arsenic acid in sulfuric acid. The fastness of its scarlet aluminum lake does not equal that of alizarin. Anthragallol, on the other hand, yields with chrome mordants on wool or leather full brown shades of excellent fastness. It is usually made by heating benzoic acid with gallic acid in the presence of sulfuric acid.

1,2,4-Trihydroxyanthraquinonecarboxylic acid, Boletol,[174] has been isolated by Kögl from the mushroom Boletus satanas. It corresponds to either the 5- or the 8-carboxylic acid.

The yellow meat of these mushrooms has the peculiar property of turning blue when cut. Kögl ascribes this to enzyme action resulting in diquinone formation.

[174] See Kögl in Klein, "Handbuch der Pflanzenanalyse," Vol. III, Part 2, Julius Springer, Vienna, 1932, p. 1414.

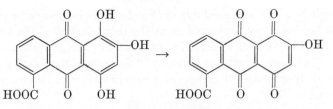

The introduction of more than three hydroxyl groups into the anthraquinone molecule is achieved by the Bohn-Schmidt reaction. Although
only two sulfonic groups can be introduced normally with sulfuric acid,
at higher temperatures sulfur trioxide oxidizes and forms the sulfuric
esters with the hydroxyl groups thus created. The addition of boric
or arsenic acid to the reaction mixture protects these hydroxyls by the
formation of boric esters (Schmidt, 1895).

The introduction of a plurality of hydroxyl groups shifts the shade
from red to blue. At the same time, the anthraquinone dyes carrying
a plurality of hydroxyl groups lose their character as cotton dyes and
become wool dyes. It is not possible to introduce more than six hydroxyl
groups. The Bohn-Schmidt reaction can also be applied to aminoanthraquinone and the anthraquinonesulfonic or -carboxylic acids. Three dyes
of this group are: Alizarin Bordeaux B (CXII), obtained by oxidation
of alizarin with a great excess of oleum and saponification of the sulfuric
ester; Alizarin Cyanine R (CXIII), formed from CXII by oxidation
with manganese dioxide and reduction of the intermediate anthradiqui-
none with sulfur dioxide; Anthracene Blue WR (CXIV), resulting from
treating 1,5-dinitroanthraquinone with oleum of high percentage.

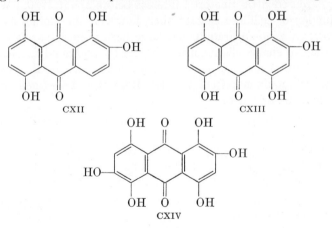

All these dyes, in the form of their chromium lakes, produce very fast
dyeings on wool. Their importance, however, has decreased in favor
of other fast dyes with easier modes of application.

Carminic acid is a natural dye of this class. It is the dyeing principle of the cochineal dye, obtained from the dried bodies of the female of the insect *Coccus cacti*, which lives on a cactus native to Mexico. This red dye has been shown by Dimroth [175] to possess the following structure with four hydroxyl groups and asymmetric carbon atoms in the side chain.

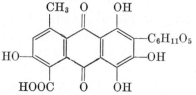

In the dye houses of the middle ages cochineal replaced another anthraquinonoid dye, Kermes, also explored by Dimroth.[176] Known since

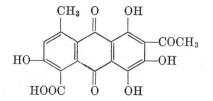

antiquity and valued as Venetian Scarlet, it gave way to the better and more powerful product of the new world in the same way as 300 years later cochineal had to yield to the much cheaper azo dyes.

**Aminoanthraquinones.** The aminoanthraquinones, devoid of sulfonic groups, aroused little tinctorial interest before about 1930. With the introduction of cellulose acetate fiber, however, the amino- as well as the hydroxyamino-anthraquinones have been used extensively for the production of shades distinguished by clarity and good fastness properties. Mention may be made of Celliton Fast Violet B, 5-nitro-1,4-diaminoanthraquinone; Celliton Fast Blue B, 1,4-*bis*-(methylamino)-anthraquinone; and also:

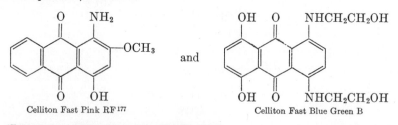

Celliton Fast Pink RF [177]                  Celliton Fast Blue Green B

[175] Dimroth and Kämmerer, *Ber.*, **53**, 471 (1920).
[176] Dimroth and Fick, *Ann.*, **415**, 315 (1916).
[177] Albrecht and Mueller, U. S. pat. 1,964,971 (1934) [*C. A.*, **28**, 5253 (1934)].

Such dyes, because of their solubility properties, are applicable also for the dyeing of spirit lacquers, oils, waxes, and printing inks, and their ability to sublime has led to their use in signal flares.

The amino group exerts a much greater bathochromic effect than the hydroxyl group, and this effect becomes more pronounced by the use of alkyl or aryl substituents.

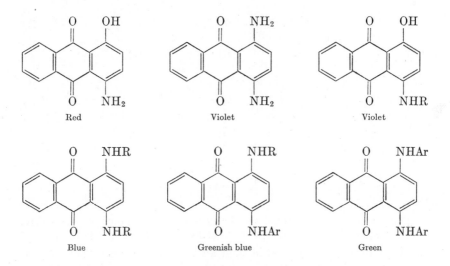

|       |              |        |
|-------|--------------|--------|
| Red   | Violet       | Violet |
| Blue  | Greenish blue | Green  |

**Sulfonated Derivatives.** Through the introduction of sulfonic groups, the dyes mentioned above become important fast wool dyes. Experience has shown that only α-aminoanthraquinones are valuable.

One of the oldest dyes of this class is Alizarin Saphirol B (CXV), obtained by the disulfonation of 1,5-dihydroxyanthraquinone with 20% oleum or chlorosulfonic acid, nitration, and reduction. Its fastness is generally very good with the exception of the fastness to perspiration and water spotting.* It is interesting to note that the corresponding dye with only one sulfonic group, Alizarin Saphirol SE, is superior in this respect. Much used for the dyeing of wool and silk, especially for draperies and rugs, is Alizarin Saphirol A (CXVI) and its homologs, as Alizarin Brilliant Blue BE [178] and Alizarin Sapphire. Green shades are represented by dyes of the type of Alizarin Cyanine Green B (CXVII).[179]

---

* By "water spotting" is meant the change in color of a dyed fabric when wet or moist. The fabric returns to its original color when dry.

[178] Hentrich and Engelbrecht, U. S. pat. 2,335,412 (1943) [*C. A.*, **38**, 2830 (1944)].

[179] Stowell, U. S. pat. 1,548,768 (1925) [*C. A.*, **19**, 3024 (1925)]; Koch and Weinand, U. S. pat. 2,042,757 (1936) [*C. A.*, **30**, 5049 (1936)].

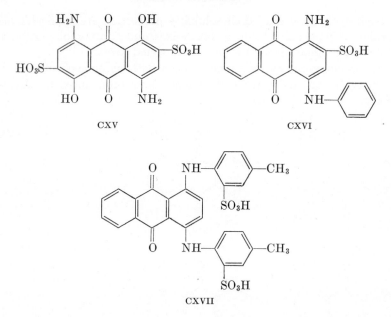

CXV                                              CXVI

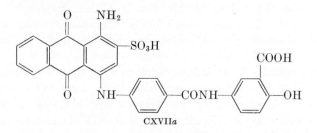

CXVII

The last may be obtained by the action of two moles of *p*-toluidine on one mole of leucoquinizarin followed by sulfonation. This dye and similar representatives excel in their all-around fastness. They may be chromed to give dyeings of improved fastness but without changing the shade appreciably. This direction has been further pursued by the preparation of compounds exemplified by CXVIIa.[180]

CXVIIa

Another logical step of progress is represented by Alizarin Light Gray 2BL (CXVIII).[181] This diaminoanthrimide dye possesses excellent fastness but does not level too well, which in view of the large molecule is understandable.

[180] Kränzlein *et al.*, U. S. pat. 2,122,798 (1938) [*C. A.*, **32**, 6877 (1938)].
[181] Raeder and Mieg, Ger. pat. 414,865 (1925) [*Friedländer*, **15**, 681].

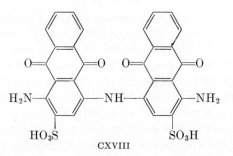

CXVIII

**Miscellaneous Types.** Acid dyes of the anthraquinone class are also known where another ring has been molded into the anthraquinone residue. One way in which this may be accomplished is by ring closure of acetylated 1-aminoanthraquinones with dilute caustic to give the corresponding anthrapyridone (CXIX); this on condensation with p-toluidine and sulfonation yields Alizarin Rubinol R (CXX),[182] a dye of outstanding fastness to light and level dyeing.

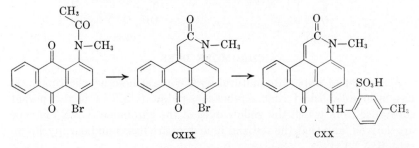

CXIX                    CXX

Anthrapyrimidones are obtained by condensation of 1-amino-4-p-toluidinoanthraquinone with urea and the sulfonated product, Alizarin Geranol B [183] is a dye of reddish violet shade having very good fastness (CXXI). The ring attached to the anthraquinone residue may also be morpholine, or thiomorpholine (CXXII); if thiomorpholine, green dyes result.

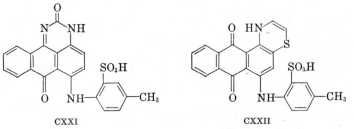

CXXI                         CXXII

---

[182] Tomaschewski, U. S. pat. 1,004,107 (1911) [*C. A.*, **6**, 299 (1912)].
[183] Tomaschewski, U. S. pat. 928,891 (1909) [*C. A.*, **3**, 2383 (1909)].

In each of the foregoing dyes the amino group has been attached in the $\alpha$-position. There are a score of dyes of more scientific than technical interest where this attachment is in the $\beta$-position. Anthraquinonepyridines were discovered first accidentally by Prud'homme (1877) in attempting to recover alizarin and nitroalizarin from printing pastes containing glycerol. He obtained a blue dye instead. Brunck [184] synthesized the new blue dye, and Graebe [185] cleared up the constitution, establishing it as the pyridine derivative (CXXIII) of alizarin. The work of Graebe was the basis for the quinoline synthesis by Skraup. Upon treatment with oleum this Alizarin Blue is converted into an oxidation product, Alizarin Blue Green, which again on treatment with sulfuric acid is converted into Alizarin Green X (CXXIV). The importance of these dyes today is small in spite of their good properties.

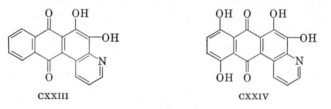

CXXIII                    CXXIV

## CHROMONE DYES

A number of important natural dyes contain heterocyclic rings. It has been established that $\alpha,\beta$-benzo-$\gamma$-pyran (CXXV) is the parent substance from which the yellow dyes of the chromone (CXXVI) type are derived, and that the red and blue dyes are based on benzopyrillium salts (CXXVII).

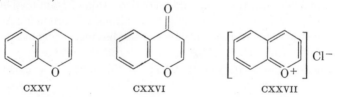

CXXV                CXXVI                CXXVII

The former, in the form of their 2-phenyl derivatives, are the flavone dyes explored extensively by von Kostanecki,[186] Perkin, *et al.* Examples are dyes like Fisetin,[187] Morin, and Quercetin (CXXVIII).[188]

Blue and red flowers and berries owe their color to the presence of anthocyanines, glycosidic compounds which on cleavage with acids and

[184] Brunck, *Ber.*, **11**, 522 (1878); von Auwers and Schmidt, *Ber.*, **46**, 367 (1913).
[185] Graebe, *Ber.*, **11**, 1646 (1878); **12**, 1416 (1879); *Ann.*, **201**, 333 (1880).
[186] Tambor, *Ber.*, **45**, 1701 (1912).
[187] von Kostanecki *et al.*, *Ber.*, **37**, 784 (1904).
[188] Attree and Perkin, *J. Chem. Soc.*, 234 (1927).

enzymes are degraded to the anthocyanidines. The latter represent pyrillium salts, i.e., oxo compounds. Dyes of this class are, for instance, Pelargonidin,[189] Cyanidin,[190] Delphinidin,[191] and Hirsutidin. The constitution of Cyanidin (CXXIX) discloses the close relationship between the anthocyanines and the flavones.

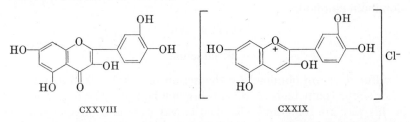

|  CXXVIII  |  CXXIX |

The field has been explored extensively by Willstätter, Robinson, Karrer, et al., and a comprehensive survey of their work is available by Link.[192]

Of technical interest are the chromone dyes contained in logwood and redwood. Logwood belongs to the species *Haematoxylon campechianum*, which flourishes in Central America and the Caribbean Isles. Its chief use is for black dyeings on silk and wool. The coloring principle occurs therein as a glucoside of the colorless leuco compound haematoxylin, which on oxidation is transformed into the dye Haematein. The dye from redwood, *Caesalpinia brasiliensis*, also is present in the wood in the form of its leuco compound brasilin, which is oxidized to the dye Brasilein. Haematein and Brasilein differ only by the presence of one additional hydroxyl group in Haematein. Their constitution has been clarified by the investigations of Pfeiffer[193] and Perkin,[194] partly based on previous work by Liebermann, Herz, and von Kostanecki.

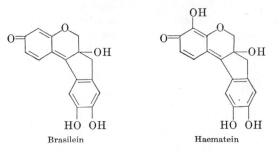

|  Brasilein  |  Haematein |

[189] Willstätter, *Ber.*, **57**, 1938 (1924); Robertson, *J. Chem. Soc.*, 1533 (1928).
[190] Willstätter, *Ann.*, **401**, 227 (1913).
[191] Pratt and Robinson, *J. Chem. Soc.*, 166 (1925).
[192] See Chapter 18, p. 1315, in Vol. II of this Treatise.
[193] Pfeiffer, *Ber.*, **58**, 1947 (1925).
[194] Perkin and Robinson, *J. Chem. Soc.*, 489 (1908).

Brasilein is used very little today.  Its mordant dyeings on cotton goods are of violet and bordeaux shades of low fastness.  Logwood extract, Haematein, on the other hand, still enjoys extensive use as a mordant dye for a variety of purposes.  It forms black shades on iron mordants, reddish violet hues with tin salts, and grayish violet with aluminum mordants.

## SULFUR DYES

### Introduction

Sulfur dyes are obtained by the action of sulfur, alkali sulfides, or other sulfur compounds on diverse organic bodies.  The dyes obtained in this way are sometimes classified as vat dyes in a broader sense of the term, inasmuch as they can be dissolved in aqueous solutions of alkali sulfides in the form of their leuco compounds, which after dyeing on the fiber are reoxidized by atmospheric oxygen.  Since Croissant and Bretonnière obtained in 1873 their "cachou de Laval" by melting sawdust with sulfur and sodium sulfide and Vidal later used well-defined benzene and naphthalene derivatives, great strides have been made in the manufacture of these dyes and in the knowledge of their constitution.

**Preparation.**  The formation of most technical sulfur dyes takes place at temperatures of 100–250°, with or without additions of alcohol or water.  Concentration of the "melt," as well as temperature and duration of the heating period, is of great importance since entirely different dyes may be obtained from the same starting materials when the conditions are varied.  Occasionally, there are additions of zinc or manganese salts to the "melt" and, for green dyes, copper salts.  After dye formation is complete the melt is blown into water and the leuco form may be salted out or the finished dye obtained directly by first blowing air through the solution of the leuco form.  Often, it is advantageous to subject the isolated dye after filtration to another "sulfur melt." [195] Sulfur dyes are also obtained in some cases by the use of sulfur chloride instead of sulfur, sometimes in the presence of aluminum chloride, and in other cases by the oxidation of mercapto compounds.[196]  The generally accepted opinion is that during the fusion the sulfur enters the organic molecule, primarily as the mercapto group, favoring a position *ortho* to hydroxy or amino groups, thereby creating alkali solubility.

**Structure.**  This group alone, however, without a strong chromophore, cannot explain the powerful coloristic properties or the stability of the dyes.  The presence of sulfur in other forms of linkage must be postu-

[195] Fierz-David, "Künstliche organische Farbstoffe," Springer, Berlin (1926), p. 394.
[196] Chenicek, U. S. pat. 2,342,663 (1944) [*C. A.*, **38**, 6544 (1944)]; Fox, U. S. pat. 2,369,666 (1945) [*C. A.*, **40**, 215 (1946)].

lated. Where the possibility of ring formation is present, the existence of nuclei containing the sulfur atom is highly probable, and the presence of thiazine and thiazole rings in sulfur dyes has been proved by Bernthsen,[197] Gnehm,[198] Gattermann,[199] Herz, and Fierz-David.[200] There is also evidence for the presence of open sulfur bridges:

$$—C—S—C—, \quad —C—S—S—C—; \text{ and sulfoxide linkages: } —C—\overset{\overset{\textstyle O}{\|}}{S}—C—;$$

and in certain vattable dyes obtained by fusion with sulfur the presence of thioketones, $>C=S$, and even thiophene rings appears probable.

Since, in the production of dyes on a technical scale, the fusion is terminated as soon as a dye with the desired properties is obtained, a technical dye usually represents a certain phase of the thionation process. The fastness of the sulfur dyes towards light and washing is usually good; their weakness, in general, is a sensitivity towards chlorine, but, in certain exceptional dyes even this is satisfactory. The shades of the typical sulfur dyes extend from yellow to black with a gap in the bright red hues. Black and blue dyes can be reduced easily to their colorless leuco compounds which reoxidize on exposure to air. The yellow, orange, and brown shades usually cannot be reduced.

## Classification and Examples

It has been customary to classify the sulfur dyes according to their colors. Inasmuch as this classification indicates a certain chemical similarity, this usage will be followed here.

**Yellows.** The yellow sulfur dyes are obtained primarily by thionation of dehydrothiotoluidines or *m*-arylenediamines and their acetyl, urea, or thiourea derivatives. All these compounds are characterized by the presence of alkyl or alkylamino substituents. Thus, the contingency for the formation of thiazole rings exists. The constitution of Immedial Yellow GG, the thionation product of dehydrothiotoluidine and benzidine, has been established in the main as shown, with three similar

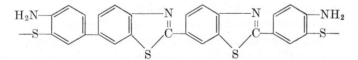

[197] Bernthsen, *Z. angew. Chem.*, **21**, 2068 (1908); *Chem. Ztg.*, **32**, 956 (1908).

[198] Gnehm and Kaufler, *Ber.*, **37**, 2617, 3032 (1904).

[199] Gattermann, *Ber.*, **22**, 424, 1064 (1889).

[200] Keller and Fierz-David, *Helv. Chim. Acta*, **16**, 585 (1933); Jones and Reid, *J. Am. Chem. Soc.*, **54**, 4393 (1932); Fierz-David, "Künstliche organische Farbstoffe," Springer, Berlin (1935), Suppl. pp. 25–31.

dyes present in lesser amount. The solubility of Immedial Yellow GG in sodium sulfide is due to the presence of disulfide groups *ortho* to amino groups. Sulfur enters the molecule preferably prior to the condensation. There is no formation of thiophene rings on the benzidine nucleus.[201]

Immedial Yellow D is obtained from *m*-toluylenediamine, Kryogen Yellow R from N,N-*bis*-(thiocarbamyl)-*m*-toluylenediamine, and Kryogen Yellow G from the same starting material with the addition of benzidine. The fastness to light of these dyes varies from moderate to good. They are powerful dyes and used extensively.

**Oranges.** Orange shades are obtainable from the same starting materials as the yellows, but at elevated temperatures. Thus, by raising the temperature of the thionation reaction to 250°, *m*-toluylenediamine will not yield a yellow, but Immedial Orange C; its constitution has not been proved exactly, but available data [201] favor either CXXX or CXXXI.

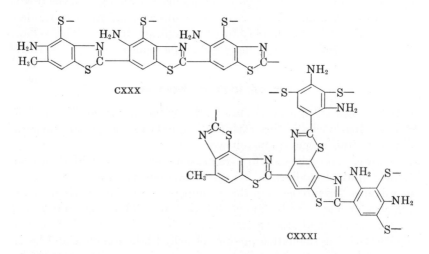

CXXX

CXXXI

**Browns.** The brown sulfur dyes can be made from the most heterogeneous materials provided that the fusion temperature is high enough. Mention has been made of cachou de Laval. Other raw materials used are the wastes from sulfite cellulose production.[202] Such dyes are, for instance, Sulfaniline Brown B.[203] The thionation of dinitronaphthalene,

[201] Zerweck et al., Angew. Chem., **A60,** 141 (1948).

[202] Robeson, U. S. pat. 1,316,742 (1919) [C. A., **13,** 3019 (1919)]; Coombs, U. S. pat. 1,327,862 (1920) [C. A., **14,** 848 (1920)].

[203] Seidel, U. S. pat. 687,581 (1901).

pretreated with sodium bisulfite, yields Sulfogen Golden Brown G.[204] The art knows other dyes, for instance, Immedial Dark Brown A from 2,4-dinitro-4'-hydroxydiphenylamine.[205] As a matter of fact, materials that at lower temperature may yield blacks will furnish brown dyes at elevated temperatures. Sometimes the fusion with sulfur is carried out in the presence of metal salts as in the process for Immedial Black Brown S, where 1,8-dinitronaphthalene is thionated in the presence of copper sulfate at 260–270°.[206]

**Reds.** All efforts to obtain bright red shades by the thionation reaction have failed. The shades obtained from aminohydroxyphenazines or dinitrohydroxydiphenylamines in the presence of copper salts, Sulfogene Bordeaux B [207] and Thiogen Dark Red G,[208] respectively, are unattractive, dull shades. It is claimed that a rather bright Bordeaux red shade is obtained by careful thionation of p-anisidine in cyclohexanol.[209, 210] It represents a quinoneimine type of sulfur dye in contradistinction to the thiazole dyes mentioned before. The former are more closely related in their behavior to the vat dyes than to the thiazoles. Solubility in sodium sulfide with the thiazole dyes is a function of the disulfide bridges; in the case of the quinoneimine-sulfur dyes, this solubility is available through the vatting of the quinonoid system and is helped further by the disulfide linkages.

**Blues.** The blue sulfur dyes are second in importance only to the blacks in this class. They are obtained by the action of polysulfides on indophenols or indoanilines. Since, during the sulfur fusion, the indophenols are reduced to the corresponding diphenylamine derivatives, the derivatives may be utilized likewise as starting materials. The thionation is carried out advantageously at comparatively low temperatures, around 100°; at higher temperatures black dyes often result. Such blue dyes generally are characterized by good fastness to light but low fastness to chlorine bleach. The first blue of this class, Immedial Pure Blue,[211] is obtained from p-dimethylamino-p'-hydroxydiphenylamine or the indoaniline obtained from phenol and p-aminodimethyl-

[204] Badische Anilin- und Sodafabrik, Ger. pat. 92,538 (1897) [*Friedländer*, **4**, 353 (1899)].

[205] Cassella, Ger. pat. 112,484 (1900) [*Friedländer*, **6**, 695 (1904)]; U. S. pat. 660,058 (1900).

[206] Crossley and Dahlen, Quartermaster Textile Series Report 18, P.B. No. 39562, U. S. Dept. Commerce, Washington, D. C. (1946).

[207] Weinberg, U. S. pat. 701,435 (1902); Lehmann, U. S. pat. 866,939 (1907).

[208] Akt.-Ges. für Anilin-Fabrik., Ger. pat. 194,198 (1907) [*C. A.*, **2**, 1894 (1908)].

[209] Kalischer and Ritter, Ger. pat. 502,071 (1927) [*C. A.*, **24**, 4939 (1930)].

[210] Zuercher, Dissertation, Zürich (1934).

[211] Weinberg and Herz, U. S. pat. 693,632–3 (1902).

aniline.   According to Fierz-David and Keller [212] it has the constitution shown.

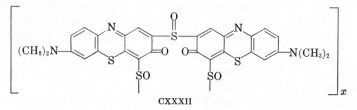

CXXXII

Other important dyes are Pyrogene Indigo,[213] obtained by thionation of the indoaniline obtained from nitrosophenol and diphenylamine, and Sulfogene Direct Blue BR,[214] from 2,4-dinitro-4'-hydroxydiphenylamine at 90–106°.   If, in the Pyrogene Indigo synthesis, the indoaniline from diphenylamine is replaced by the corresponding one from carbazole, the very important blue dye Hydron Blue R,[215] which is fast to chlorine, is formed.   The constitution of this dye is given by Bernasconi [216] as shown.

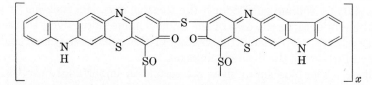

Similar dyes of equally excellent properties are obtained from N-ethyl-carbazole and from chlorinated carbazoles.

**Blacks.**   Sulfur blacks not only comprise the largest group in the sulfur dye series but also furnish one of the few really big bulk products of the coal-tar dyes.   The first technically usable black was made by Vidal when he heated p-phenylenediamine and p-aminophenol with alkali sulfides. This first black was not very powerful, though fast, and was replaced by the product of thionation of a mixture of o- and p-aminophenol, or rather of the crude nitration mixture of phenol.   Both these dyes, however, need aftertreatment on the fiber with copper salts.   The discovery of Immedial Black FF by Kalischer in 1897 [217] was of great

[212] Bernasconi, *Helv. Chim. Acta*, **15**, 287 (1932); Keller and Fierz-David, *ibid.*, **16**, 585 (1933).

[213] Herz, U. S. pat. 723,154 (1903); Manss, U. S. pat. 1,471,854 (1923) [*C. A.*, **18**, 172 (1924)].

[214] Bertschmann, U. S. pat. 665,726 (1901).

[215] Haas, U. S. pat. 919,572 (1909) [*C. A.*, **3**, 1815 (1909)]; U. S. pat. 931,598 (1909) [*C. A.*, **3**, 2618 (1909)]; Herz, U. S. pat. 956,348 (1910) [*C. A.*, **4**, 1685 (1910)].

[216] Bernasconi, *Helv. Chim. Acta*, **15**, 287 (1932); see, also, Shah *et al.*, *Proc. Indian Acad. Sci.*, **28A**, 111 (1948).

[217] Kalischer, U. S. pat. 610,541 (1898); U. S. pat. 678,884 (1901).

importance since it was the first sulfur black to yield deep black shades
directly. It is the higher thionation product of 2,4-dinitro-4'-hydroxy-
diphenylamine. All these black dyes had to give way, however, to the
black obtained by Vidal and Priebs when they subjected dinitrophenol
or dinitrochlorobenzene to the sulfur melt. The resultant Sulfur Black
T [218,219] became one of the most important dyes on the market. It is
unexcelled in fastness to light and washing, although its fastness to
chlorine could stand improvement.

**Greens.** Practically all green shades are obtained by the addition of
copper salts to blue sulfur melts. Thionation of $p$-nitrophenol at 180–
200° in the presence of copper salts yields Pyrogene Green B, and of
hydroxythiocarbanilide yields Thiongreen B. The best results are obtained by the use of the indophenol from 8-anilinonaphthalene-1-sulfonic
acid, which on thionation yields Katigen Brilliant Green G.[220] The
constitution of this dye has been established by Fierz-David, Keller,
and Vanotti as shown.

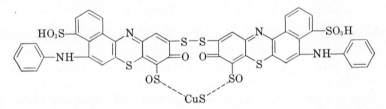

A jade-green sulfur dye of the phthalocyanine series has been described. Dyes of this type may be obtained by reduction of copper
phthalocyaninesulfonyl chloride with zinc followed by oxidation [221] or
by reaction of copper phthalocyanine with sulfur chloride in the presence
of aluminum chloride.[222] These dyes yield bright dyeings which are
fast to washing and light.

When the normal sulfur melt is carried further than usual, products
result which frequently require hydrosulfite for reduction and dyeing.
Such dyes take on the character of true vat dyes and will, therefore,
be dealt with in a subsequent section.

[218] Vidal, U. S. pat. 618,152 (1899); U. S. pat. 655,650 (1900).

[219] Flachsländer, U. S. pat. 935,009 (1909) [C. A., **4**, 116 (1910)].

[220] Boeniger, U. S. pat. 776,885 (1904); Reber and Frölich, U. S. pat. 1,568,622 (1926)
[C. A., **20**, 3822 (1926)].

[221] Haddock, U. S. pat. 2,342,662–3 (1944) [C. A., **38**, 4810, 4811 (1944)].

[222] Fox, U. S. pat. 2,369,666 (1945) [C. A., **40**, 215 (1946)].

## VAT DYES

### Introduction

The family of the vat dyes is composed of a great variety of hetero-geneous pigment dyes, insoluble in water and in this state possessing no affinity for textile fibers. They all contain $>C=O$ groups which are reducible to water-soluble leuco compounds which in turn are substantive to animal or vegetable fibers or both. On reoxidation *in situ* by oxygen of the air or other means, the original insoluble dye is re-created on and throughout the fiber, and its insolubility in water and alkali is the reason for the excellent wash-fastness of dyes of this class.

**Application.** The old technical methods of reduction by fermentation, lime-iron sulfate, or zinc-dust vats have been abandoned entirely in favor of the reduction by means of salts of hyposulfurous acid, sodium hydro-sulfite being preferred.

$$Na_2S_2O_4 + 2NaOH + H_2O \rightarrow Na_2SO_4 + Na_2SO_3 + 2H_2$$

Since alkali is required for this reduction, the main field of application of the vat dyes lies in the dyeing of vegetable fibers. There are, however, vat dyes with far greater affinity for and better fastness on animal fibers than cotton, as, for instance, indigo. For such dyes a minimum of alkali is a prerequisite to avoid degradation of the animal fiber. It is essential, furthermore, for successful dyeing operations, that the optimum conditions of reduction for each dye be established, since otherwise reduction might be carried too far, leading to losses of dye. It has also been established that the affinity of a vat leuco dye for the fiber is profoundly influenced by the temperature at which the dyeing is carried out, and for technical usage the vat dyes are classified accord-ingly.

The reduction to the leuco compound results in the change of the $>C=O$ groups into $>C—OH$. This explains their alkali solubility. Though it is true that the leuco compounds of the indigoid and thio-indigoid types are only slightly yellowish, they are not universally so. Those of the anthraquinone series are deeply colored, and in several others the color is deeper than that of the reoxidized dyes.

**Classification.** A scientific classification of vat dyes is difficult in view of the great many heterogeneous dyes known. One may, however, with a certain degree of reservation, adopt the following: (*a*) indigo and derivatives; (*b*) acylaminoanthraquinones, anthraquinonylureas; (*c*) anthraquinoneimines, anthrimides, carbazoles; (*d*) anthraquinone di-hydroazides, acridones, thioxanthones; (*e*) flavanthrones, pyranthrones;

(*f*) benzanthrone and derivatives; (*g*) anthanthrones, dibenzpyrene-quinones; (*h*) perylene tetracarboxylic acid and derivatives; (*i*) dipyra-zolanthrones.

Not all compounds falling chemically under this classification are vat dyes, since many of the leuco compounds of these products do not show the necessary affinity for fibers or sufficient solubility in dilute alkali. A general rule governing the relation between substantivity and chemical constitution is not known.

The excellent fastness of the better vat dyes is proverbial. Yet, not all vat dyes have this good property as a generic attribute. There are many dyes of this class which have distinctly poor fastness to light. A great difference between the fastness of the same dye on different types of fibers likewise exists. Indigo, for example, possesses much better fastness on wool than on cotton, and the light-fastness of many of the best vat dyes on nylon fibers is unbelievably poor.

Vat dyes are used to an overwhelming degree for the printing and dyeing of cotton, to a far lesser degree for wool. In their pigment form these dyes find increasing use in the graphic arts and lacquer trade.

## Indigo Types

**Indigo.** Indigo occurs in many plants, particularly those belonging to the *Indigofera* species, not as a dye but in the form of a colorless gluco-side, indican. Indican, on treatment with water, may be hydrolyzed by enzymes or acids to glucose and indoxyl (CXXXIII), which in turn is oxidized to indigo (CXXXIV).

Indican($C_{14}H_{17}O_6N \cdot 3H_2O$) →

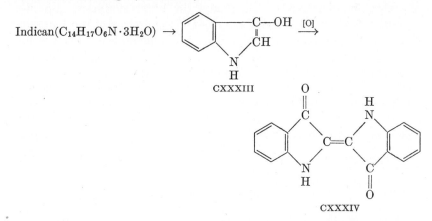

CXXXIII

CXXXIV

Indigo is one of the oldest known organic coloring agents. Its use as a dye was known to the inhabitants of Asia for over four thousand years.  Between the thirteenth and sixteenth centuries, its use spread throughout Europe and its position of prominence as one of the most important natural dyes prompted investigations of its constitution by several early chemists.  Dumas established its analytical formula in 1857.[223]  Unverdorben obtained aniline in 1841 by dry distillation of indigo, and in the same year Fritzsche obtained anthranilic and salicylic acids by fusion with potassium hydroxide.  Erdmann and Laurent [224] subjected indigo to oxidative degradation with chromic acid and discovered isatin, the constitution of which was postulated by Kekule in 1869 [225] and proved later by Baeyer and Claisen.[226]  The structure of indigo was solved finally by Baeyer in 1883 after long years of research.[227] He devised several ingenious synthetic methods, which, however, did not attain technical success since the starting materials were too expensive or the yields too low.  Baeyer's proposals all start with materials having the structure

as, for example, o-nitrophenylpropiolic acid,[228] o-nitrocinnamic acid, dinitrodiphenylbutadiene,[229] and o-nitrobenzaldehyde.[230]

The first successful commercial synthesis was found by Heumann in 1890.[231]  Phenylglycine, obtained from aniline and chloroacetic acid, cyclizes on fusion with potassium hydroxide to indoxyl, which can be oxidized readily to indigo.  Better yields were obtained starting with phenylglycine-o-carboxylic acid,[232] and the latter synthesis, also discovered by Heumann, became the basis of the process of the Badische Aniline and Soda plant in 1897.  Since phthalimide was necessary for conversion to anthranilic acid, this synthesis also led to the production of phthalic anhydride by oxidation of naphthalene.

The low yield of the first Heumann synthesis starting from phenylglycine is due to the elimination of water by the ring closure, an equilibrium being reached at a point of incomplete conversion, and to the high temperature of the melt (300°), which is harmful to the indoxyl.

[223] Dumas, *Ann.*, **22**, 72 (1857).
[224] Erdmann and Laurent, *Ann.*, **48**, 254, 260 (1843).
[225] Kekule, *Ber.*, **2**, 748 (1869).
[226] Baeyer, *Ber.*, **11**, 582, 1228 (1878); Claisen and Shadwell, *Ber.*, **12**, 350 (1879).
[227] Baeyer and Bloem, *Ber.*, **17**, 963 (1884).
[228] Baeyer, *Ber.*, **13**, 2254 (1880).
[229] Baeyer, *Ber.*, **15**, 50, 775 (1882).
[230] Baeyer and Drewsen, *Ber.*, **16**, 2205 (1883).
[231] Heumann, *Ber.*, **23**, 3043 (1890).
[232] Heumann, *Ber.*, **23**, 3431 (1890).

Use of sodium amide in the melt [233] overcame both these defects: the temperature could be lowered to 180–210° and the amount of sodamide could be regulated in such a way that no free water was present during the reaction. Phenylglycine became the basis for the second commercial process, to be replaced later in part by N-β-hydroxyethylaniline, which likewise will yield indigo under the conditions of the alkali fusion.

There are altogether some thirty indigo syntheses, none of which, however, has been able to replace on a commercial scale the processes sketched above. In spite of inroads by other, faster vat and azoic dyes, indigo is still today one of the few great bulk dyes derived from the coal-tar industry. The production from natural sources is comparatively small and competitively in a hopeless position.

**Substitution Products of Indigo.** Even though the substituted indigos cannot match their prototype in size of production, very important dyes are found in this class. The substitution products are numbered according to the scheme shown.

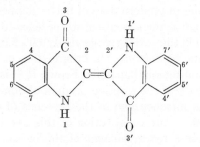

Although substitution in no case causes a radical change of color, there are certain rules governing the coloristic effects of substituents in the benzene nuclei. Substitution in position 4 has the least influence, in 6 a hypsochromic effect. Methyl groups in position 7 and halogen in position 5 or 7 tend to yield somewhat greener shades.

Sulfonated indigo (5,5'-indigodisulfonic acid),[234] in spite of its name, Indigocarmine, dyes wool a pleasant blue of very low light-fastness. It is of no technical importance.

Methylated indigos (5,5' or 7,7') [235] dye somewhat faster and greener shades than indigo. Since the chlorinated indigos are still better, the methylated ones were not practical. Naphthalene indigos from α- and β-naphthylamine [236] give blue to green shades, but are without great technical value. Substitution by halogens enhances the coloristic properties of indigo, the brightness, fastness to chlorine, and affinity

[233] Homolka and Liebknecht, U. S. pat. 704,804 (1902).
[234] Crum et al., Ann., **22**, 72 (1837).
[235] Heumann, U. S. pat. 617,651–2 (1899); Koetschet, U. S. pat. 662,073–5 (1900).
[236] Wichelhaus, Ber., **26**, 2547 (1893).

to fibers being improved.   Substitution with bromine is carried out best in various solvents, e.g., nitrobenzene, dichlorobenzene, and sulfuric acid, or by direct action of bromine.[237]   Chlorinated indigos are generally obtained from chlorinated starting materials.   The most important halogenated indigos are listed.

Ciba Blue 2B or Brilliant Indigo 4B,[238] 5,7,5′,7′-tetrabromoindigo, has a somewhat brighter shade than indigo, better fastness to chlorine and light, and a greatly improved affinity to fibers.   It is prepared by bromination of indigo in boiling nitrobenzene.

Brilliant Indigo 4G,[239] 4,4′-dichloro-5,5′-dibromoindigo, gives a very greenish blue shade.

Indigo 5B is the Tyrian purple obtained in antiquity from the purple snail (*Murex brandaris*).   Friedländer [240] isolated 1.4 g. from twelve thousand mollusks and identified the dyeing principle as 6,6′-dibromoindigo.   The dye is of only historical interest since its rather dull reddish violet shade so highly favored in ancient times cannot compete with more brilliant shades of modern dyes of better fastness.

Nitration of indigo in the absence of water leads to 6,6′-dinitroindigo, which on reduction in the vatting stage yields 6,6′-diaminoindigo, having a bluish green shade on cotton.   On bromination of the latter, 6,6′-diamino-5,7,5′,7′-tetrabromoindigo, Ciba Brown R,[241] is obtained.

Indigo Yellow 3G [242] is the reaction product obtained from indigo and benzoyl chloride in nitrobenzene in the presence of copper powder by heating to 150–160°.   The constitution of this dye was established by Posner.[243]   Probably a rearrangement of the indigo molecule with enlargement of the five-membered heterocyclic rings occurs.

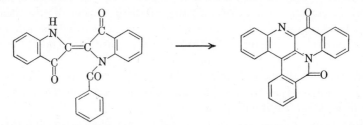

[237] Engi, *Chem. Ztg.*, **32**, 1178 (1908); Strosacker and Rupright, U. S. pat. 1,473,887 (1923) [*C. A.*, **18**, 475 (1924)].
[238] Strosacker and Rupright, U. S. pat. 1,473,887 (1923) [*C. A.*, **18**, 475 (1924)].
[239] Julius *et al.*, U. S. pat. 957,683 (1910) [*C. A.*, **4**, 2380 (1910)]; Engi, U. S. pat. 872,115 (1907) [*C. A.*, **2**, 1060 (1908)].
[240] Friedländer, *Ber.*, **42**, 765 (1909); **55**, 1655 (1922).
[241] Engi and Kappeler, U. S. pat. 940,586 (1909) [*C. A.*, **4**, 517 (1910)].
[242] Engi and Froelich, U. S. pat. 994,988 (1911) [*C. A.*, **5**, 2727 (1911)]; U. S. pat. 1,026,-574 (1912) [*C. A.*, **6**, 1995 (1912)].
[243] Posner and Hofmeister, *Ber.*, **59**, 1827 (1926).

It is no longer a true indigo derivative, and its relation to the anthraquinone vats is evident from the blue-red color of its vat.

**Thioindigo and Derivatives.** Efforts were made early to substitute
the imino group of the heterocyclic rings in indigo by other atoms.
Gabriel and Colman [244] in 1899 obtained the so-called ketoindigo.

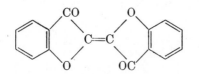

The coloristic properties of this compound, however, are worthless.
The thioindigos, on the other hand, discovered by Friedländer in
1906,[245] represent a very valuable addition to the family of dyes. They
yield bright shades extending from orange through red and violet to
brown and black, of very good fastness. It is interesting to note that,
in addition to their ability to be vatted with those agents usable for
vat dyes, they form their leuco compounds also by action of sodium
sulfide. They may, therefore, be dyed in conjunction with sulfur dyes.
Numerous examples of both symmetrical and unsymmetrical types are
known.

The methods of synthesis of symmetrical thioindigos are analogous
to those for indigo, being based principally either on *o*-carboxyarylthio-
glycolic acids (CXXXV) or arylthioglycolic acids (CXXXVI).

The prototype of this series, the original Thioindigo Red of Friedländer, or Algol Red 5B (CXXXVII),[246] dyes cotton and wool fibers
in bluish red shades of very good fastness. Its substitution products are

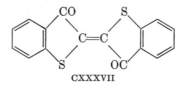

CXXXVII

even brighter and faster. Contrary to the minor effects caused by
substitution in indigo, the entrance of substituents into the thioindigo

[244] Gabriel and Colman, *Ber.*, **33**, 996 (1900).
[245] Friedländer, *Ber.*, **39**, 1060 (1906); *Ann.*, **351**, 390 (1907).
[246] Friedländer, U. S. pat. 819,348 (1906).

molecule causes major changes.　Substitution in the 6-position shifts
the shade to the orange, in the 5-position to the blue side of the spectrum.

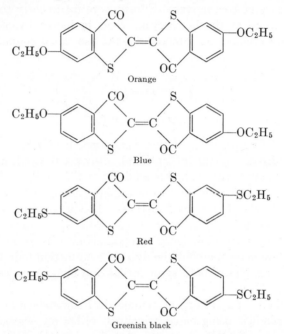

Orange

Blue

Red

Greenish black

A large number of compounds of the thioindigo series have been
prepared by replacing the hydrogen atoms of the aryl nuclei by a great
many substituents such as —$CH_3$, —Cl, —Br, —$OC_2H_5$, —$SCH_3$, and
—$NH_2$.　A few of the more important are listed.

| | |
|---|---|
| Algol Rubine B or Helindone Red B: | 5,5'-dichlorothioindigo [247] |
| Ciba Bordeaux B: | 5,5'-dibromothioindigo [248] |
| Indanthrene Red Violet RH: | 5,5'-dichloro-6,6'-dimethylthioindigo |
| Indanthrene Brown RRD: | 2,1-bis-naphthothioindigo [249] |
| Algol Orange RF or Helindone Orange R: | 6,6'-diethoxythioindigo [250] |
| Sulfanthrene Pink FB or Helindone Pink BN: | 4,4'-dimethyl-6,6'-dichlorothioindigo [251] |

The last compound of the above series was prepared according to the
interesting synthesis of Herz.

[247] Schmidt, U. S. pat. 861,624 (1906); Schmidt and Bryk, U. S. pat. 916,029–30 (1909)
[C. A., 3, 1465 (1909)].

[248] Engi, U. S. pat. 867,715 (1907) [C. A., 2, 909 (1908)].

[249] Soc. anon. pour l'ind. chim. à Bâle, Ger. pat. 455,280, 481,598 (1928) [C. A., 24,
247 (1930)]; Staudinger et al., U. S. pat. 1,600,743 (1926) [C. A., 20, 3577 (1926)].

[250] Schirmacher and Deicke, U. S. pat. 867,305 (1907) [C. A., 2, 907 (1908)].

[251] Kalle & Co., Ger. pat. 239,094 (1911) [Friedländer, 10, 491].

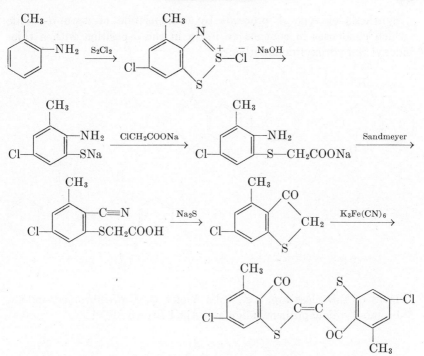

Replacement of the sulfur in the thioindigos by selenium is feasible and leads to dyes of similar shades and properties.[252]   No technical dyes of this nature are in use.

**Unsymmetrical Indigo and Thioindigo Dyes.**   The dyes considered so far have been symmetrical.   Unsymmetrical dyes are known of the following main types (X = N, Y = S, or vice versa).

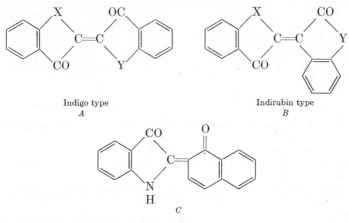

| Indigo type | Indirubin type |
|:---:|:---:|
| A | B |

C

[252] Lesser, *Ber.*, **45**, 1835 (1912); **46**, 2640 (1913).

Synthesis of type *A* proceeds by condensation of isatin-α-anilide (which condenses in contrast to isatin in the α-position with a thioindoxyl (3-hydroxythionaphthene).

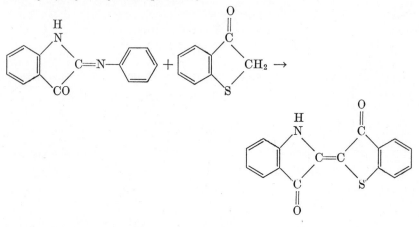

Dyes of this class are, e.g., Ciba Violet B,[253] 5,7-dibromo-2-indole-5'-bromo-2'-thionaphtheneindigo and Algol Brown 3R,[254]

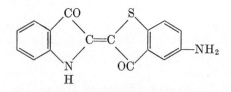

Condensation of isatin with indoxyl or thioindoxyl compounds, on the other hand, yields dyes of the Indirubin type (B).

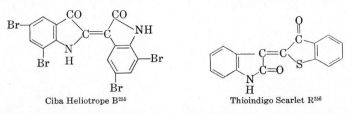

Ciba Heliotrope B[255]					Thioindigo Scarlet R[256]

[253] Engi, U. S. pat. 836,309 (1906) [*C. A.*, **1**, 502 (1907)]; U. S. pat. 848,355–6 (1907) [*C. A.*, **1**, 1635 (1907)].

[254] Schmidt *et al.*, U. S. pat. 968,697 (1910) [*C. A.*, **4**, 3008 (1910)].

[255] Engi, U. S. pat. 876,158 (1908) [*C. A.*, **2**, 1499 (1908)]; U. S. pat. 898,452 (1908) [*C. A.*, **3**, 379 (1909)].

[256] Engi, U. S. pat. 841,003 (1907) [*C. A.*, **1**, 793 (1907)]; Albrecht, U. S. pat. 874,649 (1907) [*C. A.*, **2**, 1202 (1908)]; Homolka and Welde, U. S. pat. 943,687 (1909) [*C. A.*, **4**, 674 (1910)].

Type *C* dyes are formed by reaction of certain *o*-diketones such as isatins, *β*-naphthoquinones, and acenaphthene quinones, of *α*-haloketones, or of *α*-anilinoketones such as *α*-isatinanilide, with compounds containing reactive methylene groups (indoxyls, naphthols, *α*-anthrols, etc.). Specific dyes of this class are shown.

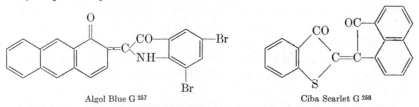

Algol Blue G [257]                    Ciba Scarlet G [258]

The possibility of variations in this series is very large. Inasmuch as their fastness in most cases is also excellent, their practical use is limited only by their cost, which is often quite high.

### Acylaminoanthraquinones and Dianthraquinonylureas

Almost all benzoylated *α*-aminoanthraquinones possess the properties of technical vat dyes. Probably because of the rather small molecule, their fastness is not quite equal to that of more complex vat dyes, but their dyeings are acceptable for normal requirements and their moderate cost has assured for them a definite use in the dyeing of textiles as well as for pigment color purposes.

Their synthesis is effected principally by the action of aromatic acids or acid chlorides on aminoanthraquinones in nitrobenzene or pyridine, benzoyl chloride being the preferred reactant. When using dibasic acids, two aminoanthraquinones may be linked together. Monobasic aliphatic acids confer no substantivity.

Coloristically, the same rules prevail as for the acid alizarin dyes. When substituents are present, the hydroxyl group yields redder shades than the amino group; alkylation of the latter shifts the shade toward green.

Specific dyes of this class are listed.

1. Algol Yellow WG,[259] 1-benzoylaminoanthraquinone, is the prototype of the series and was used for dyeing and printing of cotton but its present importance is very small. The color of its vat is red.

[257] Bauer, U. S. pat. 961,396 (1910) [*C. A.*, **4**, 2576 (1910)]; U. S. pat. 980,140 (1910) [*C. A.*, **5**, 996 (1911)]; Elbel and Wray, U. S. pat. 999,439 (1911) [*C. A.*, **5**, 3161 (1911)].
[258] Grob, U. S. pat. 891,690 (1908) [*C. A.*, **2**, 2999 (1908)]; U. S. pat. 915,346 (1909) [*C. A.*, **3**, 1464 (1909)]; Elbel, U. S. pat. 965,170 (1910) [*C. A.*, **4**, 2738 (1910)].
[259] Deinet, U. S. pat. 957,041 (1910) [*C. A.*, **4**, 2379 (1910)]; Schmidt, U. S. pat. 964,-816 (1910) [*C. A.*, **4**, 2738 (1910)]; Deinet, U. S. pat. 978,138 (1910) [*C. A.*, **5**, 994 (1911)].

2. Heliofast Yellow 6GL,[260] 1-salicylaminoanthraquinone, is a very fast greenish yellow pigment color.

3. Indanthrene Red 5G,[261] 1,4-dibenzoylaminoanthraquinone.

4. Indanthrene Brilliant Violet RK,[262] 4,8-*bis*-(*p*-methoxybenzoylamino)-1,5-dihydroxyanthraquinone.

An example of the linkage of two aminoanthraquinone nuclei by an aliphatic dibasic acid is Algol Yellow 3GK,[263] N,N'-*bis*-(1-anthraquinonyl)-succinamide.

Other dibasic acids like oxalic, adipic, maleic, isophthalic, and phthalic may be used. The linkage may also be obtained through the use of phosgene, the resultant urea derivatives forming valuable dyes such as Algol Yellow 4GK,[264] *sym*-*bis*-(2,2'-anthraquinonyl)-urea, and Helindone Brown 3GN.[264]

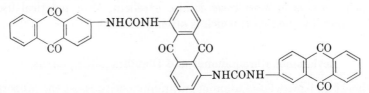

The only other bridging component of importance is cyanuric chloride, which is also used in the field of direct azo colors (cf. p. 293). Thus, two moles of an aminoanthraquinone can be reacted readily with one mole of cyanuric chloride and the third chlorine replaced by amino, anilino, alkoxy, or phenoxy, etc. A third aminoanthraquinone residue can be introduced but generally is more difficult and does not have a proportionate effect on the properties of the dye. An example is Cibanone Orange 6R.[265]

## Anthraquinoneimines

**Anthrimides.** The direct linkage of two or more anthraquinone nuclei with each other by —NH— may be effected by the action of haloanthraquinones on aminoanthraquinones in the presence of copper.[266] Occa-

[260] Tomaschewski, U. S. pat. 957,125 (1910) [*C. A.*, **4**, 2380 (1910)]; Schmidt, U. S. pat. 964,816 (1910) [*C. A.*, **4**, 2738 (1910)].

[261] Deinet, U. S. pat. 957,042 (1910) [*C. A.*, **4**, 2380 (1910)]; Schmidt, U. S. pat. 964,816 (1910) [*C. A.*, **4**, 2738 (1910)].

[262] Tomaschewski, U. S. pat. 957,125 (1910) [*C. A.*, **4**, 2380 (1910)].

[263] Fischer, U. S. pat. 938,566 (1909) [*C. A.*, **4**, 516 (1910)]; Schmidt, U. S. pat. 964,816 (1910) [*C. A.*, **4**, 2738 (1910)].

[264] Schmidt and Kränzlein, U. S. pat. 958,325 (1910) [*C. A.*, **4**, 2381 (1910)].

[265] Soc. anon. pour l'ind. chim. à Bâle, Ger. pat. 390,201 (1924) [*Friedländer*, **14**, 878]; Ger. pat. 399,485 (1924) [*Friedländer*, **14**, 880].

[266] Ullmann et al., *Ann.*, **381**, 17 (1911); *Ber.*, **47**, 564 (1914); **49**, 2162 (1916); Frey, *Ber.*, **45**, 1363 (1912); Ger. pat. 162,824 (1905) [*Friedländer*, **8**, 363]; Ger. pat. 174,699 (1906) [*Friedländer*, **8**, 365]; Ger. pat. 194,253 (1907) [*Friedländer*, **9**, 758]; Ger. pat. 208,162 (1909) [*Friedländer*, **9**, 761]; Ger. pat. 216,688 (1909)[*Friedländer*, **9**, 763]; Ger. pat. 220,581 (1910) [*Friedländer*, **9**, 764].

sionally nitroanthraquinones [267] or even sulfo derivatives [268] may be employed instead of the halo compounds. By judicious substitution, the resultant anthrimides yield shades from yellow to violet. Experience has shown that as a rule $\alpha,\alpha$-dianthraquinonylamines have poor affinity to the fiber when employed as vat dyes and are not fast to light. $\alpha,\beta$-Condensates, however, yield very satisfactory vat dyes. Furthermore, the direct —NH— linkage between anthraquinone nuclei may be replaced by certain groups without destroying their dyeing character, e.g.:

Anthraquinone—NH—⟨⟩—NH—Anthraquinone

Anthraquinone—NH—⟨⟩—⟨⟩—NH—Anthraquinone

The shade of the anthrimide dyes is influenced less by the size of the molecule than by the nature of the substituents. The majority of these dyes show very good fastness. As examples may be mentioned Indanthrene Orange 6RTK,[269] 1,2'-dianthraquinonylamine; and Algol Bordeaux 3B.[270]

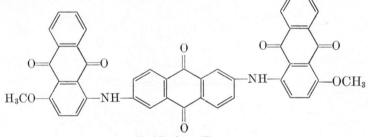

Algol Bordeaux 3B

The substitution of the anthraquinone radicals need not be limited to simple substituents. Other nuclei may be attached as in Algol Red B,[271]

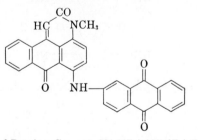

[267] Meister, Lucius, and Brüning, Ger. pat. 201,327 (1908) [*Friedländer*, **9**, 774].
[268] Meister, Lucius, and Brüning, Ger. pat. 216,083 (1909) [*Friedländer*, **9**, 775].
[269] Isler, U. S. pat. 814,137 (1906).
[270] Frey, Ger. pat. 216,668 (1909) [*Friedländer*, **9**, 763].
[271] Tomaschewski, U. S. pat. 875,390 (1907).

the first red dye discovered in the anthraquinone vat series. It is made by condensation of 1-chloroanthraquinone with methylamine, acetylation, and condensation to N-methylanthrapyridone. Bromination of the last in the 4-position and condensation with 2-aminoanthraquinone yields the dye.

**Carbazoles.** The $\alpha,\alpha'$-anthrimides, not usable as such for vat dyes, are important as intermediates since, under the influence of condensing agents such as sulfuric acid, aluminum chloride, aluminum chloride and pyridine, or chlorosulfonic acid, valuable vat dyes are formed. Presumably, condensation takes place in the o-position to the imino bridge, and carbazole derivatives are formed.

Other methods of formation are the condensation through the loss of ammonia of 1,1'-diamino-2,2'-bis-anthraquinonyl in concentrated sulfuric acid or with zinc chloride at 300–360°,[272] and the action of two moles of phthalic anhydride on carbazoles (N-alkylated preferred).[273] These are only a few of the known reactions, and the examples of important dyes of this class given below represent only a small part of a series distinguished by excellent fastness.

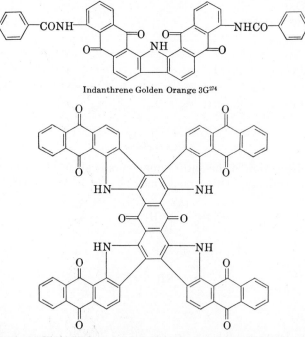

Indanthrene Golden Orange 3G[274]

Indanthrene Khaki GG from α-aminoanthraquinone and tetrachloroanthraquinone

[272] Meister, Lucius, and Brüning, Ger. pat. 267,833 (1912) [C. A., **8**, 1018 (1914)].
[273] Cassella & Co., Ger. pat. 261,495 (1912) [C. A., **7**, 3547 (1913)].
[274] Gassner, U. S. pat. 1,667,848 (1928) [C. A., **22**, 2278 (1928)].

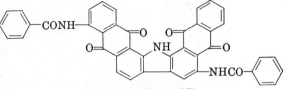

Carbanthrene Brown AR[275]

Anthraquinone and its derivatives possess the property of being con-verted into molecules with additional cyclic nuclei, thereby forming a host of complex ring systems. In principle, three main types may be expected.

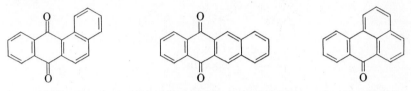

The added nuclei may be isocyclic or heterocyclic and even part of other condensed systems. It is obvious that a multitude of compounds are theoretically possible. Experience has shown, however, that for coloristically useful dyes the number of combinations is definitely limited and that the vat dyes of this class used in practice are confined to the dihydroazine, acridone, thioxanthone, thiazole, or oxazole derivatives.

**Dihydroazines.** When Bohn in 1901 attempted to form an anthracene-indigo from N-($\beta$-anthraquinonyl)glycine by fusion with alkali, he obtained a blue dye which he named indanthrene (indigo of anthracene). He found subsequently that the same dye is obtained by alkali fusion of $\beta$-aminoanthraquinone itself at 200–250°. The reaction was elucidated by investigations of Scholl [276] and Bohn; it consists of the condensation of two anthraquinone nuclei, with the intermediate formation of the leuco compound, to N,N'-dihydro-1,2,1',2'-anthraquinonazine, also known as indanthrone or Indanthrene Blue R.

Yields of 48–50% are obtainable; in addition alizarin (p. 343) and flavanthrone (CXXXVIII) are formed in the melt. Indanthrene Blue R is one of the fastest dyes known. Its defect is a pronounced sensi-tivity to chlorine, which has a tendency to oxidize or substitute the hydrogen atoms of the dihydroazine ring. The oxidation products, either the azhydrin, azine, or the chlorimine, N—Cl, are yellow but can be reconverted to Indanthrene Blue by means of reducing agents. Puri-fied indanthrones show a somewhat greater resistance to chlorine.

[275] Tomaschewski et al., U. S. pat. 986,521 (1911) [C. A., **5**, 2000 (1911)].
[276] Scholl et al., Ber., **36**, 3410, 3421, 3710 (1903); **40**, 320, 326, 390, 395, 924, 933 (1907); **44**, 1727 (1911).

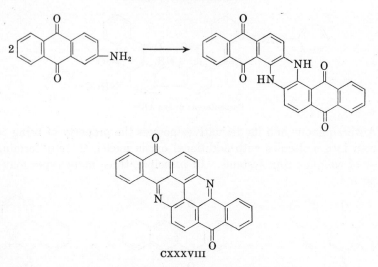

CXXXVIII

Of the several other methods for the synthesis of indanthrone, only the self-condensation of 1-amino-2-bromoanthraquinone (Kugel and Tomaschewski, 1903) in nitrobenzene in the presence of sodium acetate and copper powder is important. This synthesis, even though not competitive with the Bohn process, is valuable for the production of substituted indanthrone-type dyes. Thus, 1-methylamino-2-bromoanthraquinone gives Indanthrene Blue RK (CXXXIX),[277] and 1-amino-2-bromo-4-hydroxyanthraquinone gives Indanthrene Blue 5G (CXL).[278]

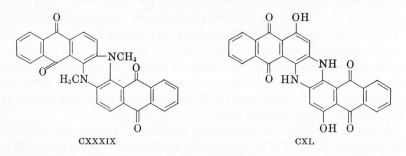

CXXXIX                                           CXL

Indanthrene Blue RK has no better fastness to chlorine than Indanthrene Blue R, even though the imino hydrogens are substituted by methyl.

The halogen derivatives of indanthrone, as a rule, give greener shades than their prototype. They may be obtained either by halogenation

[277] Kugel, U. S. pat. 775,368 (1904); U. S. pat. 1,150,863 (1915) [C. A., 9, 2817 (1915)].
[278] Tomaschewski, U. S. pat. 801,418 (1905).

of the parent dye in a variety of media with thionyl chloride, sulfuryl chloride, antimony pentachloride, bromine, aqua regia, etc., or by the choice of proper starting compounds in the Kugel synthesis. These halogenated indanthrones are improved in their fastness to chlorine. They constitute the commercial brands Indanthrene Blue GC,[279] GCD,[280] and BC,[281] which are, respectively, the dibromo-, monochloro-, and dichloro-indanthrones.

Green shades are obtainable from amino-substituted indanthrones such as Indanthrene Green BB.[282]

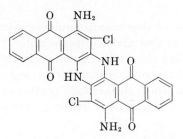

The indanthrone blues are used for the dyeing and printing of cotton, linen, and rayon. They are utilized also as pigments in the graphic art and lacquer industries.

**Acridones.** Certain acridone derivatives of anthraquinone also have excellent fastness. Of the two theoretical possibilities, 2,1- or 1,2-acridones, only the former yield dyes of value. They may be obtained easily in several ways. There is first the condensation of α-chloroanthraquinone with anthranilic acid in the presence of sodium acetate and copper.[283]

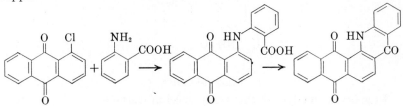

[279] Bohn, U. S. pat. 739,579 (1903); Kugel, U. S. pat. 775,369 (1904); U. S. pat. 808,762 (1906); Steindorff and Welde, U. S. pat. 1,145,934 (1915) [C. A., **9**, 2454 (1915)].

[280] Bohn, U. S. pat. 739,579 (1903); U. S. pat. 753,659 (1904); Atack and Soutar, U. S. pat. 1,452,774 (1923) [C. A., **17**, 2510 (1923)]; Kalischer and Salkowski, U. S. pat. 1,509,808 (1924) [C. A., **18**, 3727 (1924)].

[281] Badische Anilin- und Sodafabrik, Ger. pat. 157,449 (1903) [*Friedländer*, **8**, 351]; Ger. pat. 168,042 (1905) [*Friedländer*, **8**, 352].

[282] Kugel, U. S. pat. 775,367 (1904).

[283] Ullmann et al., Ber., **43**, 536 (1910); Ann., **380**, 336 (1910); **381**, 1 (1911).

Another synthesis uses as starting material 1-chloro-2-carboxyanthra-quinone or 1-nitro-2-carboxyanthraquinone, which on condensation with arylamines yields acridones.[284]

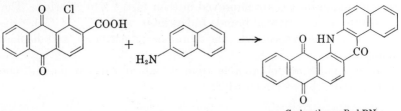

Carbanthrene Red BN

Other methods use *o*-halogenoanthraquinone-nitriles and amines [285] or *o*-chlorobenzaldehydes and aminoanthraquinones.[286] Diacridones like-wise are known. Ring closure is effected preferably with concentrated sulfuric acid or phosphorus pentachloride and aluminum chloride. Substitution by halogen in the benzene portion of the acridones leads to bluish red dyes; amino groups in the anthraquinone residue yield blue shades.

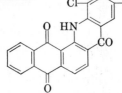

Indanthrene Red Violet RK [287]

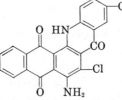

Indanthrene Blue 8GK [288]

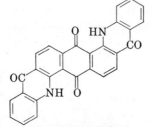

Ponsol Violet BN [289]

In general, the dyes of this group excel in fastness.

[284] Lüttringhaus, U. S. pat. 1,011,068 (1911) [*C. A.*, **6**, 430 (1912)]; Thomas, U. S. pat. 1,504,164 (1921) [*C. A.*, **18**, 3279 (1924)].

[285] Schaarschmidt, *Ann.*, **405**, 95 (1914).

[286] Mayer and Bansa, *Ber.*, **54**, 16 (1921).

[287] Ullmann, U. S. pat. 961,047 (1910) [*C. A.*, **4**, 2574 (1910)]; Lüttringhaus, U. S. pat. 1,010,930 (1911) [*C. A.*, **6**, 430 (1912)]; U. S. pat. 1,011,068 (1911) [*C. A.*, **6**, 430 (1912)]; Just and Eckard, U. S. pat. 1,150,863 (1915) [*C. A.*, **9**, 2817 (1915)].

[288] Berliner, Ger. pat. 531,013 (1928) [*C. A.*, **25**, 5574 (1931)].

[289] Ullmann, U. S. pat. 961,047-8 (1910) [*C. A.*, **4**, 2574 (1910)]; Bally, U. S. pat. 1,086,-123 (1914) [*C. A.*, **8**, 1211 (1914)].

**Thioxanthones and Thiazoles.** The replacement of the imino group in the acridones by sulfur yields yellow to orange thioxanthones, the shade of which may be deepened to red where the introduction of two thioxanthone groups is possible. The synthesis of these compounds proceeds along orthodox lines, as, for instance, by the condensation of α- or β-chloroanthraquinones with thiosalicylic acid followed by ring closure.

Dithioxanthones are accessible from the dichloroanthraquinones.[290] 1,4-Chloroaminoanthraquinones will lead to 4-aminoanthraquinone-1,2-thioxanthones, in which the amino group is capable of the usual reactions of this substitutent.[291] The thioxanthones, like the acridones, may be halogenated in a number of ways. Thus, this group offers many possibilities of variation. 2,3-Thioxanthone also has been made.[292] The following may be mentioned as specific examples.

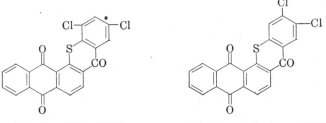

Indanthrene Yellow GN[293]        Indanthrene Golden Orange GN[293]

The action of mercaptoanthraquinones and their derivatives (for instance, xanthogenates, thiocyanates) on hydroxyanthraquinones in the presence of sulfuric acid leads to reddish vat dyes of the structure (CXLI).[294] Thianthrene derivatives of structure CXLII [295] yielding

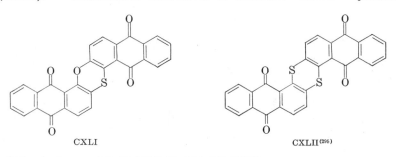

CXLI                    CXLII[295]

[290] Bayer, Ger. pat. 216,430 (1908) [*C. A.*, **4**, 832 (1910)].

[291] Meister, Lucius, and Brüning, Ger. pat. 243,587 (1910) [*C. A.*, **6**, 2325 (1912)].

[292] Soc. anon. pour l'ind. chim. à Bâle, Fr. pat. 427,189 (1910) [*C. A.*, **6**, 2006 (1912)].

[293] Lüttringhaus and Schwarz, U. S. pat. 1,044,674 (1912) [*C. A.*, **7**, 262 (1913)]; Thomas, U. S. pat. 1,504,164 (1924) [*C. A.*, **18**, 3279 (1924)].

[294] Bayer, Ger. pat. 235,094 (1910) [*C. A.*, **5**, 3168 (1911)].

[295] Badische Anilin- und Sodafabrik, Ger. pat. 248,171 (1911) [*C. A.*, **6**, 2689 (1912)].

reddish shades have been prepared from 1,2-dimercaptoanthraquinone and 1,2-dichloroanthraquinone.

None of these dyes has attained commercial importance.

Thiazole derivatives of anthraquinones, on the other hand, are encountered in the trade and are very valuable dyes. There are a number of ways by which they can be made, a few of which may be outlined: the action of sulfur on 1-chloro-2-acetamidoanthraquinone [296] or oxalyl chloride upon 1-mercapto-2-aminoanthraquinone [297] yields a thiazole (CXLIII). 2,6-Diaminoanthraquinone when melted with sulfur and benzotrichloride forms a greenish yellow dye, Algol Yellow GCN (CXLIV).[298]

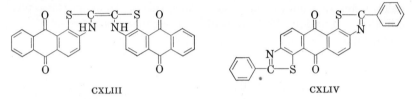

CXLIII                                    CXLIV

The same dye may also be obtained by reaction of sulfur with benzyl or benzylidine derivatives of the diaminoanthraquinone.

Another thiazole dye of this series is Indanthrene Yellow GF (CXLV) obtained by reaction of sulfur with two moles of 2-methylanthraquinone and one mole of benzidine.[299] This dye has excellent fastness.

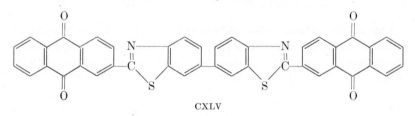

CXLV

The technically important Cibanone Blue 3G (CXLVI) is derived from benzanthrone and obtained by reaction of sulfur with β-methyl-

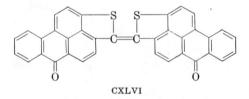

CXLVI

[296] Badische Anilin- und Sodafabrik, Ger. pat. 280,882 (1913) [*C. A.*, **9**, 1999 (1915)].
[297] Badische Anilin- und Sodafabrik, Ger. pat. 280,883 (1913) [*C. A.*, **9**, 1999 (1915)].
[298] Unger and Boehner, Ger. pat. 492,447 (1928) [*C. A.*, **24**, 2893 (1930)].
[299] Weinberg, *Ber.*, **63A**, 117 (1930).

benzanthrone.[300]   Its constitution has been proved by synthesis from 1,3-benzanthronylthioglycolic acid.[301]

## Flavanthrones and Pyranthrones

**Flavanthrones.**  It has been mentioned before (p. 371) that a by-product of the indanthrene synthesis from $\beta$-aminoanthraquinone is a yellow vat dye, flavanthrone.  This dye predominates when fusion is carried out at higher temperatures (330–350°) or in the presence of reducing agents, or when alcoholic potassium hydroxide is employed in the melt.[302]  The best method of obtaining it is to boil $\beta$-aminoanthraquinone with antimony pentachloride in nitrobenzene solution.[303]  Its constitution was established by Scholl in a series of investigations as CXLVII.[304]

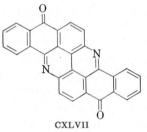

CXLVII

From a dark blue-violet vat, flavanthrone dyes cotton yellow shades having excellent fastness to light, washing, and chlorine.  The 3,3′-dibromo derivative, Indanthrene Yellow R, is obtained by a similar reaction starting with either 1,3-dibromo-2-aminoanthraquinone [305] or 3-bromo-2-aminoanthraquinone.[306]

**Pyranthrones.**  Replacement of one nitrogen in flavanthrone by carbon leads to pyranthridone (CXLVIII); of both, to pyranthrone (CXLIX). Pyranthridone has been synthesized by Scholl.[307]  It is a powerful orange-red vat dye, yellower than pyranthrone but much redder than flavanthrone.  It is not used technically.  Pyranthrone, on the other

[300] Mayer and Weil, U. S. pat. 1,044,797 (1912) [C. A., **7**, 262 (1913)].

[301] Lüttringhaus et al., Ger. pat. 483,154 (1927) [C. A., **24**, 508 (1930)].

[302] Badische Anilin- und Sodafabrik, Ger. pat. 133,686 (1901) [Friedländer, **6**, 417]; Ger. pat. 135,408 (1901) [Friedländer, **6**, 416].

[303] Scholl, Ber.. **40**, 1691 (1907).

[304] Bülow and Sproesser, Ber., **41**, 1691 (1908); Scholl, Ber., **41**, 2304 (1908); Scholl and Mansfield, Ber., **43**, 1740 (1910).

[305] Ullmann, Ger. pat. 248,999 (1911) [C. A., **6**, 2851 (1912)]; Bayer, Ger. pat. 172,733 (1904) [Friedländer, **8**, 354].

[306] Kugel, U. S. pat. 808,762 (1906); Goodrich, U. S. pat. 1,581,111 (1926) [C. A., **20**, 1910 (1926)]; Scholl, Ber., **40**, 1700 (1907).

[307] Scholl and Dischendorfer, Ber., **51**, 441 (1918).

hand, has attained great commercial importance under the name of
Indanthrene Golden Orange G. It may be obtained from 2,2'-di-
methyl-1,1'-dianthraquinonyl by heating with zinc chloride or alcoholic
potassium hydroxide.[308] Other syntheses are known, one being the
condensation of pyrene with benzoyl chloride and aluminum chloride to

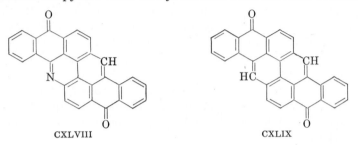

CXLVIII                                         CXLIX

give dibenzoylpyrene, which upon heating with aluminum chloride
yields pyranthrone.[309] The dye has a remarkable fastness to chlorine
and alkali wash and dyes extremely bright orange shades from a cherry-
red vat. The dichloro derivative, Indanthrene Golden Orange R, and
the dibromo compound, Indanthrene Golden Orange 2RT, dye in redder
shades and may be obtained either by direct halogenation or, synthetically, from the corresponding halodimethyldianthraquinonyls.[310]

The tetrabromo compound may serve as a dye itself or as an intermediate. By further condensation with α-aminoanthraquinone and
aminodibenzanthrone, a very fast vat black is obtained of good affinity
to the fiber which does not require the oxidizing after-treatment of
Indanthrene Black BB. It is known in the trade as Indanthrene Direct
Black RB.

### Benzanthrone and Derivatives

When Bally in 1904 applied the Skraup reaction of β-aminoalizarine
(Prud'homme and Brunck, 1878) to β-aminoanthraquinone, he observed that acrolein (from glycerol) entered twice into the molecule.[311]

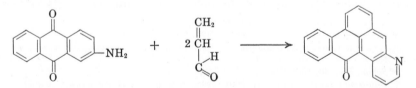

[308] Scholl, *Ber.*, **43**, 346, 512 (1910); **44**, 1448, 1662 (1911); U. S. pat. 828,778 (1906);
U. S. pat. 845,129 (1907) [*C. A.*, **1**, 1070 (1907)]; U. S. pat. 856,811 (1907) [*C. A.*, **1**, 2503
(1907)]; Isler, U. S. pat. 1,004,433 (1911) [*C. A.*, **6**, 300 (1912)].

[309] Scholl and Seer, *Ann.*, **394**, 111 (1912).

[310] Scholl, *Ber.*, **43**, 352 (1910).

[311] Badische Anilin- und Sodafabrik, Ger. pat. 171,939 (1904) [*Friedländer*, **8**, 369].

He found, furthermore, that anthraquinone and anthranol likewise condense readily with glycerol in the presence of sulfuric acid to form benzanthrone (CL).[312]

The formation of benzanthrones in this manner is a general reaction, taking place with many derivatives [313] of anthraquinone as well as with anthraquinone itself, provided that a free $\alpha$-position is available. A few types that have been used are 1,2-benzanthraquinones,[314] hydroxyanthraquinones,[315] and haloanthraquinones,[316] but it has not been found possible to effect benzanthrone formation with both carbonyl groups.

Another method of synthesis is the fusion of phenyl $\alpha$-naphthyl ketone with aluminum chloride.[317] It has proved of great value in the study of the more complex benzanthrones.

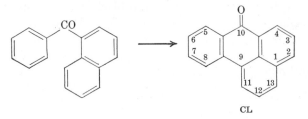

CL

Halogenation of benzanthrone,[318] either in aqueous suspension or in the presence of organic solvents such as nitrobenzene or acetic acid, is readily accomplished. The halogen atoms first enter the Bz ring, and these halogens are much more reactive than those attached to the anthraquinone.

**Dibenzanthrones.** The benzanthrones are yellow compounds, devoid of dyeing character, but by fusion with potassium hydroxide a dark blue vat dye of excellent fastness to light, chlorine, and washing is obtained. The constitution of this dye was established by Scholl,[319] and the reaction underlying the fusion evidently is as shown.

[312] Bally, *Ber.*, **38**, 194 (1905); Bally and Scholl, *Ber.*, **44**, 1656 (1911).

[313] Badische Anilin- und Sodafabrik, Ger. pat. 200,335 (1905) [*C. A.*, **2**, 3411 (1908)].

[314] Badische Anilin- und Sodafabrik, Ger. pat. 181,176 (1904) [*C. A.*, **1**, 1805 (1907)].

[315] Badische Anilin- und Sodafabrik, Ger. pat. 187,495 (1904) [*C. A.*, **2**, 217 (1908)].

[316] Badische Anilin- und Sodafabrik, Ger. pat. 205,294 (1905) [*C. A.*, **3**, 1596 (1909)].

[317] Scholl and Seer, *Ann.*, **394**, 143 (1912); **398**, 82 (1913); *Ber.*, **55**, 109 (1922); Scholl and Neuman, *Ber.*, **55**, 118 (1922); *Monatsh.*, **33**, 522 (1912); **34**, 1493 (1913); Schaarschmidt, *Ber.*, **50**, 294 (1917); Schaarschmidt and Korten, *Ber.*, **51**, 1074 (1918).

[318] Badische Anilin- und Sodafabrik, Ger. pat. 193,959 (1906) [*C. A.*, **2**, 1893 (1908)].

[319] Scholl *et al.*, *Ber.*, **43**, 2208 (1910); *Ann.*, **394**, 111 (1912); see, also, Lüttringhaus and Neresheimer, *Ann.*, **473**, 263 (1929).

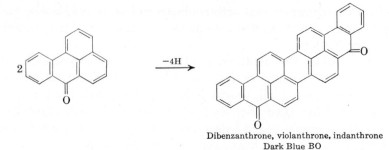

Dibenzanthrone, violanthrone, indanthrone
Dark Blue BO

Halogenated derivatives are dyes of redder shades of similarly excellent fastness, e.g., Indanthrene Violet RT.[320]

Nitration of dibenzanthrone [321] yields a green vat dye, Indanthrene Green B (CLI), which is very fast to light and on treatment with hypochlorite on the fiber turns into a deep black of extraordinary fastness. It is thus known as Carbanthrene Black B.[321] Mononitration of dibenzanthrone has not been accomplished successfully, a mixture of mono and dinitro compounds always being obtained along with unreacted dibenzanthrone.

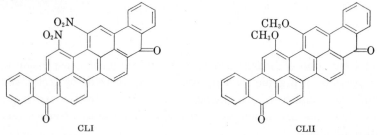

CLI                                          CLII

Oxidation of dibenzanthrone with nitric acid or manganese dioxide in concentrated sulfuric acid results in quinones which may be reduced to green dihydroxydibenzanthrones. These are of no technical interest. The dimethyl ether of 12,12′-dihydroxydibenzanthrone, however, represents the most important green vat dye known today, Jade Green (CLII).[322] Its constitution has been determined by Schirmacher.[323]

Reduction of (CLI) and condensation of the aminodibenzanthrone thus obtained with α-nitronaphthalene, α-chloroanthraquinone, hydroxylamine,[324] etc., leads to interesting black vat dyes which do not require after-treatment when dyed.

[320] Neresheimer, U. S. pat. 1,589,303 (1926) [C. A., **20**, 3088 (1926)].
[321] Badische Anilin- und Sodafabrik, Ger. pat. 226,215 (1909) [C. A., **5**, 1195 (1911)].
[322] Davis and Thomson, U. S. pat. 1,531,261–3 (1925) [C. A., **20**, 114 (1926)].
[323] Schirmacher et al., Ger. pat. 413,738 (1923) [Friedländer, **15**, 765].
[324] Shepherdson and Thornley, Ger. pat. 485,567 (1927) [C. A., **24**, 1224 (1930)].

When Bz-halogenated benzanthrones are subjected to a fusion with potassium hydroxide,[325] a halogen-free vat dye results which is isomeric with dibenzanthrone but yields decidedly redder shades. It is isodibenzanthrone (CLIII) and is known in the trade as Indanthrene Violet R.

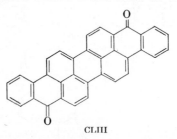

CLIII

The dichloro derivative is Indanthrene Brilliant Violet RR; the dibromo compound, Indanthrene Brilliant Violet 3B.[326]   All these dyes are extraordinarily fast.

The 3,12′-dimethoxyisodibenzanthrone is blue [327] in contrast with Jade Green above.

Halogenated benzanthrones may also be condensed with various amino compounds to yield valuable dyes, such as Indanthrene Olive Green B [328] (CLIV).

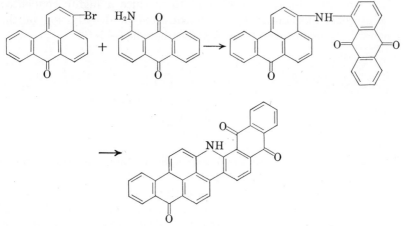

CLIV

[325] Bally, Ger. pat. 194,252 (1906) [C. A., **2**, 1893 (1908)]; Bally and Wolff, U. S. pat. 906,367 (1908) [C. A., **3**, 956 (1909)]; Lüttringhaus et al., U. S. pat. 1,580,062 (1926) [C. A., **20**, 1721 (1926)].

[326] Badische Anilin- und Sodafabrik, Ger. pat. 217,570 (1909) [C. A., **4**, 1549 (1910)]; Soc. anon. pour l'ind. chim. à Bâle, Ger. pat. 480,487 (1928) [C. A., **23**, 5047 (1929)].

[327] Nawiasky et al., Ger. pat. 442,511 (1924) [Friedländer, **15**, 772].

[328] Honold and Boehner, U. S. pat. 1,903,181 (1933) [C. A., **27**, 3343 (1933)]; Honold, U. S. pat. 1,936,716 (1933) [C. A., **28**, 1543 (1934)].

When using pyrazole compounds, easily obtainable from α-anthra-quinonylhydrazines by boiling with water or acetic acid,[329] dark navy blue shades result.

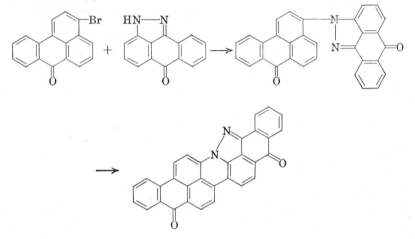

## Anthanthrones, Dibenzpyrenequinones

Kalb in 1914 described a method to produce a highly condensed benzanthrone, anthanthrone, which consisted of dehydration of the isomeric 1,1′-dinaphthyl-2,2′- or 8,8′-dicarboxylic acids.[330]

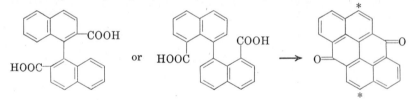

The starting material for the dicarboxylic acid may be acenaphthene or 8-naphthylamine-1-sulfonic acid.

Anthanthrone has little affinity for cotton fiber when applied as a vat dye. Its halogen derivatives, however, are powerful reddish orange dyes. They are readily obtainable by halogenation of anthanthrone in such solvents as trichlorobenzene, nitrobenzene, or sulfuric acid.[331] The dibromo derivative is known commercially as Indanthrene Brilliant Orange RK; the dichloro compound, as Indanthrene Brilliant Orange GK. They represent very fast dyes of extremely bright shades. The

[329] Bayer, Ger. pat. 171,293 (1904) [*Friedländer*, **8**, 304].

[330] Kalb, *Ber.*, **47**, 1724 (1914).

[331] Herz and Zererck, Ger. pat. 492,344 (1927) [*C. A.*, **24**, 2893 (1930)]; Ger. pat. 495,-367-8 (1928) [*C. A.*, **24**, 3379 (1930)]; Ger. pat. 478,738 (1926) [*C. A.*, **23**, 4328 (1929)].

halogen atoms are present to a large extent in the positions marked with asterisks.

Closely related to the anthanthrones are the dibenzpyrenequinones. In this group only the *trans*-dibenzpyrenequinones, reaction products of benzanthrones and benzoyl chloride with aluminum chloride,[332] are of technical importance. The simplest member of the group is the unsubstituted 3,4,8,9-dibenzopyrene-5,10-quinone, Indanthrene Golden Yellow GK (CLV), which can also be obtained by ring closure of 1,5-dibenzoylnaphthalene.[333]

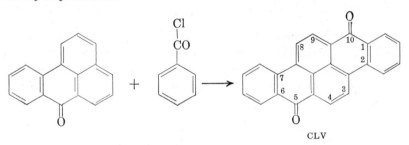

CLV

Halogenation again leads to other valuable dyes as, for instance, Indanthrene Golden Yellow RK.[334]

Later developments in this field brought forth still larger anthraquinones. Kunz and Koeberle have investigated intensively the *dianthrones* and have shown that many of them yield excellent vat dyes of yellow to orange shade. The dianthrones have the structures shown.

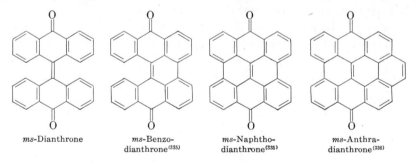

*ms*-Dianthrone     *ms*-Benzo-       *ms*-Naphtho-      *ms*-Anthra-
                    dianthrone[335]   dianthrone[335]    dianthrone[336]

Available information does not indicate whether any of the dianthrones have found technical application.

[332] Kränzlein *et al.*, Ger. pat. 412,053 (1922) [*Friedländer*, **15**, 731].

[333] Kränzlein *et al.*, U. S. pat. 1,564,584 (1925) [*C. A.*, **20**, 510 (1926)]; Zahn *et al.*, U. S. pat. 1,693,447 (1928) [*C. A.*, **23**, 715 (1929)].

[334] Kunz *et al.*, U. S. pat. 1,804,880 (1931) [*C. A.*, **25**, 3668 (1931)]; Kränzlein *et al.*, U. S. pat. 1,855,293 (1932) [*C. A.*, **26**, 3263 (1932)]; Kunz *et al.*, U. S. pat. 1,957,892 (1934) [*C. A.*, **28**, 4246 (1934)]; U. S. pat. 1,959,679 (1934) [*C. A.*, **28**, 4605 (1934)].

[335] Scholl and Mansfield, *Ber.*, **43**, 1734 (1910).

[336] Kunz and Koeberle, Ger. pat. 457,494 (1926) [*Friedländer*, **16**, 1294].

## Perylenetetracarboxylic Acid and Derivatives

Dibenzanthrone and isodibenzanthrone dyes may be considered derivatives of the hydrocarbon perylene (CLVI).

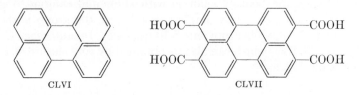

CLVI                                      CLVII

For vat-dye purposes the tetracarboxylic acid (CLVII) and the *bis*-methylimide (CLVIII) have been employed successfully, the latter representing a red vat dye which is used commercially. It may be obtained by a fusion of potassium hydroxide with naphthalene-1,8-di-

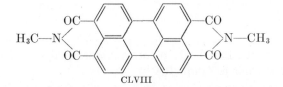

CLVIII

carboxylic acid methylimide [337] or of the naphthindandion which on oxidation will yield the free acid and on methylation the dye.[338]

In this connection a series of vat dyes may be mentioned which, though they are not perylene derivatives, show a certain similarity in structure. Examples are derivatives of naphthalene-1,4,5,8-tetra-carboxylic acid. The imidazoles of this acid represent excellent vat dyes. Two methods of synthesis available for the tetracarboxylic acid are the oxidation of pyrene [339] or the method shown, starting from acenaphthene.[340]

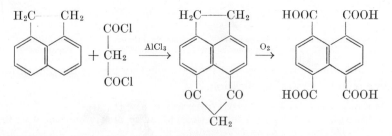

[337] Neugebauer and Schmidt, Ger. pat. 394,794 (1921) [*Friedländer*, **14**, 482].
[338] Kalle, Ger. pat. 408,513 (1922) [*Friedländer*, **14**, 483].
[339] Volmann and Corell, U. S. pat. 2,009,596 (1935) [*C. A.*, **29**, 6251 (1935)].
[340] Eckert, Ger. pat. 439,511 (1924) [*Friedländer*, **15**, 294].

Similar methods are described in several patents.[341]

Dyes of this type are obtained by condensation of an *o*-phenylene-diamine with the tetracarboxylic acid, mixtures of the *cis*- and *trans*-isomers being obtained. The pure isomers generally have markedly different shades as indicated in the unsubstituted compound shown.

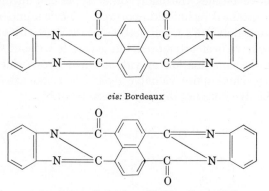

*cis:* Bordeaux

*trans:* Orange (Indanthrene Brilliant Orange GR)

The isomeric mixture obtained directly from the reaction is a scarlet (Indanthrene Scarlet 2G).[342]

By the use of 4-ethoxy-1,2-phenylenediamine instead of *o*-phenylene-diamine, the shade becomes a reddish brown.[342] These and similar dyes of this series are surprisingly fast and excellent for printing purposes.

## Dipyrazolanthrones

Pyrazolanthrone may be converted into a yellow vat dye by fusion with potassium hydroxide. Contrary to the statements in the original patent,[343] the reaction consists in the linking of two pyrazolanthrone nuclei.

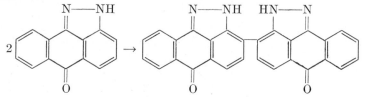

---

[341] Greune, U. S. pat. 1,803,182 (1931) [*C. A.*, **25**, 3669 (1931)]; Eckert *et al.*, U. S. pat. 1,913,798 (1933) [*C. A.*, **27**, 4414 (1933)]; Kränzlein and Vollmann, U. S. pat. 1,920,406 (1933) [*C. A.*, **27**, 4816 (1933)]; Greune and Eckert, U. S. pat. 1,970,651 (1934) [*C. A.*, **28**, 6159 (1934)]; Eckert *et al.*, U. S. pat. 2,011,805 (1935) [*C. A.*, **29**, 6609 (1935)].

[342] Baumann, U. S. pat. 1,730,186 (1929) [*C. A.*, **23**, 5597 (1929)].

[343] Griesheim-Elektron, Ger. pat. 255,641 (1912) [*C. A.*, **7**, 1981 (1913)].

Pyrazolanthrone Yellow dyes from a blue vat in bright yellow shades, fast to chlorine, but not to alkali. The alkali salts may be alkylated easily, and the alkylated compounds represent red dyes of technical importance.[344]

There are infinitely more variations of the main types of the vat dyes discussed above besides the many other types not mentioned which have not yet attained technical importance. Their number is too great for detailed consideration. Combinations of vat dyes with other chromophoric groups have been attempted, but generally without success. The exception is the combination of vat and azo dyes, which in certain associations produce quite valuable dyes. It is remarkable that the vatting of the dye does not destroy the azo bond.[345]

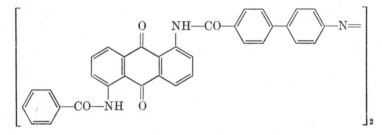

**Solubilized Vat Dyes**

Dyeing with vat dyes as a rule requires skill and experience. The relatively large amount of alkali for the vatting operation, i.e., the creation of the substantive leuco compound of the dye, restricts the use of the great majority of the vat dyes to the dyeing of cellulosic fibers. It is, therefore, not surprising that many efforts were made towards an easier and broader application of this class of colorants. Bader in 1921 proposed the use of the sodium salts of the disulfuric esters of the indigoid or anthraquinoid leuco vats for the dyeing or printing of textile

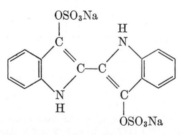

[344] Griesheim-Elektron, Ger. pat. 301,554 (1918) [*C. A.*, **13**, 380 (1919)].

[345] Honold and Schubert, U. S. pat. 2,228,455 (1941) [*C. A.*, **35**, 3102 (1941)]; Besler, U. S. pat. 2,316,758 (1943) [*C. A.*, **37**, 5872 (1943)]; U. S. pat. 2,347,027 (1944) [*C. A.*, **38**, 6573 (1944)].

fibers in general. The first representative was the sodium salt of the disulfuric ester of leuco indigo, and products of this type have since been known as indigosols even though the majority are not derivatives of indigo.

Two general methods of preparation have been used. The first to be developed follows a procedure described first by Verley,[346] which consists of the sulfation of leuco compounds with chlorosulfonic acid in the presence of tertiary amines (pyridine, dimethylaniline, etc.).[347] This reaction was further simplified when it was found that reduction of the dye to the leuco compound and esterification may be carried out simultaneously.[348] Much more recently it was found that certain tertiary amine-sulfur trioxide compounds $(R_3N \cdot SO_3)$ would react in aqueous solution with the leuco forms of many vat dyes to give the desired sulfuric esters.[349] This method is particularly useful when the desired leuco can be obtained from the vat dye by an aqueous reduction.

The esters obtained are stable in alkaline or neutral solutions; they may be dyed on the fiber and be reconverted on the fiber to the original dye by acid hydrolysis and oxidation.

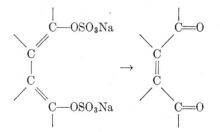

Not all vat dyes can be converted into indigosols, and of those which lend themselves to esterification, quite a few are too insoluble in their esterified form to be of technical value. There exists, however, a very complete line of shades which may be used not only for dyeing or printing of wool or cellulosic fibers but also for the dyeing of uniform shades of mixed fibers. A few of the dyes commercially offered are: Indigosol Blue O4B (vat dye, Ciba Blue 2B), Indigosol Orange HR (from Algol Orange RF), and Indigosol Red IFBB (from Indanthrene Red FBB).

[346] Verley, *Bull. soc. chim. France*, **25**, 46 (1901).
[347] Bader and Sunder, U. S. pat. 1,448,251 (1923) [*C. A.*, **17**, 2195 (1923)].
[348] Morton *et al.*, U. S. pat. 1,790,759 (1931) [*C. A.*, **25**, 1683 (1931)].
[349] Lecher *et al.*, U. S. pat. 2,403,226 (1946) [*C. A.*, **40**, 6264 (1946)]; Lecher and Hardy, *J. Am. Chem. Soc.*, **70**, 3789 (1948).

## PHTHALOCYANINES

In 1927 Diesbach and von der Weid obtained by reaction of aryl-*o*-dibromides with copper cyanide or aryl-*o*-dinitriles with copper bromide in pyridine a stable blue pigment without recognizing its true constitution.[350] A year later chemists of Scottish Dyes Ltd.[351] observed the formation of a blue pigment in the technical process of making phthalimide by treating molten phthalic anhydride with ammonia. This discovery provided the dye industry with an entirely new group of organic dyes of great beauty and stability. The structure and mode of formation were elucidated in 1934 by Linstead and co-workers,[352] who also proposed the name phthalocyanines. They proved that phthalocyanine, readily formed by the reaction of many metals with phthalonitrile, is tetrabenzporphyrazine and, therefore, closely related to the porphin nucleus present in chlorophyll and hemin.

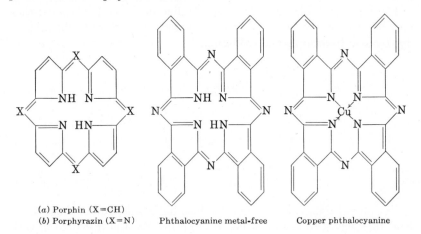

(a) Porphin (X=CH)
(b) Porphyrazin (X=N)      Phthalocyanine metal-free      Copper phthalocyanine

The two imino hydrogens of phthalocyanine can be replaced by metals, thus forming stable metal-complexes. Intermediate rings in which the methine bridges of the porphin structure have been replaced partly have been synthesized by Helberger[353] and Dent.[354] They represent dyes of properties similar to phthalocyanine.

The phthalocyanines are formed by heating aromatic *o*-dicarboxylic acids or their amino or imino derivatives with metals or metal salts in

[350] Diesbach and von der Weid, *Helv. Chim. Acta*, **10**, 886 (1927).

[351] Dandridge *et al.*, Brit. pat. 322,169 (1928) [*C. A.*, **24**, 2890 (1930)].

[352] Linstead, *J. Chem. Soc.*, 1016 (1934).

[353] Helberger, *Ann.*, **529**, 205 (1937); Helberger and von Rebay, *Ann.*, **531**, 279 (1937); Helberger *et al.*, *Ann.*, **533**, 197 (1938); Helberger and Hever, *Ann.*, **536**, 173 (1938).

[354] Dent, *J. Chem. Soc.*, 3 (1938).

the presence of ammonia.   The reaction seems to proceed most easily
with o-dinitriles.   According to Linstead, in order to be usable for the
synthesis, the o-dinitriles should meet the following specifications: [355]
(a) the carbons carrying the nitrile groups must be connected with each
other through a double bond; (b) they must have the faculty to form
heterocyclic rings similar to the anhydrides or imides of the o-dicar-
boxylic acids; (c) they must be stable to the temperature of the reaction;
the reaction is exothermic and seems to suggest a polymerization of
phthalonitriles.

Several technical processes are in use for the production of phthalocyanines.   Important starting materials are the aromatic o-dinitriles,
especially for the synthesis of metal-free nuclear substituted dyes.[356]
In the latter case, the correspondingly substituted o-dinitriles are used.
Another process uses phthalic anhydride and urea [357] as starting materials.   The reactions may be carried out either in the form of a melt or
in the presence of an inert solvent.   A further suggestion is to use as
starting materials mononitriles with halogen or sulfonic acid group in the
ortho position, adding to the reaction mixture copper cyanide, thereby
forming the dinitriles in situ.[358]   Catalytic additions of such substances
as boric acid or tungsten [359] result in yields close to the theory.

Copper phthalocyanine is a deep blue pigment of a very pure hue.
It is extraordinarily stable, not affected by boiling hydrochloric acid or
molten alkali.   It is completely insoluble in all the usual organic solvents.
The metal-free phthalocyanine may be obtained from lead or magnesium
phthalocyanines by treatment with acids.   Its shade is a greenish blue
of properties similar to those of the metal complex.   Phthalocyanine is
not stable against oxidizing agents of an acidic character.

Substitution in the benzene nuclei of the phthalocyanine will yield
green dyes if the molecule is enlarged sufficiently; two examples are
1,2-naphthalocyanine [360] and tetraphenylphthalocyanine.[361]   Other substitutions by amino, acylamino, alkoxy, carboxy, and aroyl groups have
been effected.

The halogenated phthalocyanines are important commercially, those

[355] Linstead, Ber., **72A**, 93 (1939).

[356] Linstead and Dent, U. S. pat. 2,056,944 (1936) [C. A., **30**, 8639 (1936)]; Heilbron
et al., U. S. pat. 2,124,419 (1938) [C. A., **32**, 7282 (1938)].

[357] Wyler, U. S. pat. 2,197,458 (1940) [C. A., **34**, 5674 (1940)].

[358] Linstead et al., U. S. pat. 2,075,043 (1937) [C. A., **31**, 3711 (1937)].

[359] Riley, U. S. pat. 2,214,477 (1940) [C. A., **35**, 911 (1941)].

[360] Bradbrook and Linstead, J. Chem. Soc., 1744 (1936); Gassner and Biener, U. S. pat.
2,116,196 (1938) [C. A., **32**, 5225 (1938)]; Heilbron et al., U. S. pat. 2,116,213 (1939)
[C. A., **33**, 8428 (1939)].

[361] Bienert and Gassner, Ger. pat. 682,542 (1939) [C. A., **36**, 3367 (1942)].

containing 14 to 16 chlorine atoms [362] having very brilliant bluish green shades of excellent fastness.

Copper phthalocyanine and its chlorinated derivatives are used for a variety of purposes in the paint, lacquer, and printing ink industry.

Water-soluble derivatives obtained by sulfonation [363] of the phthalocyanines or synthetically from the sulfophthalic acids [364] dye cellulosic fibers directly in very fast shades. A dye of this type is Fastusol Turquoise Blue LGLA. The tetraphenyl copper-phthalocyanine tetracarboxylic acid, Sirius Light Green FFGL, likewise is a direct cotton dye. Although these dyes are relatively fast to light and show good fastness to alkali and acid they are deficient in their resistance to bleaching agents and washing.

The action of trichloroacetic acid on metal phthalocyanine at elevated temperature is reported to give fast acid wool dyes.[365] The condensation products of phthalocyanines and benzalchloride or benzotrichloride contain aromatic nuclei as well as halogen and constitute fast and bright green to blue-green pigments.[366]

Proposals for using aminophthalocyanines in the azo or azoic field as diazo components have not progressed beyond the patent stage.[367]

Of technical interest, however, is the use of copper phthalocyanines for sulfur dyes, whereby a sulfonyl chloride of the former is reduced by zinc or iron to the corresponding mercaptan and oxidized.[368] The sulfur dye obtained is a bright jade green of high fastness.

Another development is based on the chloromethylation of copper phthalocyanine. The resulting chloromethyl derivative when reacted with an equivalent amount of a volatile amine gives a water-soluble quaternary salt which can be used for either dyeing or printing. The pigment is fixed on the fiber by a mild alkaline hydrolysis which liberates the volatile amine at the same time. Alcian Blue 8G represents a dye of this type.[369]

[362] Schmidt et al., Ger. pat. 692,977 (1940) [C. A., 35, 4604 (1941)]; Barrett et al., J. Chem. Soc., 1820 (1939).

[363] Dandridge et al., Brit. pat. 322,169 (1930) [C. A., 24, 2890 (1930)].

[364] Bienert and Thielert, U. S. pat. 2,266,404 (1941) [C. A., 36, 2419 (1942)].

[365] I. G. Farbenind. A.-G., Brit. pat. 487,261 (1938) [C. A., 32, 9515 (1938)]; Niemann, Ger. pat. 677,667 (1939) [C. A., 33, 9667 (1939)].

[366] Mühlbauer, Ger. pat. 700,225 (1940) [C. A., 35, 7206 (1941)].

[367] Haddock, U. S. pat. 2,280,072 (1942) [C. A., 36, 5359 (1942)]; Blackshaw and Haddock, U. S. pat. 2,339,740 (1944) [C. A., 38, 4138 (1944)]; Haddock, U. S. pat. 2,349,089–91 (1944) [C. A., 39, 1545 (1945)]; U. S. pat. 2,351,119 (1944) [C. A., 38, 5414 (1944)].

[368] Fox, U. S. pat. 2,369,666 (1945) [C. A., 40, 215 (1946)]; Haddock, U. S. pat. 2,342,663 (1944) [C. A., 38, 4810 (1944)].

[369] Haddock and Wood, U. S. pat. 2,464,806 (1949) [C. A., 43, 8172 (1949)]; U. S. pat. 2,435,307 (1948) [C. A., 42, 8482 (1948)]; Haddock, Research, 1, 685 (1948); Chem. Trade J., 122, 87 (1948).

It is evident from the above that the phthalocyanines may be used for a variety of applications. Their exceptional fastness has secured for them a broad and permanent place in commerce despite their very short period of existence.

## GENERAL REFERENCES

Barnett, "Anthracene and Anthraquinone," Bailliere, Tindall & Cox, London (1921).

Cain, "The Manufacture of Dyes," Macmillan & Co., London (1922).

Cain, "The Chemistry and Technology of the Diazo Compounds," Edward Arnold, London (1920).

Curtis, "Künstliche organische Pigmentfarben und ihre Anwendungsgebiete," Springer, Berlin (1929).

Diserens, "Die neuesten Fortschritte in der Anwendung der Farbstoffe," Birkhaeuser, Basel (1946); Reinhold Publishing Corp., New York (1948). Translated by Wengraf and Baumann.

Fierz-David, "Künstliche organische Farbstoffe," Springer, Berlin (1926–1935), 2 vols.

Fischer and Orth, "Die Chemie des Pyrrols," Band II, Akademische Verlagsgesellschaft, Leipzig (1937).

Fox, "Vat Dyestuffs and Vat Dyeing," Chapman & Hall, London (1946).

Georgievics and Grandmougin, "A Text-Book of Dye Chemistry," Scott, Greenwood & Son, London (1920).

Hewitt, "Synthetic Colouring Matters. Dyestuffs Derived from Pyridine, Quinoline, Acridine and Xanthene," Longmans, Green & Co., London (1922).

Holzach, "Die aromatischen Diazoverbindungen," Enke, Stuttgart (1947).

Houben, "Das Anthracen und die Anthrachinone," Thieme, Leipzig (1929).

Mayer, "Chemie der organischen Farbstoffe," Springer, Berlin (1934–1935), 2 vols.

Remick, "Electronic Interpretations of Organic Chemistry," John Wiley & Sons, New York (1949), 2nd ed.

Rowe, "The Development of the Chemistry of Commercial Synthetic Dyes (1856–1938)," Inst. of Chemistry of Great Britain and Ireland, London (1938).

Saunders, "The Aromatic Diazo-Compounds and Their Technical Applications," Edward Arnold, London (1936).

Schultz, "Farbstofftabellen," Akademische Verlagsgesellschaft, Leipzig (1931).

Venkataraman, "The Chemistry of Synthetic Dyes," Academic Press, New York (1952).

Wheland, "The Theory of Resonance and Its Application to Organic Chemistry," John Wiley & Sons, New York (1949), 2nd ed.

## ACKNOWLEDGMENT

The author is grateful to Dr. R. S. Long for gracious assistance.

# CHAPTER 5

## SOME ASPECTS OF CHEMOTHERAPY

### H. R. ING

*University of Oxford*

## CONTENTS

## INTRODUCTION

The term "chemotherapy" was invented by Paul Ehrlich. It means literally the treatment of disease by means of chemical substances, and as such the practice is as old as civilization. Ehrlich, however, gave the term a more specialized meaning. He was concerned with diseases caused by infection with microörganisms—bacteria, spirochetes, or protozoa—and he believed that chemical substances could be found which would be toxic to the infecting microörganisms but relatively harmless to the infected host. His belief was amply justified in his own lifetime, and the word chemotherapy is best reserved for the treatment of diseases due to parasitic microörganisms by chemical substances which have a specific toxicity for the microörganisms. It is important to remember that chemotherapy in Ehrlich's sense is still a branch of therapeutics, but the great innovation which Ehrlich made was to enlist the help of the organic chemist, for he was convinced that it was among organic, rather than inorganic, compounds that chemical agents fulfilling his twofold requirement were to be discovered.

To the chemist, therefore, chemotherapy is a branch of applied organic chemistry, and it is interesting to reflect that it was a pathologist who laid down the principles which should guide the chemist in his search for new chemotherapeutic agents. These principles were extremely simple, even naive, in conception. First, the chemotherapeutic agent must have an affinity for the protoplasmic constituents of the parasite, i.e., it must be fixed by the parasite, or, as Ehrlich expressed it, "Corpora non agunt nisi fixata," but it should have little affinity for the tissues of the host. In Ehrlich's terminology it should be "parasitotropic" but not "organotropic." Second, the agent should be toxic to the parasite. Ehrlich regarded toxicity as due to particular chemical groups, "toxophoric groups," in the drug molecule, distinct and different from the structural features which conferred affinity for the parasite, and consequently lack of toxicity for the host was to be achieved by avoiding structural features which conferred affinity for the tissues of the host.

Penicillin is probably the nearest approach to the ideal chemotherapeutic agent in Ehrlich's sense since it combines high bactericidal activity with a remarkable lack of toxicity to the host; most synthetic agents fall well below this standard. Their usefulness therefore depends upon the relation between their toxicities to the host and to the parasite, and this relation has frequently been gauged by the ratio:

$$\frac{\text{Maximum tolerated dose or MTD}}{\text{Minimum curative dose or MCD}}$$

This ratio is called the "chemotherapeutic index," and the larger it is the safer the drug will be. The chemotherapeutic index raises difficult questions of the measurement of biological effects which will be referred to later. Meanwhile it is sufficient to say that the final selection of a new chemotherapeutic agent for investigation in human disease is the responsibility of the biologist. The problem for the chemist is how he is to set about discovering new compounds with desirable therapeutic properties.

Ehrlich began his search for chemotherapeutic agents among dyes. As a young man he had investigated the staining of microörganisms and had discovered several of the stains now commonly used in bacteriology. Since some dyes have a pronounced affinity for microörganisms, they offered, in Ehrlich's view, the possibility of being used as chemotherapeutic agents. His first success was achieved with trypan red, a *bis*-azo dye, which was both curative and prophylactic in mice infected with the disease mal de caderas, a form of trypanosomiasis. This was the first cure of an experimentally produced disease with a synthetic organic compound (1907). Later he investigated dyes of the acridine group and discovered trypaflavine, 2,8-diamino-10-methylacridinium chloride, which had considerable curative activity in trypanosome infections and which, under the name acriflavine, has since been widely used as an antiseptic.

In all his work it is noteworthy that Ehrlich had clearly in mind the idea that the drug must combine in some way with certain protoplasmic constituents, "chemoreceptors," as he called them, of the parasite. Thus, in his early work on arsenical drugs, when he found that atoxyl was without effect upon trypanosomes *in vitro* he did not test it on infected animals; but directly atoxyl had been shown to cure some forms of trypanosomiasis, in mice by Thomas and Breinl and in man by Koch, he returned to its investigation. Moreover, it is characteristic of him that he first reinvestigated its structure. Atoxyl was thought to be the anilide of arsenic acid, but Ehrlich and Bertheim proved that it was the sodium salt of $p$-aminophenylarsonic acid ($NH_2C_6H_4AsO_3HNa$).  The discovery of the true nature of atoxyl opened the possibility of preparing a wide range of compounds containing organically bound arsenic, but Ehrlich turned first to the problem of why atoxyl was trypanocidal *in vivo* but not *in vitro*.  He found that atoxyl was readily reduced by ordinary reagents to $p$-aminophenylarsenoxide * ($NH_2C_6H_4AsO$), which was powerfully trypanocidal *in vitro*, but highly toxic to the host as well as to the parasite *in vivo*.  He concluded that atoxyl was probably reduced *in vivo* to the arsenoxide and that the latter was the active trypanocidal agent in the animal.  He was immensely impressed by the contrast between this trivalent arsenic compound and atoxyl, which contains pentavalent arsenic, and it was in order to avoid the high toxicity of the arsenoxides but at the same time retain trivalent arsenic that he began to investigate arsenobenzene derivatives, work which led to his greatest practical achievement, the discovery of salvarsan (arsphenamine).

Later workers in the chemotherapeutic field have not always kept so clearly in mind as Ehrlich did the biological nature of the problem. Organic chemists have usually started from some substance already known to possess chemotherapeutic activity, either a natural product such as an alkaloid or a synthetic compound, and have prepared series of compounds of similar or related structure in the hope of finding compounds with enhanced activity.  Thus Ehrlich's discovery of the curative and prophylactic activity of trypan red in experimental trypanosomiasis led, by a series of developments that will be discussed later, to the discovery of suramin (Bayer 205, Fourneau 309), a valuable drug in the treatment of African sleeping sickness.  Similarly, the first synthetic antimalarials were developed from methylene blue, which Ehrlich had found to have some antimalarial activity.  This general method of the organic chemist is of considerable interest because it presupposes a chemical basis for drug action: that chemotherapeutic activity is to be associated with particular structural features and that suitable changes in the structure of an active molecule may not only lead to more active compounds but also reveal what structural features are essential for a particular chemotherapeutic response.

The relation between chemical constitution and physiological action is a baffling subject of study, and some authors have despaired of finding any relation.  Thus A. J. Clark [1] wrote that it was "a subject of notorious

---

* Also named $p$-aminophenylarsine oxide.

[1] Clark, Heffter's "Handbuch der experimentellen Pharmakologie," Ergänzungswerk, Band 4, *General Pharmacology*, Springer, Berlin (1937), Chapter 18, p. 190.

difficulty. It may be said that there are scarely any general rules discernible and that every cell-drug system is a law unto itself." Since much of this chapter will be concerned with the structure-action relationships of drugs, the reader must decide for himself whether he agrees with Clark's dictum or not. If structure-action relationships cannot be found, the organic chemist may be reduced to a hit-or-miss method in his search for new chemotherapeutic agents, to testing indiscriminately a wide selection of synthetic compounds of different types in the hope of discovering one with some useful activity. But if he succeeds in finding one, he will not easily resist the belief that other compounds of similar type may also be active.

It must be remembered that the living cell is a highly complex system and that interference with its manifold metabolic processes may occur at numerous points; thus a cell may be killed by such a wide variety of different chemical substances that it would be futile to try to find structure-action relationships among them all. Progress can be made only by considering structure-action relationships within groups of compounds, closely related in structure, for which a common mechanism of action can be reasonably assumed. Even so, the problem is often more difficult in chemotherapy than it is in classical pharmacology, because the system being studied, host-parasite-drug, is even more complicated. The chemotherapeutic effect observed is the resultant of so many diverse events: not only the effect of the drug upon the parasite, already sufficiently complex, but also the absorption of the drug, its distribution throughout the tissues of the host, the metabolic changes which it may undergo, and the method and rate of its excretion. Structural changes which do not materially alter the toxicity of a drug to a particular microörganism *in vitro* may destroy its curative activity; e.g., the modified drug may no longer be able to penetrate to the site occupied by the infecting organism, or it may be metabolized too rapidly for it to attain the concentration in the body fluids required for its therapeutic action to take effect.

Structure-action relationships should be discerned more readily when drugs are tested against microörganisms *in vitro*, since this method simplifies the system to be studied, but the technical difficulties of doing so are sometimes formidable. The absorption of a drug, its distribution in the tissues, and the method and rate of its excretion can all be studied separately in healthy animals. In practice it is best, whenever possible, to test drugs against microörganisms both *in vitro* and *in vivo*. If drugs are tested only *in vitro*, therapeutically active compounds may be missed since it sometimes happens that drugs that are inactive *in vitro* are active *in vivo*. It is usually assumed that such drugs are converted in the host into chemically different substances, which are active *in vivo* and would be so *in vitro*, but it is often difficult to identify the active substance with certainty. Atoxyl has already been mentioned as an example of a drug inactive *in vitro* but active *in vivo*. Drugs may also appear much less active *in vitro* than *in vivo*; e.g., quinine has no effect upon the malaria parasite *in vitro* in concentrations that are attainable in the blood of an infected animal.

The converse also happens: drugs that are highly active *in vitro* may be only feebly curative or entirely inactive in infected animals; this is true of many antiseptics. But a substance that is active only *in vitro* at least reveals an intrinsically active structure which the organic chemist may be able to modify in such a way as to produce substances active *in vivo* also.

**Chemotherapy of Bacterial Diseases.** Ehrlich's success in finding a remedy for syphilis convinced people of the possibilities of chemotherapy, and his ideas had a profound influence on the development of the chemotherapy of tropical, and particularly protozoal, diseases. Indeed, many advances in this field were made by men who had at one time worked in his laboratory, such as Browning, Roehl, and Kikuth. There was, however, one large group of diseases, namely those caused by bacterial infections, which appeared to be incurable by chemotherapeutic means. In the early thirties the opinion was widely held that chemotherapeutic methods were unsuitable for combating these infections and that the most promising methods were immunological. Domagk's discovery of Prontosil in 1935 was therefore an important turning point in chemotherapy. Prontosil cured streptococcal and staphylococcal infections in man, and it was soon shown by workers in Fourneau's laboratory that its action was due to its reduction in the body to sulfanilamide, which was the effective substance.

The discovery of the sulfonamide drugs has had an immense influence on the more recent development of chemotherapy: e.g., it is doubtful whether anyone would have devoted the immense amount of time and labor required to the isolation and purification of penicillin if the sulfonamide drugs had not demonstrated the possibility of curing bacterial diseases by means of chemical substances with highly specific bacteriostatic properties. The fact that microörganisms, particularly fungi, produce substances that inhibit the growth of other microörganisms had been well known to bacteriologists for many years before Fleming chanced to observe the inhibitory effects of *Penicillium notatum* on his bacterial cultures, but the discovery of the sulfonamides constituted a fresh and powerful incentive to the reinvestigation of such "antibiotic" substances; and the isolation of penicillin by Florey and his colleagues has led to a world-wide search for new antibiotics which may be used in combating bacterial infections.

The discovery of the sulfonamides had also a profound effect upon chemotherapeutic theory. Only a few years after Domagk's announcement of Prontosil, Woods discovered that sulfanilamide was antagonized by $p$-aminobenzoic acid, and he suggested (1) that $p$-aminobenzoic acid was an essential metabolite of bacteria, (2) that the bacteriostatic effect of sulfanilamide was due to the drug's blocking some enzyme system involved in the utilization of $p$-aminobenzoic acid, and (3) that this inhibitory effect was the result of a structural resemblance between sulfanilamide and $p$-aminobenzoic acid. These suggestions have led to a new way of looking at chemotherapeutic action. Woods belonged to a small group of workers who were engaged in studying bacterial metabolism; they had developed ideas about the action of bacteriostatic substances, ideas which led directly to Woods' discovery and which were given formal expression in an article by Fildes,[2] the leader of the group.

Briefly, their view was that chemotherapeutic substances interfered with metabolic processes, necessary to the life of the microörganism, either by combining with, and so immobilizing, essential metabolic substances or by competing with them for enzymes and so blocking their utilization. Essential metabolites were defined as substances without which the growth of the cell could not be maintained. They might be synthesized normally by the cell itself, and, if so, the effect of the chemotherapeutic agent might be defeated by an increase in the synthetic activity of the cell. If, however, the cell were incapable of synthesizing a particular metabolite and had to rely for its supply upon its environment, a chemotherapeutic agent which immobilized such a metabolite or prevented its utilization would, if present in sufficient amount, bring the growth of the cell to an end. Essential metabolites which the cell was incapable of manufacturing itself were called "growth factors," and the aim of chemotherapy was to find agents which would combine with growth factors or prevent the cell's making use of them.

These ideas were not really novel. Voegtlin some fifteen years earlier had suggested that all arsenical drugs acted by combining with, and so rendering unavailable to the organism, vital SH-compounds; and the idea that enzyme systems could be inhibited by substances related in structure to their normal substrates was familiar to all biochemists. The importance of Fildes's article lay in the emphasis which it put upon these two ideas—combination with or prevention of the utilization of growth factors—as ones which should govern the search for new chemotherapeutic remedies.

[2] Fildes, *Lancet*, **238**, 955 (1940).

Subsequent workers have concentrated mainly on the discovery of substances, chemically related to some known metabolites, which might be expected to interfere with the normal function of that metabolite in living cells; such substances are called "metabolite antagonists."[3] Three examples may be briefly mentioned. Pantoyltaurine (I) is bacteriostatic to some organisms, e.g., streptococci and pneumococci, which require preformed pantothenic acid (II), but not to organisms which synthesize their own pantothenic acid. Its bacteriostatic effect is annulled by the addition of pantothenic acid, and it will not protect animals against streptococcal infections unless, as in rats, the normal blood level of pantothenic acid is low.

A dichloro analog of riboflavin, namely 6,7-dichloro-9-($d$-1'-ribityl)$iso$-alloxazine (III), is a potent antagonist of riboflavin (IV) and inhibits the growth of numerous organisms at concentrations of the order of 0.01 mg./ml. Its bacteriostatic action is annulled by added riboflavin.

$$HOCH_2C(CH_3)_2CHOHCONHCH_2CH_2SO_3H$$
I

$$HOCH_2C(CH_3)_2CHOHCONHCH_2CH_2CO_2H$$
II

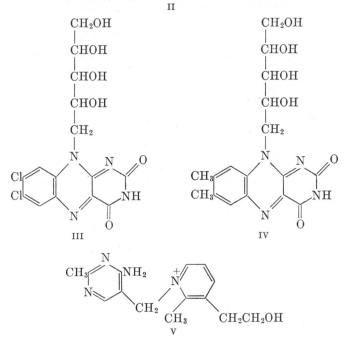

III                                        IV

V

[3] See reviews by Roblin, *Chem. Revs.*, **38**, 255 (1946); and Woolley, *Physiol. Revs.*, **27**, 308 (1947).

Finally pyrithiamine (V) inhibits the growth of microörganisms which require preformed thiamine (VI) and produces characteristic symptoms of thiamine deficiency in animals. It will be noticed that all these

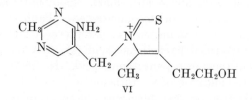

VI

metabolite antagonists have strong structural resemblances to the vitamins which they antagonize. Thus pantoyltaurine has a sulfonic acid group in place of the carboxyl of pantothenic acid; 6,7-dichloro-9-ribitylisoalloxazine contains Cl in place of $CH_3$ groups (chloro- and methyl-substituted benzene compounds are known to form mixed crystals); and pyrithiamine contains a pyridine ring which is isosteric with the thiazole ring of thiamine. Numerous other examples are known, but so far no new chemotherapeutic remedies have been discovered in work of this kind. At the same time, the work is of great interest, and it has served among other purposes to introduce into chemotherapy the idea of "fit" between drug molecules and cell constituents.

The idea of fit goes back to Pasteur, who used it to explain stereo-chemical specificity in biological effects. Thus Piutti observed that d-asparagine had a sweet taste whereas the naturally occurring l-isomer was insipid. Pasteur attributed this to the presence of an optically active substance in the nervous mechanism of taste and compared it with the stereochemical specificity of enzymes, to explain which he had earlier used his well-known analogy of the lock and key. Ehrlich does not appear to have used this idea—he thought more in terms of direct chemical combination—and although the idea of fit between drug mole-cules and the organized structures of living tissues haunted pharma-cology for many years, it was for a long time regarded with some dis-favor, mainly, no doubt, because it was too vague, lacked a firm physical basis, and was not fertile in suggesting fresh experimental work. How-ever, Lansteiner's work [4] on the antigen-antibody reaction did much to revive the idea. Also Michaelis's concept of the enzyme-substrate complex led biochemists more and more to think of substrate specificity and of competitive inhibition in terms of fit between the substrate or inhibitor molecules and the enzyme. Moreover, the previous disad-vantage that fit between molecules lacked a physical basis no longer

---

[4] Lansteiner, "The Specificity of Serological Reactions," Harvard University Press, Cambridge, Mass. (1943).

holds, since it is realized that molecules may be held in intimate contact by van der Waals forces and by hydrogen bonding. The idea of fit is implicit in the operation of van der Waals forces since they are both weak and short range; to be held together by them molecules must come into intimate contact at numerous points. Thus if a drug molecule is to be attached by these forces to a cell structure it must be of such a size and shape as to accommodate itself closely to the molecular architecture of the biological structure (enzyme, cytoplasmic membrane, or whatever it may be) upon which it exerts its disturbing effect.

This idea of fit is a valuable concept in chemotherapy. It makes reasonable the fact that some molecules are taken up by microörganisms more readily than others; i.e., it provides a physical explanation of what Ehrlich called the "parasitotropic" properties of drug molecules. If a drug molecule is of the right size and shape it may be waylaid by the microörganism and firmly bound by some macromolecular unit of structure in the cytoplasmic membrane. Some such process undoubtedly takes place with many chemotherapeutic agents, although it must not be regarded as the only way in which the uptake of drugs can occur. With some agents this primary fixation may so alter the properties of the cell membrane that the drug may achieve its effect without penetrating further into the cell. Other agents may have to be transported across the cell membrane and penetrate into the interior of the cell before their action can be exerted. The idea of fit is of course also implicit in the concept of competitive inhibition of enzymes which Woods invoked in order to account for the mutual antagonism of $p$-aminobenzoic acid and sulfanilamide.

Although the ideas we have been discussing have enriched the theoretical content of chemotherapy it must be confessed that the discovery of new chemotherapeutic agents still largely relies upon empirical methods. In order to develop rational methods it would be necessary to know much more than we do at present about the metabolic processes of microörganisms, in particular to know how they differ from those of the host, for the ideal point of attack of a chemotherapeutic agent would appear to be some unique metabolite or process in the microörganism. Many metabolic processes appear to be common to most living cells, and it is natural that these should have been among the first to be discovered and studied in detail; but, even among these, certain biochemical reactions may be relatively more important to the microörganism than to the host. Indeed it seems that this must be so: e.g., sulfonamide drugs must presumably inhibit the utilization of $p$-aminobenzoic acid by the host as well as by the invading bacteria, but a short interruption in $p$-aminobenzoic acid metabolism may be less harmful to the host than to the infecting organism.  More detailed investigation of the metabolism of microörganisms may, however, reveal unique processes, or more probably unique metabolites, upon which attack might be made with appropriately designed drugs.  But even if a drug is designed to block some uniquely important metabolic process in a microörganism, the chemist is still faced with the twin problems of uptake by the parasite and distribution in the host.  The drug must be readily absorbed by the parasite, and it must reach the sites occupied by the invading organism in sufficient amount.  Even less is known about the factors that govern the uptake of drugs by microörganisms and their distribution in the tissues of the host than is known about the metabolism of microörganisms.  Therefore, it is not surprising that new chemotherapeutic remedies are nearly always the result of empirical observations; nor, when the urgency of the human problems involved in disease is considered, will anyone wish to discourage any methods, however empirical, which may lead to the discovery of new and useful remedies.

**The Chemotherapeutic Index.**  We have already defined the chemotherapeutic index as the ratio of the maximum tolerated dose to the minimum curative dose.  Unfortunately these terms cannot be given precise meanings, except for an individual animal.  Even in apparently uniform populations, animals vary considerably in their susceptibility to any given drug.  A dose that is safe for some animals in a population may kill others, and there is often a surprisingly large gap between the minimum dose which will kill every animal in a population (Lethal Dose 100 or LD100) and the maximum dose which will kill none (LD0).  For some drugs the ratio LD100/LD0 may be as high as 5 to 10.  For this reason Trevan proposed that toxicities should be measured in terms of the dose that would kill 50% of a large number of animals (LD50).  The advantage of the LD50 as a measure of toxicity is that simple statistical methods can be used in its determination, and large numbers of animals are not required.[5]  Some authors have found it convenient to substitute the LD50 for the MTD and to replace the MCD by the CD50, i.e., the dose which would cure 50% of a large number of animals.  Both the LD50 and the CD50 can be estimated by statistical methods with greater precision than the MTD or MCD, but the ratio LD50/CD50 does not tell us what we need to know, which is the probable ratio between the safe and the curative doses in any animal.  The mortality in a population of animals may increase with increasing doses of a drug more rapidly than the cures, and consequently a dose which will cure 100% of animals may be very near or even within the toxic range

[5] See Burn, Finney, and Goodwin, "Biological Standardization," Oxford University Press, London (1950).

for some of them. Trevan has suggested that the index LD50/CD50 should be replaced by LD0.1/CD99.9, i.e., by the ratio of the dose which would kill one in a thousand animals to the dose which would cure nine hundred and ninety-nine of them. Trevan's index is really the statistical equivalent of the older chemotherapeutic index, MTD/MCD, and the values LD0.1 and CD99.9 can be obtained by extrapolation of the regression lines obtained from toxicity and therapeutic data.

If the chemotherapeutic index is to have any real meaning both toxicity and therapeutic efficiency must be estimated in the same species. The question naturally arises whether indices determined for small laboratory animals can have any bearing on the treatment of human disease. It may be said that so long as an index is measured for small mammals (mice, rats, rabbits) it is a useful indication, but no more, of the sort of relation between toxicity and therapeutic efficiency which may obtain in man, but that indices determined for species more remote from man, e.g., birds, give no reliable indication of the probable safety of new drugs in human therapeutics. In any case the physician will always have to proceed cautiously with a new drug, even if it has a high index in small mammals. It is interesting that in the extensive survey of antimalarials carried out during the war years all attempt to measure chemotherapeutic indices was abandoned; both curative activities and toxicities were estimated in terms of those of a standard drug, usually quinine. The use of a standard reference substance is becoming more and more the practice in chemotherapy, as it has been for many years in pharmacology, and when the chemotherapeutic properties of the standard are well known this method of measuring activity or toxicity has much to recommend it.

**Scope of Chapter.** Chemotherapy is now so vast a subject that it is impossible to give more than a mere outline of some branches of it in a single chapter. Since the whole range of chemotherapeutic agents could not be covered, topics have been selected with a view to their interest to organic chemists, and attention has been mainly confined to structure-action relationships and possible mechanisms of action. No attempt has been made to discuss the clinical evidence upon which an assessment of the value of particular drugs in human disease must be based. For this the reader is referred to Findlay.[6] Nor has the biochemical background of chemotherapy [7,8] been discussed, although

[6] Findlay, "Recent Advances in Chemotherapy," Churchill, London (1950).

[7] Work and Work, "The Basis of Chemotherapy," Interscience Publishers, New York (1948).

[8] Sexton, "Chemical Constitution and Biological Activity," Van Nostrand, New York (1950).

some attempt has been made to indicate the difficulties and complexities of the biological side of chemotherapeutic investigations.

## CHEMOTHERAPY OF BACTERIAL INFECTIONS

A very large number of chemical substances will kill bacteria or inhibit their growth and multiplication, but comparatively few have any clinical value.  At the outset it will be convenient to distinguish between three main classes: (1) Disinfectants, which kill bacteria.  These substances are more precisely defined as bactericidal agents.  They can rarely be used even for local application in man, except for disinfection of the intact skin, because they will usually kill any living cell; they are mainly used to disinfect inanimate objects.  (2) Antiseptics or bacteriostatic agents, which inhibit the growth and multiplication of bacteria. Many of these agents can be used for only local application, e.g., the treatment of wounds and of infections of the eye, nose, throat, urethra, etc.  (3) Chemotherapeutic remedies, which are capable of suppressing and, in conjunction with the normal defense mechanisms of the body, of eradicating systemic infections.  Some substances of this class can also be used as antiseptics for local application, e.g., penicillin and some of the sulfa drugs.  Apart from the sulfa drugs, most of the really valuable agents of this group are substances of natural origin, the so-called "antibiotics," such as penicillin, streptomycin, aureomycin, and chloromycetin.  These are discussed in Chapter 6 by Cheney.  In this chapter are considered only selected groups of synthetic substances: (1) alcohols, phenols, and synthetic detergents—these are disinfectants, but are worth considering as examples of "physical toxicity"; (2) dyes, which, apart from their historical importance as antiseptics, have considerable theoretical interest because they illustrate the effect of certain physical properties on bacteriostatic activity; and (3) sulfonamides, which provide the most convenient introduction to modern bacterial chemotherapy.  Before dealing with particular classes of compounds, however, one must briefly consider the methods of evaluating substances for use as disinfectants, antiseptics, or chemotherapeutic agents.

It is a matter of considerable difficulty to devise a satisfactory means of estimating antiseptic or disinfectant potency.*  Bacteria vary greatly in their resistance to toxic agents, and the efficiency of any given agent against a particular species of bacteria is partly dependent on the

* The terms "antiseptic" and "disinfectant," or their more precise equivalents "bacteriostatic" and "bactericidal," are convenient, but the distinction between them is not always sharp or easy to make.  Some antibiotics appear to be bacteriostatic at low but bactericidal at higher concentrations (see Florey et al., "Antibiotics," Oxford University Press, London (1949), Vol. 2, Chapter 47).

nature of the medium. Most agents are less potent in the presence of organic material, particularly serum and other protein solutions, than they are in simple aqueous suspensions of bacteria.

Obviously, there can be no absolute measure of potency; some substance must be taken as a standard and other substances compared with it. The classical standard was *phenol* simply because it was the first antiseptic to be used clinically (Lister, 1867), and for many years antiseptic or disinfectant potencies were measured as phenol coefficients by a method devised by Rideal and Walker. The principle of the method is to find the minimum concentration of phenol required to kill a particular microörganism in a given time under carefully defined conditions, and similarly the minimum concentration of the substance of unknown potency which will do the same under identical conditions. The ratio of the concentration of phenol to that of test substance is the phenol coefficient. The numerical value of this coefficient depends upon numerous variables, such as the temperature, the time allowed for the drug to act, the species and even the strain of bacteria, the number of organisms used, the nature of the culture medium, and the presence of organic material.

Phenol coefficients have fallen into disrepute, partly because much more potent substances than phenol have been discovered and consequently a much more potent standard is required. In practice it has been found more convenient to compare antiseptics by the method of serial dilutions. Bacteria are treated with serial dilutions of the antiseptic, say 1/5,000, 1/10,000, 1/20,000, etc., and the minimum dilutions for no growth and full growth are measured under standardized conditions. The statement that a particular antiseptic will prevent all growth of a given microörganism at some specified dilution under some defined conditions is more informative than a phenol coefficient. Bactericidal substances usually give a sharper end point than bacteriostatic agents, which need to be incubated with the test organism for relatively long times (24–48 hours) if their full effect is to be observed.

Chemotherapeutic agents can also be tested by the method of serial dilution if they are active *in vitro*, but it is always desirable to test them against a systemic infection in a laboratory animal. The details of the test will depend upon the particular infection being studied, but the aim is always to choose an animal in which the particular species of bacteria produces a disease resembling closely that which occurs in man. It is also necessary to study in healthy animals the toxic reactions to the proposed remedy, its absorption and distribution in the body of the host, and the method and rate of its excretion.

## Alcohols and Phenols

**Homologous Series.** It will be convenient to consider alcohols and phenols together because in some respects they resemble each other closely. The aliphatic alcohols, $C_nH_{2n+1}OH$, are in general much weaker disinfectants than phenols, and only one of them, ethyl alcohol, has been widely used. Its maximum effect is exerted in concentrations between 50% and 80%; absolute ethanol has a relatively feeble disinfectant action. Seventy per cent ethanol and 50% n-propanol have been used as disinfectants for intact skin (e.g., the hands) and for syringes.

Phenol is too toxic for general use; the cresols are more active and less toxic, and a mixture of the three cresols as a 50% solution in soap, Lysol, has been widely used. The xylenols are more active and less soluble than the cresols and are usually emulsified with oil or gum. Chlorinated xylenols are even more active.

TABLE I

NORMAL PRIMARY ALCOHOLS, R—OH

| | B. typhosus | | | Staph. aureus | | |
|---|---|---|---|---|---|---|
| R | Phenol Coef- ficient | Molar Coef- ficient | Ratio | Phenol Coef- ficient | Molar Coef- ficient | Ratio |
| Methyl | 0.026 | 0.009 | | 0.030 | 0.010 | |
| | | | 2.2 | | | 1.9 |
| Ethyl | 0.040 | 0.020 | | 0.039 | 0.019 | |
| | | | 3.25 | | | 2.8 |
| Propyl | 0.102 | 0.065 | | 0.082 | 0.053 | |
| | | | 3.30 | | | 3.30 |
| Butyl | 0.273 | 0.215 | | 0.22 | 0.175 | |
| | | | 3.39 | | | 3.37 |
| Amyl | 0.78 | 0.73 | | 0.63 | 0.59 | |
| | | | 3.39 | | | |
| Hexyl | 2.3 | 2.5 | | | | |
| | | | 3.38 | | | |
| Heptyl | 6.8 | 8.4 | | | | |
| | | | 3.46 | | | |
| Octyl | 21.0 | 29.0 | | | | |

The most striking feature of the disinfectant properties of the normal primary alcohols is that the molar potencies increase in geometrical progression as the number of carbon atoms increases in arithmetical progression; this is illustrated in Table I, which gives the phenol coefficients of the first eight members of the homologous alkanols for *Bacillus typhosus* and of the first five for *Staphylococcus aureus*.[9] The molar

[9] Tilley and Schaffer, *J. Bact.*, **12**, 303 (1926).

coefficient is defined as

$$\text{Phenol coefficient} \times \frac{\text{Molecular weight of substance}}{\text{Molecular weight of phenol}}$$

and it will be seen that, if methanol is omitted, the ratios between consecutive molar coefficients are approximately constant, the mean value being 3.36 for *B. typhosus*. This means that, if the logarithms of the molar coefficients are plotted against the number of carbon atoms, a linear relation will be obtained. A similar "logarithmic increase" in molar phenol coefficients also appears to hold approximately for alkylphenols. Tables II and III record results obtained by Tilley and Schaffer [10] for 4-alkylphenols and 4-alkylresorcinols. The particular

TABLE II

p-n-ALKYLPHENOLS, R⟨ ⟩OH

| | *B. typhosus* | | | *Staph. aureus* | | |
|---|---|---|---|---|---|---|
| R | Phenol Coefficient | Molar Coefficient | Ratio | Phenol Coefficient | Molar Coefficient | Ratio |
| Methyl | 2.5 | 2.9 | | 2.2 | 2.5 | |
| | | | 3.3 | | | 3.1 |
| Ethyl | 7.4 | 9.6 | | 6 | 7.8 | |
| | | | 3.2 | | | 3.1 |
| Propyl | 21.6 | 31 | | 16.5 | 24 | |
| | | | 3.5 | | | 3.3 |
| Butyl | 68 | 108 | | 50 | 79 | |
| | | | 3.2 | | | 3.0 |
| Amyl | 197 | 344 | | 139 | 243 | |
| | | | 2.7 | | | 2.9 |
| Hexyl | 500 | 950 | | 375 | 710 | |

strain of *B. typhosus* used in these experiments appears to have been unusually sensitive; with four other strains a maximum coefficient was observed in the resorcinol series for the hexyl member, and in the phenol series for the butyl or amyl member. Table IV records some more results for these two series including those obtained by Leonard,[11] who was the first to examine the resorcinol series.

The occurrence of maximum potency for one member of such homologous series, higher members being much less active or even inactive, is commonly observed, and the maximum occurs at different positions in the series for different organisms. In general, it appears that for Gramnegative organisms (like *B. typhosus*) the maximum occurs at a lower

[10] Tilley and Schaffer, *ibid.*, **14**, 259 (1927).
[11] Leonard, *J. Am. Med. Assoc.*, **83**, 2005 (1924).

## TABLE III

4-$n$-ALKYLRESORCINOLS R⟨OH⟩OH

| | B. typhosus | | | Staph. aureus | | |
|---|---|---|---|---|---|---|
| R | Phenol Coef- ficient | Molar Coef- ficient | Ratio | Phenol Coef- ficient | Molar Coef- ficient | Ratio |
| Ethyl | 1.6 | 2.35 | | 1.5 | 2.2 | |
| | | | 3.32 | | | 2.7 |
| Propyl | 4.8 | 7.8 | | 3.7 | 6 | |
| | | | 3.39 | | | 3.0 |
| Butyl | 15 | 26.5 | | 10.2 | 18 | |
| | | | 3.39 | | | 3.2 |
| Amyl | 47 | 90 | | 30.6 | 59 | |
| | | | 3.37 | | | 3.4 |
| Hexyl | 147 | 303 | | 98 | 202 | |
| | | | 2.53 | | | 3.1 |
| Heptyl | 350 | 770 | | 280 | 630 | |
| | | | 1.22 | | | 2.7 |
| Octyl | 400 | 940 | | 725 | 1710 | |
| | | | | | | 1.5 |
| Nonyl | | | | 1000 | 2500 | |

point in a series than for Gram-positive organisms * (like staphylococci and streptococci). Coulthard, Marshall, and Pyman [12] examined homologous alkyl derivatives of $o$-, $m$-, and $p$-cresols and found maximum phenol coefficients against B. *typhosus* for the $n$-amyl member in each

## TABLE IV

| | Phenol Coefficients against B. *typhosus* of | | | |
|---|---|---|---|---|
| $n$-Alkyl Group | 4-Alkylphenols | | 4-Alkylresorcinols | |
| | Ref. 10 | Ref. 12 | Ref. 10 | Ref. 11 |
| Methyl | 2.4 | 2.5 | .... | .. |
| Ethyl | 6.6 | 7.5 | .... | .. |
| Propyl | 18 | 20 | 4.75 | 5 |
| Butyl | 64 | 70 | 15 | 22 |
| Amyl | 54 | 104 | 45 | 33 |
| Hexyl | .. | 90 | 59 | 46–56 |
| Heptyl | .. | 20 | 37 | 30 |

series. Klarmann, Shternov, and Gates [13] tested homologous $o$-alkyl-$p$-chloro- and $p$-alkyl-$o$-chlorophenols against six different organisms; some of their results are recorded in Tables V and VI. It will be noticed

* For the meaning of the terms Gram-positive and Gram-negative see p. 420.
[12] Coulthard, Marshall, and Pyman, *J. Chem. Soc.*, 280 (1930).
[13] Klarmann, Shternov, and Gates, *J. Am. Chem. Soc.*, **55**, 2576 (1933).

## TABLE V

*Eberthella typhi*

| n-Alkyl Group | o-Alkyl-p-chlorophenols | | | p-Alkyl-o-chlorophenols | | |
|---|---|---|---|---|---|---|
| | Phenol Coefficient | Molar Coefficient | Ratio | Phenol Coefficient | Molar Coefficient | Ratio |
| None | 4.3 | 5.9 | | 2.5 | 3.4 | |
| | | | 3.22 | | | 2.79 |
| Methyl | 12.5 | 18.9 | | 6.3 | 9.6 | |
| | | | 2.52 | | | 3.00 |
| Ethyl | 28.6 | 47.6 | | 17.2 | 28.6 | |
| | | | 3.54 | | | 2.41 |
| Propyl | 93 | 168.7 | | 38 | 68.9 | |
| | | | 1.64 | | | 2.48 |
| Butyl | 141 | 276.8 | | 87 | 170.8 | |
| | | | 1.19 | | | 0.99 |
| Amyl | 156 | 329.5 | | 80 | 169 | |
| Hexyl | (23) | ..... | | .. | | |

## TABLE VI

*Staphylococcus aureus*

| n-Alkyl Group | o-Alkyl-p-chlorophenols | | | p-Alkyl-o-chlorophenols | | |
|---|---|---|---|---|---|---|
| | Phenol Coefficient | Molar Coefficient | Ratio | Phenol Coefficient | Molar Coefficient | Ratio |
| None | 4.3 | 5.9 | | 2.9 | 4.0 | |
| | | | 3.22 | | | 2.87 |
| Methyl | 12.5 | 18.9 | | 7.5 | 11.4 | |
| | | | 3.03 | | | 2.30 |
| Ethyl | 34.4 | 57.3 | | 15.7 | 26.2 | |
| | | | 2.97 | | | 2.22 |
| Propyl | 94 | 170.4 | | 32 | 58.0 | |
| | | | 2.96 | | | 3.18 |
| Butyl | 257 | 504.4 | | 94 | 184.5 | |
| | | | 2.09 | | | 3.27 |
| Amyl | 500 | 1056 | | 286 | 604 | |
| | | | 2.68 | | | 2.67 |
| Hexyl | 1250 | 2826 | | 714 | 1614 | |
| | | | 1.28 | | | |
| Heptyl | 1500 | 3620 | | ... | | |
| | | | 0.98 | | | |
| Octyl | 1750 | 3556 | | 375 | | |

that with *Eberthella typhi* (a Gram-negative organism) maximum activity occurred for the butyl or amyl members, but with *Staphylococcus aureus* (a Gram-positive organism) for higher members. The molar coefficients have been calculated for these series in order to show that the logarithmic increase is approximately obeyed.

It does not seem to have been generally recognized, in spite of Tilley and Schaffer's papers, that the molar phenol coefficients of homologous alkylphenols increase logarithmically as the series is ascended. Few authors have calculated the molar coefficients, but a survey of representative data suggests that such a rule does hold approximately; accurate agreement with the rule is unlikely in view of the approximate nature of phenol coefficients. The implications of the rule are important. It has long been recognized that the simple aliphatic narcotics—hydrocarbons, alcohols, ethers, esters, amides, etc.—obey the rule fairly accurately; i.e., within any homologous series the isonarcotic molar concentrations decrease, or the molar narcotic potencies increase, logarithmically. A similar regularity has been observed for a variety of other pharmacological effects, such as hemolysis of red blood cells by urethanes, alcohols, esters, and ketones,[14] the toxicity of alcohols, esters, etc., to plant cells,[15] and the inhibition of sodium permeability into erythrocytes by alkyl carbamates.[16]

Ferguson [17] has suggested that a logarithmic decrease in equiactive molar concentrations (or a like increase in molar potencies) as a homologous series is ascended is the result of an equilibrium between two phases, the phase in which the drug is applied and its concentration measured and the "biophase" in which it has its effect. He has drawn attention to the fact that all the physical properties of homologous series which depend upon an equilibrium between two phases (and are, of course, measured when equilibrium is established) change in a similar logarithmic manner. Such properties are solubility, vapor pressure, surface tension, and differential solubility between immiscible solvents. If these properties, expressed on a molar basis, are plotted as logarithms against the number of carbon atoms, linear relations closely similar and sometimes parallel to those for certain pharmacological properties are obtained.

The conclusion to be drawn is that, whenever the molar potencies within a homologous series increase logarithmically, the pharmacological effect must depend primarily upon some physical property, although the

[14] Fuhner and Neubauer, *Arch. exptl. Path. Pharmakol.*, **56**, 333 (1907).

[15] Stiles and Stirk, *Protoplasma*, **16**, 79 (1932).

[16] Davson and Danielli, "The Permeability of Natural Membranes," Cambridge University Press, London (1943), Chapter 16.

[17] Ferguson, *Proc. Roy. Soc. (London)*, **B127**, 387 (1939).

parallelism between the pharmacological properties and those physical properties which also change logarithmically does not enable us to identify the particular physical property involved. The narcotic activity of simple aliphatic compounds has long been regarded as due to some physical property, but the rival claims of such properties as differential solubility in fat solvents and adsorption have not even yet been settled.

It is easy to believe that in a readily reversible effect like narcosis an equilibrium is set up between the circumambient fluid containing the drug and the biophase (whatever it may be) in which the drug exerts its effect, but it may seem curious to apply the same ideas to toxicity toward bacteria. But the lethal action of alcohols and phenols on bacteria is not immediate; the primary process is almost certainly reversible, and the irreversible effects culminating in death must be due to secondary processes.

The antiseptic potencies of homologous alcohols and phenols do not increase indefinitely; a homolog with maximum potency is eventually reached, and higher homologs are less active or even inactive. Ferguson has suggested a reason for the attainment of a maximum: the ratio between equiactive molar concentrations or potencies in such series is usually about 3, whereas the ratio between the water solubilities of successive members lies between 4 and 4.5; i.e., the solubilities of successive members decrease more rapidly than the equiactive concentrations. Consequently, a member will be reached for which a saturated solution is insufficiently concentrated for the standard effect being measured to be achieved. The position of the maximum within the series will depend on the organism. It has already been noted that the maximum phenol coefficient for alkylphenols does not occur for all bacteria at the same point in a series, and inspection of Tables II, III, V, and VI will reveal that, the more resistant the organism, the lower in the series is the maximum reached. This is illustrated diagrammatically in Fig. 1. If curves $A$ and $B$ represent the decrease in equiactive molar concentrations (plotted as logarithms) of homologous disinfectants and curve $S$ represents the steeper decrease in solubility (expressed in similar concentration terms), curve $A$ will obviously refer to a more resistant organism than curve $B$ and maximum activity will occur at a lower point in the series, since beyond a certain member the attainment of the theoretically required concentration will be impossible.

Figure 1 represents the ideal situation. In practice, it will usually be found that the logarithmic relation is not accurately followed by the first few members of the series; e.g., among alcohols, methanol is anomalous (Table I), but the chemical reactivity of the first member of a homologous series is often much greater than that of higher members. Consequently, we may expect to find a chemical action superimposed upon the physical effect in the lowest members of a series, but as the series is ascended the logarithmic increase in activity may become established. Similarly, the logarithmic relation is frequently not accurately followed at or near the point of maximum activity; thus the

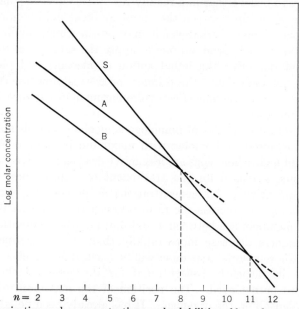

FIG. 1.  Equiactive molar concentrations and solubilities of homologous disinfectants (schematic only).

ratios between the molar coefficients in Tables II, III, V, and VI decline at or near the maximal values. This may well be due to micelle formation in solutions of the higher members, which will reduce the effective concentration of the drug.

The general conclusions to be drawn from this discussion are that the disinfectant properties of alcohols and phenols are due to some physical property and that the relative molar potencies depend upon the attainment of an equilibrium between the circumambient solution and the bacterial biophase, whatever it may be, in which these compounds have their effect. This conclusion will be reinforced by the regularity with which structural changes other than those within homologous series affect the disinfectant potency.[18]

[18] For an interesting review of phenolic disinfectants, see Suter. *Chem. Revs.*, **28**, 269 (1941).

CHEMOTHERAPY 413

**Effect of Branched Chains.** Among both alcohols and phenols branched-chain compounds are invariably less active than their straight-chain isomers. Among the simple alkanols (Table VII) secondary

TABLE VII

MOLAR PHENOL COEFFICIENTS FOR ALKANOLS

|  | B. typhosus | | | Staph. aureus | |
|---|---|---|---|---|---|
|  | Butyl | Amyl | Hexyl | Butyl | Amyl |
| Primary | 0.215 | 0.73 | 2.50 | 0.175 | 0.590 |
| Secondary | 0.120 | 0.36 | 1.10 | 0.103 | 0.300 |
| Tertiary | 0.064 | 0.17 | 0.49 | 0.050 | 0.133 |

alcohols are about half as active as isomeric primary alcohols, and tertiary alcohols about half as active as isomeric secondary alcohols, at least for B. typhosus and Staph. aureus. Data are lacking for so complete a comparison among alkyl phenols and resorcinols, but branched-chain compounds that have been tested were invariably less active than their straight-chain isomers.

**Effect of Halogens.** Bechhold and Ehrlich [19] were the first to observe that the introduction of chlorine or bromine into phenol or β-naphthol increased their antiseptic potency considerably. Using B. diphtheriae and Staph. aureus they found that pentabromophenol was five hundred times as effective as phenol on a molar basis. Bromine is more effective than chlorine. Table VIII summarizes data of Klarmann,[20] but his

TABLE VIII

MOLAR PHENOL COEFFICIENTS OF HALOGENATED PHENOLS

| Position of Halogen | Chlorophenols | | Bromophenols | |
|---|---|---|---|---|
|  | B. typhosus | Staph. aureus | B. typhosus | Staph. aureus |
| 2 | 4.9 | 5.2 | 7.0 | 6.8 |
| 3 | 10.1 | 7.9 | .... | .... |
| 4 | 5.3 | 5.3 | 9.9 | 8.5 |
| 2,4 | 22.6 | 22.6 | 64.4 | 74.5 |
| 2,4,6 | 48.8 | 53.1 | .... | .... |

phenol coefficients have been converted into molar coefficients which reveal the superior effect of bromo substitution more clearly. Little is known about iodinated phenols, and fluorophenol differs little from phenol in its antiseptic potency. Halogenation and alkylation of phenols appear to increase antiseptic potency independently; thus if the molar

[19] Bechhold and Ehrlich, Z. physiol. Chem., **47**, 173 (1906).
[20] Klarmann, J. Bact., **17**, 440 (1929).

coefficients for $p$-alkylphenols against *Staph. aureus* (Table II) are compared with those for $p$-alkyl-$o$-chlorophenols against the same organism (Table VI) it will be seen that the alkyl chlorophenols are consistently more active than their unchlorinated analogs.

**Effect of Hydroxyl Groups.** Increasing the number of hydroxyl groups in both alcohols and phenols decreases the bactericidal activity. In phenols the introduction of a second phenolic hydroxyl can be compensated for by alkyl or halogen substitution; thus in the $p$-alkylphenols maximum activity against *B. typhosus* occurs with the $n$-amyl member, but in the 4-alkylresorcinols with the $n$-hexyl member. Similarly, comparison of the data for *Staph. aureus* in Tables II and III will show that the 4-alkylresorcinols are consistently less active than their 4-alkylphenol analogs. Three hydroxyl groups in the benzene ring cannot be compensated for by increasing the size of the alkyl chain.

**Mechanism of Action.** All the evidence so far mentioned suggests that the bactericidal action of phenols and alcohols is due to some physical process. It is known that these substances are readily adsorbed by proteins, which they frequently denature. It has been revealed that phenols have a detergent-like action on bacteria, making the cell membrane permeable to simple molecules, and it will be convenient to consider this evidence in connection with detergent disinfectants.

## Surface-Active Disinfectants

It has long been known that soap has some disinfectant action, but the development of synthetic detergents has revealed new and powerful bactericidal substances.[21] Hartmann and Kaegi [22] reported in 1929 that a series of cationic detergents were bactericidal; these were long-chain fatty acid amides of the general formula I, where R was an alkyl group or hydrogen. In 1935 Domagk [23] published an account of the

$$C_nH_{2n+1}CONRCH_2CH_2N(C_2H_5)_2$$

I

$$C_{12}H_{25} \diagdown \overset{+}{\underset{C_6H_5CH_2 \diagup}{N(CH_3)_2Cl}}\overset{-}{}$$

II

$$C_nH_{2n+1}OSO_3Na$$

III

bactericidal properties of dodecyldimethylbenzylammonium chloride (II). Since then an increasing number of bactericidal cationic detergents, including ammonium, phosphonium, arsonium, and sulfonium

[21] For a useful symposium on surface-active agents, see *Ann. N. Y. Acad. Sci.*, **46**, 347–529 (1946).

[22] Hartmann and Kaegi, *Z. angew. Chem.*, **41**, 127 (1928).

[23] Domagk, *Deut. med. Wochschr.*, **61**, 829 (1935).

salts, have been described. Anionic detergents,[24, 25] e.g., the sodium salts of long-chain alkylsulfates (III), were also found to be bactericidal, particularly against Gram-positive organisms. Soap is, of course, also an anionic detergent, and Stanley et al.[26] found that the sodium salts of numerous aliphatic carboxylic acids, particularly dialkylacetic acids, had a powerful bactericidal action on acid-fast bacteria. Phenolic disinfectants also behave in some ways like anionic detergents.

It is reasonable to assume that cationic and anionic detergents are adsorbed at the surface of the bacterial cell by virtue of their hydrophobic or lipophilic groups, but the ionic character of these agents is of fundamental importance. Thus the intensity of their action depends on the pH of the medium, and unionizable surface-active agents are not bactericidal. The bactericidal action of cationic detergents increases with increasing pH, whereas that of anionic agents decreases. This is what would be expected if these agents form salts with the acidic or basic groups of the cytoplasmic membrane. If, as is frequently true, the detergents are salts of strong acids (e.g., acid sulfates) or strong bases (e.g., "onium" salts) they will remain fully ionized over a considerable range of pH, but the ionization of the acidic and basic groups of the lipoprotein in the cell membrane will change with changing pH. The ionization of acidic groups (carboxylic and phenolic) will be increased as the pH increases, and salt formation with cationic agents will be encouraged. On the other hand, increasing pH will depress the ionization of the basic (amino) groups, and salt formation with anionic agents will be discouraged. If the detergents are salts of weak acids (e.g., phenols or fatty acids) or weak bases (e.g., amines) increasing the pH will increase the ionization of the anionic agents and depress that of the cationic agents. The overall effect on bactericidal action will depend upon the respective dissociation constants of the detergent and of the acidic and basic groups of the bacterial protein. At neutral pH bacteria usually carry a negative charge, owing to a preponderance of acidic groups at the cell surface, and this may explain the greater efficiency of cationic compared with anionic detergents in neutral solution.

The adsorption of detergents at the cell surface appears to disorganize the cytoplasmic membrane in some way and make it more permeable to solutes. Hotchkiss [27] discovered that, when detergents are allowed to act in lethal concentrations on bacteria, nitrogen and phosphorus compounds rapidly leak out of the cells but that at bactericidally ineffective concentrations no such leakage occurs. This happens both

[24] Cowles, *Yale J. Biol. and Med.*, **11**, 33 (1938).
[25] Birkeland and Steinhaus, *Proc. Soc. Exptl. Biol. Med.*, **40**, 86 (1939).
[26] Stanley *et al.*, *J. Pharmacol.*, **45**, 121 (1932).
[27] Hotchkiss, *Ann. N. Y. Acad. Sci.*, **46**, 479 (1945–46).

with cationic agents, such as dodecyldimethylbenzylammonium and cetylpyridinium salts, the basic polypeptide tyrocidin, and anionic agents like sodium lauryl sulfate and aersol O.T. (dioctylsulfosuccinate). It also occurs with phenol, the cresols, $o$-chlorophenol, and hexylresorcinol, which must, therefore, be regarded as belonging to the group of anionic detergents in this respect.

This cytolytic action of bactericidal detergents has been studied by Gale and Taylor,[28] who have developed methods of estimating the amounts of free lysine and glutamic acid inside bacterial cells and in the medium by measuring the carbon dioxide evolved from these amino acids by the action of specific decarboxylases. *Strept. faecalis* has a high internal concentration of lysine and of glutamic acid, and these acids do not leak out when the bacteria are suspended in distilled water; but when the bacteria are exposed to cetyltrimethylammonium bromide (1 mg./ml.), aersol O.T. (1 mg./ml.), phenol (10 mg./ml.), or the basic polypeptides tyrocidin and gramicidin, all the lysine and glutamic acid rapidly leaks out of the cells. This does not happen with antiseptics of other types, such as gentian violet, acriflavine, sulfathiazole, and penicillin.

Whether this cytolytic action of phenols and detergents is the sole cause of their bactericidal effect must remain an open question. There is already reason to think that the disinfectant action of phenols depends upon some physical process, and one must now consider some structure-action relationships among cationic and anionic detergents. It may be said at the outset that in any homologous series of detergents maximum bactericidal activity occurs for a certain range of chain length, usually between 12 and 20 carbon atoms; above or below this range activity is weak or absent.

The work of Stanley, Adams, and their colleagues[26] on the bactericidal action of the sodium salts of aliphatic carboxylic acids on acid-fast bacteria has already been mentioned. The purpose of the work was to find a synthetic substitute for chaulmoogric acid (IV; $n = 12$) in the

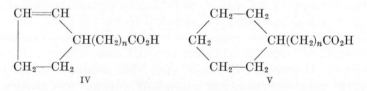

treatment of leprosy. The organisms used were *Mycobact. leprae* and *Mycobact. tuberculosis;* all acids were tested as their sodium salts *in vitro* by the method of serial dilution. Since reduction of the cyclopentenyl ring in chaulmoogric acid decreases but does not abolish activity,

[28] Gale and Taylor, *J. Gen. Microbiol.*, **1**, 77 (1947).

attention was first directed to the more readily accessible cyclohexyl compounds (V). It was found that the bactericidal efficiency of the sodium salts depended upon the value of $n$. Acids with $n < 4$ were only feebly active, but as $n$ increased from 5 onwards the effectiveness increased, reaching a maximum for the acids with $n = 8$ or 9 and then declining progressively from $n = 10$ to $n = 12$. The most effective acids were therefore those containing 15 or 16 carbon atoms.

Since branched-chain acids of the type $RR'CHCO_2H$ are more readily prepared than acids of the type V, a series of cyclohexyl aliphatic acids of general formula VI was next investigated where $m$ was varied

$$\langle hexagon \rangle\!-\!(CH_2)_m\!-\!CH\!-\!(CH_2)_nCH_3 \qquad CH_3(CH_2)_m\!-\!CH\!-\!(CH_2)_nCH_3$$
$$\underset{CO_2H}{|} \qquad\qquad\qquad\qquad \underset{CO_2H}{|}$$
$$\text{VI} \qquad\qquad\qquad\qquad\qquad\qquad \text{VII}$$

from 0 to 4 and $n$ chosen so as to make the individual acids contain 12 to 20 carbon atoms. All the acids were bactericidally more effective than their isomeric $\omega$-cyclohexyl acids (V), and all the most active acids had 17 or 18 carbon atoms in the molecule (Table IX). It was also

## TABLE IX

COMPARISON OF BACTERICIDAL POTENCIES AGAINST ACID-FAST BACTERIA OF ISOMERIC ACIDS OF SIX CYCLOHEXYL SERIES

$$C_6H_{11}\!-\!(CH_2)_m\!-\!CH\!-\!(CH_2)_n\!-\!CH_3$$
$$\underset{CO_2H}{|}$$

| $m$ | $n$ | Total No. of C Atoms | Maximum Effective Dilution of Na Salts (thousands) |
|---|---|---|---|
| 0 | 7 | 16 | 110 |
| 0 | 8 | 17 | 190 |
| 0 | 9 | 18 | 180 |
| 1 | 6 | 16 | 190 |
| 1 | 7 | 17 | 190 |
| 2 | 5 | 16 | 160 |
| 2 | 6 | 17 | 220 |
| 2 | 7 | 18 | 320 |
| 3 | 4 | 16 | 170 |
| 3 | 5 | 17 | 240 |
| 3 | 6 | 18 | 220 |
| 4 | 3 | 16 | 190 |
| 4 | 4 | 17 | 220 |
| 4 | 5 | 18 | 180 |
| $C_6H_{11}(CH_2)_nCO_2H$ { 9 | | 16 | 20 |
| 10 | | 17 | 10 |
| 11 | | 18 | 20 |

found that the sodium salts of acids of type VI in which the cyclohexyl group was replaced by cyclopentyl, cyclopentenyl, cyclobutyl, or cyclopropyl had similar potencies, the most active acids containing 17 or 18 carbon atoms. Finally, it was found that dialkylacetic acids (VII) also had a similar order of activity, the most effective being those with 16 carbon atoms. Among nine isomeric hexadecanoic acids (VII; $m + n = 12$) the most active were those in which the two alkyl groups differed little, if at all, in size, e.g., the hexyloctyl- and diheptylacetic acids.

It will be noticed that the total carbon content for maximum activity varied somewhat in the different series. For acids of type V it was 15 to 16; for VI, 17 to 18; and for dialkylacetic acids VII it was 16. A similar variability in the position of the maximum has been observed for cationic detergents; reference may be made to a series of papers by Kuhn, Jerchel, et al.,[29] and to the work of Valko and Dubois.[30] The position of the maximum also depends upon the species of organism used in the test. Thus, with alkyldimethylbenzylammonium salts (VIII; X = N) and either *Staph. aureus* or *Eberthella typhosa* maximum

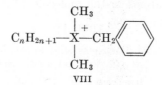

VIII

potency occurred with the dodecyl or tetradecyl chain, but when the benzyl group was replaced by ethyl the maximum was reached with the hexadecyl member. Jerchel,[29] who studied the action of analogous ammonium, phosphonium, and arsonium salts (VIII; X = N, P, or As) on *Lactobacillus casei*, found the hexadecyl (cetyl) members most active; also the order of activity was ammonium < phosphonium < arsonium. When the alkyl chain in compounds of type VIII, X = N, contains a double bond, activity may be markedly increased; e.g., the octadecenyl compound was much more active than the octadecyl compound against *Staph. aureus* and more active even than the dodecyl and tetradecyl compounds, which have maximum activity in the saturated series.

Cationic and anionic detergents are reasonably water-soluble substances, and it seems likely that the decline in bactericidal potency beyond a certain member of a homologous series is due to an increasing tendency to micelle formation, which will reduce the effective concen-

[29] Kuhn, Jerchel, et al., Ber., **73**, 1080, 1092, 1095, 1100, 1105, 1109 (1940); **74**, 941, 949 (1941); **75**, 75 (1942); **76**, 600 (1943).
[30] Valko and Dubois, J. Bact., **50**, 481 (1945).

tration of the active molecule. Thus, whereas low concentrations of soap solution increase the bactericidal activity of phenol by lowering interfacial surface tension, higher concentrations at which micelle formation occurs diminish it markedly, the effective concentration of phenol being reduced by absorption into the micelles. This effect was well shown by Alexander and Trim [31] for the absorption of hexylresorcinol by pig roundworms (*Ascaris lumbricoides*) in the presence of varying concentrations of soaps like sodium oleate and cetyltrimethylammonium bromide.

Detergents and phenols are bactericidal only *in vitro*. They are so avidly adsorbed by proteins that in the presence of serum or other tissue fluids they have little disinfectant power. They can be used for external application and for sterilizing instruments, etc.

### Alkyl Ethers of Hydrocupreine and Apoquinine

Since quinine had for a long time been believed to have beneficial effects in the treatment of pneumonia, Morgenroth [32] made a careful study of alkyl ethers of hydrocupreine. Cupreine itself is difficult to obtain and cannot be prepared by the demethylation of quinine. Dihydroquinine, however, is readily demethylated, and from the product, dihydrocupreine (IX; R = H), Morgenroth prepared a series of homologous alkyl ethers (IX; R = $C_nH_{2n+1}$) and tested them by the method of serial dilution against a variety of microörganisms *in vitro*. It was

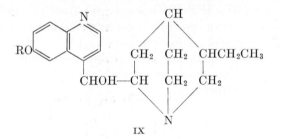

IX

found that as the number of carbon atoms in the alkyl group increased the bactericidal activity increased to a maximum and then declined. The position of the maximum depended upon the particular microorganism used. Thus with pneumococcus the most active member was

[31] Alexander and Trim, *Proc. Roy. Soc. (London)*, **B133**, 220 (1946); see also Trim and Alexander, "Selective Toxicity and Antibiotics," Cambridge University Press, London (1949), pp. 111–142.

[32] Morgenroth and Levy, *Berlin. klin. Wochschr.*, **48**, 1560, 1979 (1911); Morgenroth and Bieling, *ibid.*, **54**, 723 (1917).

the ethyl ether (optochin), which was lethal at 1 in 400,000; with *Corynebacterium diphtheriae* it was the isoöctyl ether (vuzin), lethal at 1 in 750,000. Vuzin was also the most active against staphylococci, but only at 1 in 100,000.

The high specificity of optochin against pneumococcus (it was twice as active as the propyl ether and more than four times as active as the methyl and amyl ethers) led to its being tested against experimental pneumococcal infections in mice. Encouraging results were obtained, but extensive trials in human pneumonia were disappointing. Moreover, optochin is likely to cause damage to the retina and even blindness.

A more promising compound was found in a series of ethers of apo-quinine (X; R = H) synthesized by Butler, Renfrew, and Cretcher.[33] The ethyl ether (X; R = $C_2H_5$) was again the most active member of the series against pneumococcus; indeed, it was more active than opto-

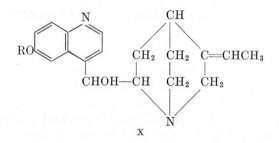

chin, but like it was liable to produce retinal damage. The β-hydroxy-ethyl ether (X; R = $HOCH_2CH_2$) was free from this defect and, although less active than optochin, it compared favorably with sulfapyridine in protecting mice against pneumococcal infections.[34,35] Its use in human pneumonia had already given encouraging results when the discovery of sulfa drugs more active and less toxic than sulfapyridine diverted attention from it.[36]

## Dyes as Antiseptics

Some bacteria are stained by dyes more readily than others, and it is customary to classify then in terms of an arbitrary staining test devised by Gram. A film of bacteria on a microscope slide is treated with 1% aqueous crystal violet (a basic triphenylmethane dye) and then washed

[33] Butler, Renfrew, and Cretcher, *J. Am. Chem. Soc.*, **57**, 575, 738, 1083 (1935).
[34] Johnston *et al.*, *J. Pharmacol.*, **61**, 364 (1937).
[35] Bracken *et al.*, *ibid.*, **68**, 259 (1940).
[36] For a more detailed account of antipneumococcal activity in the cinchona series, see Renfrew and Cretcher, *Chem. Revs.*, **30**, 49 (1942).

with a mild oxidizing agent (e.g., 0.3% I$_2$ in 0.6% KI).  The film is now dried and washed with an organic solvent (alcohol, acetone, etc.) in which the dye is soluble, after which it is treated with a contrasting dye such as basic fuchsine, which is red.  If the film has retained the violet dye, it will now appear blue-black in color, and the bacteria are called Gram-positive; if the organic solvent removed the violet dye, the bacteria will now appear red, and they are called Gram-negative.  The test distinguishes between bacteria that are dyed fast by crystal violet or some other basic dye (Gram-positive) and bacteria from which the dye is readily removed by organic solvents in which it is soluble (Gram-negative).

The significance of the Gram test was greatly clarified by the Stearns,[37] who showed that the retention of either acidic or basic dyes by bacteria

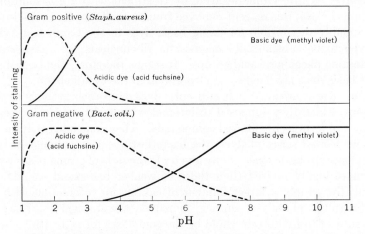

FIG. 2.  Effect of acidic and basic dyes on Gram-positive and Gram-negative bacteria (adapted from Stearn and Stearn;[37] courtesy of the publisher).

depended upon the pH of the medium.  They found that *Staph. aureus*, a typical Gram-positive organism, was maximally stained by methyl violet in the Gram test at all pH values above 3, but that *Bact. coli*, a typical Gram-negative organism, retained this dye and remained fully stained only at pH values above 8.  On the other hand, *Bact. coli* retained acidic dyes (acid fuchsine) up to pH 3, but *Staph. aureus* did so only below about pH 1.  Their results are illustrated in Fig. 2, which shows that below pH 3 *Staph. aureus* will behave as a Gram-negative organism and above pH 8 *Bact. coli* will behave as a Gram-positive organism.  For each organism there is an intermediate range of pH over

[37] Stearn and Stearn, *J. Bact.*, **9**, 463, 479, 491 (1924).

which there is little retention of either basic or acidic dyes; this is the isoelectric range. It is assumed that the cell surface is composed partly of protein and partly of phospholipids; it will then contain both acidic and basic groups, and if the acidic include phosphoric acid groups, the isoelectric range will lie on the acid side of $pH$ 7. The lower the $pH$ of the isoelectric range, the lower the $pH$ at which basic dyes will be retained in the Gram test, and vice versa. The distinction between Gram-positive and Gram-negative organisms is thus seen to depend upon the position of the isoelectric range in the $pH$ scale. The term isoelectric *range* is used because the cell surface is a complex structure and does not, like a pure protein, have an isoelectric *point*.

The Stearns' views have received striking confirmation by the work of Henry and Stacey,[38] who found that Gram-positive organisms could be converted into Gram-negative by treatment with a 2% solution of sodium cholate; this reagent removed from the cell surface a constituent, presumably responsible for fixing basic dyes in the Gram test, which proved to be substantially magnesium ribonucleate, i.e., a substance containing phosphoric acid groups. It seems, therefore, highly probable that basic dyes are fixed by nucleoprotein in the cytoskeleton.

The Stearns assumed that antiseptic dyes owed their activity to their cations, which they supposed to interact with acidic groups in the cell surface to form feebly ionized compounds. They concluded that, in any closely related series of dyes, the bacteriostatic power should increase with basic strength, since at any given $pH$ the salts of strong bases would be more highly ionized than those of weaker bases and would, consequently, supply a larger number of cations for interaction with the acidic groups of the cell surface; moreover, the stronger the base, the less subject to hydrolysis would be the complexes formed with bacterial protein.

It is certainly true that high bacteriostatic power is associated among dyes only with the more strongly basic compounds. Fairbrother and Renshaw [39] tested a large number of basic dyes for antibacterial action on a variety of organisms. They used di- and triphenylmethane, acridine, phenazine, thiazine, oxazine, and azo dyes, and inspection of the formulas of the more active compounds suggests that all were relatively strong bases. Azo dyes were for the most part inactive.

The two most fully investigated groups of antiseptic dyes are the acridine and the triphenylmethane groups, and these will be considered in some detail.

[38] Henry and Stacey, *Nature*, **151**, 671 (1943); *Proc. Roy. Soc.* (*London*), **B133**, 391 (1946).
[39] Fairbrother and Renshaw, *J. Soc. Chem. Ind.* (*London*), **41**, 134T (1922).

**The Acridine Group.** The most widely used acridine dyes are 2,8-di-aminoacridine hydrochloride (XI; R = H), called proflavine; 2,8-di-amino-10-methylacridinium chloride (XI; R = CH$_3$), called euflavine; and a mixture of the two, called acriflavine.* Rivanol or 2,5-diamino-7-ethoxyacridine (XII) has also been studied in some detail but has

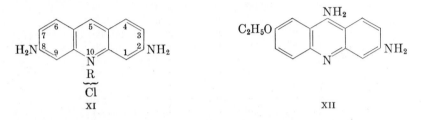

XI                                                            XII

been used chiefly in amebic dysentery. Browning introduced acriflavine into the treatment of wounds in 1917, largely because he found that its bacteriostatic activity, unlike that of most other antiseptics, was not reduced by the presence of serum.[40] Acridine dyes may appear to be more active in the presence of serum; this is due to the fact that serum usually becomes alkaline (owing to the loss of carbon dioxide), and, as will be seen, acridine dyes are more effective in alkaline media. If the pH is accurately controlled acridine dyes do not appear more active in the presence of serum.

The acridine group has been extensively investigated by Albert and his colleagues.[41] Their work will be considered in some detail because it not only has clarified the structure-action relationships of the acridine dyes but also has illuminated previous work on other types of antiseptic dyes. They studied a hundred and seven acridine compounds, seventy-seven of which were synthesized for the first time specially for the investigation. Five organisms were used: *Clostridium welchii*, *Streptococcus pyogenes* A, *Staphylococcus aureus*, *Bacterium coli*, and *Proteus* (unidentified species). The first three are Gram-positive and the last two Gram-negative, and they are named in the order of decreasing susceptibility to acridine compounds. The compounds were tested in broth, to which 10% ox serum was added, at pH 7.2–7.4. Geometrical dilutions of each compound were made in serum broth commencing at 1 in 5000. The greatest dilution completely preventing visible

* In order to facilitate reference to the literature referred to in the sequel, the acridine ring has been numbered as shown in formula XI.

[40] Browning, *Edinburgh Med. J.*, new series, **44**, 497 (1937).

[41] Rubbo, Albert, and Maxwell, *Brit. J. Exptl. Path.*, **23**, 69 (1942); Albert, Rubbo, Goldacre, Davey, and Stone, *ibid.*, **26**, 160 (1945); Albert, Rubbo, and Burvill, *ibid.*, **30**, 159 (1949). For synthetical work see Albert, *J. Chem. Soc.*, 121, 484 (1941); 244 (1947); 1225 (1948). See also Albert, "The Acridines," Arnold, London (1951).

growth after 48 hours' incubation at 37° was taken as the end point of bacteriostasis, and to each dilution was assigned a code number according to the key shown.

KEY

| | | | | | | | |
|---|---|---|---|---|---|---|---|
| 0 | signifies growth at 1 in 5000 of base | | | | | | |
| 1 | " | inhibition of growth at 1 in | | | | | 5,000 |
| 2 | " | " | " | " | " | " 1 " | 10,000 |
| 3 | " | " | " | " | " | " 1 " | 20,000 |
| 4 | " | " | " | " | " | " 1 " | 40,000 |
| 5 | " | " | " | " | " | " 1 " | 80,000 |
| 6 | " | " | " | " | " | " 1 " | 160,000 |
| 7 | " | " | " | " | " | " 1 " | 320,000 |
| 8 | " | " | " | " | " | " 1 " | 640,000 |
| 9 | " | " | " | " | " | " 1 " | 1,280,000 |
| 10 | " | " | " | " | " | " 1 " | 2,560,000 |

The sum of the code numbers for the inhibitory dilutions for each organism was taken as the "bacteriostatic index" (B.I.). A difference of 5 units in B.I. represents on the average a twofold difference in inhibitory dilutions. A B.I. of less than 10 was taken as indicating poor antibacterial activity, a B.I. of 15 as suggesting moderate activity, and a well-distributed B.I. above 20 as indicating marked activity. These arbitrary conventions were based on the B.I. values for acridine derivatives of established clinical usefulness, e.g., proflavine and euflavine.

The $pK_a$, or negative logarithm of the "acidic dissociation constant," was measured for each compound by potentiometric titration, and the percentage ionization at any $pH$ was calculated from the mass-action equation:

$$\text{Percentage ionized} = \frac{100}{1 + \text{antilog } (pH - pK_a)}$$

*Aminoacridines.* The five possible monoaminoacridines and eight diaminoacridines were examined. Inspection of the results in Table X will show that only those compounds which are highly ionized at $pH$ 7.3 have B.I. values above 15 and that these are confined to substances containing an amino group in the 2- or the 5-position. The reason for the stronger basicity (higher $pK_a$ values) of the 2- and 5-aminoacridines is that the cations of these bases can exist as resonance hybrids and are consequently more stable. Thus 2-aminoacridinium can exist as a resonance hybrid of forms (XIIIa) and (XIIIb), and 5-aminoacridinium as a resonance hybrid of forms (XIVa) and (XIVb), but this ionic resonance, extra to that of the acridine nucleus itself, is not possible to other aminoacridinium ions.*

* It is assumed that *ortho*-quinonoid forms, possible to 4-aminoacridines, are unlikely to contribute substantially to resonance hybrids.

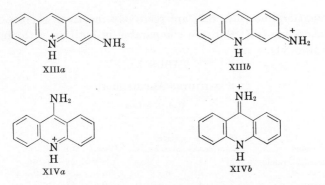

XIIIa

XIIIb

XIVa

XIVb

Table X also reveals that a high $pK_a$ value is not the only factor involved in high antibacterial activity, since the 2,5- and 3,5-diaminoacridines, although fully ionized at $pH$ 7.3 were significantly less active

TABLE X

MONO- AND DIAMINOACRIDINES

| | Code Numbers | | | | | | | Per Cent Ionized at 20° |
|---|---|---|---|---|---|---|---|---|
| Compound | Cl. welchii | Strep. pyogenes | Staph. aureus | B. coli | Proteus | B.I. | $pK_a$ | at $pH$ 7.3 |
| Acridine | 3 | 1 | 1 | 0 | 1 | 6 | 4.8 | 0.3 |
| Monoaminoacridines | | | | | | | | |
| 1-amino | 2 | 1 | 1 | 0 | 0 | 4 | 4.2 | 0.1 |
| 2-amino | 6 | 5 | 3 | 4 | 3 | 21 | 8.2 | 88 |
| 3-amino | 5 | 2 | 1 | 0 | 0 | 8 | 5.8 | 3.0 |
| 4-amino | 5 | 2 | 1 | 1 | 0 | 9 | 6.2 | 7.4 |
| 5-amino | 7 | 6 | 4 | 4 | 4 | 25 | 9.9 | 100 |
| Diaminoacridines | | | | | | | | |
| 1,9-diamino | 0 | 0 | 0 | 0 | 0 | 0 | 4.3 | 0.1 |
| 2,5-diamino | 7 | 6 | 2 | 2 | 0 | 17 | 11.4 | 100 |
| 2,6-diamino | 7 | 7 | 4 | 4 | 4 | 26 | 9.2 | 99 |
| 2,7-diamino | 7 | 6 | 4 | 5 | 4 | 26 | 8.2 | 88 |
| 2,8-diamino | 7 | 6 | 4 | 3 | 2 | 22 | 10.0 | 100 |
| 2,9-diamino | 4 | 3 | 0 | 2 | 0 | 9 | 7.2 | 44 |
| 3,5-diamino | 7 | 6 | 2 | 2 | 1 | 18 | 10.5 | 100 |
| 3,7-diamino | 5 | 3 | 1 | 0 | 0 | 9 | 6.2 | 7.4 |

than the 2,6-, 2,7-, and 2,8-isomers, although only against *Staph. aureus* and the two Gram-negative organisms.

*Chloro Derivatives.* The introduction of a chlorine atom into aminoacridines reduces the $pK_a$ by about 1 unit; this will reduce the ionization at $pH$ 7.3 significantly only if the $pK_a$ of the unsubstituted aminoacridine is below a critical value (about 8.5); thus the chloro derivatives of 2-aminoacridine ($pK_a$ 8.2) are relatively inactive, whereas those of 5-aminoacridine ($pK_a$ 9.9) are comparable in activity with the parent base (Table XI).

## TABLE XI

### Substituted Aminoacridines

| Compound | | Cl. welchii | Strep. py- ogenes | Staph. aureus | B. coli | Proteus | B.I. | $pK_a$ | Per Cent Ionized at pH 7.3 |
|---|---|---|---|---|---|---|---|---|---|
| 2-aminoacridine | | 6 | 5 | 3 | 4 | 3 | 21 | 8.2 | 88 |
| 5-Chloro- | " | 1 | 0 | 0 | 0 | 0 | 1 | 6.5 | 13 |
| 7-Chloro- | " | 5 | 4 | 3 | 1 | 0 | 13 | 7.0 | 33 |
| 8-Chloro- | " | 5 | 4 | 3 | 2 | 0 | 13 | 7.3 | 50 |
| 5-aminoacridine | | 7 | 6 | 4 | 4 | 4 | 25 | 9.9 | 100 |
| 1-Chloro- | " | 6 | 5 | 4 | 3 | 2 | 20 | 8.3 | 91 |
| 2-Chloro- | " | 7 | 6 | 5 | 5 | 3 | 26 | 9.0 | 98 |
| 3-Chloro- | " | 7 | 6 | 5 | 4 | 4 | 26 | 8.8 | 97 |
| 4-Chloro- | " | 6 | 6 | 4 | 4 | 2 | 22 | 8.4 | 93 |
| 1-Nitro- | " | 6 | 7 | 4 | 4 | 3 | 24 | 7.8 | 76 |
| 2-Nitro- | " | 6 | 10 | 6 | 5 | 3 | 30 | 7.8 | 76 |
| 3-Nitro- | " | 7 | 6 | 5 | 4 | 2 | 24 | 7.9 | 80 |
| 4-Nitro- | " | 7 | 8 | 6 | 4 | 2 | 27 | 7.5 | 61 |
| 3-Cyano- | " | 7 | 5 | 4 | 4 | 3 | 23 | 8.0 | 83 |
| 1-Methyl- | " | 7 | 7 | 5 | 4 | 4 | 27 | 10.2 | 100 |
| 2-Methyl- | " | 6 | 6 | 4 | 3 | 2 | 21 | 10.2 | 100 |
| 3-Methyl- | " | 7 | 6 | 4 | 4 | 2 | 23 | 10.0 | 100 |
| 4-Methyl- | " | 6 | 6 | 4 | 4 | 4 | 24 | 10.0 | 100 |
| 1-Hydroxy- | " | 5 | 5 | 3 | 3 | 3 | 19 | 8.3 | 91 |
| 2-Hydroxy- | " | 2 | 4 | 0 | 0 | 0 | 6 | 7.7 | 71 |
| 3-Hydroxy- | " | 4 | 6 | 2 | 0 | 0 | 12 | 9.1 | 98 |
| 4-Hydroxy- | " | 3 | 3 | 1 | 0 | 0 | 7 | 6.5 | 11 |
| 1-Methoxy- | " | 7 | 6 | 4 | 3 | 2 | 22 | 9.9 | 100 |
| 2-Methoxy- | " | 7 | 6 | 5 | 4 | 3 | 25 | 10.1 | 100 |
| 3-Methoxy- | " | 7 | 7 | 5 | 4 | 2 | 25 | 9.6 | 100 |
| 4-Methoxy- | " | 7 | 6 | 4 | 3 | 2 | 22 | 10.2 | 100 |

*Nitro Derivatives.* The nitro group is an even more powerful base-weakening group, but, although its introduction into 5-aminoacridine reduces the $pK_a$ by about 2 units, the nitro-5-aminoacridines are not less active (Table XI); indeed, two of them, the 2-nitro and 4-nitro derivatives, are more active than 5-aminoacridine, the 2-nitro derivative being one of the most active acridine compounds known. Inspection of the individual code numbers for 5-amino-2-nitroacridine will show that its high bacteriostatic index is mainly due to the sixteenfold increase in activity against *Strep. pyogenes* and the fourfold increase in activity against *Staph. aureus* which the introduction of the 2-nitro group into 5-aminoacridine produces.

These results suggest that the nitro group makes its own independent contribution to the antibacterial action of these derivatives, but it is worth noting that the 3-cyano group reduces the $pK_a$ of 5-amino-acridine by practically the same amount as the 3-nitro group does, but the bacteriostatic index remains high (23) and about equal to that of 3-nitro-5-aminoacridine (24). Other 3-substituted 5-aminoacridines, e.g., 3-methyl and 3-phenyl, with as high bacteriostatic indexes have higher $pK_a$ values (3-methyl-5-amino: $pK_a$ 10.0, B.I. 23; 3-phenyl-5-amino: $pK_a$ 9.7, B.I. 24).

*Methyl Derivatives.* The introduction of a methyl group into amino-acridines does not decrease the $pK_a$, and in some positions a methyl group may enhance antibacterial activity; in 5-aminoacridine the introduction of a 1-methyl group increases the bacteriostatic index slightly (Table XI), but in proflavine (B.I. = 22) the introduction of two methyl groups into the 1- and 9-positions produces a marked increase in antibacterial activity (B.I. = 30). The 3,7- and 4,6-dimethyl-derivatives of proflavine were not more active than proflavine itself (B.I. values 21 and 22 respectively).

The introduction of a methyl group into the 10-position involves quaternization of the nuclear nitrogen of the acridine ring and should increase the basicity of the molecule. Several of these compounds, however, e.g., 3- and 4-amino-10-methylacridinium bromides, are readily oxidized, when their buffered solutions are shaken with air, to the corresponding acridones which are not ionized and are not anti-bacterials; 10-methylacridinium bromide behaves similarly. When the 5-position is blocked this oxidation does not occur, and 3-amino-5,10-di-methylacridinium bromide was moderately active (B.I. = 15). A 2- or a 5-amino group also appears to stabilize the 10-methylacridinium ring, but quaternization of the 10-nitrogen in 5-amino- and 2,8-diamino-acridine does not increase the bacteriostatic index.

*Hydroxy Derivatives.* Of the five possible hydroxyacridines only the 1-hydroxy derivative has appreciable activity (B.I. = 12). These are all poorly ionized substances, and it is suggested that the activity of 1-hydroxyacridine ($pK_a$ = 4.7) may be due to its removing divalent metals essential to cellular respiration by chelation. A similar effect may account for the well-known antiseptic properties of 8-hydroxy-quinoline (oxine).[42]

The hydroxy derivatives of 5-aminoacridine (Table XI) are less active than their $pK_a$ values would lead one to expect. Thus, the 2- and 3-derivatives are well ionized but their antibacterial activity is

[42] Albert *et al.*, *Brit. J. Exptl. Path.*, **28**, 69 (1947); Albert and Magrath, *Biochem. J.*, **41**, 534 (1947).

poor. The 1-hydroxy derivative is again the most active. The four methoxy-5-aminoacridines (Table XI) differ little from 5-aminoacridine itself, and 2,5-diamino-7-ethoxyacridine (Rivanol) had a B.I. of 20.

*Other Structural Features.* The predominant factor in determining antibacterial activity in the acridine derivatives so far mentioned is certainly basic strength, and this is borne out by other facts: e.g., acetylation of 1-, 2-, 3-, 4-, or 5-aminoacridines reduces the bacteriostatic efficiency to negligible values. The introduction of acidic groups, e.g., hydroxyl (except in the 1-position), also reduces the antibacterial activity substantially. Stronger acidic groups, e.g., carboxylic and sulfonic groups, reduce the activity to zero. The basic character cannot, however, be the only important factor. We have already noted that a nitro group or even a methyl group in suitable positions may increase activity, and the acridine ring system itself must be presumed to contribute in some way to the antibacterial activity. Thus 4-amino-

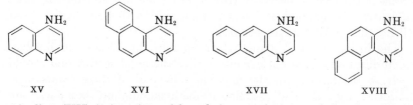

|  XV  |  XVI  |  XVII  |  XVIII  |

quinoline (XV) is inactive, although it contains two of the three ring systems of 5-aminoacridine and its cation is similarly capable of extra ionic resonance ($pK_a$ = 9.1). If, however, the area of the 4-aminoquinoline molecule is increased by the fusion of a third aromatic ring in the 5,6-, 6,7-, or 7,8-positions, bacteriostatic activity is restored. Thus the 4-amino derivatives of 5,6-benzoquinoline (XVI), 6,7-benzoquinoline (XVII), and 7,8-benzoquinoline (XVIII) have bacteriostatic indices of 16, 19, and 19. These are all flat (or planar) molecules of approximately the same area as 5-aminoacridine. Increasing the area of the 5-aminoacridine molecule by one more aromatic ring, so retaining the flatness, does not reduce the bacteriostatic activity appreciably; thus the 5-amino derivatives of the 1,2-, 2,3-, and 3,4-benzacridines (XIX, XX, and XXI) have bacteriostatic indices of 23, 24, and 23, respectively.

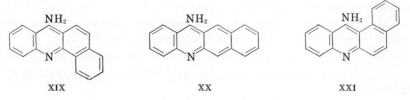

|  XIX  |  XX  |  XXI  |

The importance of the flatness of the aminoacridines is illustrated by the observation that 1,2,3,4-tetrahydro-5-aminoacridine (XXII) is devoid of bacteriostatic activity. In this molecule the reduced ring is not planar and the flat area is reduced to that of 4-aminoquinoline. Activity can, however, be partially restored by the fusion of a third aromatic ring as in 6,7-benzo-1,2,3,4-tetrahydro-5-aminoacridine (XXIII),

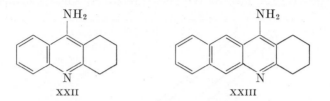

which has a B.I. of 13. This figure should be compared with the figures for 4-amino-6,7-benzoquinoline (XVII; B.I. = 19) and 5-amino-2,3-benzacridine (XX; B.I. = 24); either the attachment of a saturated ring to XVII or the hydrogenation of one ring in XX reduced activity.

These results suggest that both dimensional and geometrical factors (area and flatness) are of importance, probably in governing the extent of adsorption of the cation at the bacterial surface.

Another interesting comparison is that of quinacrine (XXIV) with 5-amino-2-chloro-7-methoxyacridine (XXV), which lacks the side chain. Quinacrine is the stronger base ($pK_a$ of quinacrine, 10.2; of XXV, 8.6) but a very much weaker antibacterial compound (B.I. of quinacrine, 7; of XXV, 21).

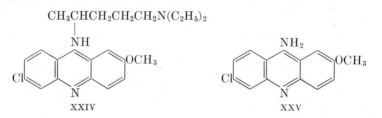

N-Alkylation of aminoacridines also reduces activity, although it does not reduce basic strength. The reduction in activity is particularly striking with long-chain alkyl groups, which confer high olive oil/water partition coefficients, and it may be the result of lipophilic factors as well as dimensional and geometrical factors.

*Effect of pH.* It is well known that acridine antiseptics are less effective in acidic than in alkaline media. By estimating the limiting bacteriostatic dilutions of several aminoacridines at different $p$H values,

Albert and his colleagues were able to show that there was a linear relation between the limiting inhibitory molar concentration of the *cation* and the *p*H. In Fig. 3 the limiting inhibitory log molar concentrations $\times 10^6$ of the cations of two highly active and two weakly active aminoacridines are plotted against the *p*H. It will be seen that the experimental figures fit parallel straight lines approximately well, and that the vertical displacement of the lines is relatively small; i.e., equiactive

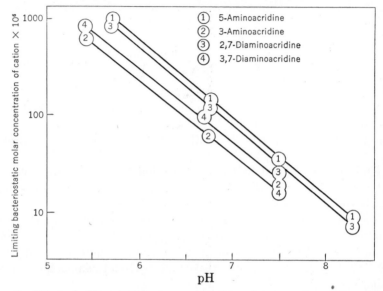

FIG. 3. Effect of *p*H on inhibitory concentrations of some aminoacridine cations (after Albert *et al.*;[41] courtesy of the publisher).

*cationic* concentrations are of the same order for strongly and weakly active salts. The simplest interpretation of these results is that the drug cations compete with hydrogen ions for some "receptor" on the surface of the bacteria, and from the slope of the lines it can be deduced that a sixteenfold increase in hydrogen-ion concentration (i.e., a fall of 1.2 *p*H units) can be compensated by a tenfold increase in the cationic concentration of the drug. The ratio of drug cationic concentration to hydrogen-ion concentration at the limiting inhibitory dilution proved to vary only about threefold for a four-hundredfold change in hydrogen-ion concentration (*p*H 5.7 to 8.3), and the mean ratio was about 800. Thus, for inhibition of growth, aminoacridinium ions must be about 800 times as numerous as hydrogen ions.

*Mechanism of Action.* The general viewpoint indicated here differs from that of the Stearns in one respect. It is assumed that the dye cation is held by adsorptive or van der Waals forces at the bacterial surface, whereas the Stearns assumed, rather paradoxically, that the dye formed feebly ionized salts with acidic groups in the cell surface. Their view is difficult to reconcile with the evidence that dimensional and geometrical factors profoundly affect bacteriostatic potency in this group of dyes. It is also inconsistent with accepted physicochemical theory. The nature of the competition between dye cations and hydrogen ions is, however, not clear. It might involve a weakly acidic group, such as a phenolic group, thus:

$$S]{-}OH + \overset{+}{D}H \rightleftarrows S\left]\begin{matrix}-\overset{-}{O}\\ \underset{\cdots\cdots\overset{+}{D}H}{+}\end{matrix}\right. + \overset{+}{H} \qquad (1)$$

where S] represents the cell surface, $\overset{+}{D}H$ the drug cation, and the dotted line indicates that $\overset{+}{D}H$ is held by van der Waals forces. Alternatively adsorption of the dye cation might suppress the ionization of more weakly basic groups, thus:

$$S\left]\begin{matrix}-\overset{+}{N}H_3\\ -CO_2{}^-\end{matrix}\right. + \overset{+}{D}H \rightleftarrows S\left]\begin{matrix}-NH_2\\ -CO_2{}^-\end{matrix}\cdots\cdots\overset{+}{D}H\right. + \overset{+}{H} \qquad (2)$$

In equation 2 the cell surface is represented as a zwitterion. Both equations are purely schematic and are introduced simply to suggest possible types of competition. It must be remembered that the cation $\overset{+}{D}H$ itself exists in equilibrium with undissociated dye (D) and hydrogen ions; and that the same is true of the no doubt numerous acidic and basic groups in the lipoprotein of the cell surface. It may be noted that equation 2 suggests a physical reason for the decrease in potency of these basic dyes in an acidic medium, since the presence of $-\overset{+}{N}H_3$ groups in the surface will repel the similarly charged dye cations.

**Other Dyestuff Antiseptics.** No other group of dyes has been so well investigated as the acridine group, but it seems probable that the conclusions that we have drawn for the acridine antiseptics would apply *mutatis mutandis* to other groups. We have already mentioned the conclusion which Fairbrother and Renshaw [39] drew from their wide survey, that high antiseptic potency is only found among strongly basic dyes, and, as will be seen, many highly active dyes must, owing to resonance, have flat cations. Three groups call for mention: triphenylmethane dyes, styryl- and anilquinoline derivatives, and cyanine dyes.

Triphenylmethane dyes have the general structure **XXVI**. Among highly bacteriostatic dyes of the group are malachite green (X = H, R = $CH_3$), brilliant green (X = H, R = $C_2H_5$), methyl violet (X = $NHCH_3$, R = $CH_3$), and crystal violet (X = $N(CH_3)_2$, R = $CH_3$).

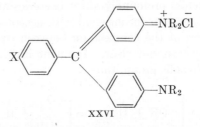

XXVI

The cations are regarded as resonating hybrids of two forms when X is not a basic group and of three when it is. Thus in crystal violet (**XXVII**) any of the three benzene nuclei can become quinonoid and the cation is best regarded as a resonance hybrid of the three possible forms. This resonance will tend to produce a flat cation and to increase its stability, i.e., to increase the basic strength. The free bases are, however, unstable and isomerize more or less rapidly into colorless and feebly basic carbinols (**XXVIII**) so that the following equilibrium is set up as the pH increases. For this reason the measurement of $pK_a$ values presents

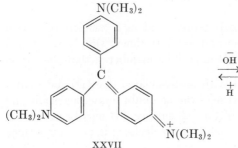

XXVII

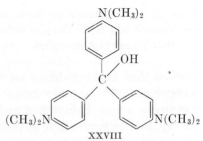

XXVIII

exceptional difficulty and no data are available for attempting to correlate bacteriostatic potency with basic strength.

Gale and Mitchell [43] made the interesting observation that triphenyl-methane dyes inhibit the glutamic acid metabolism of *Strept. faecalis.* This organism assimilates glutamic acid from the medium, provided that glucose is also available.  Some of the glutamic acid is then metabolized so that the content of free glutamic acid inside the bacterial cells repre-sents a balance between the amount assimilated and the amount metabo-lized.  The free glutamic acid content of the cells and of the medium can be estimated by measuring the volume of carbon dioxide evolved in contact with a specific glutamic acid decarboxylase.  Gale and Mitchell found that cells exposed to triphenylmethane dyes in a medium containing glucose and glutamic acid had a higher glutamic acid content than control cells and that the extent of this increase in glutamic acid content ran roughly parallel with the bacteriostatic efficiency of the dyes (Table XII).  They were also able to show, by drawing up a

## TABLE XII

| Name | Substituents | Growth (+) or Inhibition of Growth (−) at Dilutions of 1 in: | | | | | | | | Effect on Glutamic Acid Uptake at $1/10^4$ * | Partition Coefficient Iso-butanol-Water |
|---|---|---|---|---|---|---|---|---|---|---|---|
| | | $10^4$ | $5 \times 10^4$ | $10^5$ | $2 \times 10^5$ | $3 \times 10^3$ | $5 \times 10^5$ | $7 \times 10^5$ | $10^6$ | | |
| p-Rosaniline | $3NH_2$ | − | − | + | + | + | + | + | + | 4 | 12.5 |
| Fuchsin | $3NH_2$, $CH_3$ | − | − | + | + | + | + | + | + | 25 | 14.7 |
| Methyl violet | $2N(CH_3)_2$, $NHCH_3$ | − | − | − | − | − | + | + | + | 85 | 62 |
| Crystal violet | $3N(CH_3)_2$ | − | − | − | − | − | − | + | + | 100 | 76 |
| Malachite green | $2N(CH_3)_2$ | − | − | − | − | − | − | − | + | 100 | 125 |
| Brilliant green | $2N(C_2H_5)_2$ | − | − | − | − | − | − | − | + | 140 | 480 |
| Methyl green | $2N(CH_3)_2$, + $N(CH_3)_3$ | + | + | + | + | + | + | + | + | 0 | 0.2 |
| Soluble blue | $3(NHC_6H_4SO_3H)$ | − | − | + | + | + | + | + | + | 7 | 0.1 |

* On scale of crystal violet = 100.

balance sheet for glutamic acid inside and outside the cells, that the increase in internal glutamic acid was due to a decrease in its metabolism. Since the dyes must be absorbed in order to affect internal metabolic reactions, they also measured the partition coefficients of the dyes be-tween isobutanol and water and found that they too ran roughly paral-lel with bacteriostatic potency (Table XII).

[43] Gale and Mitchell, *J. Gen. Microbiol.*, **1**, 299 (1947).

The order of increasing potency indicated in Table XII is very similar to that which other authors have found, e.g., Kligler,[44] who studied a large number of dyes on a representative selection of microörganisms. It will be noticed that methyl green which contains one quaternary ammonium group was not bacteriostatic. Presumably it was not absorbed, since it had no effect on glutamic acid uptake and its iso-butanol-water partition coefficient was very small; the same was true for the acidic dye, soluble blue.

The antiseptic properties of the anil- and styrylquinolines and of the cyanine dyes were discovered by Browning and his collaborators.[45] The compounds, which are all dyes, were investigated because all their salts contain the conjugated system $-NR{=}C-(CH{=}C)_n-N{<}$ which occurs in acriflavine. In acriflavine (XXIX), $n = 1$; in the carbocyanines (XXX), $n = 2$; and in the styrylquinolines (XXXI), $n = 3$. In the anilquinolines (XXXII) $n = 2$ but the system also includes the analogous unit $(-CH{=}N-)$. This conjugated system will

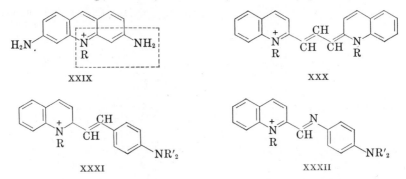

XXIX                                          XXX

XXXI                                          XXXII

obviously confer "extra ionic resonance" on the cations, similar to that which we noted for 2- and 5-aminoacridines. Thus the anilquinolinium ions will be resonance hybrids of the forms XXXII and XXXIII. One

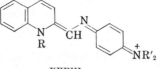

XXXIII

would expect this resonance to stabilize the cations, i.e., to increase basic strength and the extent of ionization at physiological pH, and to

[44] Kligler, *J. Exptl. Med.*, **27**, 463 (1918).
[45] Browning, Cohen, Ellingworth, and Gulbransen, *Proc. Roy. Soc. (London)*, **B96**, 317 (1924); **100**, 293 (1926); **103**, 404 (1928); **113**, 300 (1933); **115**, 1 (1934).

make them flat.   Thus the analogy with acriflavine was more far-reaching than Browning and his collaborators could have foreseen in 1924.   The importance of the extra ionic resonance is illustrated by the observation that *o*-dialkylamino-anil- and -styrylquinolines are less active than their *para* isomers and that the *meta* isomers, in which the conjugated system is broken, have only negligible activity.   Unfortu-nately the $pK_a$ values of these isomers have not been measured, but it is highly probable that the *para* isomers would be stronger bases than the *meta* isomers.

All the compounds were tested on *Staph. aureus* (Gram positive) and *Bact. coli* (Gram negative) by the method of serial dilution in simple peptone water and in the presence of serum.   In general, these dyes resembled the acridine dyes in that their activity was not substantially reduced by serum, also in being slow-acting antiseptics, i.e., bacterio-static agents.

Some of the cyanine dyes were powerful antiseptics for *Staph. aureus* but much less active against *Bact. coli*.   Thus 1,1'-dimethyl-6,6'-di-methoxycarbocyanine iodide (XXX; R = $CH_3$, 6-$CH_3O$ in each quino-line ring) was lethal to *Staph. aureus* at $10^{-6} - 2.5 \times 10^{-6}$, whereas against *Bact. coli* a concentration of $5 \times 10^{-4}$ was required.

In the anil- and styrylquinoline series, *p*-dimethylamino and *p*-di-ethylamino compounds were more effective than the *p*-amino; i.e., in XXXI and XXXII, R' = $CH_3$ or $C_2H_5$ was better than R' = H.   The metho salts (XXXI and XXXII; R = $CH_3$) were also more active than the salts of tertiary bases.   Acetylation of the amino group in *p*-amino compounds abolished activity, a result which recalls the effect of acetylation on aminoacridines.

Further substitution in the quinoline nucleus revealed some curious differences between the anil and the styryl compounds.   Thus the in-troduction of a 6-acylamino group into the anils (XXXIV) increased

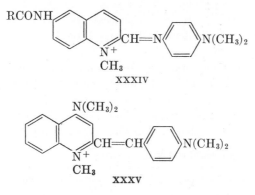

XXXIV

XXXV

activity considerably, particularly against *Bact. coli*, but had little effect in the styryl compounds. Considerable variation in the nature of the acyl group could be made without loss of activity; thus, in XXXIV, R might be $C_nH_{2n+1}(n = 1, 2, 3, 4, 5)$, $C_6H_5$, $CH_3O$, or $C_2H_5O$. On the other hand, the activity of the styryl compounds was increased by the introduction of a 4-dimethylamino group (as in XXXV), whereas that of the anils was decreased.

## Sulfonamides

None of the antiseptics thus far discussed has been proved useful in the treatment of bacterial septicemias, although many of them have proved to be valuable for external use, e.g., the treatment of wounds and in surgery. In spite of the success of chemotherapeutic agents in the treatment of protozoal and spirochetal infections, no substance capable of combating bacterial infections was known in 1930. Promising results were, however, obtained in the early thirties by the I. G. Farbenindustrie, and in 1935 Domagk [46] described the cure of acute and chronic infections of mice with hemolytic streptococci by oral treatment with a new drug Prontosil or 4-sulfonamido-2′,4′-diaminoazobenzene (XXXVI). Clinical trials reported in the period 1933–1935 showed that

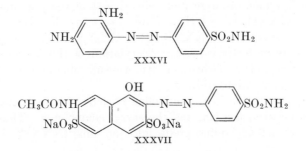

the new drug cured acute staphylococcal and streptococcal infections in man. A more soluble drug of the same type, Prontosil-S (XXXVII), was also announced by Domagk.

Domagk's results with mice were soon confirmed in France by Levaditi and Vaisman.[47] Meanwhile, Trefouel, Trefouel, Nitti, and Bovet [48] suggested that Prontosil was broken down in the body at the azo link liberating *p*-aminobenzenesulfonamide or sulfanilamide (XXXVIIIa), which they found to be therapeutically active in streptococcal infections

[46] Domagk, *Deut. med. Wochschr.*, **61**, 250 (1935).
[47] Levaditi and Vaisman, *Compt. rend.*, **200**, 1694 (1935).
[48] Trefouel, Trefouel, Nitti, and Bovet, *Compt. rend. soc. biol.*, **120**, 756 (1935).

of mice and rabbits. Their results were soon confirmed in England by Buttle, Gray, and Stephenson.[49] Colebrook and Kenny [50] also showed that, although Prontosil was inactive *in vitro*, it did confer bacteriostatic power on the blood of patients treated with it. A year later

XXXVIII*a*

Nitti, Bovet, and Depierre [51] found that sulfanilamide was bacteriostatic to hemolytic streptococci *in vitro*, without being immediately lethal, and that its *o*- and *m*-isomers and its acetyl derivative were inactive.

Since 1935 an enormous number of sulfonamide derivatives have been prepared. Northey,[52] who reviewed the subject in 1940, stated that the synthesis of some thirteen hundred new compounds derived from sulfanilamide had been disclosed in five years. The first really effective one was sulfapyridine, which was found to be particularly active in pneumococcal infections but to have marked toxic actions. This result led to the synthesis of many other sulfonamides with heterocyclic nuclei attached to the amide N-atom; representatives of this class, besides sulfapyridine, are sulfathiazole, sulfadiazine, sulfamerazine, sulfamezathine, and gantrisin (XXXVIII*b*). Table XIII lists the most important sulfonamides used in medicine with their structural features.

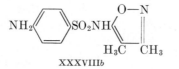

XXXVIII*b*

In naming sulfonamides, substituents of the amide group are called $N^1$-substituents and those of the amino group $N^4$-substituents; thus sulfacetamide (Table XIII) has an $N^1$-acetyl group, but the acetyl derivative of sulfanilamide which the French workers found to be inactive *in vitro* has an $N^4$-acetyl group.

The sulfonamide drugs have the advantage of being relatively easy to prepare. The general method consists in treating the appropriate amine with N-acetylsulfanilyl chloride, $CH_3CONHC_6H_4SO_2Cl$, and removing the $N^4$-acetyl group by hydrolysis with acid or, preferably, alkali. N-Acetylsulfanilyl chloride is obtained by sulfonating acetanilide

[49] Buttle, Gray, and Stephenson, *Lancet*, **230**, 1286 (1936).

[50] Colebrook and Kenny, *ibid.*, **230**, 1279 (1936).

[51] Nitti, Bovet, and Depierre, *Compt. rend. soc. biol.*, **124**, 16 (1937).

[52] Northey, *Chem. Revs.*, **27**, 86 (1940). See also Northey, "The Sulfonamides and Allied Compounds," Reinhold Publishing Corp., New York (1948).

with chlorosulfonic acid. The free drugs are sparingly soluble in water, but all those which contain an H atom on $N^1$ form readily soluble sodium salts.

TABLE XIII

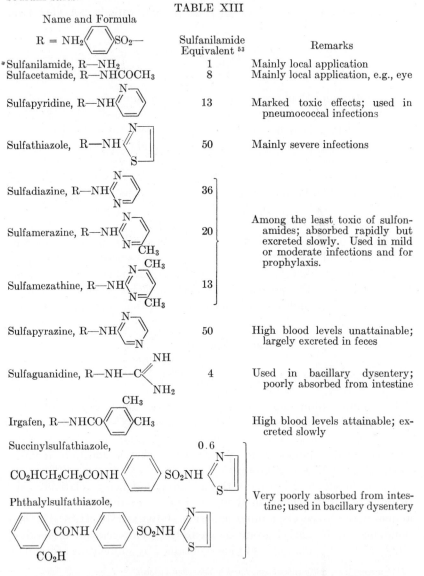

| Name and Formula<br>$R = NH_2$⟨⟩$SO_2$— | Sulfanilamide<br>Equivalent [53] | Remarks |
|---|---|---|
| Sulfanilamide, R—$NH_2$ | 1 | Mainly local application |
| Sulfacetamide, R—$NHCOCH_3$ | 8 | Mainly local application, e.g., eye |
| Sulfapyridine, R—NH⟨⟩ | 13 | Marked toxic effects; used in pneumococcal infections |
| Sulfathiazole, R—NH⟨⟩ | 50 | Mainly severe infections |
| Sulfadiazine, R—NH⟨⟩ | 36 | Among the least toxic of sulfonamides; absorbed rapidly but excreted slowly. Used in mild or moderate infections and for prophylaxis. |
| Sulfamerazine, R—NH⟨⟩$CH_3$ | 20 | |
| Sulfamezathine, R—NH⟨⟩ | 13 | |
| Sulfapyrazine, R—NH⟨⟩ | 50 | High blood levels unattainable; largely excreted in feces |
| Sulfaguanidine, R—NH—C⟨NH, $NH_2$⟩ | 4 | Used in bacillary dysentery; poorly absorbed from intestine |
| Irgafen, R—NHCO⟨⟩$CH_3$ | | High blood levels attainable; excreted slowly |
| Succinylsulfathiazole,<br>$CO_2HCH_2CH_2CONH$⟨⟩$SO_2NH$⟨⟩ | 0.6 | Very poorly absorbed from intestine; used in bacillary dysentery |
| Phthalylsulfathiazole,<br>⟨⟩CONH⟨⟩$SO_2NH$⟨⟩<br>$CO_2H$ | | |

The sulfonamides are bacteriostatic, not bactericidal. Their therapeutic effect is achieved by preventing the multiplication of the infecting

[53] Lawrence, "The Sulfonamides in Theory and Practice," H. K. Lewis, London (1946).

organism and so allowing the normal defense mechanisms of the host to eradicate the infection.  When bacteria are exposed to inadequate concentrations of sulfonamides, so that some growth occurs, they eventually become resistant to the whole group (but not to antibacterial agents of a different type, such as penicillin and acriflavine).  In order to avoid this, intensive treatment for short periods must be given.

The bacteriostatic action of sulfonamides is confined to certain types of bacteria, particularly cocci; streptococci, pneumococci, staphylococci, meningococci, and gonococci.  They also act on coliform bacteria of the intestine and on the organisms causing gas gangrene, plague, and malaria.  The drugs are normally tested against experimental infections in mice, but they can also be tested *in vitro*.  The effectiveness of any given sulfonamide in human disease depends on numerous variables, but particularly on the nature of the infection, the concentration of drug attainable in the blood, and its rate of excretion.

Some sulfonamides are more effective against certain organisms than others.  This is probably not due to a selective action but to quantitative differences in activity.  Some bacteria, e.g., hemolytic streptococci, are very sensitive to most sulfonamides; pneumococci are more resistant, and most strains of staphylococci more resistant still.  Infections with resistant species can be cured only by the most active drugs.

The concentration in the blood depends on absorption from the intestine and the rate of excretion.  Fortunately, sulfonamides are easily estimated in blood and urine.  Protein is precipitated with trichloroacetic acid, and the filtrate is diazotized and coupled with N-(1-naphthyl)-ethylenediamine to give a soluble red dye which can be estimated colorimetrically.  Since the amino group ($N^4$) is often acetylated in the body and the drug largely excreted in the urine as its $N^4$-acetyl derivative, the total sulfonamide content can be obtained only after hydrolyzing the protein-free filtrate with acid.  The difference between estimations before and after hydrolysis gives the content of acetylated drug.

Sulfonamides in therapeutic doses are not free from toxic effects.  Many of these are mild, but a few are serious and may prove fatal, e.g., agranulocytosis.  The toxicology of the sulfonamides is discussed by Goodman and Gilman.[54]

Sulfanilamide itself inhibits the enzyme carbonic anhydrase and so diminishes the carbon dioxide-combining power of the blood.  $N^1$-substituted sulfonamides do not have this effect.

**Structure-Action Relationships.**  All the minimum structural requirements for bacteriostatic activity in the sulfonamide group are contained

[54] Goodman and Gilman, "The Pharmacological Basis of Therapeutics," The Macmillan Co., New York (1941), Chapter 57.

in sulfanilamide and appear to be those represented in **XXXIX**. The *para*-amino group is essential and can be replaced only by groups which

XXXIX

are converted into a free amino group in the body, such as $NO_2$, $NHOH$, and the azo group. Acylation of the amino group abolishes activity *in vitro* but not necessarily *in vivo*, where deacylation may occur. Thus succinyl and phthalyl sulfathiazoles (Table XIII) are effective in bacillary dysentery. Both drugs are poorly absorbed in the intestine, only about 5% being excreted by the kidney, but there is evidence that their action on intestinal flora is due to the liberation of small amounts of sulfathiazole. Other compounds which are converted *in vivo* into the free amine are formaldehyde bisulfite and formaldehyde sulfoxalate derivatives and certain anils.

Nuclear-substituted sulfonamides are usually inactive; the most profitable form of substitution is that at $N^1$. Alkylation of $N^1$ reduces activity. Conflicting reports have been made about $N^1$-phenyl and substituted phenyl derivatives, but there is no doubt that the substitution of heterocyclic aromatic nuclei on $N^1$ has led to highly active substances; the order of increasing effectiveness appears to be 2-pyridine, 2-pyrimidine, 2-thiazole. These heterocyclic $N^1$-derivatives can exist in prototropic forms; e.g., sulfapyridine can exist as **XL**a and b. Replacement of the $N^1$-hydrogen in **XL**a by methyl gives an almost in-

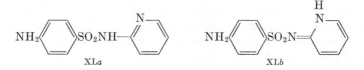

XLa                              XLb

active compound, but the Py-methyl derivative of **XL**b is as active as sulfapyridine.[55]

Substitution of an amidine group on $N^1$ gives sulfaguanidine (Table XIII), which is more active than sulfanilamide; it is poorly absorbed in the intestine and has been used to combat intestinal infections. $N^1$-Acyl derivatives may be highly active, and two are included in Table XIII. Sulfacetamide is a useful drug because its sodium salt solutions are nearly neutral and are therefore suitable for local application to delicate tissues like those of the eye; the sodium salts of most sulfonamides other than $N^1$-acyl derivatives form strongly alkaline solutions.

[55] Shepherd, Bratton, and Blanchard, *J. Am. Chem. Soc.*, **64**, 2532 (1942).

Replacement of the sulfonamide group by $SO_3H$ destroys activity, but the analogous sulfinic acid was tested as its $N^4$-acetyl derivative, $CH_3CONHC_6H_4SO_2H$, by Gray et al.[56] and found to be active; the acyl derivative (XLI) was described as being as active as sulfanilamide and less toxic.

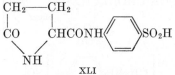

XLI

Buttle et al.[49] found that $p,p'$-diaminodiphenyl sulfone, $NH_2C_6H_4SO_2$-$C_6H_4NH_2$, was very potent in experimental streptococcal infections, but it is much more toxic than sulfanilamide. Fourneau et al.[57] also found that activity was retained by compounds in which the sulfonamide group of sulfanilamide was replaced by

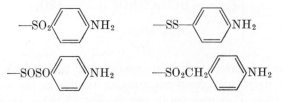

and $-SO_2C_nH_{2n+1}$ (max. for $n = 3$). If sulfoxides and sulfides are oxidized in vivo to sulfones, these results are in keeping with the view that the essential structural features are

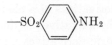

Diaminodiphenyl sulfone is mainly of interest because some of its derivatives have been found to have therapeutic activity in tuberculosis and leprosy. A related sulfone with similar properties is Promizole, or $p$-aminophenyl 2-amino-4-thiazolyl sulfone (XLII). The toxicity of

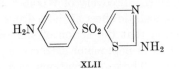

XLII

diaminodiphenyl sulfone and its insolubility in water led to the search for less toxic and more soluble derivatives. Promin (XLIII), its bis-

[56] Gray, Buttle, and Stephenson, Biochem. J., 31, 724 (1937).

[57] Fourneau et al., Compt. rend. soc. biol., 127, 393 (1938); Bull. acad. med. (Paris), 118, 210 (1937).

glucose sulfonate, was the first derivative shown to have a striking action against experimental tuberculosis and against human leprosy. Other derivatives are Diasone (XLIV), its *bis*-formaldehyde sulfox-

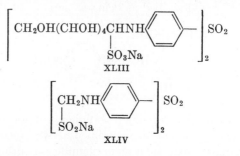

XLIII

XLIV

alate, and Sulfetrone, to which formula XLV is assigned. None of

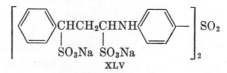

XLV

these compounds are so active in experimental tuberculosis as streptomycin, but they have given encouraging results in the treatment of human leprosy. It is reasonably certain that all these derivatives owe their chemotherapeutic activity to the liberation of diaminodiphenyl sulfone,[58, 59, 59a] and good results have been obtained in the treatment of leprosy with diaminodiphenyl sulfone itself. It is not always advantageous to use less toxic derivatives of a chemotherapeutic agent when the curative effect of such derivatives is due to the liberation of the toxic agent itself. Less toxic derivatives may be uneconomical in use owing to their rapid excretion, and blood concentrations of the effective agent may be more reliably maintained with the toxic drug itself than with its less toxic derivatives.

**Mechanism of Action.** The key to the mechanism of action of sulfonamides was provided by the discovery of Woods [60] that *p*-aminobenzoic acid prevents the bacteriostatic effect of these drugs. During 1938–1940 several workers observed that the action of sulfanilamide *in vitro* was inhibited by the addition of peptone or extracts of yeast, bacteria, etc., to the culture medium. These observations were of great interest to

[58] Titus and Bernstein, *Ann. N. Y. Acad. Sci.*, **52**, 719 (1949).

[59] Francis and Spinks, *Brit. J. Pharmacol.*, **5**, 565 (1950).

[59a] The drug Promacetin (4,4'-diamino-2-N-acetylsulfonamidodiphenylsulfone) also deserves mention. It contains both sulfone and sulfonamide units of structure and has given promising results in the treatment of leprosy.

[60] Woods, *Brit. J. Exptl. Path.*, **21**, 74 (1940).

Fildes and his group, to which Woods belonged, because their general view of bacteriostasis was that the drug immobilized some essential metabolite of the microörganism, either by irreversible combination with it or by blocking some enzyme system concerned in its utilization. It seemed reasonable to assume that the extracts referred to might contain an essential bacterial metabolite, and by fractionating an ammoniacal extract of yeast, Woods obtained a fraction that was highly active in antagonizing sulfanilamide and did so competitively. The active substance in the yeast fraction appeared to be an aromatic carboxylic acid containing a feebly basic amino group. Since substances which inhibit enzymes competitively are frequently related structurally to the normal substrates, it seemed likely that the yeast fraction contained a substance with some structural resemblance to sulfanilamide. The simplest aminoarylcarboxylic acid fulfilling this condition, and the first that Woods tested, was $p$-aminobenzoic acid. It completely prevented the bacteriostatic action of sulfanilamide at approximately $\frac{1}{5000}$ of the molar concentration of the latter, and this ratio remained constant over a twenty-five-fold range of sulfanilamide concentrations.

The only other compounds related to $p$-aminobenzoic acid that had comparable activity, out of some sixteen which Woods tested, were procaine (diethylaminoethyl $p$-aminobenzoate) and $p$-hydroxyaminobenzoic acid. Both these compounds, the former by hydrolysis and the latter by reduction, might easily be converted into $p$-aminobenzoic acid in the bacterial cell. Woods therefore concluded that the active substance in his yeast extract was $p$-aminobenzoic acid. At the same time he boldly suggested that $p$-aminobenzoic acid was an essential metabolite of bacteria and that the enzymic reaction involved in its further utilization was subject to competitive inhibition by sulfanilamide. This inhibition was regarded as due to a structural relationship between sulfanilamide and $p$-aminobenzoic acid, the latter being the normal substrate of the enzyme in question.

Substantial corroboration of these suggestions was soon forthcoming. $p$-Aminobenzoic acid was found to prevent the curative effect of sulfanilamide in streptococcal infections of mice,[61] it was isolated from yeast,[62, 63] in which it was found to occur as a glutamic acid peptide;[64] it was shown to be a growth factor for *Clostridium acetobutylicum*[62] and later for a wide variety of microörganisms;[65] it has also been shown to be

[61] Selbie, *ibid.*, **21**, 90 (1940).

[62] Rubbo and Gillespie, *Nature*, **146**, 838 (1940).

[63] Blanchard, *J. Biol. Chem.*, **140**, 919 (1941).

[64] Ratner *et al.*, *ibid.*, **155**, 689 (1944).

[65] Knight, *Vitamins and Hormones*, **3**, 105 (1945); Woods, *Ann. Rev. Biochem.*, **16**, 115 (1947).

synthesized by many organisms that do not require a supply of it in the culture medium. The sulfonamide-$p$-aminobenzoic acid antagonism has been found to occur with all microörganisms that are susceptible to these drugs, except *Bact. tularense*, and with a wide variety of sulfonamide drugs.

$p$-Aminobenzoic acid appears to be involved in the synthesis of folic acid, which is a member of the vitamin B complex and an essential growth factor for some microörganisms, mainly enterococci and lactobacilli. Folic acid is also involved in the nutrition of animals and occurs widely in animal and vegetable tissues. It is probably not a single substance but a group of closely related substances. One substance with full folic acid activity for *Lactobacillus casei* and other folic acid-requiring organisms has been isolated and synthesized,[66] namely, pteroylglutamic acid (XLVI). The compound also occurs in poly-

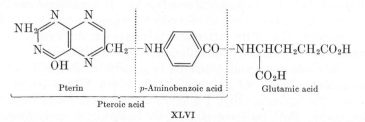

XLVI

peptides with extra glutamic acid residues, e.g., pteroyltriglutamic and pteroylpentaglutamic acids.

The presence of $p$-aminobenzoic acid in pteroylglutamic acid naturally suggests that one purpose for which the former is utilized in the bacterial cell is the synthesis of folic acid. If this is the main function of $p$-aminobenzoic acid in bacteria we should expect organisms which require preformed folic acid, i.e., which cannot synthesize it, to be insensitive to sulfonamides; organisms which can synthesize it if they are provided with $p$-aminobenzoic acid to be very sensitive to sulfonamides; and finally sensitive organisms to be rendered insensitive to sulfonamides in the presence of adequate amounts of folic acid. Moreover, folic acid should overcome sulfonamide inhibition of growth in a non-competitive fashion. Evidence is accumulating in support of all these expectations.[67] In what follows it will be assumed that inhibition of bacterial growth by sulfonamides can be satisfactorily accounted for by their effect upon the utilization of $p$-aminobenzoic acid alone.

[66] Angier *et al.*, *Science*, **103**, 667 (1946); *J. Am. Chem. Soc.*, **70**, 14, 19, 23, 25, 27 (1948).
[67] For a fuller account see Woods and Nimmo-Smith, "Society for Experimental Biology Symposia." III. "Selective Toxicity and Antibiotics," Cambridge University Press, London (1949), pp. 177–192.

The amount of $p$-aminobenzoic acid required to reverse the bacterio-static action of sulfonamides appears to depend on the intensity of the biological effect and is not directly related to the concentration of the drug. Thus Rose and Fox [68] observed that a constant concentration of $p$-aminobenzoic acid ($5 \times 10^{-7}$ $M$) was required to reverse the effect of the minimum effective concentrations (MEC) of various sulfonamides, although the MEC varied from $2.5 \times 10^{-3}$ $M$ for sulfanilamide to $4 \times 10^{-6}$ $M$ for sulfathiazole, a six-hundred-fold range. Results of this kind suggest that the sulfonamides compete with $p$-aminobenzoic acid for the same receptor, probably an enzyme, and their varying potencies are due to different affinities for the receptor.

The same authors [69] also noted that at the minimum effective concentration the ionic concentrations of various sulfonamides were of the

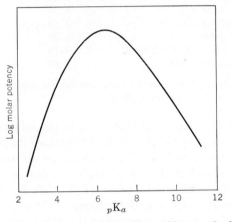

FIG. 4. The $pK_a$ values of representative sulfonamides vs. the logarithm of their potencies (after Bell and Roblin; [70] courtesy of the publisher).

same order. They suggested that the active form of sulfonamides was the anion and supported their suggestion by the observation that the MEC of sulfanilamide at $p$H 7.8 was one-eighth of that at $p$H 6.8, but the ionization at $p$H 7.8 was ten times that at $p$H 6.8. Moreover, $p$-aminobenzoic acid at $p$H 7 exists almost entirely as $p$-aminobenzoate anions, and consequently the sulfonamide anion might be expected to compete with it on more favorable terms than the undissociated mole-cule. However, when the $pK_a$ values for a representative range of sulfonamides are plotted against the logarithms of the potencies (ex-

[68] Rose and Fox, *Science*, **95**, 412 (1942).
[69] Fox and Rose, *Proc. Soc. Exptl. Biol. Med.*, **51**, 102 (1942).
[70] Bell and Roblin, *J. Am. Chem. Soc.*, **64**, 2905 (1942).

pressed as the reciprocals of the minimum effective molar concentrations for complete bacteriostasis of *Bact. coli* in synthetic medium at $pH$ 7), a parabolic curve is obtained (Fig. 4). The most potent sulfonamides have $pK_a$ values of between 6 and 7, and both weaker and stronger acids are less potent (see Table XIV).

TABLE XIV

| Compound | $pK_a$ | MEC * $\times 10^5$ |
|---|---|---|
| $N^1$-Methylsulfanilamide | 10.77 | 30 |
| Sulfanilamide | 10.43 | 20 |
| $N^1$-Phenylsulfanilamide | 9.60 | 3.0 |
| Sulfapyridine | 8.43 | 0.6 |
| 3-Sulfanilamidopyridine | 7.89 | 0.2 |
| Sulfathiazole | 7.12 | 0.08 |
| Sulfadiazine | 6.48 | 0.08 |
| Sulfapyrazine | 6.04 | 0.08 |
| Sulfanilylurea | 5.42 | 10 |
| Sulfacetamide | 5.38 | 0.7 |
| $N^1$-Chloroacetylsulfanilamide | 3.79 | 10 |
| Sulfanilylcyanamide | 2.92 | 100 |

* MEC = minimum effective molar concentration for complete bacteriostasis of *Escherichia coli* in synthetic medium, $pH$ 7.

Bell and Roblin [70] explained this curve in the following way. They postulated that the more closely the drug resembled the $p$-aminobenzoate ion the greater would be its ability to block the utilization of that ion. The actual dimensions of the $NH_2C_6H_4SO_2$-radical in sulfonamides are very similar to those of $p$-aminobenzoate (Fig. 5), but in the latter the $CO_2$-radical carries unit negative charge. Consequently, Bell and Roblin argued that, the more negative the $SO_2$-group of an N-substituted sulfanilamide derivative, the more potent the latter should be. The $SO_2$-group is itself a negative or electrophilic group and will attract part of the charge in the sulfonamide ion (Fig. 5); consequently, the sulfonamides should be more active in the ionized state. But the acidic strength of N-substituted sulfonamides will depend on both the $SO_2$-group and the N-substituent. If the latter is also electrophilic the acidic strength will be increased, and this is why sulfathiazole, sulfadiazine, sulfacetamide, etc., are much stronger acids than sulfanilamide (Table XIV). But the more electrophilic the N-substituent is, the more it will compete with the $SO_2$-group for a share of the negative charge of the sulfonamide anion, and in the strongest acids the $SO_2$-group may be less negative than in the moderately strong acids. Thus the right-hand arm of the curve in Fig. 4 represents decreasing potency as acidic strength declines (or $pK_a$ increases), and the left-hand arm, increasing potency as the $SO_2$-group becomes more negative owing to a decrease in the electrophilic character of the N-substituent, which is, of course, accompanied by a decline in acidic strength. The maximum in the curve represents the optimum balance of these two effects, i.e., sulfonamides sufficiently strongly acid to produce a high proportion of anions but with N-substituents which do not make such great demands on the negative charge as to reduce appreciably the negativity of the $SO_2$-group.

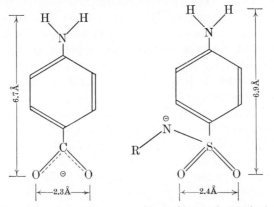

FIG. 5. A dimensional comparison of sulfonamides and p-aminobenzoate anion (after Bell and Roblin;[70] courtesy of the publisher).

It is interesting that maximum potency occurs for sulfonamides with $pK_a$ values in the range 6–7, since at pH 7 these drugs will be approximately 50% ionized; this result suggests an alternative explanation of the parabolic curve in Fig. 4. It is well known that undissociated molecules generally penetrate cell membranes more readily than ions. If this is true for sulfonamides, the extent to which these drugs penetrate into the bacterial cell may depend upon the concentration of undissociated molecules. As soon as the undissociated molecules are inside the cell the ionization equilibrium will be restored and the anion may be the bacteriostatically effective agent. Thus the left-hand arm of the curve in Fig. 4 would represent the effect of increasing penetration, and the right-hand arm that of decreasing ionization, the maximum representing the optimal balance of these two effects.[71]

A decision between these two ways of accounting for the parabolic curve of Fig. 4 might be reached by eliminating one of the variables. Thus if the enzyme system concerned in the utilization of p-amino-benzoic acid could be isolated from bacterial cells it would become possible to study the inhibitory action of sulfonamides upon it apart

[71] Cowles, *Yale J. Biol. and Med.*, **14**, 599 (1942).

from the complicating factor of their penetration into living cells. If Bell and Roblin's view is correct, the curve relating inhibitory power and $pK_a$ should also be parabolic with a maximum around $pK_a = 6$–$7$; but if the curve in Fig. 4 represents a balance between penetration and ionization, the inhibitory power on the isolated enzyme system would be expected to run parallel with the extent of ionization, i.e., to rise with decreasing $pK_a$ to a maximum and then remain approximately constant. The isolation of what may well be a complicated enzyme system would, however, be a difficult matter, and it has not yet been achieved.

Competitive antagonism to $p$-aminobenzoic acid is displayed by a larger range of compounds than that represented by the sulfonamides. It is shown by $p$-aminophenyl derivatives of the general type $p$-$NH_2C_6H_4X$, where X is a sufficiently acidic or "negative" group. Thus, besides $SO_2NHR$ or $SO_2R$, X may be the arsonic acid group $AsO_3H_2$, the sulfydryl group SH, the phosphonous acid group $PO_2H_2$, or the carbonyl group as in 4,4'-diaminobenzophenone or 4,4'-diaminobenzil (XLVII). The last compound has a bacteriostatic activity on some organisms comparable with that of 4,4'-diaminodiphenyl sulfone.[72] A free amino group in the *para* position to the acidic or negative group is essential for antagonism to $p$-aminobenzoic acid; thus Marfanil (XLVIII) is bacteriostatic, but its action is not annulled by $p$-aminobenzoic acid.

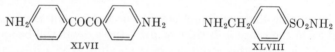

XLVII  XLVIII

Some nuclear substituted $p$-aminobenzoic acids are also bacteriostatic and their action is antagonized by $p$-aminobenzoic acid itself. Thus Wyss, Rubin, and Strandskov[73] described 2-chloro-4-aminobenzoic acid as almost as active as sulfapyridine on *Escherichia coli*, and its action was antagonized by $p$-aminobenzoic acid. Martin and Rose,[74] on the other hand, found that the 2-chloro acid had antisulfanilamide action on *Strept. pyogenes*. On this organism the 3-chloro-4-amino- and 3-hydroxy-4-aminobenzoic acids had the highest bacteriostatic activity of numerous substituted 4-aminobenzoic acids. Wyss *et al.*[73] found the 3-hydroxy acid inactive on *E. coli*. In their experiments the 2-fluoro acid was a growth factor for *Clostridium acetobutylicum* one-third as effective as $p$-aminobenzoic acid, but 3-fluoro-4-aminobenzoic acid was bacteriostatic.

[72] Kuhn *et al.*, *Ber.*, **75**, 711 (1942); **76**, 405 (1943).

[73] Wyss, Rubin, and Strandskov, *Proc. Soc. Exptl. Biol. Med.*, **52**, 155 (1943); see also Schmelkes and Rubin, *J. Am. Chem. Soc.*, **66**, 1631 (1944).

[74] Martin and Rose, *Biochem. J.*, **39**, 91 (1945).

Johnson, Green, and Pauli [75] found that methyl and methoxy substituents also conferred bacteriostatic properties on *p*-aminobenzoic acid. They confirmed many of the observations of Wyss *et al.*[73] but reported that the 2-chloro-4-aminobenzoic acid exhibited antisulfonamide action on some organisms (compare Martin and Rose [74]). They also studied a group of heterocyclic analogs of *p*-aminobenzoic acid; 6-aminonicotinic acid (XLIX) was bacteriostatic for *E. coli* and streptococci in approximately the same concentrations as sulfapyridine, but the isosteric thiazole acid (L) was inactive. 5-Nitrothiophene-2-carboxylic acid (LI) and its amide were bacteriostatic, but the analogous 5-nitrofuroic acid (LII) was not. All the active heterocyclic compounds had their

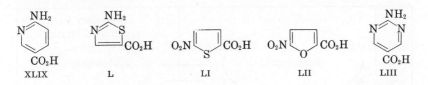

| XLIX | L | LI | LII | LIII |

bacteriostatic effect annulled by *p*-aminobenzoic acid. Finally, Martin *et al.*[76] found that 2-aminopyrimidine-5-carboxylic acid (LIII) prevented the action of sulfanilamide on *Strept. pyogenes*, but much less effectively than *p*-aminobenzoic acid. It will be noticed that this compound differs from the bacteriostatic acid (XLIX) only by the replacement of one CH in the ring by N. It seems clear that the subtleties of the structure-action relationships of these near relatives of *p*-aminobenzoic acid have been very far from completely unraveled. A full understanding of them must probably await the isolation of the enzyme system involved in the utilization of *p*-aminobenzoic acid.

## CHEMOTHERAPY OF MALARIA

Before World War II it was estimated that about a quarter of the population of the world suffered from malaria. About 800 tons of quinine were being produced per annum, but even this was only a small fraction of the amount that would have been used if every infected person had been treated. The chemotherapy of malaria is thus of massive importance.

Malaria is caused by infection with a parasitic protozoal organism called *Plasmodium* which has a complicated life cycle involving particular species of mosquitoes and other animals. This cycle must be briefly

[75] Johnson, Green, and Pauli, *J. Biol. Chem.*, **153**, 37 (1944).
[76] Martin, Rose, and Swain, *Nature*, **154**, 639 (1944).

described. When an infected mosquito bites an animal, it transfers from its own salivary glands to the animal a form of the parasite called a *sporozoite*. The sporozoites disappear rapidly from the blood, and the parasites appear to reside in the tissues of the host for several days, weeks, or even months. These "tissue forms," or primary exoerythrocytic forms, as they are called to distinguish them from forms which infest the red blood cells, eventually give rise to forms (*merozoites*) which invade the red blood cells, where they undergo a period of active growth. The growing parasites (*trophozoites*) develop either into asexual parasites (*schizonts*) or into sexual forms (*gametocytes*). Each schizont multiplies

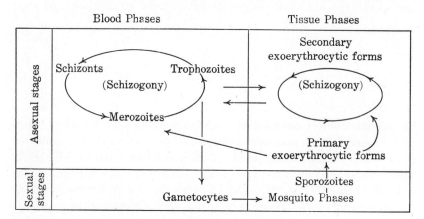

Diagram of the main features in the life cycle of plasmodia.

by dividing into a large number of small individuals, a process known as *schizogony*. The periodic disruption of the red cells and the appearance of these smaller parasites in the plasma, on their way to fresh red cells, coincide with the periods of high fever so characteristic of the disease. The gametocytes are the forms that infect mosquitoes when these insects suck the blood of infected animals. The gametocytes conjugate in the intestine of the mosquito, initiating a succession of developmental forms culminating in the sporozoites, which collect in the salivary glands of the insect. The asexual erythrocytic forms can also revert to exoerythrocytic forms which disappear from the blood into the tissues; it is these secondary exoerythrocytic forms that give rise periodically to relapses since they provide a reservoir from which the red blood cells may again be invaded.

The relations between the various forms of the parasite are represented in the diagram. Whether, indeed, the primary exoerythrocytic forms (formed from sporozoites) are identical with the secondary exoerythrocytic forms (formed from trophozoites) is uncertain, but it is these tissue forms that provide the ideal point of attack for antimalarial drugs in an established infection. In practice the erythrocytic forms (preschizonts and schizonts) are more susceptible to most of the common antimalarial drugs, and consequently most antimalarials are primarily suppressive drugs; they suppress the symptoms of the disease by destroying the rapidly multiplying erythrocytic forms but do not eradicate the causative agents. A drug that would destroy both the primary and secondary exoerythrocytic forms would be a causal prophylactic, since it would prevent the appearance of parasites in the red cells; it would also be a radical curative agent; that is, it would not merely suppress the attack but also would prevent relapses from occurring after the cessation of treatment.

There are numerous species of *Plasmodia*, and different species infect different animals. Man is susceptible to four species: *Plasmodium vivax*, which causes benign tertian malaria in which the bouts of fever are separated by 48 hours, i.e., they occur every third day; *P. falciparum*, which produces malignant tertian (or subtertian) which has an irregular cycle of about 48 hours; *P. malariae*, which causes quartan fever and has a cycle of 72 hours, i.e., fever occurs every fourth day; and the relatively uncommon *P. ovale*.

Other *Plasmodia* which have been used in experimental work are *P. relictum* and *P. cathemerium*, commonly studied in canaries; *P. gallinaceum* and *P. lophurae*, used in chickens and ducks; and *P. cynomolgi* and *P. knowlesi*, in monkeys. Different species of *Plasmodia* show different susceptibilities to drugs, and this is one of the major difficulties in devising methods of testing antimalarial drugs.[77]

## Methods of Testing Antimalarials

So long as antimalarial drugs could be tested only on man, no progress could be made in devising new drugs and it was very difficult even to assess the relative therapeutic efficiencies of the well-known cinchona alkaloids. Consequently, the discovery of a laboratory method of testing antimalarials by Roehl in 1926 constitutes a landmark in the development of the subject. Roehl made use of canaries infected with *P. relictum*. He transmitted the disease by injecting blood from infected birds intramuscularly into healthy birds, and he treated the disease by administering drugs orally for 4–6 days. In untreated birds parasites first appeared in the peripheral blood on the fourth to fifth day after

[77] For a review of the literature on the activity of antimalarials in avian, simian, and human malaria, see Curd, *Ann. Trop. Med. Parasitol.*, **37**, 115 (1943).

inoculation, but adequate daily doses of an effective antimalarial delayed the appearance of parasites in the blood beyond this period. Thus, after daily doses of 2.5–3.0 mg. of quinine for four days, parasites might not appear in the blood until twelve days after they had appeared in the blood of untreated birds. Roehl regarded a substance as promising if, administered in the maximum tolerated dose, it prolonged the delay in the appearance of parasites in the blood for five or more days beyond that in the control birds.[78]

Roehl's method was a test of suppressive and not of curative activity, and it allowed only qualitative judgments of relative activities. Fortunately, some substances that were active in the Roehl test were also found to be active in human malaria, but the converse was not necessarily true; e.g., in the later thirties it was discovered that some sulfonamide drugs that had a beneficial effect in human malaria were completely inactive in *P. relictum* infections of canaries. Substances have also been found that are active in the Roehl test but ineffective in human malaria. For these reasons, among others, a search was made early in the war years for alternative methods. Two methods were eventually developed, one using *P. gallinaceum* in chickens and the other using *P. lophurae* in ducklings. Both infections were sensitive to certain sulfonamides, and the former will be briefly described.[79]

When young chicks are injected intravenously with blood from heavily infected chicks, the infection climbs rapidly to a peak, the number of red blood cells containing parasites increasing sharply, reaching a maximum on the fourth or fifth day after inoculation and then declining. If the birds are treated orally with adequate doses of an active antimalarial twice daily for four days the number of parasitized red cells on the fifth day is markedly less than in untreated birds. By counting the number of parasitized red cells in a random 500 cells from treated and control birds a measure of activity can be obtained. An interesting feature of the method is that experience shows that, when an antimalarial is administered according to a particular dosage regime (e.g., twice daily), a critical dose can be found which accomplishes practically everything of which the drug is capable, and increasing the dose beyond this critical level will not materially improve the results.

The method as described above tests only suppressive activity, but prophylactic activity can be simply tested by infecting chicks with sporozoites, either by allowing them to be bitten by infected mosquitoes or by injecting a preparation of the salivary glands of infected mosquitoes intravenously.

[78] For an excellent account of the chemotherapy of avian malaria up to 1942, see Bishop, *Parasitology*, **34**, 1–54 (1942).

[79] Curd, Davey, and Rose, *Ann. Trop. Med. Parasitol.*, **39**, 139 (1945).

Most of the results of antimalarial tests were recorded, until comparatively recently, as chemotherapeutic indices, i.e., as ratios of the maximum tolerated dose to the minimum curative dose (MTD/MCD). This method has, however, several disadvantages. The terms MTD and MCD cannot be given precise meanings, and even if they are replaced by statistically precise terms, such as LD0.1 and CD99.9, the toxicity of an antimalarial for the canary or the chick has no certain bearing on its toxicity for man. It is better to estimate toxicities in small mammals such as mice and rats, but if this is done no chemotherapeutic index can be recorded.

A very useful method of comparing antimalarial activities without regard to toxicity for the host, and one which was adopted in the Antimalarial Survey, 1941–1945, is to use an antimalarial of acknowledged potency in human malaria as a standard and compare other synthetic compounds with it. Quinine is one of the obvious standards to use, and Buttle, Henry, and Trevan (1934) were the first to express their results as "quinine equivalents." They were using the Roehl test, and they defined the quinine equivalents as that dose of quinine which would produce the same delay in the appearance of parasites in the blood as unit dose of the substance under assay. Since, in *gallinaceum* infections of chicks and in other avian methods of tests, it is now customary to estimate the antimalarial effect in terms of the extent of parasitemia, the quinine equivalent is now defined as the ratio by weight of the dose of quinine to the dose of the drug under assay when the two drugs, administered under identical conditions, produce the same effect upon the parasitemia of infected birds. The degree of parasitemia can be estimated either by counting the number of parasites in an arbitrarily chosen number of red cells or by estimating the percentage of red cells that contain parasites. The former method gives higher values because some of the parasitized cells invariably contain more than one parasite.

It will be obvious that the higher the quinine equivalent the more effective the substance under assay will be, relative to quinine, in the particular type of infection studied; but a high quinine equivalent does not necessarily mean that the substance will surpass quinine equally in the treatment of human malaria. Moreover, it is important to remember that the quinine equivalent is not a constant, but depends upon numerous variables, not only upon the species of plasmodium and of host but also upon the technical details of the assay, such as dosage regimen and the age and weight of birds.[80]

---

[80] For a more detailed account of methods of testing the activity and toxicity of antimalarials see Marshall, *Federation Proc.*, **5**, 298 (1946), and "Survey of Antimalarial Drugs, 1941–1945," edited by Wiselogle, Edwards, Ann Arbor (1946), Chapter 2, pp. 59–71.

Quinine is not the only possible standard, and, since sulfadiazine is a causal prophylactic for *P. gallinaceum* infections in the chick, some workers have found it useful to estimate a "sulfadiazine equivalent," which is that dose of sulfadiazine which would achieve the same degree of prophylaxis (e.g., the same delay in the appearance of parasites in the blood) as unit dose of the substance under assay. The sulfadiazine equivalent, therefore, bears the same relation to causal prophylaxis as the quinine equivalent does to the treatment of an established infection.

Toxicities in mice or rats are also usefully estimated in terms of a standard. In exploring a large number of new substances, closely related in chemical structure to some known antimalarial, such as pamaquin or quinacrine, it is convenient to use one of the latter as a standard, but with new types of antimalarial quinine is probably the best standard of toxicity. The standard drug-equivalent of toxicity is defined as the ratio of the dose of the standard to the dose of the substance under assay when the two drugs, administered under identical conditions, produce the same toxic response. Toxic response is usually evaluated in terms of mortality, but suppression of growth can also be used. Toxicity tests should be designed to imitate as closely as possible the conditions under which an antimalarial will be administered in the treatment of human malaria; i.e., chronic toxicity is more illuminating than acute toxicity, and the effect of oral administration more useful than that of intravenous injection.

Vincke and Lips [81] have described a new strain of the malarial parasite, *P. berghei*, which can be used to infect mice. This discovery should prove of great value in the chemotherapy of malaria since it opens the possibility of testing drugs both for antimalarial activity and for toxicity in a small mammal, easily bred and handled in the laboratory.

In dealing with the several types of antimalarial drugs, and the structure-action relationships which obtain among them, it will be convenient to consider the cinchona alkaloids first and to classify synthetic compounds in terms of some common structural unit, e.g., the quinoline nucleus. No attempt will be made to assess the relative merits of different drugs in the treatment of human malaria (for this, see Ref. 6). Only the experimental aspects of the subject will be considered here, and the reader is warned not to regard the amount of space devoted to any group of drugs as a measure of their clinical importance.

[81] Vincke and Lips, *Ann. soc. belg. med. trop.*, **28**, 97 (1948).

## Cinchona Alkaloids

The cinchona alkaloids [82] are derived from the fundamental structure
I.   In quinine and quinidine, $R = OCH_3$ and $R' = CH{=}CH_2$; and in

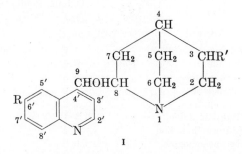

I

the corresponding hydroquinine and hydroquinidine, $R' = C_2H_5$.   In
cinchonine and cinchonidine, $R = H$ and $R' = CH{=}CH_2$; and in the
corresponding hydrocinchonine and hydrocinchonidine, $R' = C_2H_5$.
In cupreine, $R = OH$ and $R' = CH{=}CH_2$.

The cinchona alkaloids are suppressive drugs.   Their action is exerted
on the rapidly multiplying erythrocytic forms, and they do not affect
the gametocytes or the exoerythrocytic forms.   In human malaria it
appears to be agreed that quinine and quinidine are practically equivalent and more active than cinchonine and cinchonidine.

Several groups of workers have compared the activities of the main
cinchona alkaloids in bird malaria.   Their results do not agree in detail,
but this is not surprising because it is always difficult to obtain consistent values for relative activities among a group of compounds that
do not differ widely in their potencies.   Moreover, it is not an easy task
to separate the individual alkaloids in a state of high purity, and few
workers have paid sufficient attention to this aspect of the problem.
Buttle, Henry, and Trevan [83] did obtain the main alkaloids in a highly
purified state, and their results in the Roehl test are given in Table XV,
column 2.   The figures represent the dose of quinine necessary to produce
the same degree of protection as unit dose of the alkaloid named.   Quinine and hydroquinine were the most active, quinidine and cinchonidine
were both about half as active as quinine, and cinchonine was much less
active.   Giemsa, Weise, and Tropp [84] had previously found that there

[82] For the chemistry of the cinchona alkaloids and an excellent account of their pharmacology see Henry, "The Plant Alkaloids," Churchill, London (1949), 4th ed., pp. 418–483;
see also Manske and Holmes, "The Alkaloids," Academic Press, New York (1950).

[83] Buttle, Henry, and Trevan, *Biochem. J.*, **28**, 426 (1934).

[84] Giemsa, Weise, and Tropp, *Arch. Schiffs- u. Tropen-Hyg.*, **30**, 334 (1926).

was little difference between the activities of quinine, hydroquinine, and quinidine in the Roehl test, but that cinchonine was definitely inferior.

TABLE XV

|  | Quinine Equivalents | |
| Alkaloid | P. relictum in Canaries | P. gallinaceum in Chicks |
| --- | --- | --- |
| l-Quinine | 1.0 | 1.0 |
| d-Quinidine | 0.5 | 1.6 |
| l-Cinchonidine | 0.5 | 1.5 |
| d-Cinchonine | <0.2 | 1.9 |
| l-Hydroquinine | 1–2 | 2.0 |
| d-Hydroquinidine | 0.5–1 | |
| l-Hydrocinchonidine | <0.2 | |
| d-Hydrocinchonine | <0.2 | |

Marshall,[85] using the same highly purified alkaloids as Buttle et al.,[83] but testing them against P. gallinaceum in chicks, obtained entirely different results (Table XV, column 3). In this test hydroquinine and cinchonine were equally active, quinidine and cinchonidine were somewhat less active, and quinine was least active. It is of interest that quinine was the most rapidly destroyed by chick liver and that cinchonidine and cinchonine were not metabolized by this tissue.

Formula I contains four asymmetric centers, viz., carbon atoms 3, 4, 8, and 9. In cinchonine and quinidine all four centers are dextrorotatory. In quinine and cinchonidine centers 8 and 9 are levo- and centers 3 and 4 dextrorotatory. It will be noticed (Table XV) that in the Roehl test each levorotatory alkaloid affords greater protection than its dextrorotatory isomer, but that in the chick test the reverse is true. The stereochemical configurations around $C^8$ and $C^9$ appear to be more important than those around $C^3$ and $C^4$. Thus epiquinine [$C^8(-)$, $C^9(+)$] and epiquinidine [$C^8(+)$, $C^9(-)$] are only slightly active or, according to Dirscherl and Thron,[86] inactive, but destruction of the asymmetry around $C^3$, as in $\alpha$- and $\beta$-isoquinine (II; R = $CH_3$), diminishes activity only slightly (quinine equivalents: 0.62 and 0.69 respectively).

Hydrogenation of the vinyl group in quinine and quinidine appears to increase activity, if anything, but not in cinchonine and cinchonidine (Table XV). Oxidation of the vinyl group to carboxyl, as in quitenine (I; R = $OCH_3$, R' = $CO_2H$), destroys antimalarial activity, but this is not surprising since the introduction of an acidic radical alters the

[85] Marshall, J. Pharmacol., **85**, 299 (1945).
[86] Dirscherl and Thron, Ann., **521**, 48 (1935).

physicochemical properties of the molecule profoundly. Activity can be recovered to some extent by esterification of quitenine, which restores the purely basic character of the molecule.[83, 87] Activity is not restored by conversion of quitenine into its amide or methylamide.[88] Oxidation of the vinyl group to an aldehyde group as in quininal (I; R = $OCH_3$, R' = CHO) scarcely affects activity, but the corresponding carbinol, quininol (I; R = $OCH_3$, R' = $CH_2OH$) is inactive. Ozonization of β-isoquinine gives a ketone (I; R = $OCH_3$, R' = $COCH_3$) which is still active.[89]

The significance of the 6'-methoxy group in the cinchona alkaloids is puzzling and has been the subject of much discussion. A methoxy group in the same relative position enters into the structure of many synthetic antimalarials and, as will be seen, has frequently been found to be an essential feature for high activity. There is also little doubt that the presence of the 6'-methoxy group in the cinchona alkaloids insures higher activity in human malaria, but in bird malaria anomalous results have been obtained. Thus, Marshall found cinchonidine more active than quinine, and cinchonine more active than quinidine, in *P. gallinaceum* infections of chicks (Table XV). Similarly Buttle et al.[90] found that the two apoquinines (II; R = H) were about equal to quinine in activity but their methylated products, α- and β-isoquinine, were less active (about two-thirds that of quinine).

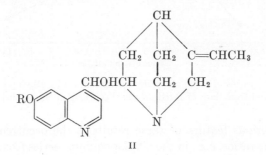

II

Buttle et al.[90] examined two interesting series of homologous *n*-alkyl ethers, viz., those of dihydrocupreine (I; R = OH, R' = $C_2H_5$) obtained by demethylating hydroquinine, and those of apoquinine (II; R = H) obtained by demethylating quinine. Their results, which are illustrated graphically in Fig. 6, were expressed in "quinine ratios." If $x$ is the mean delay in days for the appearance of parasites in the blood of

[87] Goodson, Henry, and MacFie, *Biochem. J.*, **24**, 874 (1930).
[88] Cohen and King, *Proc. Roy. Soc. (London)*, **B125**, 49 (1938).
[89] Work, *J. Chem. Soc.*, 334 (1944).
[90] Buttle, Henry, Soloman, Trevan, and Gibbs, *Biochem. J.*, **32**, 47 (1938).

control birds in the Roehl test, $y$ the mean delay for quinine, and $z$ that for the substance being tested, the quinine ratio for the last is given by $(z - x)/(y - x)$. No regularity can be detected in either series as a whole, but if they are divided into subseries according to whether the alkyl groups contain odd or even numbers of carbon atoms, a definite trend will be seen, the quinine ratio rising to a maximum and then falling as each subseries is ascended.

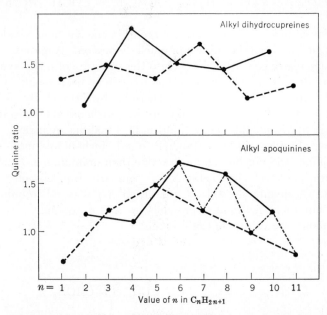

Fig. 6.    Quinine ratios of some alkyldihydrocuprienes and alkylapoquinines (constructed from data of Buttle et al.; [90] courtesy of the publisher).

Another curious feature of these results is the occurrence of alternating quinine ratios, e.g., in the alkylapoquinine series from the $n$-amyl to the $n$-undecyl member, ethers with an odd number of carbon atoms in the alkyl group being less active than those with an even number. This alternation is indicated by the dotted line in Fig. 6; it does not occur for ethers lower in the series than $n$-amyl. Alkyldihydrocupreines with an odd number of carbon atoms in the alkyl group also show alternating quinine ratios, but this is not true for the ethers with an even number of carbon atoms, or for the series as a whole except for the last four members, $n$-octyl to $n$-undecyl. Alternation has also been observed in the chemotherapeutic indices of some homologous synthetic antimalarials (see below).

The carbinol ($\rangle$CHOH) group at $C^9$ of the cinchona alkaloids is undoubtedly an essential feature for their antimalarial action, since changes in it lead to completely inactive substances. Replacement of the hydroxyl by chlorine ($\rangle$CHCl), reduction of the carbinol to methylene ($\rangle$CH$_2$) as in the desoxy alkaloids, or oxidation to carbonyl ($\rangle$CO) as in quininone, all produce inactive compounds.[84, 88] The ethyl carbonyl derivative ($\rangle$CHOCOC$_2$H$_5$) of quinine is the only active acyl derivative known.[88]

Isomeric changes in the cinchona alkaloids which involve the carbonyl group also destroy activity: thus the isoquinidines (III), in which the hydroxyl group has formed an ether linkage with the vinyl group, are almost inactive. The quinicines or quinatoxines (IV), in which the quinuclidine ring has been broken, are also inactive. When quinicine is reduced two dihydroquinicinols (V) are obtained, both of which are inactive, and so is the methylation product, $d$-N-methyldihydroquinicinol.[91]

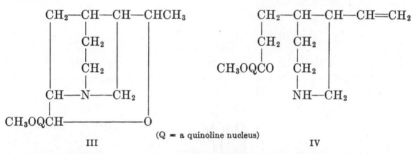

(Q = a quinoline nucleus)

The inactivity of quinicine and the dihydroquinicinols is remarkable. It cannot be attributed solely to the rupture of the quinuclidine ring structure since niquine, niquidine, and isoniquidine (VI) are all active (quinine equivalents 0.86, 1.45, and 1.05 respectively).[90] These compounds are obtained by the action of water, alkalies, or silver nitrate on the hydrogen chloride addition products of quinine and quinidine,

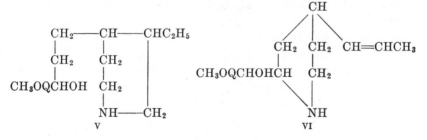

[91] Ainley and King, *Proc. Roy. Soc.* (*London*), **B125**, 60 (1938).

and their formation involves the loss of one carbon atom as formalde-hyde.[92]  Hydrogenation of niquine and niquidine reduces activity slightly; quinine equivalents: dihydroniquine 0.63, dihydroniquidine 1.06.

## Quinoline Derivatives

**Quinolylcarbinolamines.**  Although Giemsa and his colleagues,[84] by their investigation of the effect of the main cinchona alkaloids and their simple derivatives in the Roehl test, had made it clear in 1926 that the important structural features for antimalarial activity were the meth-oxyquinoline nucleus, the carbinol group, and the basic character, syn-thetical work was not at first directed to obtaining molecules embodying these three features.  Indeed, it was not until 1938 that Ainley and King [91] succeeded in synthesizing 6'-methoxyquinolyl-2-piperidylcarbi-nol (VII); two diastereoisomeric carbinols were obtained, both of which

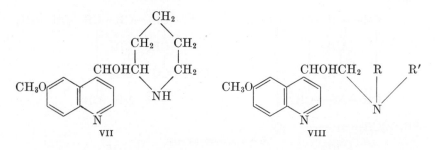

were active in the Roehl test, the more active stereoisomer being about half as active as quinine but just as toxic.  It will be noticed that they differ from niquine and niquidine (VI) in not containing the propylene chain.  Analogous carbinols without the 6'-methoxy group were inactive, and so were the N-methyl, N-propyl, and N-butyl derivatives of (VII). The last result is surprising, since these N-alkyl derivatives are so closely related in structure to quinine and the N-butyl compound differs in com-position from hydroquinine only by two additional hydrogen atoms.

The activity of VII and the inactivity of the dihydroquinicinols (V) suggested that the strongly basic center should not be separated by more than one carbon atom from the carbinol group.  King and Work [93] there-fore prepared a series of 6-methoxyquinolyl carbinolamines of the general formula VIII in which R and R' were n-alkyl groups.  Only three sub-stances were active, viz., those in which R = R' = butyl, amyl, or hexyl;

[92] Gibbs and Henry, *J. Chem. Soc.*, 240, 1294 (1939); Solomon, *ibid.*, 77 (1941); Butler, Renfrew, and Cretcher, *J. Am. Chem. Soc.*, **65**, 2038 (1943).

[93] King and Work, *J. Chem. Soc.*, 1307 (1940); 401 (1942).

higher and lower homologs were inactive, and so were compounds in which R and R' were different, e.g., R = butyl, R' = hexyl.

An interesting development of this work on quinolylcarbinolamines arose from the discovery that quinine is oxidized in animals to the corresponding carbostyryl, 2'-hydroxyquinine.[94] If compounds of type VIII are similarly oxidized, they might be rendered more stable in the animal by substituents in the 2-position of the quinoline ring. A considerable number of such 2-substituted compounds have been made;[95] some typical results of antimalarial tests are collected in Table XVI.[96] The most

TABLE XVI

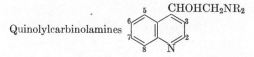

Quinolylcarbinolamines

| R | Other Substituents | SN | Quinine Equivalents | |
| | | | *P. galli-naceum* Chick | *P. lophurae* Duck |
|---|---|---|---|---|
| Butyl | 2-Phenyl | 10,509 | 0.1 | 0.3 |
| Butyl | 2-*p*-Chlorophenyl | 13,841 | 2 | 8 |
| Butyl | 2-*p*-Chlorophenyl-6-chloro | 14,273 | 4 | 20 |
| Hexyl | 2-*p*-Chlorophenyl-6-chloro | 14,934 | | 15 |
| Butyl | 2-*p*-Chlorophenyl-7-chloro | 13,710 | 20 | 20 |
| Hexyl | 2-*p*-Chlorophenyl-7-chloro | 12,711 | 6 | 15 |
| Butyl | 2-*p*-Chlorophenyl-8-chloro | 13,634 | 2 | 8 |
| Hexyl | 2-*p*-Chlorophenyl-8-chloro | 12,673 | 3 | 8 |
| Butyl | 2-*p*-Chlorophenyl-6,8-dichloro | 14,062 | 15 | 30 |
| Hexyl | 2-*p*-Chlorophenyl-6,8-dichloro | 12,678 | 8 | 8 |
| Butyl | 2-Phenyl-6-methoxy | 10,525 | 1 | 1 |
| Hexyl | 2-Phenyl-6-methoxy | 11,395 | | 1 |
| Butyl | 2-*p*-Chlorophenyl-6-methoxy | 14,285 | 4 | 20 |
| Butyl | 2-*p*-Chlorophenyl-6-methoxy-7-chloro | 14,883 | 15 | 15 |

effective substituent in position 2 appears to be *p*-chlorophenyl, and on the whole the dibutylamino compounds are more active than their dihexylamino analogs. Activity is enhanced by a 6-methoxy group in the quinoline nucleus (compare SN 10,525 with SN 10,509 and SN 14,285 with SN 13,841) and particularly by a 7-chlorosubstituent (SN 13,710 and SN 14,883). Substitution of chlorine at position 6 or 8 is less effec-

[94] Kelsey *et al.*, *J. Pharmacol.*, **80**, 391 (1944); Mead and Koepfli, *J. Biol. Chem.*, **154**, 507 (1944).

[95] Lutz *et al.*, *J. Am. Chem. Soc.*, **68**, 1813 (1946); Rapport *et al.*, *ibid.*, **68**, 2697 (1946).

[96] "Survey of Antimalarial Drugs, 1941–45," edited by Wiselogle, Edwards, Ann Arbor (1946).

tive, but disubstitution at the 6,8-positions is highly effective (SN 14,062). None of these compounds is more than two or three times as toxic to the mouse as quinine, but several of them are many times more active than quinine in avian malaria.

**8-Aminoquinoline Derivatives.** It was not the structure of quinine but an early observation of Ehrlich and Guttmann that methylene blue (IX) had some antimalarial activity which provided the starting point for the discovery of the first successful synthetic antimalarial. Schulemann, Schönhöfer, and Wingler found that higher activity was obtained by replacing one dimethylamino group of methylene blue by diethylaminoethylamino; the new substance (X) was, however, a dyestuff, and

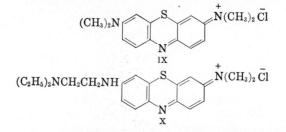

in order to avoid this undesirable character they introduced the diethylaminoethylamino group into the 8-position of quinoline and obtained an active substance. An extensive search was then made for the most effective basic side chain and for other substituents in the quinoline nucleus which might enhance activity. Ultimately 8-(4'-diethylamino-1'-methylbutylamino)-6-methoxyquinoline (XI) was selected as the most promising compound. It was called "plasmochin," the anglicized form being "plasmoquin"; its official name is "pamaquin." [97]

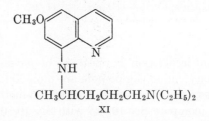

The discovery of pamaquin was made possible by Roehl's method of testing drugs against *P. relictum* in canaries, and it is a good example of the way in which chemotherapy advances when a method of testing new

[97] Schulemann, Schönhöfer, and Wingler, *Klin. Wochschr.*, **11**, 381 (1932). For an account of the steps leading to the discovery of plasmochin see Schulemann, *Proc. Roy. Soc. Med.*, **25**, 897 (1932).

substances in small animals under laboratory conditions becomes available. Pamaquin was soon found to be active in human malaria, and Roehl was the first to discover that it attacked the gametocytes of *P. falciparum*. That discovery showed that pamaquin was not so much a synthetic substitute for quinine as a new type of antimalarial with a different kind of chemotherapeutic action. The selective action of pamaquin on the gametocytes, especially of malignant tertian infections, and its relatively feeble action on the trophozoites of human malaria, have led to its use in combination with quinine, which exerts its action on the schizonts.

The discovery of pamaquin, the formula of which was published in 1928, naturally stimulated a great deal of new work on synthetic antimalarials in countries other than Germany, and, as the German workers never published their extensive researches in detail, most of our knowledge of how antimalarial activity varies with structure in the 8-aminoquinoline group derives from work led by Fourneau [98] in France, Barger and Robinson [99] in England, and Magidson [100] in Russia; and more recently from the work of the Antimalarial Survey [96] in the United States during 1941–1945. As a result of this work two other 8-aminoquinoline derivatives have been found to be of interest in the treatment of human malaria, viz., 8-(3'-diethylaminopropylamino)-6-methoxyquinoline (XII), called F710, plasmocide, and 8-(5'-isopropylaminoamylamino)-6-methoxyquinoline (XIII), named pentaquine (SN 13,276). Penta-

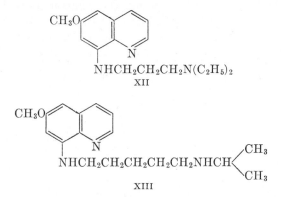

$$CH_3O$$

$$NHCH_2CH_2CH_2N(C_2H_5)_2$$
XII

$$CH_3O$$

$$NHCH_2CH_2CH_2CH_2CH_2NHCH \begin{cases} CH_3 \\ CH_3 \end{cases}$$
XIII

[98] Fourneau *et al.*, *Ann. inst. Pasteur*, **46**, 514 (1931); **50**, 731 (1933); Bovet and Demanche, *ibid.*, **51**, 528 (1933); Bovet, Benoit, and Altmann, *Bull. soc. path. exotique*, **27**, 236 (1934); Altmann, *Rec. trav. chim.*, **57**, 941 (1938).

[99] Barger and Robinson, *J. Chem. Soc.*, 2947 (1929); Robinson *et al.*, *ibid.*, 2952, 2959, 2965 (1929); 1356 (1930); 3089, 3096 (1931); 1467 (1933); 1264, 1267, 1322, 1520, 1534 (1934); 1143, 1421 (1935); 555, 557, 561 (1943).

[100] Magidson *et al.*, *Arch. Pharm.*, **271**, 359, 569 (1933); **272**, 74 (1934); **273**, 320 (1935); Kritschewski and Sternberg, *Z. Immunitätsforsch.*, **80**, 438 (1933).

quine is about half as toxic as pamaquin to laboratory animals but nearly as active in bird malaria. It was discovered in a systematic attempt by American workers to find a less toxic substitute for pamaquin for the treatment, in combination with quinine, of benign tertian malaria.

It will be noticed that both the compounds XII and XIII, like pamaquin, contain a 6-methoxy group, and it appears to be generally accepted that higher activity is displayed by 6-methoxy derivatives of 8-aminoquinoline than by other derivatives. Thus in the 8-diethylaminopropylaminoquinoline series Fourneau *et al.* found the following chemotherapeutic indices ($t/c$) with *Haemoproteus orizivorae* infections of rice finches.

| 6-Substituent: | H | OH | OCH$_3$ | OC$_2$H$_5$ | CH$_3$ |
|---|---|---|---|---|---|
| $t/c$: | 80 | 40 | 100 | 4 | Inactive |

In the same series Magidson *et al.* found that the chemotherapeutic index of the 6-methoxy compound was twice that of the 6-ethoxy in canaries. Robinson *et al.* also state that 6-methoxy compounds are usually more active than 6-ethoxy analogs. The 6-methoxy group is not, however, indispensable; a 6-hydroxy analog of pamaquin (Cilional or Certuna) is also active but has not been used much in human malaria.

The effect of the length of the basic side chain has been studied in some detail. Magidson *et al.* using *P. praecox* (syn. *relictum*) infections of siskins observed a curious alternation in the chemotherapeutic indices of the 8-diethylaminoalkyl-6-methoxyquinoline series. Their results are illustrated in Fig. 7. Unfortunately, the compounds with octa- and decamethylene chains were not made, but the alternation between the

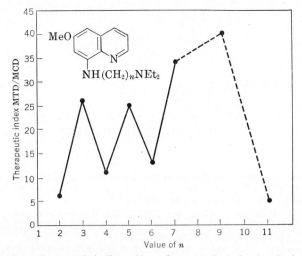

FIG. 7. The chemotherapeutic indices of homologous 8-diethylaminoalkyl-6-methoxyquinolines (after Magidson *et al.*; [100] courtesy of the publisher).

ethylene and heptamethylene compounds is striking. The chemotherapeutic index is so complex a measure of activity, depending as it does upon both the plasmodicidal activity of the drug and its toxicity to the host, that it is doubtful whether any theoretical implications can be

TABLE XVII

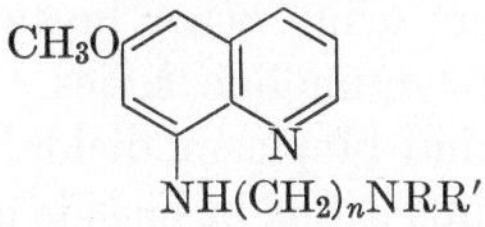

$NH(CH_2)_nNRR'$

| | | | Quinine Equivalents | | | | |
|---|---|---|---|---|---|---|---|
| | | | P. cathemerium | | P. gallinaceum | P. lophurae | |
| $n$ | NRR' | SN | Canary | Chick | Chick | Chick | Duck |
| 2 | $NH_2$ | 3,553 | | | 30 | | 3 |
| 3 | " | 1,452 | 30 | 10 | 60 | 80 | 3 |
| 4 | " | 3,883 | 20 | | 80 | | 10 |
| 5 | " | 3,851 | 2 | | 4 | | 0.8 |
| 6 | " | 12,352 | 8 | | 20 | 40 | 6 |
| 8 | " | 13,082 | | | 6 | | 3 |
| 10 | " | 5,692 | | | 0.6 | | <1 |
| 2 | $NHCH(CH_3)_2$ | 13,704 | | | 20 | | 80 |
| 3 | " | 3,559 | 15 | | 40 | | 80 |
| 4 | " | 13,275 | 20 | | 40 | | 40 |
| 5 | " | 13,276 | | | 80 | | 150 |
| 6 | " | 13,232 | | | 40 | | 80 |
| 2 | $N(C_2H_5)_2$ | 3,114 | | | 10 | | 40 |
| 3 | " | 3,115 | 20 | 60 | 20 | | 30 |
| 5 | " | 12,904 | • | | 30 | | 30 |
| 6 | " | 11,191 | 40 | 200 | 30 | | 100 |
| 7 | " | 13,576 | | | | | 40 |
| 9 | " | 167 | 8 | | 2 | | 3 |
| 10 | " | 12,892 | | | 0.6 | | 6 |
| 11 | " | 11,425 | | | 0.3 | | 8 |
| | $NHCH(CH_3)(CH_2)_3$-$N(C_2H_5)_2$ | 971 | 60 | 150 | 15 | 40 | 60 |

drawn from this alternation. It should be noted, however, that these 8-aminoquinoline derivatives are homologs of the general type $X(CH_2)_nY$ (where X and Y are functional groups), and alternation in physical properties (e.g., solubilities and melting points) is known to occur in homologous series in which a polymethylene chain separates two functional groups; aliphatic dibasic acids provide a classic example. It may well be that the alternation in chemotherapeutic indices observed by Magidson et al. is due to some alternating physical property of the series affecting either the toxicity or the plasmodicidal activity of the compounds or both. Such variables as absorption, distribution, metabolism, and excretion might also be influenced by physical properties. It must be admitted, however, that there is no evidence either to support or to refute these speculations.

Some indications of alternation in chemotherapeutic indices were also observed by other workers using other hosts but the same 8-diethyl-aminoalkylamino-6-methoxyquinoline series. Bovet and Demanche [98] also observed that the kind of plasmodicidal activity changed as the number of methylene groups in the basic side chain increased. Increase in the length of the side chain was accompanied by a reduction in the action on gametocytes and an increase in the action on trophozoites.

When antimalarial activities were measured as quinine equivalents in a variety of hosts no alternation was observed. Table XVII records a representative sample of homologous compounds which were included in the Antimalarial Survey.[96] Data for pamaquin are included for comparison. It will be noticed that the maximum quinine equivalent in any series appears to depend to some extent upon the nature of the terminal basic group. In the diethylamino series the hexamethylene chain appears to be optimal whereas in the isopropylamino series the pentamethylene chain is clearly the best.

The effect of branching of the side chain was studied by Fourneau et al.[98] In Haemoproteus infections of Java sparrows any branching of the chain was disadvantageous, as the following figures for chemotherapeutic indices show (all compounds contained a 6-methoxy group and a diethylamino terminal group).

| | | | |
|---|---|---|---|
| $CH_2CH_2CH_2$ | 100 | $CH_2CH_2CH_2CH_2CH_2$ | 150 |
| $CH(CH_3)CH_2$ | 10 | $CH(CH_3)CH_2CH_2CH_2$ | 40 |
| $CH_2CH_2CH_2CH_2$ | 20 | $CH_2C(CH_3)_2CH_2$ | 40 |
| $CH(CH_3)CH_2CH_2$ | 10 | $CH(C_2H_5)CH_2CH_2$ | 4 |

The same was true in P. relictum infections of siskins except for compounds with a 1'-methyl group which had a slightly higher index than the isomeric straight chain compounds.

| | |
|---|---|
| $NH—CH_2CH_2CH_2CH_2N(C_2H_5)_2$  10.6 | $NH—CH_2CH_2CH_2CH_2CH_2N(C_2H_5)_2$  25 |
| $NH—CH(CH_3)CH_2CH_2N(C_2H_5)_2$  25 | $NH—CH(CH_3)CH_2CH_2CH_2N(C_2H_5)_2$  40 |

The success of pamaquin and quinacrine (see below), which both contain the 1'-methylbutyl chain, suggests that branching to this extent is also of value in human malaria. Two other useful drugs of the 6-methoxy-8-aminoquinoline class which contain the same 1'-methylbutyl chain are isopentaquine, which has a terminal isopropylamino group, and primaquine, which has a terminal $NH_2$ group.

**4-Aminoquinoline Derivatives.** Shortly before the outbreak of war in 1939 German patents appeared dealing with 4-aminoquinoline derivatives as antimalarials, and when the Allied Forces occupied Tunis in

TABLE XVIII

$$CH_3CHCH_2CH_2CH_2N(C_2H_5)_2$$

| Substituents | SN | Quinine Equivalents | | | | | Toxicity Mouse |
|---|---|---|---|---|---|---|---|
| | | *P. cathemerium* | | *P. gall.* | *P. lophurae* | | |
| | | Canary | Duck | Chick | Chick | Duck | |
| 7-Fluoro | 13,986 | | | | | 10 | |
| 7-Chloro | 7,618 | 15 | 60 | 15 | 30 | 15 | 5 |
| 7-Bromo | 7,373 | 8 | 30 | 15 | | 15 | 4 |
| 7-Iodo | 7,620 | 6 | 10 | 10 | | 6 | 6 |
| 3-Methyl-7-fluoro | 8,797 | | 2 | 2 | | 1 | 1.5 |
| 3-Methyl-7-chloro | 6,911 | 3 | 20 | 4 | 6 | 6 | 8 |
| 3-Methyl-7-bromo | 7,284 | 4 | 30 | 3 | | 6 | |
| 3-Methyl-7-iodo | 9,904 | | | 1 | | 3 | 3 |
| 2-Methyl-7-chloro | 7,135 | 2 | 15 | 1.5 | 6 | 6 | 6 |
| 2-Phenyl-7-chloro | 10,556 | | | <0.8 | | <0.4 | |
| 6-Methoxy | 3,294 | 1.5 | 4 | 2 | 2 | 2 | 3 |
| 7-Methoxy | 11,421 | | | 2 | | 2 | 3 |
| None | 6,732 | | 4 | 1 | | 1 | |

1943 they found a German drug which had been sent there to be tested as an antimalarial agent. It was known as Sontoquin and was soon found to be 4-(4'-diethylamino-1'-methylbutylamino)-7-chloro-3-methyl-quinoline (XIV; R = CH₃).

$$CH_3CHCH_2CH_2CH_2N(C_2H_5)_2$$

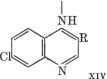

XIV

A large number of compounds of this type were prepared and tested under the auspices of the Antimalarial Survey, particular attention being paid to the nature of the side chain, of the alkyl groups in the terminal basic group, and of the substituents in the quinoline nucleus. The most promising compound appeared to be one differing from Sontoquin only in the absence of the 3-methyl group, viz., XIV, R = H, which was called chloroquine. The choice of chloroquine was fully justified in large-scale trials in human malaria, and at the end of the war it bade fair to replace quinacrine, on which, owing to the lack of quinine, the Allied Forces had previously relied. It cures malignant tertian malaria, but relapses occur after its use in benign tertian malaria.

The outstanding feature of the 4-aminoquinoline series is the predominant influence of a 7-chloro (or -bromo) substituent. Chlorine is far more effective in increasing antimalarial activity at position 7 than it is at positions 5, 6, or 8. Chlorine at position 7 is also more efficacious than bromine, iodine, or fluorine at the same position (Table XVIII).[96] No other substituent rivals chlorine in enhancing antimalarial activity; neither a 6- nor a 7-methoxy group increases the activity appreciably. The introduction of a 3-methyl group into 7-halo derivatives decreases activity (Table XVIII).

A considerable number of 7-chloro compounds with different basic side chains had relatively high activity. Table XIX gives results for some simple chains.[96] As far as evidence is available the introduction of a 1'-methyl group appears to be advantageous. The diethylamino group appears to be the most satisfactory terminal basic group, but relatively high activity also occurs in many compounds containing secondary amino groups attached to a trimethylene chain.

An interesting development of the chloroquine type was the attachment of the basic chain to the 4-amino group through a phenolic nucleus as in XV. Only 7-chloro and 7-bromo compounds had relatively high activity. The compound XV, in which R = $C_2H_5$, had about the same

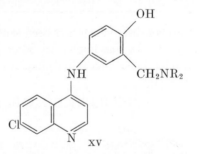

activity as chloroquine on *P. gallinaceum* and *P. lophurae* infections but was less active on *P. cathemerium*;[96] this compound is called Camoquin.

TABLE XIX

| Nature of R | SN | Quinine Equivalents | | | | | Toxicity Mouse |
|---|---|---|---|---|---|---|---|
| | | P. cathemerium | | P. gallinaceum | P. lophurae | | |
| | | Canary | Duck | Chick | Chick | Duck | |
| $(CH_2)_2N(C_2H_5)_2$ | 9,551 | 3 | 6 | 10 | 15 | 3 | 3 |
| $(CH_2)_3N(C_2H_5)_2$ | 9,584 | 8 | 30 | 30 | 30 | 6 | 5 |
| $(CH_2)_4N(C_2H_5)_2$ | 8,136 | 6 | 30 | 15 | 30 | 15 | 6 |
| $(CH_2)_6N(C_2H_5)_2$ | | | | 6 | | 3 | 10 |
| $CH(CH_3)(CH_2)_3N(C_2H_5)_2$ | 7,618 | 15 | 60 | 15 | 30 | 15 | 5 |
| $CH(CH_3)(CH_2)_4N(C_2H_5)_2$ | 10,961 | | | 15 | | 15 | 6 |

## Acridine Derivatives

Six years after the discovery of pamaquin Kikuth [101] announced the synthesis by Mauss and Mietzsch [102] of a new antimalarial compound. It was called Atebrin. Its official names are quinacrine U.S.P. and mepacrine B.P. It is 9-(4'-diethylamino-1'-methylbutylamino)-2-methoxy-6-chloroacridine (XVI). It contains a methoxy group in the same posi-

$$CH_3CHCH_2CH_2CH_2N(C_2H_5)_2$$

XVI

tion relative to the ring N-atom as in pamaquin and quinine and the same basic side chain as pamaquin and chloroquine; in fact, it can be regarded as chloroquine with a methoxybenzene ring fused to the quino-

[101] Kikuth, *Deut. med. Wochschr.*, **58**, 530 (1932).
[102] Mauss and Mietzsch, *Klin. Wochschr.*, **12**, 1276 (1933).

line ring in the 2,3-positions.  A comparison of the quinine equivalents of these three closely related synthetic drugs is interesting, and Table XX gives data taken from the Antimalarial Survey.[96]  As is at once

TABLE XX

| Drug | SN | Quinine Equivalents | | | | | Toxicity | |
|------|----|---------------------|---|---|---|---|----------|---|
| | | P. cathemerium | P. gall. | P. lophurae | | | | |
| | | Canary | Duck | Chick | Chick | Duck | Mouse | Rat |
| Pamaquin | 971 | 60 | 150 | 15 | 40 | 60 | | |
| Chloroquine | 7618 | 15 | 60 | 15 | 30 | 15 | 5 | 10 |
| Quinacrine | 390 | 4 | 15 | 2 | 1.5 | 3 | 4 | 10 |

apparent, quinacrine is by far the least active antimalarial of the three, being at best only four times as active as quinine.  This was indeed Kikuth's figure in the Roehl test.  It does not, of course, follow that the same ratios would apply for human malaria.  The great advantage of quinacrine, before the discovery of chloroquine, was that it was less toxic than pamaquin.  During the war the effect of prolonged administration of quinacrine to man was studied on a large scale, and apart from the yellow staining of the skin no adverse effects were discovered.[103]  Goodwin [104] has compared the action of quinacrine, pamaquin, and chloroquine on the P. berghei infection of the mouse.  His results (Table XXI)

TABLE XXI

| Drug | Quinine Equivalents | |
|------|---------------------|---|
| | P. gallinaceum Chick | P. berghei Mouse |
| Quinacrine | 2 | 7.8 |
| Pamaquin | 18 | 2 |
| Chloroquine | 13 | 13 |

are of great interest, since in this mammalian infection quinacrine proved to be more active than pamaquin and about half as active as chloroquine.

103 Maegraith et al., Ann. Trop. Med. Parasitol., 39, 232 (1946).
104 Goodwin, Nature, 164, 1133 (1949).

Quinacrine differs from pamaquin in having no action upon the gametocytes. Its effect, like that of quinine, is exerted on the schizonts. Its action is suppressive, but it can prevent attacks of malaria in infected persons, as experimental work during the war proved,[105] provided that 0.1 g. is taken daily. It was used on a very large scale during the war. It cured malignant tertian malaria and relapses were rare, but relapses were common after attacks of benign tertian malaria had been suppressed by its use.

Much of our information on the effects of varying the structure of quinacrine is due to Magidson et al.,[106] whose compounds were tested on P. praecox (syn. relictum) infections of siskins. The 6-chloro substituent appears to play an important part. Its absence leads to inactive compounds, and even its removal to position 7 reduces the chemotherapeutic index considerably. The introduction of a 7-chloro substituent into quinacrine also reduces the index (Table XXII). A 7-nitro group is

TABLE XXII

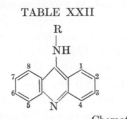

| Substituents | Chemotherapeutic Index | |
| --- | --- | --- |
|  | R = CH(CH₃)-$(CH_2)_3N(C_2H_5)_2$ | R = $(CH_2)_3$-$N(C_2H_5)_2$ |
| 2-Methoxy | 0 | 0 |
| 2-Methoxy-6-chloro | 15 | 15 |
| 2-Methoxy-7-chloro | 2 | 2 |
| 2-Methoxy-6,7-dichloro | 6 | .... |
| 2-Methoxy-7-nitro | 4 | 2.5 |
| 2-Methoxy-6-cyano | 23 | 10 |
| 2-Ethoxy-6-chloro | .. | 7.5 |
| 2-Methyl-6-chloro | .. | 6 |

more efficient than 7-chloro, and the 6-chloro substituent can be replaced by a 6-cyano group without serious loss of activity. A 2-ethoxy group leads to greater toxicity and a lower index than the 2-methoxy group. Whereas in the 8-aminoquinoline series replacement of the 6-methoxy group by a 6-methyl group destroys activity, the 2-methyl analog of quinacrine is still active.

[105] Fairley, Trans. Roy. Soc. Trop. Med. Hyg., **38**, 311 (1945).

[106] Magidson et al., Ber., **69B**, 396, 537 (1936); Krichevskii et al., J. Microbiol. Epidemiol. Immunobiol. (U.S.S.R.), **14**, 642 (1935) [C. A., **30**, 4218 (1936)]; Krichevskii et al., Giorn. batter., **13**, 685 (1934) [C. A., **31**, 3208 (1937)].

The effect of increasing the length of an unbranched basic side chain from $C_2$ to $C_6$ is to increase the chemotherapeutic index up to a maximum for the $C_4$ chain. Branching of the carbon chain to the extent of a 1'-methyl group decreases the index for a butyl chain, more than doubles it for an amyl chain, and has no effect with a hexyl chain.

### Pyrimidine and Biguanide Derivatives

In 1942 a group of workers in England led by Curd, Davey, and Rose [107] began to investigate the possibility of using the pyrimidine nucleus, instead of the conventional quinoline and acridine nuclei, as a basic unit upon which antimalarial drugs might be built. The quinoline and acridine nuclei are foreign to the animal body, but the pyrimidine nucleus is one of the most important heterocyclic systems occurring in it, and consequently the host might be expected to tolerate pyrimidine drugs more readily and, in virtue of existing enzyme systems, to metabolize and excrete them more easily. All compounds were tested in the first instance against *P. gallinaceum* infections of chicks by the method already described (p. 452).

Schönhöfer [108] had suggested that the antimalarial action of quinacrine might be connected with the possibility of tautomerism of the type XVIIa ⇌ XVIIb, and it was noted that the attachment of a similar basic side chain at the 4-position of the pyrimidine ring would permit

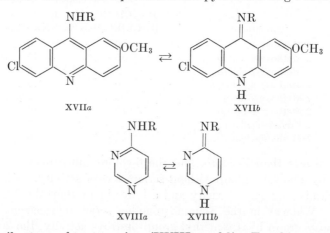

of a similar type of tautomerism (XVIIIa and b). For this reason compounds of type XIX were prepared in which a basic side chain was at-

[107] For an interesting account of the development of this work, up to the discovery of proguanil, see Curd, Davey, and Rose, *Ann. Trop. Med. Parasitol.*, **39**, 139, 157, 208 (1945).
[108] Schönhöfer, *Z. physiol. Chem.*, **274**, 1 (1942).

tached to the pyrimidine ring and R was *p*-chloro or *m*- or *p*-methoxy, but these were inactive.

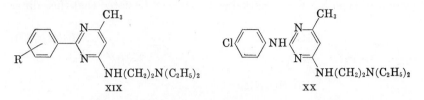

XIX

XX

The next stage was to introduce an imino group between the benzene and pyrimidine nuclei, and here activity was immediately encountered in the compound M2666 (XX). In compounds of this type (XXI) the substituent R could be Cl, Br, $NO_2$, or CN. Methoxy and ethoxy were less advantageous, and the unsubstituted compound (R = H) was inactive. Chlorine appeared to be the most advantageous substituent, and *para*-chloro was better than *ortho* or *meta*. In *p*-chloro compounds simple basic side chains with two or three methylene groups were best, and small alkyl groups on the terminal N atom like methyl or ethyl were better than larger alkyl groups or ring structures. The most active member of the series was M3711 (XXI; R = Cl, $n = 3$, $R' = CH_3$).[109]

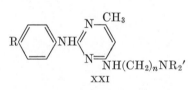

XXI

Further elaboration of type XXI by fusion of a benzene ring either to the phenyl nucleus or to the pyrimidine nucleus led to equally active or more active compounds. Thus M3502 (XXII) which contains a naphthalene nucleus was more active than M2666, and M3666 (XXIII) which contains a quinazoline nucleus was as active as M2666.[110]

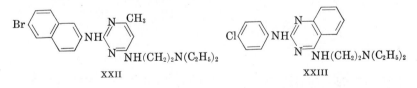

XXII                                    XXIII

Activity was retained in compounds in which the anilino and basic side-chain groups were interchanged, i.e., in 4-*p*-chloroanilino-2-dialkyl-

[109] Curd and Rose, *J. Chem. Soc.*, 343, 351 (1946).
[110] Curd, Raison, and Rose, *ibid.*, 366 (1946); Curd, Landquist, and Rose, *ibid.*, 775 (1947).

aminoalkylaminopyrimidines (XXIV) [111] but not in 4-*p*-chloroanilino-6-dialkylaminoalkylaminopyrimidines (XXV).[112]  The inactivity of compounds of type XXV is remarkable, but it may be noted that they differ

XXIV                                                    XXV

from compounds of types XXI and XXIV in the variety of tautomeric possibilities open to them.  It will be obvious that in all three types the NH of the anilino group can enter into prototropic change with either of the nitrogen atoms of the pyrimidine ring.  So, also, can the NH of the basic side chain; but whereas in types XXI and XXIV both NH groups can simultaneously undergo prototropic change of this type with the production of the tautomers XXVI and XXVII, this is impossible in compounds of type XXV because movement of either the anilino or the basic side-chain hydrogen atom into the pyrimidine nucleus, as in XXVIII*a* and *b*, converts the prototropic system

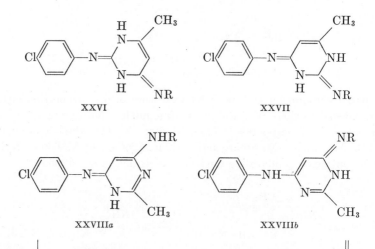

XXVI                                          XXVII

XXVIII*a*                                       XXVIII*b*

—NH—C=N— in the other part of the molecule into —NH—C—N=, which cannot undergo prototropic change.

Another development of the 2-anilino-4-dialkylaminoalkylaminopyrimidine class investigated was the replacement of the anilino group

[111] Curd, Rose, *et al.*, *ibid.*, 370 (1946).
[112] Basford, Curd, and Rose, *ibid.*, 713 (1946).

by a phenylguanidino group as in **XXIX**.[113]  This type retains the possibilities of tautomeric change inherent in types **XXI** and **XXIV** and possesses additional possibilities by virtue of the guanidino group.  Some

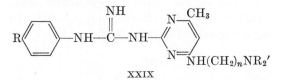

XXIX

of these compounds were more active than the anilino analogs.  In particular, not only was compound M3349 (**XXIX**; R = Cl, $n$ = 2, R' = $C_2H_5$) more active than M2666 against *P. gallinaceum*, but also a clinical trial showed that it was active in all three types of human malaria.  M3349, therefore, was a definite advance on M2666, which had given negative results in a clinical trial.

In compounds of type **XXIX**, high activity was shown when R was Cl, F, CN, or $NO_2$; *p*-bromo compounds were less active.  When R was Cl the best side chain was diethylaminoethylamino ($n$ = 2, R' = $C_2H_5$).

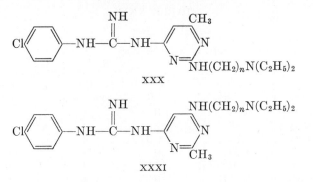

XXX

XXXI

As in the anilino series, interchanging the positions of the phenylguanidino group and the basic side chain as in **XXX** did not abolish activity; but unlike the anilino series some 4-*p*-chlorophenylguanidino-6-dialkylaminoalkylaminopyrimidines were active, e.g., **XXXI**; $n$ = 2 or 3.

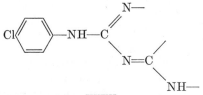

XXXII

[113] Curd, Rose, *et al.*, *ibid.*, 362 (1946); 574, 586 (1948).

At this stage of the work the possibility of simplifying the molecular types under investigation was considered.[114] All the more active pyrimidines were salts of strong bases and contained an alternating arrangement of nitrogen and carbon atoms. Thus M2666 contains the unit XXXII, and M3349 the more extended unit XXXIII, which includes a biguanide residue (enclosed within the dotted lines). Attachment of

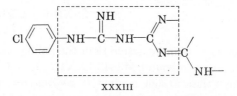

XXXIII

a dialkylaminoalkyl group to the terminal nitrogen ($N^5$) of $p$-chlorophenylbiguanide led to inactive compounds, but simple alkyl groups in this position converted the inactive $p$-chlorophenylbiguanide into a series of highly active antimalarials. The most effective group was isopropyl; Table XXIII illustrates the way in which activity varies in

TABLE XXIII

Cl—C6H4—NH—C(=NH)—NH—C(=NH)—N(R)(R')    XXXIV

| No. | R | R' | Dose mg./50 g. | Activity * |
|---|---|---|---|---|
| 3327 | H | H | 6 | − |
| 5093 | CH₃ | H | 4 | − |
| 4134 | CH₃ | CH₃ | 4 | − |
| 4967 | C₂H₅ | H | 1 | ++ |
| 3926 | C₂H₅ | C₂H₅ | 4 | ++ |
| 4887 | $n$-C₃H₇ | H | 1 | +++ |
| 4888 | $iso$-C₃H₇ | H | 0.5 | +++ |
| 4329 | $n$-C₃H₇ | CH₃ | 2 | ++ |
| 4430 | $iso$-C₃H₇ | CH₃ | 0.8 | +++ |
| 4968 | Allyl | H | 1 | ++ |
| 4565 | $n$-C₄H₉ | H | 4 | ++ |
| 4567 | $iso$-C₄H₉ | H | 16 | + |
| 4568 | $tert$-C₄H₉ | H | 2 | ++ |

* Inactive, −; slight, +; marked, ++; very high, +++.

$N^1$-$p$-chlorophenylbiguanides with the nature of the alkyl group or groups attached to $N^5$. It will be noticed that the two methyl derivatives are inactive, but marked activity occurs with the monoethyl de-

[114] Curd and Rose, *ibid.*, 729 (1946).

rivative.  The highest activity appears to be associated with a three-carbon alkyl group, the butyl derivatives being much less active.

The most active member of the series was $N^1$-$p$-chlorophenyl-$N^5$-isopropylbiguanide [XXXIV; NRR' = NHCH(CH$_3$)$_2$], which was registered as Paludrine (Proguanil B.P.).  It is one of the most interesting antimalarial drugs, because it is of an entirely new type and combines high activity against both erythrocytic and exoerythrocytic forms of plasmodia.  The next most active member of the series was the $N^5$-methyl derivative of proguanil, No. 4430 (Table XXIII).

Both proguanil and 4430 were studied in a variety of types of avian malaria and compared with quinine, quinacrine, and sulfonamides; Table XXIV records some of the results.[115]  Against infections produced

TABLE XXIV

| Test | Drug | P. cathe-merium<br>Canary | P. galli-naceum<br>Chick | P. lophurae<br>Chick | P. relictum<br>Canary |
|---|---|---|---|---|---|
| Causal prophylactic | Quinine | − | − | − | − |
| action against | Quinacrine | − | − | − | − |
| sporozoite- | Sulfonamides | − | + | − | − |
| induced | 4430 | − | ++ | − | − |
| infections | Proguanil | + | +++ | +? | + |
| | | | | | |
| Therapeutic test | Quinine | + | ++ | ++ | + |
| against blood | Quinacrine | ++ | ++ | ++ | ++ |
| infections | Sulfonamides | − | + | + | − |
| | 4430 | − | +++ | +++ | .... |
| | Proguanil | ++ | ++++ | ++++ | ++ |

Symbols indicate inactivity (−) to very high activity (++++).

by injected blood from heavily infected birds proguanil was at least as effective as quinine and quinacrine, and more so in *P. gallinaceum* and *P. lophurae* infections in chicks, as judged by the parasitemia test.  It was not so active as pamaquin, which is the most potent drug known in avian malaria.  Like sulfadiazine, proguanil was also a causal prophylactic in sporozoite-induced infections of *P. gallinaceum*.  Indeed, it was found to have a more intense action on the exoerythrocytic forms of this parasite than sulfadiazine.  Unlike sulfadiazine and 4430 it was also a causal prophylactic in infections with *P. relictum*, *P. cathemerium*, and probably with *P. lophurae*.

Proguanil has a remarkably low toxicity to chicks (LD50 oral, 400–600 mg./kg.) but is more toxic to mice and rats, in which it produces de-

[115] Curd, Davey, and Rose, *Ann. Trop. Med. Parasitol.*, **39**, 208 (1945).

layed deaths.[116]  Curiously enough, man appears to resemble the chick more than the mouse in being very little susceptible to its toxic effects, and doses of the order of 0.6 g. twice daily can be given with safety.

In human beings proguanil cures malignant tertian malaria, and relapses do not occur.  It removes clinical symptoms of benign tertian malaria but does not appear to prevent relapses.  Relapses can probably be prevented by a combination of proguanil and pamaquin.  It has the disadvantage that it can give rise to resistant forms of plasmodia; thus, strains of *P. gallinaceum*, maintained by serial blood inoculation in chicks, rapidly develop high resistance to proguanil when repeatedly exposed to subeffective doses of it.[116a]  It appears to be the erythrocytic forms of *P. gallinaceum* that develop resistance, since the development of resistance has so far failed in latent infections, in which the parasites are present mainly as exoerythrocytic forms.[116b]  Resistant strains of *P. vivax* and *P. falciparum* have also been produced in man.[116c]  The significance of these findings for the treatment of large populations in malarial districts with proguanil is still a matter of dispute among malariologists.

An even more active, but more toxic, derivative of proguanil has been described, viz., M5943 or $N^1$-3,4-dichlorophenyl-$N^5$-isopropylbiguanide (XXXV).[117]  It was, however, inactive against a proguanil-resistant strain of *P. gallinaceum*.

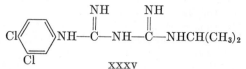

XXXV

The mechanism of action of proguanil is unknown.  Evidence is accumulating which indicates that its antimalarial action is not due to proguanil itself but to some metabolite formed from it in the host.  Proguanil has no antiplasmodial action on cultures of the exoerythrocytic forms of *P. gallinaceum* or on the endoerythrocytic forms of *P. cynomolgi* in concentrations comparable with those commonly reached in the blood during human therapy.  Serum from a fowl or monkey which has been recently treated with proguanil does, however, prevent the development of the parasites; cultures of *P. gallinaceum* are destroyed.  Incubation of proguanil with minced liver also produces material with a similar pro-

[116] Butler, Davey, and Spinks, *Brit. J. Pharmacol.*, **2**, 181 (1947).

[116a] Williamson and Lourie, *Ann. Trop. Med. Parasitol.*, **41**, 278 (1947).

[116b] Rollo, Williamson, and Lourie, *ibid.*, **42**, 241 (1948).

[116c] Seaton and Lourie, *Lancet*, **256**, 394 (1949); Adams and Seaton, *Trans. Roy. Soc. Trop. Med. Hyg.*, **42**, 314 (1949).

[117] Curd, Davey, Hendry, and Rose, *Brit. J. Pharmacol.*, **5**, 438 (1950).

nounced antiplasmodial action *in vitro*.   These results suggest that proguanil itself is not active against plasmodia but that it can be modified
in the body or by liver cells with the production of an actively plasmodicidal substance.[118]

Three metabolites of proguanil have been isolated: N-*p*-chlorophenyl-
diguanide, 4-amino-2-*p*-chloroanilino-1,6-dihydro-6,6-dimethyl-1,3,5-tri-
azine (XXXVa),[118a] both of which are inactive, and 1-*p*-chlorophenyl-2,
4-diamino-1,6-dihydro-6,6-dimethyl-1,3,5-triazine (XXXVb), which is
about ten times as active as proguanil in *P. gallinaceum* infections of
chicks.[118b]   The 3,4-dichlorophenyl analog of XXXVb, which might be
expected to be a metabolite of XXXV, is even more active, being nearly
a hundred times as effective as proguanil in *P. gallinaceum* infections of
chicks.   The active metabolite XXXVb differs in composition from
proguanil in containing two hydrogen atoms less; it is readily converted
by heating alone or in alkaline aqueous solution into the inactive compound XXXVa.

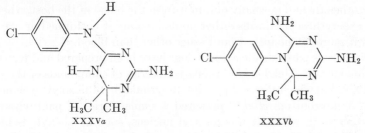

XXXVa                    XXXVb

The discovery of proguanil diverted attention from pyrimidine derivatives as potential antimalarial drugs, but Falco *et al.*[119] have reported
several derivatives of 2,4-diaminopyrimidine as powerful antimalarials.
The highest activity was shown by 2,4-diamino-5-*p*-chlorophenyl-
6-ethylpyrimidine (XXXVI), which was 60 times as active as proguanil

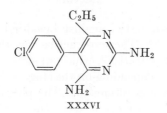

XXXVI

[118] Hawking and Perry, *ibid.*, **3**, 320 (1948); cf. Madinaveitia and Raventos, *ibid.*, **4**,
81 (1949).

[118a] Crounse, *J. Org. Chem.*, **16**, 492 (1951).

[118b] Carrington *et al.*, *Nature*, **168**, 1080 (1951).

[119] Falco *et al.*, *Brit. J. Pharmacol.*, **6**, 185 (1951); *J. Am. Chem. Soc.*, **73**, 3753, 3758
(1951); Russell and Hitchings, *ibid.*, **73**, 3763 (1951).

against *P. gallinaceum* in chicks and 200 times as active against *P. berghei* in mice. Moreover, 2,4-diaminopyrimidine derivatives of this type retain activity against proguanil-resistant strains of *P. gallinaceum* and *P. berghei*, and, consequently, clinical trials of the compound XXXVI will be awaited with interest. The structural resemblance between the pyrimidine derivative XXXVI and the triazine metabolite XXXV*b* of proguanil is worthy of notice.

### Pantothenic Acid Analogs as Antimalarials

Pantothenic acid appears to be a growth factor for the erythrocytic forms of plasmodia. Thus when blood from chicks infected with *P. gallinaceum* is inoculated into pantothenate-deficient chicks no parasitemia develops as it does in normal chicks. Infections induced by sporozoites, e.g., by mosquito bites, are, however, not suppressed in the same way. Consequently, it appears that the erythrocytic forms require preformed pantothenate and normally obtain it from the blood of the host, whereas the exoerythrocytic forms either do not require it preformed or can obtain it more abundantly from tissues other than blood.[120]

Numerous pantothenic acid analogs have been prepared and tested as antimalarials. Mead et al.[121] prepared a series of compounds of the type XXXVII in which R was 2-pyridyl, 2-pyrimidyl, 2-thiazolyl, cyclohexyl, etc.; Winterbottom et al.[122] prepared a similar series of pantoyltaurine derivatives in which R was an aryl nucleus, such as phenyl, 4-chlorophenyl, *p*-tolyl, or naphthyl. Many of these compounds had anti-

$$\text{HOCH}_2\text{CMe}_2\text{CHOHCONHCH}_2\text{CH}_2\text{SO}_2\text{NHR}$$
XXXVII

$$\text{HOCH}_2\text{CMe}_2\text{CHOHCONHCH}_2\text{CH}_2\text{R}$$
XXXVIII

malarial activity when tested against blood-induced infections of *P. gallinaceum* in chicks.[120] The most active was the 4-chlorophenyl derivative XXXVII, R = $C_6H_4Cl$, which was from four to twelve times as effective as quinine, depending on the stage of infection at which the extent of parasitemia was estimated. The phenyl and *p*-tolyl derivatives were among the next most active. The therapeutic effect of these pantoyltaurine derivatives was annulled by the administration of additional pantothenate.

---

[120] Brackett, Waletzky, and Baker, *J. Parasitol.*, **32**, 453 (1946).

[121] Mead et al., *J. Biol. Chem.*, **163**, 465 (1946).

[122] Winterbottom et al., *J. Am. Chem. Soc.*, **69**, 1393 (1947).

Senear, Rapport, and Koepfli [123] prepared a series of compounds of type XXXVIII in which R was —$SC_6H_5$, —$SO_2C_6H_5$, or the corresponding 4-chloro derivatives. Here again the $p$-chlorophenyl sulfide and sulfone were the most active. It is curious that all the most active of these pantothenic acid analogs should contain the $p$-chlorophenyl group, since they are remote in structure from the $p$-chlorophenyl-biguanides and from antimalarials like chloroquine and quinacrine which also contain a Cl substituent *para* to the point of attachment of the basic side chain.

The foregoing account of antimalarial drugs does not exhaust the multiplicity of chemical types that have been tested for antimalarial activity, nor does it even mention all the types that have been found to possess activity in some degree. The empirical character of chemotherapeutic investigation is well illustrated by the fact that the testing of several thousand synthetic compounds has resulted in providing the clinician with at least seven useful drugs besides quinine, viz., quinacrine, chloroquine, proguanil, camoquin (XV),[123a] pentaquine, isopentaquine, and primaquine.[123b] The first three of these cure malignant tertian malaria but cannot be relied upon to prevent relapses of benign tertian malaria. Camoquin and pentaquine, in combination with quinine, appear to be the most useful drugs in suppressing and preventing relapses of benign tertian malaria. It is probably too much to hope that the successful treatment or prophylaxis of malaria can ever be achieved by a single drug, but the organic chemist has reason to be proud of the help which he has already given to the clinician in dealing with this widespread scourge of mankind.

## CHEMOTHERAPY OF TRYPANOSOMIASIS

Trypanosomiasis is the name given to a group of diseases caused by parasitic protozoal organisms called trypanosomes (genus *Trypanosoma*). These parasites occur in fish, amphibians, reptiles, birds, and mammals. They are transmitted to animals by insects, although *Trypanosoma equiperdum*, which causes a disease called dourine in horses, is normally transmitted by infected animals during coitus. In some animals trypanosomes are non-pathogenic, but all those that invade man are pathogenic. The most widespread form of trypanosomiasis in man is African sleeping sickness, which is caused by *T. gambiense* (west central and east Africa) and by *T. rhodesiense* (east Africa, north and south Rhodesia,

---

[123] Senear, Rapport, and Koepfli, *J. Biol. Chem.*, **167**, 229 (1947).

[123a] Burckhalter *et al.*, *J. Am. Chem. Soc.*, **68**, 1894 (1946); *ibid.*, **70**, 1363 (1948). See also Burckhalter, *Trans. Kansas Acad. Sci.*, **53**, 433 (1950).

[123b] Edgcomb *et al.*, *J. Natl. Malaria Soc.*, **9**, 285 (1950).

Bechuanaland, etc.).  The insect vector in this disease is the tsetse fly (*Glossina* spp.), and the natural reservoir for the parasites is usually said to be the antelope and other game animals.  The disease is characterized by a preliminary period of malaise and fever and later, as the trypanosomes invade the cerebrospinal fluid and the brain, by meningoencephalitis.  The untreated disease is usually fatal.  A form of trypanosomiasis, called Chagas's disease, also occurs in South America; it is caused by *T. cruzi*, which is transmitted by bedbugs.

Horses and cattle in Africa are also subject to trypanosomiasis.  The two chief trypanosomes implicated are *T. brucei*, which causes a fatal disease called "nagana" but is non-infective to man, and *T. congolense*. Infection of cattle with the latter is very widespread, and large areas of tropical Africa are held back from full development because of it. Other important trypanosomes which occur in Africa and elsewhere are *T. evansi*, *T. equinum*, *T. equiperdum*, *T. vivax*, and *T. simiae*.

Experimental work on the chemotherapy of trypanosomiasis usually relies on infections in mice, which can be produced by inoculating healthy mice with blood from an infected animal.  Mice are susceptible to a wide range of *Trypanosoma* species, though not to all, and a particular strain of trypanosomes can be maintained for many years by passage through successive generations of mice.  Continued passage through mice often produces changes in the sensitivity of a particular strain to drugs.  Thus wild strains of *T. rhodesiense* are not normally sensitive to arsenical drugs, but after prolonged passage through mice they may become very sensitive.  Since trypanosomes can be readily detected microscopically in blood, it is easy to discover whether a drug has eliminated an infection and to detect relapses.  Mice are usually regarded as cured if the blood remains free from trypanosomes for 30 or more days.

Trypanosomiasis in mice is a blood infection, and, consequently, before a new drug is used in human sleeping sickness, it is advisable to test it on an infected animal in which trypanosomes invade the extravascular tissues and particularly the brain.  Chronic infections of rabbits provide the most convenient means of investigating the ability of a trypanocidal drug to penetrate into the deeper tissues and the brain.

In 1930 Yorke and Murgatroyd devised a method of keeping trypanosomes alive *in vitro* for about 24 hours at 37°, and since then a considerable amount of work has been done on trypanosomes *in vitro*.  Trypanosomes are remarkably active organisms, and loss of motility provides an excellent criterion of trypanocidal action.  Loss of infectivity, which may occur before loss of motility, can also be used as a criterion of the toxic effect of a drug on trypanosomes.

The early development of trypanocidal drugs was due to Ehrlich, who investigated both dyes and arsenical drugs; something has already been said about this early work in the introductory section. In this section only purely organic compounds with trypanocidal activity will be considered. It will be convenient to treat arsenical drugs, which have been used in a number of other diseases, as a class by themselves.

## Dyes as Trypanocidal Agents

Ehrlich discovered that certain *bis*-azo dyes had some trypanocidal activity, particularly trypan red (I), obtained by coupling tetrazotized benzidine with 2-aminonaphthalene-3,6-disulfonic acid, and trypan blue (II), obtained similarly from tolidine and 8-amino-1-naphthol-3,6-di-sulfonic acid (the so-called H-acid). In spite, however, of an enormous

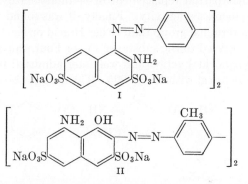

amount of work by Nicholle and Mesnil, who studied dyes prepared by coupling tetrazotized benzidine and its derivatives with the three dye-stuff intermediates H-acid, 4,6,8-acid, and Koch acid, no real advance was made until it was found in 1906 that more active compounds were

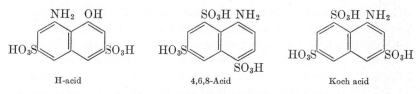

| H-acid | 4,6,8-Acid | Koch acid |

sometimes obtained by separating the benzene nuclei by a urea group, as in Afridol violet (III). Attention was then directed to compounds in

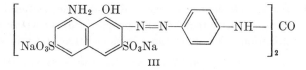

III

which the azo link was replaced by an amide group, and in 1920 a new drug, Bayer 205, for the treatment of sleeping sickness was announced, but its composition was kept secret. It was not a dye, and on acid hydrolysis it gave 4,6,8-acid, *m*-aminobenzoic acid, and *m*-amino-*p*-toluic acid.

Meanwhile Fourneau and his colleagues [124] at the Institut Pasteur made a long series of urea derivatives containing aminobenzoyl residues and, as terminal groups, H-acid, 4,6,8-acid or Koch acid. These compounds were of the general type

$$(\text{naphthylamine sulfonic acid}{-}COC_6H_4NHCOC_6H_4NH)_2CO$$

It was found that compounds containing *m*-aminobenzoyl residues as linking units were more effective than those containing *p*-aminobenzoyl groups; also that partial replacement of *m*-aminobenzoyl by *m*-amino-*p*-toluyl led to increased activity. Finally, it was found that 4,6,8-acid was better as a terminal group than either H-acid or Koch acid. In this way Fourneau was led to the substance IV, or Fourneau 309, which had a powerful trypanocidal action and was later admitted by the German workers to be identical with Bayer 205. The drug is also called suramin

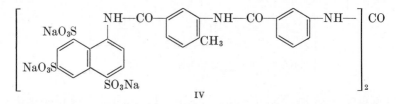

IV

sodium (U.S.P.), suramin (B.P.), moranyl, and germanin. Suramin is highly effective in experimental mouse infections, 0.06 mg./20-g. mouse curing 100% of animals and rendering them immune to infection for about three months. It also acts prophylactically in healthy mice, preventing infection. It is relatively non-toxic and has a high chemotherapeutic index. In sleeping sickness it is effective in the early stages of *T. rhodesiense* infections, but less so in *T. gambiense* infections. It is useless for the treatment of advanced cases because it is unable to penetrate into the cerebrospinal fluid and the brain. Its solutions are colloidal (mol. wt. = 1430), and this fact may account for its inability to penetrate the so-called blood-brain barrier and for its persistence in the blood stream. The last property enables it to act prophylactically, and it can be used to protect healthy people in areas where they are exposed to infection. There is some evidence that suramin sensitizes

---

[124] Fourneau, Trefouel, Trefouel, and Vallee, *Ann. inst. Pasteur*, **38**, 81 (1924).

trypanosomes to phagocytosis in the reticulo-endothelial system, since, if this system is inactivated by splenectomy and the intravenous injection of colloidal copper, the efficacy of suramin is greatly diminished.

The most remarkable feature of suramin is its high degree of structural specificity; the slightest change in structure leads to diminution or abolition of trypanocidal activity. Thus the compound V in which the *m*-aminobenzoyl and *m*-amino-*p*-toluyl units of suramin have been interchanged is inactive. The replacement of the methyl group of suramin by methoxyl, halogens, or higher alkyl groups also diminishes or abolishes activity. Replacement of the terminal 4,6,8-acid groups by other naphthylamine sulfonic acids yields compounds with no or only

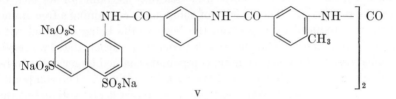

V

slight activity. The central urea grouping is an essential feature of the molecule. The analogous thiourea compound is considerably less active, and replacement of the central carbonyl group by oxalyl, malonyl, diethylmalonyl, or either of the three possible phthalyl groups abolishes activity. So also does replacement of the central urea residue by the azo or azoxy links.

Suramin is thus a unique member of its class; no compound of related structure is known which rivals it in trypanocidal activity. It is natural to conclude that by virtue of its particular molecular configuration it can fit and form stable complexes with some macromolecular structure in trypanosomes.

It has already been mentioned that Ehrlich discovered that certain acridine dyes had trypanocidal activity, e.g., 2,8-diamino-10-methylacridinium chloride (trypaflavine), and that Browning and his colleagues developed the anil- and styryl-quinoline antiseptics because they contained the unit $-N{=}\overset{|}{C}-(CH{=}CH)_n-N{<}$ which occurs in acriflavine. It is therefore of interest that some of these anil and styryl compounds have trypanocidal activity. All compounds were tested against *T. brucei* infections of mice.[125]

The anils were in general much less trypanocidal than the styryl compounds, but 2-*p*-aminoanil-6-aminoquinaldine metho salts (VI) were

[125] Browning, Cohen, Ellingworth, and Gulbrasen, *Proc. Roy. Soc. (London)*, **B105**, 99 (1929); **108**, 119 (1931); **110**, 249 (1932); **113**, 293, 300 (1933).

active and so were the compounds in which either the $p$-amino or the 6-amino group was replaced by dimethylamino. The styryl compounds were of the general formula VII. Active compounds were obtained when

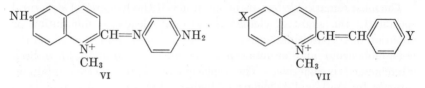

X = Y = $NH_2$ or when X = $NH_2$, Y = $N(CH_3)_2$, or X = $N(CH_3)_2$, Y = $NH_2$, but not when X = Y = $N(CH_3)_2$; the last condition produced a highly toxic substance, and this may account for its lack of curative properties. The toxicity of compounds containing a free amino group was reduced by acylation, the best results being obtained with acetyl compounds. The decreased toxicity of either the 2-$p$-acetylaminostyryl or the 6-acetylamino compounds enabled larger doses to be used and consequently enhanced the curative activity. The compound in which both X and Y were acetylamino groups was also active, but the conditions for highest curative activity appeared to be one basic group, $NH_2$ or $N(CH_3)_2$, and one acetylamino group. It is curious that either the benzene or the quinoline nucleus could carry the basic group provided that the other nucleus carried an acetylamino group. A 6-acetylamino group could be replaced by an amide group (NHR—CO—) where R = H or $CH_3$, but transference of the acetylamino group to the 4-position of the quinoline nucleus abolished activity.

It will be obvious that the structural features favoring curative properties in experimental trypanosomiasis are not identical with those which confer bacteriostatic activity. Thus $p$-acetylaminostyrylquinolinium or $p$-acetylaminoanilquinaldinium compounds were not bacteriostatic, and $p$-amino compounds were less so than $p$-dimethylamino compounds. Also, whereas a 6-acetylamino group increased the bacteriostatic activity of the $p$-dimethylaminoanils, it had little effect on analogous styryl compounds. It must, however, be remembered that these compounds were tested against bacteria *in vitro*, whereas trypanocidal activity was observed *in vivo* where other factors, particularly toxicity to the host, come into play.

## Diamidines

Trypanosomes require considerable supplies of glucose in order to maintain metabolic activity, and it occurred to Jancsó and Jancsó [126]

[126] Jancsó and Jancsó, *Z. Immunitätsforsch.*, **84**, 471 (1935).

that substances which reduce the blood sugar level in animals might, by reducing the glucose available to the trypanosomes, have a beneficial effect in trypanosomiasis. The simplest synthetic substance available was decamethylene diguanidine (VIII; $n = 10$), which had been called synthalin because its hypoglycemic action resembled that of insulin.

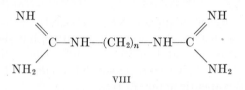

VIII

The Jancsós found that synthalin did in fact have curative properties in experimental trypanosomiasis. This result was confirmed by Lourie and Yorke,[127] using *T. equiperdum* and *T. rhodesiense*, but they also found that synthalin and synthalin B (VIII; $n = 12$) were directly trypanocidal *in vitro;* i.e., their effects were not due to a hypoglycemic action in the host. Moreover, insulin itself had negligible trypanocidal activity. These results led to an extensive investigation of polymethylene derivatives containing two amidine groups such as diguanidines (VIII), diisothioureas (IX), and diamidines (X).[128]

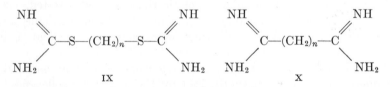

The compounds were tested on *T. rhodesiense* infections of mice and also on the same strain of trypanosomes *in vitro*. Nine diguanidines were studied, namely, those containing 4, 5, 6, 8, 10, 12, 14, 16, and 18 carbon atoms in the polymethylene chain. Maximum activity *in vitro* was associated with chains of 10 to 16 carbon atoms, these compounds being trypanocidal in dilutions of 1 in $256 \times 10^6$. The decamethylene, dodecamethylene, and tetradecamethylene members of the series also produced occasional cures of experimental infections.

Monoguanidines $C_nH_{2n+1}NHC(NH)NH_2$ ($n = 9, 12, 14, 16,$ and $18$) were not curative, but those with $n$ equal to 12, 14, or 16 were trypanocidal *in vitro* at a dilution of 1 in $4 \times 10^6$.

Diisothioureas (IX; $n = 2, 3, 6, 10, 11, 12, 14,$ and $16$) were also not curative, but those with $n = 14$ or 16 were trypanocidal *in vitro* at 1 in $64 \times 10^6$.

[127] Lourie and Yorke, *Ann. Trop. Med. Parasitol.*, **31**, 435 (1937).
[128] King, Lourie, and Yorke, *ibid.*, **32**, 177 (1938).

Eight diamidines were tested (X; $n = 8, 9, 10, 11, 12, 13, 14$, and 16). Maximum activity *in vitro* occurred for $n = 10, 11, 12, 13$, and 14, the undecamethylene member ($n = 11$) being trypanocidal at 1 in 256 $\times 10^6$, and the other four ($n = 10, 12, 13$, and 14) at 1 in $64 \times 10^6$. Moreover, all these members ($n = 10$ to 14) were curative in infected mice.

A few polymethylene diamines, $NH_2(CH_2)_nNH_2$ ($n = 8, 11, 14, 16$, and 18), were also tested; they were not curative, but the $C_{18}$ member was trypanocidal *in vitro* at 1 in $16$–$64 \times 10^6$. One diglyoxaline compound (XI) was tested; it was trypanocidal *in vitro* at 1 in $256 \times 10^6$, and had some therapeutic action *in vivo*.

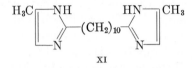

XI

The best compound of all those so far mentioned was undoubtedly undecamethylenediamidine (X; $n = 11$); a dose of 0.25 mg./20-g. mouse was capable of curing 80% of mice infected with *T. rhodesiense*. It did not, however, cure *T. congolense* infections.

Three compounds containing aromatic rings were also tested, viz., *p,p'*-diguanidinodiphenylmethane, *p,p'*-diamidinodiphenylmethane, and 2,7-diamidinonaphthalene. All three were active *in vitro* at 1 in $16 \times 10^6$, and all three were curative in *T. rhodesiense* infections.

Later Lourie and Yorke [129] tested a longer series of aromatic diamidines which had been synthesized by Ewins and his colleagues.[130] These were of the general structure XII, where the linking group X between the two benzene rings was a short carbon chain or a chain

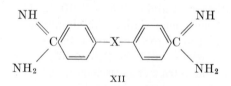

XII

containing one or two oxygen, sulfur, or nitrogen atoms. The most active members of this series were *p,p'*-diamidinostilbene (XIII), now called stilbamidine; 1,3-*p,p'*-diamidinodiphenoxypropane (XIV, $n = 3$) or propamidine; and 1,5-*p,p'*-diamidinodiphenoxypentane (XIV, $n = 5$) or pentamidine. Stilbamidine cured 100% of mice infected with *T. rhodesiense* in the dosage range 0.025–0.05 mg./20-g. mouse. Propami-

[129] Lourie and Yorke, *ibid.*, **33**, 289 (1939).
[130] Ashley *et al.*, *J. Chem. Soc.*, 103 (1942).

dine and pentamidine were a little less active, a dosage range of 0.05–0.1 mg./20-g. mouse being required to cure the majority of mice. Curiously enough, these compounds are less trypanocidal *in vitro* than many

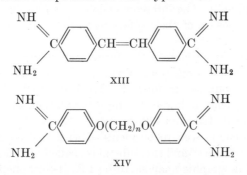

XIII

XIV

of the aliphatic compounds mentioned above, dilutions of 1 in 1–4 × $10^6$ being required for stilbamidine and of 1 in 6–8 × $10^6$ for pentamidine with *T. rhodesiense.*\*  These three compounds are also much less active against *T. congolense* infections than against *T. rhodesiense* infections, and they are inactive against *T. cruzi* infections.  Fulton and Yorke [131] found that dimethylstilbamidine (XV) was about twice as active as

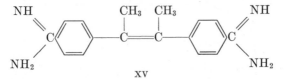

XV

stilbamidine on *T. congolense* infections but definitely less active than stilbamidine on *T. rhodesiense* infections.  According to Wien [132] the therapeutic index (LD50/CD50) of dimethylstilbamidine (XV) in *T. congolense* infections is 12–28 (depending on the strain) whereas that of stilbamidine is only 2–3.

Substitution of methoxyl, methyl, hydroxyl, or halogen in the benzene rings of the aromatic diamidines usually reduces trypanocidal activity, although halogenation as in 2,2′-dibromopropamidine may enhance the bactericidal properties of these compounds. [133]  The 3,4′- and 3,3′-diamidino compounds are also less active in trypanosomiasis than the 4,4′-compounds.

With mineral acids the aromatic diamidines form salts which are sparingly soluble in water, and they are usually administered as their

\* Unpublished results of Dr. E. M. Lourie.

[131] Fulton and Yorke, *Ann. Trop. Med. Parasitol.*, **36**, 131 (1942).

[132] Wien, *Brit. J. Pharmacol.*, **1**, 65 (1946).

[133] Wien, Harrison, and Freeman, *ibid.*, **3**, 211 (1948).

water-soluble isethionates (isethionic acid is $\beta$-hydroxyethylsulfonic acid, $CH_2OHCH_2SO_3H$). Stilbamidine exists in *cis* and *trans* forms, *cis*-stilbamidine being more toxic and less therapeutically active than *trans*-stilbamidine.[134] The interconversion of the *cis* and *trans* forms is catalyzed by exposure of their solutions to light, an equilibrium being ultimately established.[135]

*trans*-Stilbamidine, which is the form used in medicine, undergoes another photochemical reaction, in which a dimer, 1,2,3,4-tetra-(4'-amidinophenyl)cyclobutane, is formed. Hydrolysis of this dimer to a tetracarboxylic acid, followed by decarboxylation, gave two hydrocarbons, melting at 163° and 149°, respectively. The former, which was the main product, proved to be identical with the dimer obtained by irradiation of stilbene,[136] and this substance, called distilbene, was shown by x-ray crystallographic analysis to be 1,2,3,4-tetraphenylcyclobutane and to have a center of symmetry.[137] It must have the configuration (XVI), and since the tetraphenylcyclobutane, m.p. 163°, was the major product obtained from the stilbamidine dimer, it seems highly probable

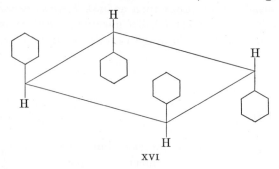

XVI

that the latter has the same configuration with amidine groups in the *para*-positions of all four phenyl radicals.

The diamidines are remarkably persistent in the body. They have been detected in the blood of patients several months after treatment has ceased. This suggests that they are firmly bound in the tissues of the host, and it may well be that their therapeutic action is partly due to their being firmly attached to trypanosomes for which they have affinity. It is difficult to imagine any type of firm attachment, particularly for polymethylene diamidines, other than salt formation. Amidines are strong monoacidic bases, and, like isothiourea derivatives, which also contain the amidine unit, they form highly crystalline, and often spar-

[134] Fulton and Goodwin, *ibid.*, **1**, 234 (1946).
[135] Henry, *J. Chem. Soc.*, 1156 (1946).
[136] Fulton, *Brit. J. Pharmacol.*, **3**, 75 (1948).
[137] Fulton and Dunitz, *Nature*, **160**, 161 (1947).

ingly soluble, salts with carboxylic acids. In such salts both the anion and the cation are resonating structures, and Walker [138] has suggested that ionic bonds are formed *simultaneously* between the two oxygen atoms sharing the negative charge in the carboxylate anion and the two nitrogen atoms sharing the positive charge in the amidinium cation. The amidinium carboxylate may then be represented as XVII, in which

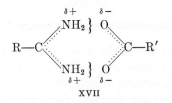

XVII

the seven atoms of the amidinium ion and the three atoms of the carboxylate ion will all be coplanar; i.e., ten atoms (plus the two atoms to which the ions are attached) will form a relatively rigid configuration of minimum potential energy. It is tempting to assume that the chemotherapeutic properties of the diamidines may be partly due to salt formation of this type with carboxylate anions in the protein of trypanosomes. The natural spacing of the carboxylate groups in the protein of the parasite will on this view determine the optimum length of chain between the amidine groups in the drug molecule.

Amidines have usually been prepared by Pinner's method, i.e., by the action of ammonia on imido ethers, but Oxley and Short [139] have described a more convenient method, which consists in heating a nitrile

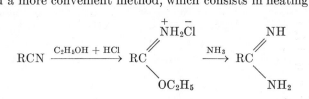

with an ammonium arylsulfonate at temperatures of the order of 250–300°. The reaction is regarded as proceeding by the following reversible steps.

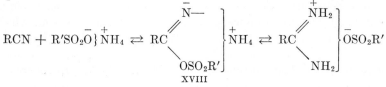

XVIII

[138] Walker, *J. Chem. Soc.*, 1996 (1949).

[139] Oxley and Short, *ibid.*, 147 (1946); Oxley *et al.*, *ibid.*, 763 (1946), and succeeding papers.

The attack of the sulfonate anion on the nitrile group is thought to produce the intermediate anion XVIII, which then degrades the ammonium ion and gives rise to the amidinium sulfonate. Amidines can similarly be obtained by heating carboxylic acids with aryl sulfonamides and ammonium arylsulfonates, this reaction involving the intermediate formation of the amide and then the nitrile of the carboxylic acid.

### Phenanthridinium Compounds

During an investigation of the general chemotherapeutic properties of phenanthridinium compounds, prepared by Morgan and Walls,[140] Browning et al.[141] discovered two substances which had a curative action on *T. brucei* infections of mice. These were 3-acetamino-9-*p*-acetaminophenyl-10-methylphenanthridinium chloride (XIX) and 7-amino-9-*p*-aminophenyl-10-methylphenanthridinium chloride (XX), now called

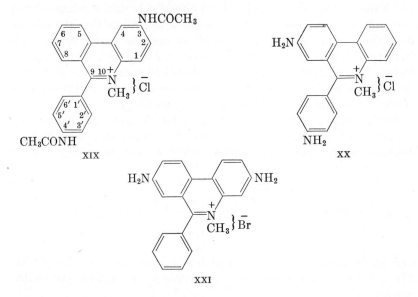

phenidium chloride. This last substance was, however, remarkable in that it cured infections of mice with *T. congolense*, a trypanosome which is normally refractory to most drugs that act powerfully on *T. brucei*. Later an even more powerful member of the series, 2,7-diamino-9-phenyl-10-methylphenanthridinium bromide (XXI) was discovered.[142]

[140] Morgan and Walls, *ibid.*, 389 (1938).
[141] Browning *et al.*, *J. Path. Bact.*, **46**, 203 (1938).
[142] Browning, Calver, and Adamson, *ibid.*, **60**, 336 (1948).

It is now called dimidium bromide and has been used to control wide-spread outbreaks of bovine trypanosomiasis.

Experimental work on *T. congolense* infections with these phenanthridinium compounds revealed that this organism undergoes changes during the course of the infection which affect its sensitivity to drugs. In order to get consistent results it is essential to transfer the trypanosomes to a fresh mouse as soon as they become abundant in the blood, that is at "acme." After acme the number of trypanosomes in the blood may remain high until the mouse dies, or it may fluctuate, a relapsing course being established. If the disease becomes chronic, i.e., if the host survives the infection for more than a few days after acme, it becomes more difficult to cure than at the acme stage, and larger doses of phenanthridinium compounds are required.[143]

The phenanthridinium nucleus incorporates both an isoquinoline and a quinoline nucleus. Its derivatives are readily obtained by the action of phosphorous oxychloride on acyl derivatives of the readily accessible *o*-aminobiphenyl. If the biphenyl nucleus or the acyl group contains

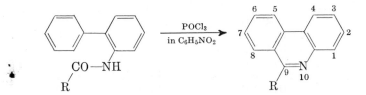

nitro groups cyclization is effected at a higher temperature in nitrobenzene solution. Quaternization of the nuclear nitrogen can also be achieved in the same solvent by means of methyl sulfate, and nitro groups can be subsequently reduced by iron and water or by ferrous hydroxide. If the acylaminobiphenyl compound contains amino groups they must be protected during cyclization, e.g., as carbethoxy derivatives.

A considerable number of phenanthridinium compounds have been prepared [144] and tested.[141, 142, 145, 146] The following structural features appear to be essential for high activity against *T. congolense* infections: (1) a quaternary nitrogen at position 10—so far only metho salts have been investigated; (2) an aryl nucleus attached directly or indirectly at position 9; (3) a free amino group, or a group like the nitro group capable

[143] Calver, *Trop. Diseases Bull.*, **42**, 704 (1945); Browning, *Nature*, **163**, 590 (1949).

[144] Walls, *J. Chem. Soc.*, 294 (1945); 1031 (1946); 67 (1947); Walls and Calderwell, 188 (1948); Walls and Whittaker, 41 (1950); Walls and Copp, 311 (1950); see also Walls, *J. Soc. Chem. Ind.* (*London*), **66**, 182 (1947).

[145] Wien, *Brit. J. Pharmacol.*, **1**, 65 (1946).

[146] Brownlee *et al.*, *ibid.*, **5**, 261 (1950).

of giving rise to an amino group. The effect of amino groups in 9-phenyl-10-methylphenanthridinium salts is illustrated in Table XXV.[146]

TABLE XXV

EFFECT OF SUBSTITUENTS ON THE ACTIVITY OF 9-PHENYL-10-METHYL PHENANTHRIDINIUM SALTS

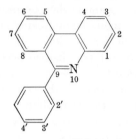

| Substituents | Activity against *T. congolense* in Mice | |
| | In Terms of Dosage * | In Terms of Dimidium Br = 1 |
| --- | --- | --- |
| None | 0 | ... |
| 4'-NH₂ | ++ | ... |
| 2-NH₂-4'-NH₂ | +++ | 0.5 |
| 3-NH₂-4'-NH₂ | + | ... |
| 6-NH₂-4'-NH₂ | +++ | 0.7 |
| 7-NH₂-4'-NH₂ | +++ | 0.3 |
| 7-NH₂-3'-NH₂ | +++ | 0.3 |
| 8-NH₂-4'-NH₂ | + | ... |
| 2-NH₂-7-NH₂ | ++++ | 1.0 |
| 2-NH₂-7-NH₂-4'-NH₂ | ++++ | 1.5 |
| | | |
| 2-NH₂-4'-NO₂ | ++ | ... |
| 6-NH₂-4'-NO₂ | +++ | 0.3 |
| 7-NH₂-4'-NO₂ | + | ... |
| 8-NH₂-4'-NO₂ | + | ... |
| 2-NH₂-7-NH₂-4'-NO₂ | ++++ | 1.3 |

* 0 = no activity at 50 mg./kg. The plus signs indicate the dosage range required to free the blood of at least 80% of mice from trypanosomes.

$$+ = 10\text{--}50 \text{ mg./kg.}$$
$$++ = 1\text{--}10 \text{ mg./kg.}$$
$$+++ = 0.1\text{--}1.0 \text{ mg./kg.}$$
$$++++ = 0.01\text{--}0.1 \text{ mg./kg.}$$

It will be noticed that a 4'-NH₂ leads to moderate activity, but much higher activity is obtained when a second amino group is introduced in the 2-, 6-, or 7-positions. A second amino group in the 3- or 8-positions does not increase activity. The most favorable arrangement of two amino groups appears to be 2,7 as in dimidium bromide, but the 2,7,4'-triamino compound (trimidium bromide) is even more active.   In the lower part of Table XXV it will be seen that replacement of the 4'-amino group by a nitro group does not abolish activity although it reduces it. Methylation or acylation of one or more amino groups invariably reduces activity.

Table XXVI [146] illustrates the effect of various 9-substituents on the activity of 2,7-diamino-10-methylphenanthridinium salts.   The high

TABLE XXVI

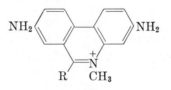

Activity against *T. congolense* in Mice

| R | In Terms of Dosage | In Terms of Dimidium Br = 1 |
|---|---|---|
| $C_6H_5$ | ++++ | 1.0 |
| $p$-$NH_2C_6H_4$ | ++++ | 1.5 |
| $p$-$NO_2C_6H_4$ | ++++ | 1.3 |
| $C_6H_5CH_2$ | +++ | 0.8 |
| $C_6H_5CO$ | ++ | 0.03 |
| $\alpha$-Thienyl | ++++ | 1.3 |
| $CH_3$ | + | |

Symbols are the same as in Table XXV.

activity of the thienyl and benzyl compounds is in sharp contrast to the weak activity of the benzoyl and methyl compounds.

It is interesting that suitable alkoxyl groups can replace amino groups without complete loss of activity (Table XXVII).[146]   Compounds containing a 7-ethoxy or 7-$n$-propoxy group and a 4'-amino group are highly active.   The corresponding 4'-nitro compounds are also active and, even more remarkable, the 7,4'-dimethoxy compound has some activity.

It has already been mentioned that acylation of free amino groups in phenanthridinium compounds invariably reduces activity against *T. congolense* infections.   Browning and his colleagues,[147] however, discovered that some phenanthridinium compounds containing urethane groups had curative properties in *T. cruzi* infections of mice.   *T. cruzi* is the trypanosome responsible for Chagas's disease, a bug-borne disease occurring in South and Central America which chiefly attacks children.

[147] Browning *et al.*, *Nature*, **157**, 263 (1946).

## TABLE XXVII

Effect of Alkoxyl Groups in 9-Phenyl-10-methylphenanthridinium Salts

| Substituents | Activity against *T. congolense* in Mice | |
| --- | --- | --- |
| | In Terms of Dosage | In Terms of Dimidium Br = 1 |
| 2-OCH$_3$-4'-NH$_2$ | + | ... |
| 7-OCH$_3$-4'-NH$_2$ | +++ | 0.3 |
| 7-OCH$_3$-3'-NH$_2$ | +++ | 0.3 |
| 7-OC$_2$H$_5$-4'-NH$_2$ | +++ | 0.7 |
| 7-n-OC$_3$H$_7$-4'-NH$_2$ | +++ | 0.7 |
| 7-iso-OC$_3$H$_7$-4'-NH$_2$ | 0 | |
| 7-n-OC$_4$H$_9$-4'-NH$_2$ | 0 | |
| 2-OCH$_3$-4'-NO$_2$ | + | ... |
| 7-OCH$_3$-4'-NO$_2$ | +++ | 0.3 |
| 7-OCH$_3$-3'-NO$_2$ | + | ... |
| 7-OC$_2$H$_5$-4'-NO$_2$ | +++ | 0.3 |
| 7-n-OC$_3$H$_7$-4'-NO$_2$ | ++ | ... |
| 7-OCH$_3$-4'-OCH$_3$ | ++ | ... |
| 7-OCH$_3$ | 0 | ... |

Symbols are the same as in Table XXV.

The only drug previously known to influence this infection favorably was a 4,6-diaminoquinaldine derivative known as Bayer 7602(Ac) (see p. 499). Two phenanthridinium compounds gave promising results in experimental *T. cruzi* infections, namely, 3-carbethoxyamino-9-*p*-carbethoxyaminophenyl-10-methylphenanthridinium chloride (XXII) and 2,7-dicarbethoxyamino-9,10-dimethylphenanthridinium methylsulfate (XXIII). Both compounds were less active in the later stages of an

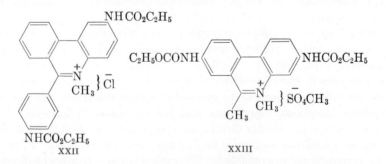

XXII                    XXIII

infection than in the early stages, but animals which had been cured were immune to infection when reinoculated even many months later.

Over 200 phenanthridine compounds have since been tested by Goodwin *et al.*[148] on mice infected with *T. cruzi*. Some eighteen compounds showed marked suppressive activity, and these were all characterized by possession of one or another of the following structural features: (1) a quaternary nitrogen (metho salts) at position 10; (2) a 9-phenyl (or in one compound a 9-$\alpha$-thienyl) group; (3) a urethane group and (4) two amino groups. Phenanthridine compounds other than quaternary salts were inactive. Most of the active compounds contained, apart from the 10-methyl group, a 9-phenyl group and a urethane group.

Most of the compounds were active, if at all, only during the incubation period of the infection. Besides the two compounds XXII and XXIII discovered by Browning *et al.*,[147] only two compounds with marked activity in an established infection were found, namely, 2-amino-9-*p*-carbethoxyaminophenyl-10-methylphenanthridinium bromide (XXIV; R = $C_2H_5$) and 3-amino-9-carbethoxyaminophenyl-10-methylphenan-

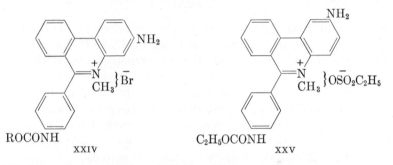

ROCONH
XXIV

$C_2H_5OCONH$
XXV

thridinium ethanesulfonate (XXV). None of the compounds with marked activity against *T. cruzi* had any but slight activity against *T. congolense*.

The difficulty of correlating structure with action in this group is well illustrated by the results obtained with homologous urethanes of the type XXIV. In the incubation period the activities were R = $C_2H_5$ > iso-$C_3H_7$ > *n*-$C_3H_7$ > *n*-$C_4H_9$ > $CH_3$, but in an established infection only the ethyl homolog had relatively high activity, the next most active being the butyl member.

## Quinaldine Derivatives

During an investigation of the bactericidal properties of numerous 4-aminoquinaldine derivatives it was discovered that antiprotozoal activity was obtained by linking two 4,6-diaminoquinaldine nuclei

[148] Goodwin *et al.*, *Brit. J. Pharmacol.*, **5**, 277 (1950).

through the 6-amino groups. The two most interesting compounds were Surfen (XXVI), in which the linking unit was a carbonyl group, and Surfen C (XXVII), which incorporated a melamine unit.[149] Surfen was introduced as a non-staining antiseptic. It has some activity against

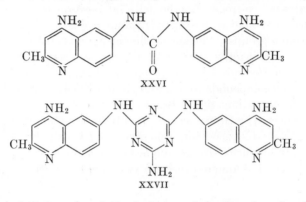

XXVI

XXVII

experimental *T. brucei* and *T. rhodesiense* infections in mice, but none against *T. congolense*. Surfen C or Congasin (XXVII), however, was at the time of its discovery one of the few compounds known which were active against *T. congolense*, and it was probably only the advent of the phenanthridinium compounds, and particularly dimidium bromide, in 1938 which prevented its exploitation on a large scale. The activity of Surfen C appears to be dependent on the presence of the 2-methyl and 4-amino groups since their elimination abolishes it. Alkylation of any of the amino groups also reduces trypanocidal activity.

An interesting development of the 4,6-diaminoquinaldine type of trypanocide is the drug antrycide [150] (XXVIII) in which a pyrimidine nucleus is attached to the 6-amino group and both heterocyclic nuclei

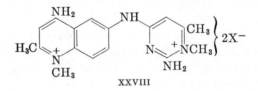

XXVIII

are quaternized. Four salts are known, the dichloride, dibromide, diiodide, and dimethylsulfate, of which only the last is readily soluble in water. Antrycide is highly active against mouse infections with *T. congolense*, *T. equiperdum*, *T. equinum*, and *T. evansi*, 100% of animals being cured by a single subcutaneous dose of 1.25 mg./kg.

[149] Jensch, *Angew. Chem.*, **50**, 891 (1937).
[150] Curd and Davey, *Brit. J. Pharmacol.*, **5**, 25 (1950).

Much higher doses (25 mg./kg.) are needed to cure 100% of mice infected with *T. rhodesiense*, *T. gambiense*, and *T. brucei*. Cure was taken to mean absence of trypanosomes in the blood for 30 days. The approximate curative doses of antrycide, suramin, and dimidium bromide in *T. congolense* infections of mice are 1–2, 100, and 2–4 mg./kg., respectively. If the sparingly soluble antrycide halides are injected subcutaneously as suspensions, it is possible to protect mice against infection with *T. congolense* for several weeks. Thus 25 mg./kg. will protect mice for 6–8 weeks. This prophylactic action is almost certainly due to the slow absorption of these insoluble salts from the site of injection into the blood stream and not to persistence in the body like that which happens with suramin or the diamidines. Preliminary field trials with antrycide have given promising results, but it is too early to say what success will attend large-scale use of it in bovine trypanosomiasis.

No details of structure-action relationships among drugs of the antrycide type have been published, but the two quaternary nitrogen atoms probably play an essential part in conferring activity on this type of molecule.

At the same time that Jensch [149] described the trypanocidal action of Surfen C against *T. congolense*, he also announced that another member of the 4,6-diaminoquinaldine group, Bayer 7602Ac (XXIX; R = R′ = allyl), which contains a diallylmalonyl linking unit, had some curative activity in experimental *T. cruzi* infections. Compounds of this type have been reinvestigated by Goble,[151] who tested a large series of dialkyl-

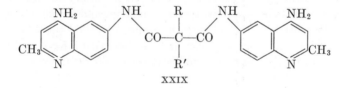

XXIX

malonyl derivatives of 4,6-diaminoquinaldine. Activity against *T. cruzi* appears to be confined to these dialkylmalonyl derivatives, and the most active members all contain at least one allyl or one propyl group. Goble arranges these compounds XXIX in the following order of decreasing activity: (1) R = R′ = allyl; (2) R = allyl, R′ = 2-thienylmethyl; (3) R = allyl, R′ = n-propyl; (4) R = R′ = n-propyl; (5) R = allyl, R′ = benzyl. His test relied on the number of mice in groups of 20 surviving for 60 days after infection. As with the phenanthridinium compounds already mentioned, the best results were obtained only by early treatment, i.e., immediately after trypanosomes appeared

[151] Goble, *J. Pharmacol. Exptl. Therap.*, **98**, 49 (1950).

in the blood. None of these dialkylmalonyl derivatives was active against *T. congolense* infections.

Goble also examined a series of diamides (XXX) where $n$ was 1, 3, 4, 5, 7, 8. None was active against *T. cruzi*, but most of them showed some activity against *T. brucei*, *T. gambiense*, and *T. equiperdum* in-

XXX

fections, the best being the adipic acid derivative ($n = 4$) which about equaled Surfen (XXVI) in activity. Two diethers, of type XXXI, viz., those with $n = 2$ and 4, were also about equal in activity to Surfen. None of these amides and ethers showed any appreciable activity against *T. congolense* infections.

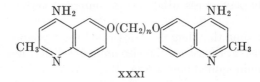

XXXI

## ARSENICAL DRUGS

Arsenical drugs have proved of value in a variety of diseases, the most important being syphilis, trypanosomiasis, and amebic dysentery. Syphilis is caused by infection with organisms called spirochetes, and most experimental work has been done either with infected rabbits or with the organism of human syphilis (*Treponema* or *Spirochaeta pallidum*) *in vitro*. These organisms cannot be cultured *in vitro*, but suspensions of them can be obtained from syphilitic lesions of rabbits. Amebic dysentery is caused by an organism called *Entamoeba histolytica* which invades the mucous membrane of the large intestine. Kittens can be infected, but a method of testing drugs on 3- to 4-week-old rats has also been devised.[152] The organism can also be used *in vitro*, but since nonabsorption in the intestine is an essential requirement of an active drug for treatment of intestinal amebiasis, it is better to test new compounds *in vivo*.

Arsenical drugs are of three types: arsonic acids, $RAsO(OH)_2$, which are used as their monosodium salts; arsenoxides, $RAsO$; and arseno-

[152] Jones, *Ann. Trop. Med. Parasitol.*, **40**, 131 (1946); *Brit. J. Pharmacol.*, **2**, 217 (1947); see also Goodwin, Hoare, and Sharp, *ibid.*, **3**, 44 (1948).

benzene derivatives, RAs=AsR; where R is an aryl group in each type. The arsonic acids are not active *in vitro*, and Ehrlich suggested that they were reduced in the tissues of the host to arsenoxides, which are active both *in vitro* and *in vivo*. The arsenoxides, however, were at first thought to be too toxic for clinical use, and it was in order to retain the high activity of trivalent arsenic compounds but avoid the high toxicity of the arsenoxides that Ehrlich developed arsenobenzene compounds. It does not seem to have occurred to Ehrlich that arsenobenzene compounds might owe their activity to *oxidation* in the host to arsenoxides, probably because the arsenobenzene derivatives are, under ordinary conditions of testing, directly trypanocidal and spirocheticidal *in vitro*.

It will be convenient at this point to give a list of representative arsenical drugs with some notes on their properties.

*Arsphenamine*, originally called 606 or Salvarsan, was probably Ehrlich's greatest practical achievement in chemotherapy. It revolutionized the treatment of syphilis and encouraged people to believe in the possibilities of chemotherapeutic methods. It is, however, a dangerous drug and difficult to use. It is 3,3'-diamino-4,4'-dihydroxy-arsenobenzene (I). It forms a dihydrochloride, solutions of which are too acidic to be injected, and a monosodium and a disodium salt, both of which form very alkaline solutions; the free base is insoluble in water. Arsphenamine is extremely easily oxidized in the air to much more toxic substances. It is usually dispensed as the dry dihydrochloride in nitrogen-filled ampoules, and the salt must be rapidly dissolved in the right amount of normal sodium hydroxide solution immediately before

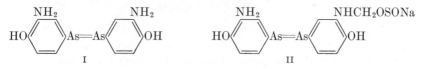

use. The neutralized product is injected intravenously or intramuscularly. Finally, there are no satisfactory physical or chemical means of establishing its purity, and each batch must be standardized biologically. Numerous attempts have been made to prepare more stable derivatives of arsphenamine; two such derivatives have been widely used, namely, *neoarsphenamine* and *sulfarsphenamine*.

Neoarsphenamine is the monosodium salt of the N-methanol sulfinic acid of arsphenamine (II). It is soluble in water, and its solutions do not need neutralization and can be injected intravenously. It is, however, very rapidly oxidized in the air to more highly toxic products. Sulfarsphenamine is a dimethylene sulfoxalate derivative of arsphenamine (III). Solutions of its disodium salt are nearly neutral and can be

injected intramuscularly and even subcutaneously. It is less rapidly
oxidized than neoarsphenamine in the air.

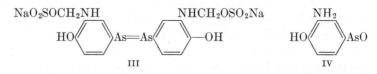

Oxophenarsine or Mapharsen (IV) is the arsenoxide corresponding to
arsphenamine. It was regarded by Ehrlich as too toxic for clinical use,
but it was introduced into medicine in 1935 after it had been shown to be
highly effective in experimental rabbit syphilis in such small doses that
its high toxicity was not a disadvantage. It is about ten times as toxic,
but also about ten times as effective, as arsphenamine. Consequently,
much smaller amounts of the drug are needed, and there is less danger
of cumulative arsenical poisoning. Moreover, it is a stable substance,
not liable to oxidation to more toxic substances, and its purity can be
checked by ordinary chemical means. It is injected as its water-soluble
hydrochloride. It is used in the treatment of syphilis and trypanosomiasis.

Acetarsol or stovarsol is the N-acetyl derivative of the arsonic acid
corresponding to arsphenamine and oxophenarsine; it is 3-acetylamino-
4-hydroxyphenylarsonic acid (V). It was introduced by Fourneau as an
oral drug for the treatment of syphilis, but its absorption is erratic. It

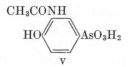

is mainly used in the treatment of amebic dysentery but is not so effective as carbarsone (see below). A similar, closely related drug is Trepar-
sol, the N-formyl derivative of 3-amino-4-hydroxyphenylarsonic acid.

Atoxyl or p-aminophenylarsonic acid (VI) was the first organic
arsenical to be used in the treatment of sleeping sickness. Its curative
action in experimental trypanosomiasis was discovered by Thomas in
1905, a year later than Ehrlich had reported its inactivity in vitro. In

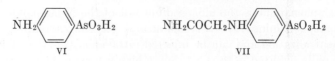

human sleeping sickness it can be used for only short courses of treatment, since it is liable to cause atrophy of the optic nerve and, therefore,

blindness. This injury to the optic nerve appears to be associated with the *p*-amino group. In a study of representative arsenicals Young and Loevenhart[153] found that only arsenicals with a free or substituted amino group *para* to the arsenic atom produced optic lesions in the rabbit; *ortho* and *meta* amino compounds produced no such injury.

*Tryparsamide* was discovered by Jacobs and Heidelberger in 1919. It is the monosodium salt of N-phenylglycineamide-*p*-arsonic acid (VII) and has been widely used in the treatment of sleeping sickness. It is less toxic than atoxyl, but like other *p*-amino compounds it can cause blindness. It has the great advantage that it penetrates into the central nervous system, the cerebrospinal fluid becoming trypanocidal. For this reason it is used in the treatment of late sleeping sickness and in neurosyphilis, in both of which conditions the infecting parasite has penetrated into the central nervous system.

*Carbarsone* (VIII) is also a derivative of atoxyl. When given orally it is not readily absorbed from the intestine; it is used in amebic dysentery.

$$NH_2CONH \text{—} \bigcirc \text{—} AsO_3H_2$$

VIII

Other additions to derivatives of atoxyl are *Melarsen* or *p*-melaminylphenylarsonic acid (IX) and *Melarsen oxide*, the corresponding arsenoxide, which have given encouraging results in African sleeping sickness.

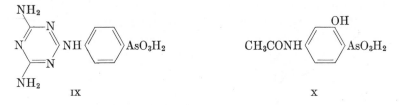

IX

X

They were introduced by Friedheim[154] in 1939.

*Orsanine* is 4-acetylamino-2-hydroxyphenylarsonic acid (X). Fourneau, who studied a large number of aminohydroxyphenylarsonic acids, found that the 4-amino-2-hydroxy compound had the highest chemotherapeutic index in *T. equiperdum* infections of mice, and its N-acetyl derivative had an even more favorable index. Orsanine resembles tryparsamide in its action but is said to be more effective and to penetrate into the central nervous system even more readily.

[153] Young and Loevenhart, *J. Pharmacol.*, **23**, 107 (1924).

[154] Friedheim, *Proc. 3rd Int. Congress Microbiol.*, N. Y., 428 (1939); *Ann. inst. Pasteur*, **65**, 108 (1940); *Ann. Trop. Med. Parasitol.*, **42**, 357 (1948).

*Butarsen* was discovered by Eagle. It is the *p*-arsenoxide of ω-phenyl-butyric acid (XI). It has the great advantage that it is active against

$$OAs\langle\ \rangle CH_2CH_2CH_2CO_2H$$

XI

trypanosomes which have acquired resistance to the more usual arsenical drugs (see below).

## Mechanism of Action

All the organic arsenicals so far discussed were discovered empirically, and no clear-cut relations between structure and curative activity are apparent. It is probable, however, that all arsenicals owe their curative action fundamentally to the same mechanism, and, consequently, it will be convenient to consider how they act before discussing why some have greater curative power than others.

It has already been mentioned that Ehrlich attributed the curative activity of arsonic acids to the formation of arsenoxides by reduction in the tissues of the host. He also suggested that the arsenoxides combined with substances containing thiol or SH groups in the parasite. The value of this suggestion was not appreciated at the time because the importance of thiol-containing substances in the animal economy was not recognized. It was only after Gowland Hopkins had isolated the tripeptide glutathione or γ-glutamylcysteinylglycine (XII) from yeast and liver (1917) and had demonstrated its wide distribution in living tissues that the important functions of thiol-containing substances, especially in the oxidation-reduction mechanisms of the body, began to be realized. Shortly after this discovery Voegtlin, Dyer, and Leonard [155]

$$
\begin{array}{cc}
NH_2 & CH_2SH \\
| & | \\
\end{array}
$$
$$HO_2CCHCH_2CH_2CONHCHCONHCH_2CO_2H$$
XII

put forward the view that the chemotherapeutic activity of arsenical drugs was due to their conversion into arsenoxides, arsonic acids being reduced and arsenobenzene compounds oxidized.

$$2RAsO(OH)_2 \xrightarrow{4H} 2RAsO \xleftarrow{2O} RAs{=}AsR$$

Three main lines of evidence were adduced in support of this view. (1) Arsonic acids are not trypanocidal *in vitro*, and arsenobenzene derivatives

---

[155] Voegtlin, Dyer, and Leonard, *U. S. Pub. Health Repts.*, **38**, 1882 (1923). See also Voegtlin, *Physiol. Revs.*, **5**, 63 (1925).

are less so *in vitro* than *in vivo*, but arsenoxides are as toxic *in vitro* as *in vivo;* i.e., they will kill trypanosomes *in vitro* at very low concentrations, comparable with those which can be safely attained in the blood of the host.   (2) Arsenoxides act very rapidly *in vivo*, the number of motile trypanosomes in the blood beginning to decline almost immediately after injection of the drug.   With arsphenamine and arsonic acids, however, there is a long latent period (1–2 hours) before the number of trypanosomes begins to decrease.   (3) Trypanosomes can be protected against the toxic action of arsenoxides by glutathione and other SH compounds like cysteine and thioglycolic acid, and arsenoxides are known to combine very readily with SH compounds to form thio-arsinites, $RAs(SR')_2$ (see below).  This protection is complete *in vitro*, provided a sufficient amount of SH compound is present, but *in vivo* the protection is temporary, its eventual diminution coinciding with the decline in the concentration of free thiol compound in the blood.   Glutathione was the most effective thiol compound in decreasing the rate of destruction of trypanosomes *in vivo*.   It would also delay the appearance of arsenical poisoning in animals to which a lethal dose of arsenoxide had been given.

In spite of this impressive body of evidence, it remained possible that arsphenamine and other arsenobenzene compounds might have a direct action of their own, since they are trypanocidal and spirocheticidal *in vitro*.   However, in a series of careful experiments Eagle [156] found that if molecular oxygen is rigorously excluded at every stage, from the making up of the solution of neoarsphenamine to the exposure of spirochetes to it, the concentration of neoarsphenamine required to kill spirochetes *in vitro* in nitrogen is 25 to 60 times greater than that which will do so when no precautions to exclude oxygen are taken.   On the other hand, oxophenarsine is just as toxic to spirochetes when oxygen is excluded as when it is present.   The difference between the lethal concentration of commercial arsphenamine in nitrogen and in air was less striking, but this was shown to be accounted for largely by the arsenoxide content of the arsphenamine preparations used.   The residual toxicity of neoarsphenamine in nitrogen may be due to a direct action of some unknown type or it may be due to slow oxidation of the drug by the spirochetes themselves.

Eagle also found that the spirocheticidal action of arsphenamine, neoarsphenamine, and even oxophenarsine *in vitro* could be almost completely abolished by the presence of a sufficient excess of cysteine, glutathione, or thioglycolic acid.   A large excess of these SH compounds was required, but this is in agreement with what is known about the

---

[156] Eagle, *J. Pharmacol.*, **66**, 423, 436 (1939).

formation of thioarsinites from arsenoxides and SH compounds. Insoluble arsenoxides dissolve immediately in neutral or acid solutions of SH compounds but are reprecipitated when the solution is made alkaline.

$$RAsO + 2HSR' \underset{\text{Alkaline}}{\overset{\text{Neutral or acid}}{\rightleftarrows}} RAs(SR')_2 + H_2O$$

Thioarsinite formation is thus a reversible reaction, and Cohen, King, and Strangeways,[157] who investigated this reaction in some detail, demonstrated that thioarsinites had curative properties in experimental trypanosomiasis little, if at all, inferior to that of the arsenoxides from which they were formed. This discovery has both practical and theoretical interest, since it provides a convenient way of administering otherwise insoluble arsenoxides, e.g., as thioarsinites of sodium thioglycolate or sodium cysteinate, and it illustrates the ready hydrolysis of thioarsinites to arsenoxides and SH compounds.

These authors also showed that arsonic acids are reduced by SH compounds like cysteine and thioglycolic acid in neutral solution to thioarsinites, a reaction which they suggest might proceed through the intermediate formation of an unstable tetrathioarsenate.

$$RAsO(OH)_2 + 4HSR' \rightarrow 3H_2O + [RAs(SR')_4] \rightarrow RAs(SR')_2 + R'SSR'$$

Arsenobenzene compounds, on the other hand, can be oxidized by disulfides in alkaline solution to arsenoxides. Thus, when arsenobenzene-4,4'-dicarboxylic acid was treated with cystine in alkaline solution and the solution subsequently neutralized, the thioarsinite (XIII$a$) was isolated. The reaction may be summarized in the following way.

$$RAs{=}AsR + 2R'SSR' + 2H_2O \xrightarrow{\text{Alkaline}}$$
$$2RAsO + 4HSR' \xrightarrow{\text{Neutral}} 2RAs(SR')_2 + 2H_2O$$

XIII$a$

Finally, arsenoxides may also be oxidized by disulfides, since after the

$$RAsO + R'SSR' + 2H_2O \xrightarrow{\text{Alkaline}} RAsO_3H_2 + 2HSR'$$

addition of an arsenoxide to an alkaline solution of cystine a positive nitroprusside reaction is obtained.

[157] Cohen, King, and Strangeways, *J. Chem. Soc.*, 3043 (1931); 2505 (1932).

The evidence so far discussed, both biological and chemical, supports Voegtlin's view that the chemotherapeutically active form of the arsenical drugs, in whatever form administered, is the arsenoxide, but the problem of why arsenoxides are toxic to the parasites remains to be considered. Voegtlin suggested that they were toxic because they combined with glutathione or similar SH compounds essential to the life of the cell. He was able to show that the protoplasm of trypanosomes contains free SH groups, since it gives a positive nitroprusside reaction, and the avidity with which arsenoxides form thioarsinites in neutral solution suggests that they would do so in living tissues if the SH compounds of protoplasm were accessible to them. Thus it is well known that arsenic is deposited in the body in just those tissues, e.g., hair and nails, which contain a high proportion of cysteine in their protein (keratein). The fact that glutathione and other SH compounds will protect trypanosomes and animals against arsenical poisoning is not, of course, evidence that the toxicity of arsenicals is due to combination with SH compounds essential to life, but Voegtlin's view that arsenoxides are specific poisons affecting SH groups in protoplasm has gained in cogency since the importance of these groups in enzyme systems has been realized. Voegtlin naturally thought at the time in terms of glutathione, but since then a number of enzyme systems have been shown to depend for their activity on the integrity of free SH groups. About thirty SH enzymes are known, several of them concerned with carbohydrate metabolism,[158] and some, but not all, are extremely sensitive to arsenicals, e.g., yeast alcohol dehydrogenase, urease, hexokinase, and phosphoglyceraldehyde dehydrogenase.

One SH enzyme system, which played an important part in the work led by R. A. Peters during the war on antidotes to arsenical gases, is the pyruvate-oxidase system of pigeon brain. This system oxidizes pyruvic acid to acetic acid and carbon dioxide. Free SH groups are known to be essential to its activity, and it is powerfully inhibited by substances that combine with SH groups, such as iodoacetate, dichlorodiethylsulfone, arsenoxides, and lewisite ($\beta$-chlorovinyldichloroarsine, $CHCl{=}CHAsCl_2$). Moreover, the blood of animals poisoned with arsenicals contains a higher concentration of pyruvic acid than normal animals. Monothiol compounds were ineffective in protecting either this enzyme system or animals against arsenite or lewisite, but when it was found that keratein (reduced keratin) combines with lewisite in such a way that 75% of the arsenic is in combination with two sulfur atoms, the protective effect of dithiols was investigated.

[158] Barron and Singer, *J. Biol. Chem.*, **157**, 221, 241 (1945).

In this way BAL (British anti-lewisite) or 2,3-dimercaptopropanol ($CH_2SHCHSHCH_2OH$) was discovered;[159] its official name is dimercaprol (B.P.). BAL, in a concentration of $10^{-4}$ molar, protected the pyruvate oxidase system completely against concentrations of lewisite which normally produced 50% inhibition. It also protected rats and guinea pigs against lethal contamination with lewisite and man against vesication by the same agent.. The protective action of BAL is probably due to the stability of the five-membered ring compounds (XIII$b$) formed with trivalent arsenicals. Thus the lewisite-BAL compound

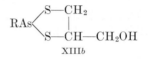

XIII$b$

is less toxic than lewisite, whereas thioarsinites formed from monothiols are often as toxic as the arsenicals from which they are derived. If the chemotherapeutic action of arsenicals is due to the formation of thioarsinites with SH groups in certain enzyme systems of parasites, the susceptibility of the parasite to these drugs will depend partly on the stability of the arsenic complex. Since thioarsinite formation is reversible, the more stable the combination of arsenical and enzyme, or the smaller its dissociation constant, the lower the concentration at which the arsenical will be effective (given equal accessibility) and the greater the concentration of SH compound required to protect the parasite. Similarly, the smaller the dissociation constant of the thioarsinite formed from the arsenical and the protecting SH compound the more effective the latter will be.

Not all "SH enzymes" are equally susceptible to arsenicals. Some are completely unaffected by concentrations of arsenoxide which inhibit others, and the same is true of trypanosome strains, although here the accessibility of the enzyme systems to the drug may also come into play. Eagle and Hogan[160] have shown that, in a series of arsenoxides varying twentyfold in systemic toxicity to mice, the amount of each bound by red blood cells *in vitro* is in proportion to its toxicity. The same is true for the uptake of arsenic by the red blood cells *in vivo* and by the tissues after intravenous injection of arsenoxides. The most striking result was that doses of tryparsamide, phenylarsonic acid, and phenylarsenoxide which produced equivalent toxic effects (LD50 level) produced compa-

[159] For a review of work leading up to the discovery of BAL, see: Peters, Stocken, and Thompson, *Nature*, **156**, 616 (1945); also: Peters, "Selective Toxicity and Antibiotics," *Symposia Soc. Exptl. Biol.* III, Cambridge University Press, London (1949), Chapter 3. pp. 36–59.

[160] Eagle and Hogan, *J. Pharmacol.*, **80**, 93 (1944).

rable tissue levels of arsenic, despite a 500-fold difference in absolute arsenic dosage. Similarly, Eagle and Magnuson [161] found that the relative trypanocidal activities of a series of some 30 arsenoxides ran parallel with the uptake of arsenic by trypanosomes *in vitro*. Ehrlich's dictum, "Corpora non agunt nisi fixata," is thus shown to be true of arsenical drugs, and as we have seen, there are reasonable grounds for regarding the arsenic receptors postulated by Ehrlich as SH groups in protoplasm, the combination of which with arsenicals blocks some process or processes essential to the life of the cell.

## Structure-Action Relationships

If the chemotherapeutically active form of organic arsenicals, in whatever form administered, is always an arsenoxide it becomes of interest to study the effect of substituents on the antiprotozoal activity of phenylarsenoxide. The unsubstituted compound is highly lethal to spirochetes and trypanosomes *in vitro*, but it is far too toxic to animals to be used therapeutically, even in experimental infections. It can, however, serve as a standard in experiments *in vitro* and in toxicity measurements, and it was so used by Eagle [162] and his colleagues in an extensive study of substituted phenylarsenoxides. Some account of their work will serve to bring out several important features of the structure-action relationships of arsenical drugs. Relative spirocheticidal and trypanocidal activities were measured *in vitro* and were expressed as potencies per gram As (i.e., relative molar potencies) on the basis phenylarsenoxide = 100. Suspensions of *S. pallida*, made by emulsifying acute testicular syphilomata of rabbits, were used for estimating spirocheticidal activity. *T. equiperdum*, harvested from heavily infected mice, was the organism used for estimating trypanocidal activity. Relative toxicities in white mice were also estimated and expressed as toxicities per gram As on the basis phenylarsenoxide = 100. Relative activity/relative toxicity ratios were taken to indicate whether particular substances were likely to be worth testing *in vivo* for curative activity. They must not be confused with chemotherapeutic indices; but they do provide a useful means of judging the relative effects of substituents on intrinsic activity and toxicity.

Both relative activity and relative toxicity are measurements of complex effects. Toxicities will obviously depend on such factors as

---

[161] Eagle and Magnuson, *ibid.*, **82**, 137 (1944).

[162] *Spirochetes;* Eagle et al., *ibid.*, **69**, 342 (1940); **74**, 210 (1942); **81**, 142 (1944). *Trypanosomes: idem, ibid.*, **85**, 265 (1945); *U. S. Pub. Health Repts.*, **59**, 765 (1944). *Chemistry: idem, J. Am. Chem. Soc.*, **62**, 168, 3010, 3012 (1940); **63**, 99 (1941); **64**, 1064 (1942); **65**, 1236 (1943); **66**, 192, 194 (1944); **67**, 719 (1945).

absorption and distribution of the drug in the tissues and rates of
excretion. Relative activity *in vitro* may at first sight appear to be a

TABLE XXVIII

| Substituent in $C_6H_5AsO$ | | Relative Activity *in vitro* per Gram As on | | Relative Toxicity (Mice) per Gram As (c) | Ratios | |
|---|---|---|---|---|---|---|
| | | Spirochetes (a) | Trypanosomes (b) | | a/c | b/c |
| None | | 100 | 100 | 100 | 1.0 | 1.0 |
| OH | ortho | 84 | 66 | 86 | 1.0 | 0.8 |
| | meta | 79 | .. | 49 | 1.6 | ... |
| | para | 72 | .. | 49 | 1.5 | ... |
| NH₂ | ortho | 88 | .. | 84 | 1.0 | ... |
| | meta | 104 | .. | 80 | 1.3 | ... |
| | para | 83 | 57 | 57 | 1.5 | 1.0 |
| Cl | ortho | 83 | 92 | 77 | 1.1 | 1.2 |
| | meta | 110 | 95 | 109 | 1.0 | 0.9 |
| | para | 85 | 90 | 99 | 0.9 | 1.0 |
| CH₃ | ortho | 84 | 91 | 88 | 1.0 | 1.0 |
| | meta | 97 | .. | 99 | 1.0 | ... |
| | para | 102 | 102 | 121 | 0.8 | 0.8 |
| NO₂ | ortho | 36 | .. | 35 | 1.0 | ... |
| | meta | 89 | .. | 80 | 1.1 | ... |
| | para | 147 | .. | 120 | 1.2 | ... |
| CO₂H | ortho | 28 | 3 | 27 | 1.0 | 0.1 |
| | meta | 13 | .. | 16 | 0.8 | ... |
| | para | 7 | 0.5 | 41 | 0.2 | 0.01 |
| p-OCOCH₃ | | 66 | .. | 44 | 1.5 | ... |
| p-OCH₃ | | 127 | .. | 118 | 1.1 | ... |
| m-NHCOCH₃ | | 42 | .. | 19 | 2.2 | ... |
| p-NHCOCH₃ | | 57 | 35 | 21 | 2.8 | 1.5 |
| p-CH₂NHCOCH₃ | | 21 | 32 | 7 | 3.0 | 4.6 |

simpler concept. It is certainly a simpler concept than therapeutic
activity, but it must also depend on several factors, e.g., uptake of the
drug by the microörganism and the efficiency of the ultimate lethal

action.  The uptake may also be complex, involving both adsorption at the surface of the cell and transport across the cytoplasmic membrane.

On *a priori* grounds it seems likely that the main effect of substituents on the activity of phenylarsenoxide *in vitro* will be exerted on the uptake of the drug by the organisms.  Substituents will of course modify to some extent the affinity of the arsenoxide group for SH compounds, or, to put it another way, substituents will affect the stability of the thio-arsinite complex assumed to be responsible for the lethal action of these drugs, but it seems unlikely that these effects will be of major importance.  There is a wealth of evidence that living cells have highly selective capacities for taking up chemical compounds, and, at least as a first approximation, it would seem justifiable to assume that the main effect of substituents will be to modify the uptake of the compounds by the cells.

The effect of simple substituents in the benzene nucleus of phenyl-arsenoxide is almost always to reduce activity *in vitro;* this is illustrated for OH, $NH_2$, Cl, $CH_3$, $NO_2$, and $CO_2H$ by Eagle's results in Table XXVIII.  With these substituents toxicity is also reduced, but to about the same extent as activity, so that the activity-toxicity ratios remain about unity.  It will be noticed that the most drastic reduction in activity is produced by the carboxyl group (see below) and that *p*-methoxy and *p*-nitro are the only groups that increase spirocheticidal activity to any appreciable extent.  An *o*-nitro group, on the other hand, decreases activity sharply.

Acetylation of *m*- and *p*-amino groups reduces activity, but it reduces toxicity even more, so that acetylamino compounds are the only ones in Table XXVIII with activity-toxicity ratios of 2 or more.  Since aromatic amines are readily acetylated in animals and frequently excreted to a large extent as acetyl derivatives in the urine, the reduced toxicity of the acetylamino compounds may be due to their being excreted more rapidly than free amines.

The effect of introducing both an OH and an $NH_2$ group into phenyl-arsenoxide is interesting; Eagle examined six of the ten possible amino-hydroxyphenylarsenoxides (Table XXIX).  It will be noticed that the spirocheticidal activities of these six isomers vary within quite narrow limits, between a third and a half that of phenylarsenoxide, but the toxicities are much more divergent.  Three isomers have toxicities of the order of a tenth that of phenylarsenoxide, and of these oxophenarsine (4-OH-3-$NH_2$) has the highest activity-toxicity ratio.  Although its spirocheticidal activity is less than half that of phenylarsenoxide, its toxicity is less than a tenth.  The therapeutic usefulness of oxophenarsine in syphilis appears then to depend on the fact that the combined effect of a 3-amino and a 4-hydroxy group is to reduce toxicity even more than spirocheticidal activity.

TABLE XXIX

| Substituents in $C_6H_5AsO$ | Relative Activity *in vitro* per Gram As on Spiro-chetes (a) | Trypano-somes (b) | Relative Toxicity (Mice) per Gram As (c) | Ratios a/c | b/c |
|---|---|---|---|---|---|
| None | 100 | 100 | 100 | 1 | 1 |
| 2-OH-3-NH₂ | 43 | 41 | 79 | 0.5 | 0.5 |
| 2-OH-5-NH₂ | 39 | .. | 22 | 1.8 | ... |
| 3-OH-2-NH₂ | 34 | .. | 10 | 3.4 | ... |
| 3-OH-4-NH₂ | 40 | 30 | 11 | 3.6 | 3.7 |
| 3-OH-5-NH₂ | 57 | .. | 74 | 0.8 | ... |
| 4-OH-3-NH₂ | 42 | 27 | 7 | 6.0 | 4.0 |

Oxophenarsine was, in Eagle's experiments, less active on trypanosomes than on spirochetes, but it still had a favorable activity-toxicity ratio. Some years earlier Fourneau and his colleagues [163] had tested the ten isomeric aminohydroxyphenylarsonic acids in experimental trypanosomiasis and had placed them in the following order in terms of the chemotherapeutic indices (given in parentheses): 2-OH-4-NH₂ (8), 4-OH-3-NH₂ (5), 3-OH-5-NH₂ (3), 3-OH-6-NH₂ (2.5), 3-OH-2-NH₂ (2.2), 3-OH-4-NH₂ (2); and the remaining four (2-OH-3-NH₂, 2-OH-5-NH₂, 2-OH-6-NH₂, 4-OH-2-NH₂) were curative only in maximum tolerated doses. The high index for the 2-OH-4-NH₂ compound is interesting because the other three isomers containing a 2-OH group were much less effective. Its N-acetyl derivative, orsanine, had an index of 20, and this is in accordance with the general finding that acylation of a 4-amino group in this series has a favorable effect on the chemotherapeutic index.

In comparing these results of Fourneau *et al.* with those of Eagle, it must be remembered that Fourneau was using arsonic acids in experimental trypanosomiasis whereas Eagle was using arsenoxides *in vitro*. Arsonic acids are excreted more rapidly than arsenoxides, and consequently Fourneau's chemotherapeutic indices are the resultants, among many other effects, of the relative rates of reduction and excretion of his compounds. Cohen, King, and Strangeways [164] attempted to throw some light on the effect of substituents in the benzene ring on the ease of

[163] Fourneau *et al.*, *Ann. inst. Pasteur*, **37**, 551 (1923); **40**, 933 (1926).
[164] Cohen, King, and Strangeways, *J. Chem. Soc.*, 2866 (1932).

reduction of phenylarsonic acids. What they actually measured were the velocity constants of the bimolecular *oxidation* of arsenoxides, since this reaction lent itself more easily to kinetic measurements than the reduction of arsonic acids. Arsenoxides are readily oxidized to arsonic acids by cystine in alkaline solution. Cysteine is formed and the reduction of cystine is accompanied by a change from $-104°$ to $-3°$ in specific rotation (mercury green line). By following the reaction polarimetrically these authors were able to calculate velocity constants from the equation $k = x/at(a - x)$, where $x =$ change in specific rotation in time $t$, and $a$ is the difference between the specific rotations of cystine and cysteine. They argued that, if arsenoxides are arranged in the order of increasing ease of oxidation, the reverse order will represent that of increasing ease of formation by reduction of arsonic acids. Since arsenoxides are always many times more toxic than the corresponding arsonic acids, it might be thought that the more easily an arsonic acid is reduced the more toxic it would be. Actually, no correlation was observed between the velocity constants measured as described above and the toxicities of the arsonic acids in mice.

It has already been noted that the introduction of a carboxyl group into phenylarsenoxide reduces activity *in vitro* drastically (Table XXVIII). With a few exceptions, to be mentioned later, it appears to be generally true that acidic groups reduce the parasiticidal activities of phenylarsenoxide derivatives to very low values. Thus Gough and King [165] observed that phenylarsonic acids containing a *meta* or *para* carboxyl or a *para* sulfonic acid group were not curative in experimental trypanosomiasis, nor were the *p*-arsonic acid derivatives of hippuric and salicylic acids. The arsenoxides corresponding to all these compounds were also ineffective, but when the acidic groups of these arsenicals were converted into amide groups, all the resulting compounds, both arsonic acids and arsenoxides, were curative, and some of them highly so. Thus *p*-benzamide arsonic acid ($NH_2COC_6H_4AsO_3H_2$) was more effective in mouse trypanosomiasis than atoxyl. This was the first record of the high trypanocidal activity of these amides, although tryparsamide was well known at the time. Eagle also studied a number of acidic arsenoxides and their corresponding amides, and some of his results, listed in Table XXX, illustrate in a striking way the effect of replacing an acidic by an amide group. With the exception of the phenylbutyric acid derivative, replacement of the acidic group by an amide group invariably increased both the trypanocidal and the spirocheticidal activity *in vitro* and usually decreased the toxicity to mice.

[165] Gough and King, *ibid.*, 669 (1930); see also Cohen, King, and Strangeways, *ibid.*, 3236 (1931).

TABLE XXX

| Substituent in $C_6H_5AsO$ | Relative Parasiticidal Activity *in vitro* per Gram As on | | Relative Toxicity (Mice) per Gram As (c) | Ratios | |
|---|---|---|---|---|---|
| | Spirochetes (a) | Trypanosomes (b) | | a/c | b/c |
| None | 100 | 100 | 100 | 1 | 1 |
| 4-CO$_2$H | 6.7 | 0.5 | 41 | 0.16 | 0.01 |
| 4-CONH$_2$ | 45 | 45 | 9.6 | 4.6 | 4.7 |
| 3-NH$_2$-4-CO$_2$H | 20 | 4 | 15 | 1.3 | 0.3 |
| 3-NH$_2$-4-CONH$_2$ | 28 | 52 | 5.6 | 5.0 | 9.3 |
| 4-CH=CHCO$_2$H | 16.6 | 2 | 9.4 | 1.8 | 0.2 |
| 4-CH=CHCONH$_2$ | 43 | 73 | 9.8 | 4.4 | 7.4 |
| 4-OCH$_2$CO$_2$H | 5 | 4.5 | 25 | 0.2 | 0.2 |
| 4-OCH$_2$CONH$_2$ | 52 | 26 | 9 | 5.7 | 2.9 |
| 4-CH$_2$CO$_2$H | 4 | 4.7 | 41 | 0.1 | 0.1 |
| 4-CH$_2$CONH$_2$ | 20 | 31 | 8.7 | 2.3 | 3.5 |
| 4-(CH$_2$)$_3$CO$_2$H | .. | 54 | 8.8 | .... | 6.1 |
| 4-(CH$_2$)$_3$CONH$_2$ | .. | 60 | 13.5 | .... | 4.4 |
| 4-SO$_3$H | 3.4 | 0.6 | 29 | 0.12 | 0.02 |
| 4-SO$_2$NH$_2$ | 29 | 24 | 4.8 | 6.1 | 5.0 |

As Gough and King pointed out, the acidic arsenoxides (assuming the arsenoxide to be the trypanocidally active molecule) will be largely present in the blood of the host as anions, whereas the corresponding amides will be neutral molecules in colloidal solution. Consequently, the amides will probably be less readily excreted by the host and more readily absorbed by the parasites, but the reason why the amides are usually less toxic to mice than the acids remains obscure. Eagle, who studied numerous examples, found that terminal amide groups, directly or indirectly attached to the benzene nucleus of phenylarsenoxide, regularly caused an 80–90% decrease in toxicity to mice but did not decrease spirocheticidal activity to anything like the same extent. Activity-toxicity ratios were about twice to six times as favorable as those of the parent arsenoxides, and somewhat smaller but still favorable chemotherapeutic indices were obtained in experimental rabbit syphilis.

That Gough and King were right in attributing the lack of curative activity of arsenicals which contain acidic groups to their existence as anions was put in a clear light by Eagle, who investigated the effect of pH on the trypanocidal activity *in vitro* of several phenylarsenoxides containing an acidic group. He found that the trypanocidal activity of arsenoxide carboxylic acids increased as the medium became more acid, i.e., as the concentration of undissociated acid increased, and, with one or two exceptions to be mentioned presently, the order of increasing activity at any given pH was the same as the order of increasing $pK$, i.e., of decreasing acidic strength. Strongly acidic compounds, such as arsenoxide sulfonic acids ($pK = <2$), and un-ionized compounds, such as amides and phenylarsenoxide itself, retained approximately the same activity over the whole range of pH used (5.7–8.7); the former because they would remain nearly fully ionized at the most acid pH used and the latter because they are not ionized at all. Moreover, Eagle showed that with arsenoxide carboxylic acids the actual amount of arsenic bound by trypanosomes increased as the pH declined and might be six times greater at pH 5.39 than at pH 8.08. That some arsenic was bound at pH 8 indicates that the anion of an arsenoxide carboxylic acid can be absorbed by trypanosomes, since at this pH most carboxylic acids are more than 99% ionized. A complicating factor, however, is that preferential absorption of the undissociated acid by a suspension of trypanosomes will displace the ionic equilibrium. It follows that in a buffered medium the heavier the trypanosomal suspension the more active an arsenoxide carboxylic acid should appear to be, relative to some un-ionized compound simultaneously tested. This was indeed so, the trypanocidal activity of two representative arsenoxide carboxylic acids [$4\text{-}CO_2H\text{-}C_6H_4AsO$ and $4\text{-}CO_2H(CH_2)_3C_6H_4AsO$] increasing, throughout the pH range 5.5–8.4, two- to fourfold for a sixfold increase in the number of organisms.

It seems clear then that the arsenoxide carboxylic acids have intrinsic parasiticidal activity, albeit of a low order, but that this activity is primarily due to the undissociated acids. Under ordinary conditions of testing arsenicals, either *in vitro* or *in vivo*, these compounds will appear inactive or only feebly active owing to their ionic dissociation at physiological pH values. There is, however, one notable exception, namely γ-phenylbutyric acid *p*-arsenoxide or butarsen ($OAsC_6H_4CH_2CH_2\text{-}CH_2CO_2H$), which displays much higher trypanocidal activity *in vitro* than either its higher or lower homologs (Table XXXI). The molar activities in Table XXXI were obtained in a medium the pH of which was not rigorously controlled ($pH$ 6.8–7.4), but it is clear from other results of Eagle that the relative molar activity of butarsen increases as the $pH$ is lowered, ranging from about 20 at $pH$ 8 to about 100 at $pH$ 5.7. This high activity is not due to butarsen's being an exceptionally weak acid, since its $pK$ is 4.9 and it is much more active than many weaker acids. At $pH$ 8 it would be 99.9% ionized, and even at $pH$ 5.7 it would

TABLE XXXI

$$OAs\langle\!\!\!\!\bigcirc\!\!\!\!\rangle(CH_2)_nCO_2H$$

| Value of $n$ | Relative Trypanocidal Activity *in vitro* per Gram As (a) | Relative Toxicity (Mice) per Gram As (b) | Ratio a/b |
|---|---|---|---|
| 0 | 0.5 | 41 | 0.01 |
| 1 | 4.7 | 41 | 0.11 |
| 2 | 2.8 | 7.3 | 0.4 |
| 3 | 54 | 8.8 | 6.1 |
| 4 | 27 | . . . | . . . |
| 5 | 9 | 8.1 | 1.1 |

be about 86% ionized. Consequently, the anion must have considerable intrinsic activity, and it may be recalled that the corresponding amide was not more active than the acid itself (Table XXX).

Butarsen is also active in mouse trypanosomiasis, a single injection of 1.6 mg./kg. curing 50% and 3.4 mg./kg. curing more than 95% of animals. Its chemotherapeutic index (LD5/CD95) in mice was 7.6, whereas that of tryparsamide, estimated similarly, was 1.6. It has the additional advantage that it is active against trypanosomes that have acquired resistance to tryparsamide and other non-acidic arsenicals. It is difficult to account for the high activity of butarsen otherwise than by assuming that the drug has a peculiarly high affinity for trypanosomes. It will be noticed (Table XXXI) that butarsen has about the same toxicity for mice as the homologous propionic and hexanoic acids but that its trypanocidal activity *in vitro* is much greater. The emergence of exceptional biological activity in one member of a homologous series is of common occurrence in pharmacology and will probably become intelligible only when more is known of the macromolecular structures in living organisms upon which such drugs act.

Another example of high intrinsic activity against trypanosomes is provided by the melaminylphenyl derivatives developed by Friedheim.[166] These are all compounds of the type XIV and include Melarsen, in which R = $AsO_3Na_2$; melarsen oxide, in which R = AsO; sodium

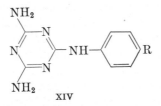

XIV

$p$-melaminylphenylstibonate, or MSb, in which R = $SbO_3HNa$; and the corresponding stibinoxide as its compound with thioglycolic acid (MSb3), where R = $Sb(SCH_2CO_2Na)_2$.

Melarsen is prepared from sodium $p$-aminophenylarsonate and cyanuric chloride. The intermediate dichlorotriazinylaminophenylarsonic acid is inactive, but trypanocidal activity appears when one chlorine atom is replaced by an amino group, and is trebled, without change in toxicity, when the second chlorine atom is replaced by $NH_2$. Alkylation of the amino groups reduces activity, and so does replacement of the amino by hydroxyl groups. The corresponding arsenoxide (melarsen oxide) and arsenobenzene derivative are also highly active.

Rollo, Williamson, and Lourie [167] made a careful comparison of all four melaminyl derivatives mentioned above with tryparsamide, oxophenarsine, and butarsen. They used mice and rabbits infected with a strain of *T. rhodesiense*, which had been passaged in mice for 25 years and had long since acquired a high sensitivity to arsenical drugs; its reactions to drugs resembled those of *T. gambiense*. Melarsen was about five to six times as toxic to mice as tryparsamide, but its curative dose (CD50) was about one-fourteenth that of tryparsamide, so that it had a somewhat more favorable index (LD50/CD50) than tryparsamide, viz., 13.0 as against 5.1. MSb was about twice as toxic as tryparsamide, but its CD50 was only about one-thirty-fifth that of the latter, so that its therapeutic ratio was 98. Melarsen oxide was slightly less toxic than oxophenarsine and butarsen but its curative dose was one-fifth that of oxophenarsine and one-ninth that of butarsen. It had a therapeutic index of 69 as against 9.0 for oxophenarsine and 5.3 for butarsen. MSb3 resembled melarsen oxide with an index of 71.

Of the four melaminyl compounds only MSb had prophylactic activity. A single intraperitoneal dose, one-quarter of the LD50, protected mice against infection for 41 weeks, whereas comparable

[166] Friedheim, *J. Am. Chem. Soc.*, **66**, 1775 (1944); Friedheim, Vogel, and Berman, *ibid.*, **69**, 560 (1947).

[167] Rollo, Williamson, and Lourie, *Ann. Trop. Med. Parasitol.*, **43**, 194 (1949).

doses of suramin and pentamidine protected mice for 10 and 4 weeks, respectively.  The persistence of MSb in the body is remarkable; whereas all trypanocidal power had vanished from the serum of rabbits within 6 days after subcutaneous injections of melarsen, melarsen oxide, tryparsamide, or oxophenarsine, it remained measurable for the extraordinary period of $7\frac{1}{2}$ months after an injection of MSb.

Melarsen, like tryparsamide, penetrates into the cerebrospinal fluid of rabbits, but melarsen oxide, in common with other trivalent arsenicals, does not.  That the cerebrospinal fluid becomes trypanocidal after administration of melarsen or tryparsamide, but not after that of trivalent arsenicals, implies that these two arsonic acids penetrate the blood-brain barrier as such and are subsequently reduced to the trypanocidally active arsenoxides.  Neither MSb nor MSb3 penetrates into the cerebrospinal fluid of rabbits.

The high trypanocidal activity of these melaminyl compounds is of great interest.  There is no reason to doubt that their lethal action on trypanosomes is ultimately due to the same mechanism as that which operates with other arsenicals.  Thus glutathione interferes with the action of melarsen oxide just as it does with that of oxophenarsine and other arsenicals, but the melaminyl group may give rise to a unique mode of fixation on, or absorption by, the trypanosome cell.  It is noteworthy that the melaminyl group contains three amidine units of structure.  We have already mentioned several classes of antiprotozoal drugs which contain two or more of these units, e.g., the anilino- and phenylguanidino-pyrimidine antimalarials, the biguanide antimalarials, the trypanocidal diamidines, and Surfen C.  In this connection it is interesting that Williamson and Lourie [168] found that Surfen C interferes selectively with the trypanocidal action of melarsen oxide *in vivo*, whereas it does not affect that of oxophenarsine or butarsen.  Moreover, it appears that it is the melamine unit of structure in Surfen C which is responsible for this interference, since melamine itself interferes with the therapeutic action of melarsen oxide but not of oxophenarsine or butarsen.  Surfen, which contains a carbamide unit linking two 4-aminoquinaldine nuclei, interferes to some extent with the action of melarsen oxide, but it also interferes with that of oxophenarsine and butarsen, i.e., exerts a less specific interference.

It is tempting to suppose that Surfen C and melamine are preferentially adsorbed on the trypanosome cell in such a way as to block the very positions at which, by virtue of the melaminyl group, the much more potent melarsen oxide would, in the absence of these interfering agents, be adsorbed; but, whatever the mechanism of this selective

[168] Williamson and Lourie, *Nature*, **161**, 103 (1948).

interference may be, it does suggest that these melaminyl arsenicals are taken up by the trypanosome cell in some way different from that which obtains for oxophenarsine or for butarsen. This conclusion, moreover, is reinforced, as will be seen, by experimental work on the drug resistance of trypanosomes to these arsenicals.

## DRUG RESISTANCE OF TRYPANOSOMES

Drug resistance by trypanosomes was discovered in Ehrlich's laboratory by Browning, Franke, and Roehl in 1907. They found that, when infected mice were fed with parafuchsin (triaminotriphenylmethyl chloride), trypanosomes disappeared from the blood but reappeared after a week or two. When the treatment had been repeated several times in an infected animal the trypanosomes ceased to disappear from the blood, i.e., they had become resistant to parafuchsin, and the blood of fresh mice infected with them could not now be cleared of parasites by feeding them with parafuchsin. The resistance extended to other triphenylmethane dyes, but the resistant strain was still sensitive to azo dyes, like trypan blue, and to arsenicals. By similar treatment of infected animals with subcurative doses trypanosome strains resistant to other dyes and to arsenicals were soon produced.

Some interesting cross-resistance relations were observed. Strains made resistant to atoxyl were resistant not only to many arsenicals but also to dyes of the acridine, oxazine, thiazine, and selenazine types (i.e., amino derivatives of I*a*, where X is CH, and of I*b*, where X is O, S, or Se). They were, however, still sensitive to triphenylmethane dyes

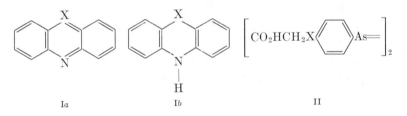

I*a*                    I*b*                          II

and to trypan blue. Similarly trypanosomes made resistant to acriflavine were found to be resistant to atoxyl too, but trypan-blue-resistant strains were resistant only to related azo dyes. There were a few exceptions also to the generality of group resistance. Thus mice infected with atoxyl-resistant strains could be cured by arsenophenylglycine (II, X = NH). Other acetic acid derivatives of the same type, e.g., arsenophenoxyacetic acid (II, X = O) and arsenophenylthioglycolic acid (II, X = S), would also cure atoxyl-resistant infections.

Since Ehrlich believed that the fixation of drugs by parasites was due to a combination of the drug with specific groups or chemoreceptors in the cell, he naturally regarded resistance as due to an alteration in the affinity of the receptors for the drug. In keeping with these ideas, it was soon found that strains made resistant to a dye were not stained by contact with dilute solutions of the dye which readily stained non-resistant parasites. Further progress on these lines was hampered by the difficulty of handling trypanosomes *in vitro;* however, Yorke and Murgatroyd [169] in 1930 devised a means of keeping trypanosomes alive and normally motile at 37° for 24 hours, and this discovery made possible a fresh experimental approach to the problem of drug resistance. They were able to show that atoxyl- and acriflavine-resistant strains were also resistant, though in varying degrees, to different organic arsenicals *in vitro*, but not to sodium arsenite. They argued that "arsenic resistance" was a definite misnomer. Their strains were not resistant to arsenic, but only to certain organic compounds of arsenic. The facts that strains made resistant to atoxyl were resistant to acriflavine, and vice versa, that they exhibited varying degrees of resistance *in vitro* to different organic compounds of arsenic, and that they were just as susceptible to sodium arsenite as the normal strain all indicated that the resistance was not to arsenic but to the substituted phenyl radical. These conclusions were reinforced by parallel experiments *in vivo*.[170]

Yorke, Murgatroyd, and Hawking [171] were also the first to demonstrate that, whereas normal trypanosomes, suspended in dilute solutions of trivalent arsenicals, rapidly remove the arsenical drug from solution, strains that have been made resistant to atoxyl do not do so. The removal of the arsenical drug from solution was detected by the diminished trypanocidal action of the supernatant fluid, after removal of the trypanosomes by centrifugation, on fresh trypanosomes. Later Hawking [172] confirmed these results by chemical estimation of the arsenic content of both trypanosomes and supernatant fluid. He found that normal trypanosomes, when suspended in dilute solutions of such trivalent arsenicals as reduced tryparsamide [$NH_2COCH_2NHC_6H_4As(SCH_2-CO_2Na)_2$], halarsol (*m*-amino-*p*-hydroxyphenyldichloroarsine), and neoarsphenamine, rapidly absorb all the available drug. At low concentrations of arsenicals no immediate damage to the trypanosomes was apparent, and absorption was complete in a few minutes so that the removal of the drug from solution could not have been due to passive

[169] Yorke and Murgatroyd, *Ann. Trop. Med. Parasitol.*, **24**, 449 (1930).
[170] Yorke, Murgatroyd, and Hawking, *ibid.*, **25**, 313 (1931).
[171] *Idem, ibid.*, **25**, 351 (1931).
[172] Hawking, *J. Pharmacol.*, **59**, 123 (1937).

absorption by dead trypanosomes. Atoxyl-resistant strains absorbed little or none of these drugs from similar dilute solutions, but absorption would occur if higher concentrations of arsenical were used. Moreover, this capacity to resist absorption of the drug was a property of living trypanosomes only. Dead trypanosomes, whether originally resistant or normal, absorbed arsenical drugs equally. Resistant strains, however, did absorb phenylarsenoxide and sodium arsenite (to which they are non-resistant *in vivo*) to the same extent as normal strains. Arseno-phenylglycine, which has a weaker curative effect on resistant than on normal infections, was absorbed to a smaller extent by resistant than by normal strains.

It is clear that resistance to particular arsenicals is not absolute. Resistant strains will absorb these drugs, but only at higher, and frequently at much higher, concentrations than normal strains will. Thus a strain will appear fully resistant to a particular arsenical *in vivo* if the threshold concentration for absorption of the drug by the trypanosomes is higher than the concentration which can be safely attained in the tissues of the host. The problem of drug resistance by trypanosomes thus becomes one of uptake. Resistant strains do not take up drugs to which they are resistant under conditions in which normal strains take them up with avidity. At the same time resistant strains will take up some arsenicals, like phenylarsenoxide and sodium arsenite, just as easily as normal strains will. The ease with which they will absorb different arsenicals varies, just as their resistance *in vivo* does. If we confine our attention to arsenoxides, it will be clear that the differing ease of absorption of various arsenicals by resistant strains must depend, as Yorke and Murgatroyd foresaw, on the nature of the substituted phenyl radical, i.e., ultimately on the nature of the substituents in the benzene nucleus. It therefore becomes of interest to study how different substituents in the phenyl group affect the trypanocidal activity of arsenicals towards normal and resistant strains. This can be done by measuring the minimum dilutions of different arsenicals required to kill normal and resistant strains *in vitro*. The ratio

$$\frac{\text{Minimum trypanocidal dilution for normal strain}}{\text{Minimum trypanocidal dilution for resistant strain}} = \frac{N}{R}$$

measures the resistance of a particular strain to any given arsenical, the larger the value of $N/R$, the greater being the resistance. Attention must be confined to trivalent arsenicals, since the pentavalent compounds are not trypanocidal *in vitro*.

Table XXXII records results on some 28 compounds taken from the work of Yorke and Murgatroyd,[169] Hawking,[172] and King and Strange-

## TABLE XXXII

| Compound | Minimum Trypanocidal Dilutions in Millions *in vitro* | | |
| --- | --- | --- | --- |
| | Normal Strain | Resistant Strain | Ratio N/R |
| Group 1 | | | |
| Phenylarsenoxide, $C_6H_5AsO$ | 409.6 | 409.6 | 1 (H) |
| | 320 | 640 | 0.5 |
| Dithioglycolylphenylthioarsinite, $C_6H_5As(SCH_2CO_2Na)_2$ | 204.8 | 204.8 | 1 (H) |
| Diglutathionylphenylthioarsinite, $C_6H_5As(SG)_2$ | 80 | 80 | 1 |
| *p*-Xylylarsenoxide, $(CH_3)_2C_6H_3AsO$ | 205 | 205 | 1 |
| | 160 | 320 | 0.5 |
| 4-Methoxyphenylarsenoxide, $CH_3OC_6H_4AsO$ | 205 | 205 | 1 |
| | 80 | 160 | 0.5 |
| 4-Thiomethylphenylarsenoxide, $CH_3SC_6H_4AsO$ | 320 | 320 | 1 |
| | 320 | 320 | 1 |
| 4-Acetophenonearsenoxide, $CH_3COC_6H_4AsO$ | 205 | 102.5 | 2 |
| | 410 | 205 | 2 |
| 4-Dimethylanilinoarsenoxide, $(CH_3)_2NC_6H_4AsO$ | 256 | 128 | 2 |
| 4-Nitrophenylarsenoxide, $NO_2C_6H_4AsO$ | 25.5 | 52 | 0.5 |
| | 2 | 2 | 1 |
| Group 2 | | | |
| 4-Carboxyphenylarsenoxide, $CO_2HC_6H_4AsO$ | 0.4 | 0.8 | 0.5 |
| | 0.8 | 0.8 | 1 |
| | 0.8 | 0.8 | 1 |
| 3-Acetamido-4-carboxyphenylarsenoxide, 3-$CH_3CONH$＼ ＞$C_6H_3AsO$ 4-$CO_2H$／ | 0.1 | 0.2 | 0.5 |
| 4-Acetamido-3-carboxyphenylarsenoxide, 3-$CO_2H$＼ ＞$C_6H_3AsO$ 4-$CH_3CONH$／ | 0.032 | 0.032 | 1 |
| 4-Phenylglycine arsenoxide, $CO_2HCH_2NHC_6H_4AsO$ | 0.8 | 0.8 | 1 |

TABLE XXXII (*Continued*)

| Compound | Minimum Trypanocidal Dilutions in Millions *in vitro* | | |
|---|---|---|---|
| | Normal Strain | Resistant Strain | Ratio N/R |
| 2,4-Dicarboxyphenylarsenoxide | 0.1 | 0.1 | 1 |
| $(CO_2H)_2C_6H_3AsO$ | 0.1 | 0.05 | 2 |
| | | | |
| Arsenophenylglycine, | 12.8 | 6.4 | 2 (H) |
| $(CO_2HCH_2NHC_6H_4As:)_2$ | 12.8 | 6.4 | 2 (H) |
| **Group 3** | | | |
| 4-Hydroxy-3-nitrophenylarsenoxide, | 8 | 4 | 2 |
| $3\text{-}NO_2$ | 26 | 6.4 | 4 |
| $\diagdown C_6H_3AsO$ | | | |
| $4\text{-}HO\diagup$ | | | |
| 4-Aminophenylarsenoxide, $NH_2C_6H_4AsO$ | 4 | 1 | 4 |
| | 4 | 1 | 4 |
| | 8 | 1 | 8 |
| Dithioglycolyl-4-aminophenylthioarsinite, | 102 | 25 | 4 (H) |
| $NH_2C_6H_4As(SCH_2CO_2Na)_2$ | | | |
| **Group 4** | | | |
| 4-Hydroxyphenylarsenoxide, $HOC_6H_4AsO$ | 51.2 | 3.2 | 16 |
| | 160 | 10 | 16 |
| | 409 | 25 | 16 (H) |
| Dithioglycolyl-3-acetamido-4-hydroxy- phenylthioarsinite, | 6.4 | 0.4 | 16 (H) |
| $3\text{-}CH_3CONH$ | | | |
| $\diagdown C_6H_3As(SCH_2CO_2Na)_2$ | | | |
| $4\text{-}HO\diagup$ | | | |
| 4-Acetanilide arsenoxide, | 51.2 | 1.6 | 32 |
| $CH_3CONHC_6H_4AsO$ | 102.4 | 3.2 | 32 (H) |
| $3\text{-}NH_2$ | 102.4 | 3.2 | 32 (H) |
| Halarsol, $\diagdown C_6H_3AsCl_2$ | | | |
| $4\text{-}HO\diagup$ | | | |
| Neoarsphenamine | 51.2 | 1.6 | 32 (H) |
| Diglutathionyl-4-acetamido-2-hydroxy- phenylthioarsinite, | 12.8 | 0.2 | 64 |
| | 25.6 | 0.8 | 32 |
| $2\text{-}HO$ | | | |
| $\diagdown C_6H_3As(SG)_2$ | | | |
| $4\text{-}CH_3CONH\diagup$ | | | |

TABLE XXXII (*Continued*)

| | Minimum Trypanocidal Dilutions in Millions *in vitro* | | |
| Compound | Normal Strain | Resistant Strain | Ratio N/R |
| --- | --- | --- | --- |
| Diglutathionyl-tryparsamide thioarsinite, $NH_2COCH_2NHC_6H_4As(SG)_2$ | 12.8 | 0.4 | 32 |
| Benzamide-4-arsenoxide, $NH_2COC_6H_4AsO$ | 51.2 | 0.8 | 64 |
| | 51.2 | 0.8 | 64 |
| Dicysteinylbenzamide-4-thioarsinite, $NH_2COC_6H_4As(SG)_2$ | 25.6 | 0.8 | 32 |
| | 51.2 | 1.6 | 32 |
| Phenyl-*p,p'*-diarsenoxide, $OAsC_6H_4AsO$ | 32 | 1 | 32 |

Results marked (H) are taken from Hawking's paper (ref. 172) and were obtained by exposure of trypanosomes to arsenicals for 24 hours at 37°; all the other results were obtained after 6 hours' exposure of trypanosomes to the drugs and are taken from the work of King and Strangeways (ref. 173). G = glutathionyl.

ways.[173] Atoxyl- and tryparsamide-resistant strains of *T. rhodesiense* were used, but atoxyl and tryparsamide, together with arsacetin, neoarsphenamine, and acriflavine, all give apparently identical resistant strains.[174] The compounds are divided into four groups: (1) phenyl-arsenoxide and derivatives of it for which the N/R ratio varies from 0.5 to 2, (2) a group of acidic arsenoxides with N/R also equal to 0.5 to 2, (3) a small group of compounds with intermediate N/R ratios (2 to 8), and (4) compounds with high N/R ratios (16 to 64). Since successive dilutions always differed by a factor of 2, compounds with N/R ratios of 0.5 to 2 may be taken as equally active on normal and resistant strains. This applies to members of groups 1 and 2, but it is convenient to consider them separately because they differ so widely in activity. Members of group 4 are very much less active on resistant than on normal strains.

Phenylarsenoxide and its derivatives in group 1 are extremely potent trypanocidal substances, most of them being active in dilutions of the order of 200 to 400 million. King drew attention to the high lipoidal content of trypanosomes—according to Kligler and Olitzki [175] 60% of the substance of *T. evansi* is lipoidal in nature—and suggested that com-

[173] King and Strangeways, *Ann. Trop. Med. Parasitol.*, **36**, 47 (1942); see also King, *Trans. Faraday Soc.*, **39**, 383 (1943).

[174] Yorke, Murgatroyd, and Hawking, *Ann. Trop. Med. Parasitol.*, **26**, 577 (1932).

[175] Kligler and Olitzki, *ibid.*, **30**, 287 (1936).

pounds like phenylarsenoxide and xylylarsenoxide, which apart from the arsenoxide group are devoid of hydrophilic groups, were taken up at a lipoid-water interface in such a way that the phenyl or xylyl group is in the lipoid and the arsenoxide group at the water interface. This would be a passive process and presumably a facile one since the action of these compounds is so pronounced. King then imagines these compounds to be transported via the lipoidal material of the cell to the site at which the arsenoxide group can exert its lethal chemical action. Since none of the other members of group 1 has markedly hydrophilic substituents in the phenylarsenoxide nucleus, they may also be capable of being taken up and transported in a similar fashion.

The members of group 2 differ vastly in activity from those of group 1 but are also as active on resistant as on normal trypanosomes. It includes arsenophenylglycine, which Ehrlich found would cure atoxyl-resistant infections, and the corresponding arsenoxide; 4-phenylglycine arsonic acid will also cure similarly resistant infections.[170] Butarsen (4-phenylbutyric acid arsenoxide) should also be included in this group since it contains a free carboxyl group and is active against tryparsamide-resistant trypanosomes.[176] It is, however, a much more active substance than the other members of this group (minimum trypanocidal dilution on *T. rhodesiense* is of the order of 100 million). All these carboxyl-containing arsenicals form easily water-soluble salts and will be present under the conditions of either *in vivo* or *in vitro* tests mainly as anions. Since they contain hydrophilic groups at each end of their molecules, they are unlikely to leave the aqueous medium and be taken up by lipoids in the trypanosome cell. King suggests that they enter the trypanosome cell by routes similar to those by which other substances that are very soluble in water, like glucose and salts, do so; this need not be, and probably is not, a simple diffusion process.

The exceptional trypanocidal potency of butarsen compared with its lower and higher homologs has been noted and it has been argued that the structure of butarsen must fit it uniquely for uptake by trypanosomes. Eagle's evidence that the undissociated acids are taken up more readily than the anions has been reviewed, but the mechanism of uptake is unknown. All that can be said with confidence is that these carboxylic acids have a means of entry into the trypanosome cell different from that open to the members of group 4 in Table XXXII, and probably different from that employed by members of group 1.

The members of group 4 illustrate admirably the remarkable phenomenon of drug resistance; they act on resistant trypanosomes only at concentrations 16- to 64-fold those which are lethal to normal strains.

[176] Eagle, *Science*, **101**, 69 (1945).

All the members of this group contain hydrophilic substituents, though none which is strongly acidic or basic; the substituents are characteristically those capable of forming hydrogen bonds, such as OH and $NH_2$. King suggests that these compounds are taken up by the normal trypanosome cell in the same way as the acridine and oxazine dyestuffs, in other words, that they are *substantive* for the same type of structure in the cytoplasmic membrane. Of this structure little is known, except that it presumably contains polar groups and is incapable of adsorbing dyes of the triphenylmethane and trypan-blue types. In resistant trypanosomes this structure has presumably been altered in such a way that it now has a markedly reduced affinity for members of this group. Moreover, this reduced affinity is maintained only in the living cell, which suggests that its maintenance is an energy-consuming process. An interesting member of the group is phenyl-$p,p'$-diarsenoxide. The introduction of a second AsO group into phenylarsenoxide has apparently altered completely the manner of its uptake by the trypanosome cell. Whereas the unsubstituted phenylarsenoxide could be taken up by lipoid structures, King suggests that the primary fixation of the diarsenoxide involves both ends of the molecule and that the molecule as a whole probably lies flat on the surface to which it is adsorbed.

Another interesting substance is benzamide-$p$-arsenoxide, which must be taken up by normal trypanosomes in some way different from 4-carboxyphenylarsenoxide. It has been noted that amide-substituted arsenoxides are considerably more active than the corresponding carboxylic acids, and the evidence presented in Table XXXII suggests that this is due to a different and much easier mechanism of uptake. Similar considerations apply to the glutathionyl derivatives of reduced tryparsamide and its corresponding acid, phenylglycine arsenoxide. It is curious that these two amides are lethal to resistant trypanosomes at about the same dilutions as the corresponding acids are to both normal and resistant strains.

Of the members of group 3, 4-hydroxy-3-nitrophenylarsenoxide probably constitutes a truly intermediate type, since its $o$-nitrophenolic radical will be less acidic than the 4-carboxyphenyl and more acidic than the 4-hydroxyphenyl radical (compare the following dissociation constants: phenol, $10^{-10}$; $o$-nitrophenol, $6 \times 10^{-8}$; benzoic acid, $7 \times 10^{-5}$). The other two members of the group are, however, much more difficult to understand. They are, of course, from the point of view of trypanocidal activity, one and the same compound, viz., the arsenoxide corresponding to atoxyl. The figures for the thioarsinite were obtained with an atoxyl-resistant strain; those for the arsenoxide, with a tryparsamide-resistant strain. It is strange that both strains should be less resistant to 4-aminophenylarsenoxide than to 4-hydroxy-phenylarsenoxide or even to 4-acetanilide arsenoxide.

One other arsenical drug must be mentioned, namely melarsen oxide. Williamson and Lourie [177] tested this substance *in vivo* on a tryparsamide-resistant strain of *T. rhodesiense*. This strain, which had maintained its resistance for 18 years, was still fully resistant to oxophenarsine, but melarsen oxide was equally as effective against it as against the parent strain. The uptake of melarsen oxide, with its melaminyl radical, by trypanosomes can scarcely be effected by the same means as that of phenylarsenoxide and its fellow members of group 1. It is equally unlikely that it will be taken up in a manner analogous to that which operates for carboxyl-substituted arsenoxides. The evidence from Williamson and Lourie's experiments proves that it is not taken up by the same means as members of group 4. It can only be concluded that it is taken up by trypanosomes in some way quite different from those which operate with all other arsenical drugs, a way, moreover, charac-teristic for melaminyl-containing substances, as evidence already quoted (p. 518) suggests. Trypanosomes can, however, be made resist-ant to melarsen, but the resistance so developed is different in character from that produced by atoxyl, tryparsamide, etc.

Strains of *T. rhodesiense* made resistant to melarsen are still sensitive to atoxyl and similar arsenicals but they are now highly resistant to pentamidine and decamethylene diamidine; they are also resistant, but less so, to stilbamidine.[178] These results suggest that melarsen oxide is taken up by trypanosomes in the same way as the diamidines. They are particularly interesting in view of the fact, to which attention has already been drawn, that the melaminyl group contains three amidine units.

The resistance that trypanosomes can acquire to arsenical drugs has been discussed in some detail because sufficient experimental evidence is available to make it clear that resistance to these drugs is primarily a matter of uptake. There is little if any doubt that the ultimate lethal action is the same for all arsenical drugs; it is certainly due to the arsenic radical, whereas the development of resistance is determined by the nature of the substituted phenyl radical. With non-arsenical drugs, however, the evidence is frequently equivocal because the mechanisms either of uptake or of the ultimate lethal action are usually not known. Moreover, with compounds that do not contain an element so readily estimated as arsenic it is often difficult to detect uptake, short of killing

[177] Williamson and Lourie, *Nature*, **161**, 103 (1948).
[178] Rollo and Williamson, *ibid.*, **167**, 147 (1951).

the organisms, or to estimate the amount of drug absorbed. The point
may be illustrated by reference to plasmodia.

Williamson and Lourie [179] found that *P. gallinaceum* made resistant
to proguanil (III) remains sensitive to 3349 (IV). The structural
resemblance between these two compounds is striking. Apart from the
basic side chain of IV, and the carbon atom to which it is attached, the

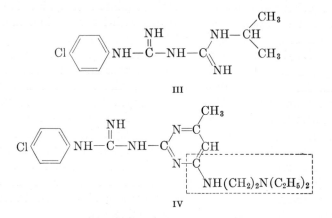

III

IV

carbon-nitrogen skeletons of these substances are identical, but it is not
known whether this resemblance entails a common ultimate mechanism of lethal action or a common mode of uptake by plasmodia. Consequently, it cannot be decided whether the sensitivity of proguanil-
resistant plasmodia to 3349 is the result of these two drugs' having different modes of uptake or different mechanisms of lethal action. If they
have a common mechanism of lethal action, as Williamson and Lourie
assumed, it must be concluded that their modes of attachment to, or
entry into, the parasite cell are different, but if their lethal actions are
of different kinds resistance to proguanil might be achieved by a change
in the biochemical mechanisms of the cell. It must not be supposed
that resistance is always and necessarily associated with changes in the
facility of uptake of drugs. There is, for example, considerable evidence
that the metabolic processes of bacteria may be modified during the
acquisition of resistance in such a way that the cell ceases to rely on the
particular process with which a bacteriostatic substance interferes.[180]
It is not impossible that protozoans may also be able to modify their
metabolic processes in such a way as to avoid the toxic effects of some
drugs, though there is as yet no evidence that this occurs.

[179] Williamson and Lourie, *Ann. Trop. Med. Parasitol.*, **41**, 278 (1947).

[180] Hinshelwood, "Chemical Kinetics of the Bacterial Cell," Oxford University Press,
London (1946).

A fundamental problem which must be briefly mentioned is how trypanosomes or other protozoans acquire resistance to particular drugs. There are several possibilities. (1) Repeated exposure of an infection to subcurative treatment with a drug might weed out sensitive individuals, leaving those naturally more resistant to multiply, until the whole population consisted of more-resistant forms; resistance would then be achieved by selection. (2) Resistance might be due to a gradual change in some or all cells, resulting from the stimulus of frequent exposure to the drug, thus giving rise to a new character transmitted unaltered through subsequent generations. In this way a new genetic strain would be produced, a process called mutation. (3) Resistant mutants might occur spontaneously, but usually be overgrown by normal forms. Exposure of populations containing such mutants to sublethal concentrations of drug might exert a selective action, sensitive forms being killed but resistant mutants multiplying until the whole population consisted of resistant forms. This process would be one of spontaneous mutation plus artificial selection.

Yorke,[181] whose fundamental work in this field has already been mentioned, inclined to the second of these views. In collaboration with Murgatroyd and Hawking [182] he demonstrated that resistant strains could be produced *in vitro* by a series of short exposures of a normal strain to reduced tryparsamide, alternating with passage of the drug-laden parasites through mice. Highly resistant strains were rapidly produced when reduced tryparsamide was used in the highest concentration possible without killing all the trypanosomes (1 in 0.8 million). All but the more-resistant trypanosomes would be killed under these conditions so that this method would be consistent with the view that the drug was acting as a means of artificial selection. On the other hand resistance to a lesser extent could be produced slowly by successive exposures to reduced tryparsamide at concentrations (1 in 12.8 million) which did not kill any appreciable number of trypanosomes. It was argued that, even if this low concentration killed a small proportion of the trypanosomes in the early stages, it could hardly have done so when the strain became several times as resistant as it had originally been. Yet the strain developed a gradual but steadily increasing resistance until after 36 exposures it was about 20 times as resistant as the parent strain. This result is difficult to account for in terms of selection, and Yorke preferred the hypothesis that resistance is fundamentally due to a process of mutation, the rapidity and degree of this mutation being

[181] Yorke, *Brit. Med. J.*, **2**, 668 (1932).
[182] Yorke, Murgatroyd, and Hawking, *Ann. Trop. Med. Parasitol.*, **25**, 521 (1931).

primarily dependent on the concentration of drug to which the trypanosomes are exposed.

Eagle and Magnuson [183] suggested the third possibility mentioned
above. They observed the spontaneous occurrence of an arsenical-
resistant strain of *T. equiperdum*. The strain had been maintained by
passage through mice untreated with drugs, but whereas it was sensitive
to such arsenicals as oxophenarsine in July, 1943, it had become resistant
to them in October of the same year. Thus, when exposed to reduced
tryparsamide *in vitro* in October, the strain took up only 1.8% of the
total arsenic in an added concentration of 1.66 $\mu$g./ml., whereas between
February and July it took up 38%. Over the same short period of July
to October the relative molar potency of reduced tryparsamide on this
strain *in vitro* fell from 14 to 0.64 (phenylarsenoxide = 100). The resistant strain retained full sensitivity to phenylarsenoxide and butarsen and
took up from solutions of these two drugs the same proportion of arsenic
as it had before resistance to other arsenicals occurred; i.e., it had
spontaneously acquired resistance of the same type as that which can be
produced by drugs like those of group 4 in Table XXXII. Eagle and
Magnuson suggested that spontaneous mutations may occur more
frequently than is suspected and that, when resistance is induced by
repeated exposure of the organisms to an arsenical drug, the drug itself
may not always "produce" the variant strain; it may only "reveal" it,
by acting as a selective factor favorable to the variant strain, killing the
susceptible organisms with which it is in competition in the host and by
which it would otherwise be overgrown. In the present state of knowledge it is probably wise to assume that more than one mechanism may
be involved in the production of resistant strains. Both mutation and
selection may be operating, although under some conditions one factor
may play a larger part than the other.

### ENVOI

This chapter provides only an introduction to some of the more
chemical aspects of chemotherapy. Many important topics have been
omitted, e.g., the chemotherapy of helminthic infections, of tuberculosis,
and of cancer. The omissions have been dictated partly by considerations of space and partly by the author's feeling that it would be better
to deal fairly thoroughly with a limited field than superficially with the
whole field. The attentive reader will also have noticed that particular
pieces of research work have been described in some detail. This has
been done deliberately, because in the author's opinion the development

---

[183] Eagle and Magnuson, *J. Pharmacol.*, **82**, 137 (1944).

of individual researches is often more illuminating to the beginner in a subject than a rounded survey of a whole literature. Research work is a highly individual activity, and beginners in it may frequently learn more from a close study of the work of one acknowledged master of it than from reading highly condensed surveys of a whole field.

This chapter has also kept to the well-trodden paths of chemotherapy and has eschewed some of its most recent developments. It is a subject much given to fashions, but he who would be well grounded in it cannot afford to neglect the main lines of its development; for this reason a considerable amount of space has been devoted to the chemotherapy of trypanosomiasis and to arsenical drugs, fields in which Ehrlich, who laid the foundations of the subject, himself worked.

One final word of warning: Chemotherapy is, of its very nature, a biological subject, but a biological subject which depends for its advancement upon the insight and ingenuity of the organic chemist. The last word will always be with the biologist or the physician. The organic chemist should always familiarize himself, as best he can, with the biological side of his problem—and the ultimate problems of the mechanism of drug actions will certainly be for him or for his colleague, the biochemist, to solve—but he must realize that the complexities of the problems involved in the treatment of disease are outside his province. Experience will teach him that the value of a new remedy is at first nearly always exaggerated, that there follows a period during which its value is underestimated, and that it is only after many years that the true status of a remedy can be assessed with confidence.

## GENERAL REFERENCES

Albert, "The Acridines, Their Preparation, Physical, Chemical and Biological Properties and Uses," Arnold, London (1951).

Burn, Finney, and Goodwin, "Biological Standardization," Oxford University Press, London (1951), 2nd ed.

Clark, "General Pharmacology," *Heffter's Handbuch der experimentellen Pharmakologie*, Erganzungswerk, Band 4, Springer, Berlin (1937).

Dubos, "The Bacterial Cell," Harvard University Press, Cambridge, Mass. (1945).

Findlay, "Recent Advances in Chemotherapy," Churchill, London, Vol. 1 (1950), Vol. 2 (1951), Vols. 3 and 4 (in press), 3rd ed.

Fischl and Schlossberger, "Handbuch der Chemotherapie," Fischer's Medizinische Buchhandlung, Leipzig (1934).

Goodman and Gilman, "The Pharmacological Basis of Therapeutics," The Macmillan Co., New York (1948), reprint.

Hawking and Lawrence, "Sulphonamides," Lewis, London (1950).

Hinshelwood, "The Chemical Kinetics of the Bacterial Cell," Clarendon Press, Oxford (1946).

Northey, "The Sulphonamides and Allied Compounds," Reinhold Publishing Corp., New York (1948).

Sexton, "Chemical Constitution and Biological Activity," D. Van Nostrand, New York (1950).

"Survey of Antimalarial Drugs, 1941–1945," edited by Wiselogle, Ann Arbor, Mich. (1946).

Symposia of the Society of Experimental Biology, No. III, "Selective Toxicity and Antibiotics," Cambridge University Press, London (1949).

Williams, "Detoxication Mechanisms," Chapman & Hall, London (1947).

Work and Work, "The Basis of Chemotherapy," Interscience Publishers, New York (1948).

CHAPTER 6

# ANTIBIOTICS

Lee C. Cheney

*Bristol Laboratories, Inc., Syracuse, N. Y.*

## CONTENTS

## INTRODUCTION

The term antibiotic is generally defined as a chemical substance of microbial origin that in low concentration seriously interferes with the growth or metabolic activities of other microörganisms, including the molds, actinomycetes, and bacteria.[1] The growing tendency to expand the definition to embrace all antimicrobial drugs of animal and botanical derivation only detracts from the recognized usefulness of the restricted term. Numerous cases of microbial antagonism have been described since Pasteur and Joubert [2] in 1877 noted that anthrax bacilli in non-sterile urine suffer marked inhibition of growth. More than fifty years later Fleming's observation [3] of antibiosis led to the discovery by Florey and his colleagues [4] of penicillin's medical potentialities. They demonstrated that a factor produced by *Penicillium notatum* was a uniquely non-toxic systemic chemotherapeutic agent of spectacular clinical promise. Through Anglo-American coöperation and military priorities second only to those for the atomic bomb, commercial penicillin was developed. The astounding potentialities of antibiotics to conquer the most dreaded diseases of mankind were thus hastened to realization through the exigencies of a world war. Without doubt the interim systematic pioneer investigations of Dubos concerning the bactericidal extract derived from a soil bacillus [5] followed by the isolation of crystalline gramicidin and tyrocidine [6] exerted a profound stimulatory effect on the course of antibiotic research.

Implemented by methods and techniques largely developed and refined since the clinical value of penicillin was appreciated, systematic world-wide antibiotic research is expanding the literature on the subject at such a tremendous pace that at best only a glimpse of a vast and dynamic field can be presented.[7] Even apart from the compounds of

[1] Waksman, "Microbial Antagonisms and Antibiotic Substances," The Commonwealth Fund, New York (1945, 1947); Oxford, *Ann. Rev. Biochem.*, **14**, 749 (1945).

[2] Pasteur and Joubert, *Compt. rend.*, **85**, 101 (1877).

[3] Fleming, *Brit. J. Exptl. Path.*, **10**, 226 (1929).

[4] Chain, Florey, and co-workers, *Lancet*, **239**, 226 (1940); Abraham and co-workers, *ibid.*, **241**, 177 (1941).

[5] Dubos, *J. Exptl. Med.*, **70**, 1 (1939).

[6] Hotchkiss and Dubos, *J. Biol. Chem.*, **132**, 791, 793 (1940); **141**, 155 (1941).

[7] (*a*) For complete information covering antibiotics and antimicrobial substances derived from plants described before 1948, consult the monumental two-volume treatise of Florey, Chain, Heatley, Jennings, Sanders, Abraham, and Florey, "Antibiotics," Oxford University Press, London (1949); (*b*) see also Baron, "Handbook of Antibiotics," Reinhold Publishing Corp., New York (1950); (*c*) for annual surveys of significant chemical developments in antibiotic research see Wintersteiner and Dutcher, *Ann. Rev. Biochem.*, **18**, 559 (1949); Carter and Ford, *ibid.*, **19**, 487 (1950); Peck and Lyons, *ibid.*, **20**, 367 (1951); and succeeding annual reviews; (*d*) Karel and Roach, "A Dictionary of Antibiosis," Columbia University Press, New York (1951).

the polypeptide class, approximately eighty significantly potent antibiotic substances have been isolated in pure form. Because of excessive systemic toxicity and/or inactivation *in vivo* only a few, however, are destined to prove eminently useful in chemotherapy. Those showing little medical promise are presented in tabular form only (Table II), arranged in conformity with the formula index of *Chemical Abstracts*. As a group they represent biologically active models exemplifying exceedingly diverse and complex structural characteristics. In consequence, only a few of the provisionally assigned structures appearing in the table have been confirmed by synthesis.

Aside from therapeutic implications, the discovery of the dramatic growth-promoting effect of certain antibiotics on poultry and swine portends far-reaching economic potentialities for antibiotic substances in animal nutrition.

### THE PENICILLINS

**Introduction.** In addition to the comprehensive monograph,[8] which delineates in detail the experimental and theoretical aspects of the chemistry of penicillin and engenders an appreciation for the magnitude of the collaborative quest for an unequivocal structure and a practical synthesis, other, more concise reviews are available.[7, 9] An elaboration of undocumented information, for which it is not possible to assign individual credit, is readily accessible through the carefully arranged index of the monograph.[8] Photostats and microfilms of the original reports may be examined.[10]

**The Various Penicillins.** During the course of structural studies, five "natural" penicillins (Table I) were isolated in pure form which differ only in the chemical nature of the acylamino moiety attached to a com-

[8] Clarke, Johnson, and Robinson, editors, "The Chemistry of Penicillin," Princeton University Press, Princeton, N. J. (1949). This volume, comprising twenty-nine chapters and over one thousand pages, is a record of approximately seven hundred confidential interim reports from seventeen participating groups in Britain and twenty-two groups in the United States. Government, industrial, and university laboratories joined forces in this wartime investigation of the chemistry of penicillin, sponsored jointly by the Office of Scientific Research and Development, Washington, D. C., and the Medicinal Research Council, London.

[9] Chain, *Ann. Rev. Biochem.*, **17**, 657 (1948); Chain, *Endeavour*, **7**, 83, 152 (1948); Cook, *Quart. Revs. (London)*, **2**, 203 (1948); Committee Med. Research, O.S.R.D., Washington, D. C., and Med. Research Council, London, England, *Science*, **102**, 627 (1945); *Nature*, **156**, 766 (1945); Editorial Board (Monograph on Chemistry of Penicillin), *Science*, **105**, 653 (1947).

[10] Bibliography of Scientific and Industrial Reports, U. S. Department of Commerce, Office of Technical Services, Washington, D. C., Vol. 6, No. 7 (1947), through Vol. 8, No. 5 (1948).

## TABLE I

THE "NATURAL" PENICILLINS

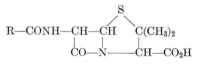

$$R—CONH—CH—CH \quad C(CH_3)_2$$
$$CO—N———CH—CO_2H$$

| Name * | Other Designations | Side Chain R | Potency against *Staph. aureus* in Units per Mg. † |
|---|---|---|---|
| 2-Pentenylpenicillin | Penicillin I or F | $CH_3CH_2CH=CHCH_2—$ | 1440–1550 |
| Benzylpenicillin | Penicillin II or G | $C_6H_5CH_2—$ | 1667 |
| p-Hydroxybenzyl-penicillin | Parasiticin [11] Penicillin III or X | $p\text{-}HOC_6H_4CH_2—$ | 850–900 |
| n-Heptylpenicillin | Penicillin K | $n\text{-}CH_3(CH_2)_6—$ | 2300 |
| n-Amylpenicillin [12] | Dihydro-F-penicillin Gigantic acid [13] Flavacidin (Flavicin) [14] | $n\text{-}CH_3(CH_2)_4—$ | 1680 |

* In general these names refer to the sodium salt of the penicillin (see ref. 8, p. 1070). A more precise nomenclature is the appropriate prefix followed by penicillinic acid, e.g., benzylpenicillinic acid to designate clearly the free acid; it follows that sodium benzylpenicillinate and methyl benzylpenicillinate are the unambiguous names for the corresponding sodium salt and the methyl ester, respectively.

† The international standard is sodium benzylpenicillinate with a potency of 1667 units per milligram; therefore by definition 1 International Unit = 0.6 $\mu$g. [*Science*, **101**, 42 (1945)].

mon nucleus. The structure of the side chain R in any individual penicillin is clearly defined by the nomenclature adopted.

The type of penicillin produced in a fermentation depends on the strain of the mold and particularly on the chemical composition of the nutrient medium. 2-Pentenylpenicillin, the main species in the impure penicillin originally studied biologically and chemically by the British, is of great historical interest. Benzylpenicillin, the first species isolated in pure crystalline form,* originated in culture broth containing corn-steep liquor, a by-product in the manufacture of corn starch. The early recognition of the chemical difference in British and American penicillins led to the discoveries that the marked stimulatory effect of

[11] Arnstein and Cook, *Brit. J. Exptl. Path.*, **28**, 94 (1947).

[12] Leigh, *Nature*, **163**, 95 (1949).

[13] Philpot, *ibid.*, **152**, 725 (1943).

[14] Adler and Wintersteiner, *J. Biol. Chem.*, **176**, 873 (1948); ref. 8, p. 103.

* Announced by MacPhillamy, Wintersteiner, and Alicino in July, 1943.

corn-steep liquor on penicillin production [15a] is explained in part by the presence of β-phenylethylamine,[15b] serving as a specific precursor for biosynthesis of benzylpenicillin by the mold, and that the yields are greatly increased by the addition of phenylacetic acid and/or its various derivatives to the fermentation broth.[15c, 16] Other important variable constituents of corn-steep liquor still remain to be identified.

Although efforts to stimulate the production of p-hydroxybenzylpenicillin by supplying the mold with various phenolic compounds have met with only moderate success, more than thirty new crystalline biosynthetic penicillins have emerged from a systematic investigation of precursor potentialities.[16] More recently, several penicillins containing a strictly aliphatic side chain have been produced biosynthetically.[17]

Benzoic and other aromatic acids are not utilized by the mold. Since only monosubstituted acetic acids are effective, the α-methylene unit appears to be essential. In place of phenyl the substituent may be an alicyclic, a heterocyclic, or a polycyclic radical. Nuclear substituents include alkoxy, alkyl, nitro, and the halogens. Various oxy- and mercapto-acetic acids are eminently satisfactory precursors, presumably because the hetero atoms interrupt β-oxidation. Effective precursors for the penicillamine moiety, common to all the penicillins, are not known.

**Production of Commercial Penicillin.** The crystalline penicillin of commerce consists almost exclusively of the non-toxic salts of relatively pure penicillin G (benzylpenicillin). Major factors that have contributed to the phenomenal increase in penicillin production * are (a) the development of higher-yielding mutants of *Penicillium chrysogenum* through the agencies of ultraviolet [18] and x-ray irradiation;[19] (b) the adoption of the submerged culture technique of fermentation; (c) the discovery of the efficacy of the corn-steep liquor and lactose medium; (d) the use of phenylacetic acid and related compounds as precursors;

[15] (a) Moyer and Coghill, *J. Bact.*, **51**, 57, 79 (1946); (b) Mead and Stack, *Biochem. J.*, **42**, xviii (1948); (c) Moyer and Coghill, *J. Bact.*, **53**, 329 (1947); Coghill and Moyer, U. S. pat. 2,423,873 [*C. A.*, **41**, 6372 (1947)]; ref. 8. pp. 9, 81–83.

[16] Behrens, ref. 8, pp. 657–679; Behrens and co-workers, *J. Biol. Chem.*, **176**, 1047 (1948) (this report provides references to the seven preceding papers in the series); Philip and co-workers, *ibid.*, **189**, 479 (1951).

[17] Thorn and Johnson, *J. Am. Chem. Soc.*, **72**, 2052 (1950).

* In 1943 the total production of penicillin (sodium salt) in the United States was 21.2 billion units (28 lb.), valued at $20 per 100,000 units (60 mg.). In 1951 the United States production totaled 324,293 billion units and was accompanied by a precipitous lowering of cost. The price for bulk crystalline potassium penicillin in June, 1951, was 4 cents per 100,000 units; in June, 1952, the price had been reduced to 2 cents per 100,000 units, or approximately $145 per pound.

[18] Backus, Stauffer, and Johnson, *J. Am. Chem. Soc.*, **68**, 152 (1946); Foster, U. S. pat. 2,458,495 [*C. A.*, **43**, 2278 (1949)]; Woodruff and Larsen, U. S. pat. 2,532,980 [*C. A.*, **45**, 1737 (1951)].

[19] Demerec, U. S. pat. 2,445,748 (1948).

and (e) the development of improved methods for isolation and purification. By virtue of the advantageous use of precursors in conjunction with superior mold strains the formation of the other penicillins is suppressed, and high yields of readily purified penicillin G can be isolated without the use of chromatographic procedures. The protein-rich mold mycelium is filtered from the broth and disposed of as fertilizer or as animal feed. After the chilled filtered broth is acidified, it is extracted countercurrently with a suitable water-immiscible organic solvent.[20] After further purification, the desired sodium or potassium salt can be precipitated metathetically by the addition of the alkali metal salt of an enol, phenol,[21] or carboxylic acid [22] to the concentrated organic solution of the benzylpenicillinic acid. Alternatively, the latter can be neutralized by means of an aqueous solution of an alkali hydroxide, followed by removal of water by azeotropic distillation.

**Some Characteristics of the Penicillins.** The penicillins are monocarboxylic acids with a $pK$ of approximately 2.8, salts of which are strongly dextrorotatory. No basic center in the molecule can be detected. The presence of two active hydrogens in the molecule is shown by the method of Zerewitinoff, which gives high values ascribable to secondary reactions, and by equilibration with deuterium oxide, wherein full biological activity is retained. With the exception of non-specific end absorption, only the intact penicillins possessing conjugation in the side chain exhibit characteristic absorption in the ultraviolet region of the spectrum. Infrared spectroscopic studies on model compounds have shown that the band common to all the penicillins at 5.62 $\mu$ is apparently characteristic of the carbonyl group of the fused $\beta$-lactam-thiazolidine ring system, whereas the band near 6.6 $\mu$ is attributed to the amide grouping of the side chain.[23]

With the exception of the stable crystalline addition product of benzylpenicillinic acid with one molecule of isopropyl ether,[24] the penicillins in the form of the free acid have not been obtained crystalline, and they undergo rapid decomposition in the presence of moisture. In sharp contrast to the amorphous forms, which require refrigeration, the pure crystalline alkali metal salts are non-hygroscopic and remarkably thermostable. Anhydrous crystalline sodium benzylpenicillinate, for example, can be heated to 100° for hours without loss of potency. In aqueous solution maximum stability prevails at $pH$ 6–7, relatively

[20] Whitmore and co-workers, *Ind. Eng. Chem.*, **38**, 942 (1946); Rowley, Steiner, and Zimkin, *J. Soc. Chem. Ind. (London)*, **65**, 237 (1946).

[21] Goldberg and Teitel, U. S. pat. 2,459,315 [*C. A.*, **43**, 2742 (1949)].

[22] Behrens, U. S. pat. 2,463,943 [*C. A.*, **43**, 4433 (1949)].

[23] Reference 8, pp. 396, 404, 405.

[24] Trenner and Buhs, *J. Am. Chem. Soc.*, **70**, 2897 (1948).

rapid deterioration ensuing outside this range. The inactivation of the penicillins by alcohols is catalyzed by metal ions such as zinc, tin, and copper, an effect which can be retarded by means of a metal-binding agent such as 2,3-dimercaptopropanol.[25]

**Carboxyl Derivatives.** Esterification of the penicillins has been accomplished (a) by treatment of the free acid or the triethylammonium salt with diazoalkanes,[26] (b) from the reaction of the anhydride of benzylpenicillin with alcohols,[27] and (c) from the condensation of potassium or sodium benzylpenicillinate with an "active halogen" compound, such as phenacyl chloride.[28] Because the esters of the penicillins are not significantly antimicrobially active *per se*, it follows that only those esters undergoing relatively facile hydrolysis appear to offer therapeutic promise in the formulation of repository (depot) forms of penicillin. Inasmuch as about three-fourths of the penicillin is destroyed under optimum conditions thus far devised for the hydrolysis of the methyl ester of benzylpenicillin, readily hydrolyzable esters are of interest for masking the carboxyl group in connection with approaches to a practical synthesis of penicillin.

By the action of ammonia or amines on a mixed anhydride[29] and the symmetrical anhydride of benzylpenicillinic acid,[27] the amide[29] and a variety of substituted amides[29,30] have been prepared that are resistant to penicillinase,[31] an enzyme elaborated by certain penicillin-resistant bacteria; the amides are significantly weaker antimicrobially than the parent benzylpenicillin.

Literally hundreds of different amine salts of benzylpenicillinic acid have been prepared in the quest for crystalline, water-insoluble products useful as processing tools and/or non-irritating salts suitable for the formulation of repository forms to produce protracted blood levels on injection. Thus far, none has proved superior to the procaine ($\beta$-diethylaminoethyl *p*-aminobenzoate) salt of benzylpenicillin for the latter application. The crystalline triethylammonium and cyclohexylammonium salts, for example, have been employed for the isolation and purification of benzylpenicillin, and N-ethylpiperidine has been utilized for the quantitative determination of benzylpenicillin in commercial mixtures.[32]

[25] Chain, Philpot, and Callow, *Arch. Biochem.*, **18**, 171 (1948).

[26] Reference 8, p. 680; Kirchner and co-workers, *J. Org. Chem.*, **14**, 388 (1949).

[27] Carpenter, *J. Am. Chem. Soc.*, **70**, 2964 (1948).

[28] McDuffie, Jr., and Cooper, U. S. pat. 2,578,570 (1951).

[29] Cooper and Binkley, *J. Am. Chem. Soc.*, **70**, 3966 (1948); Cooper, U. S. pats. 2,577,699 (1951) and 2,593,852 (1952).

[30] Holysz and Stavely, *ibid.*, **72**, 4760 (1950).

[31] Abraham and Chain, *Nature*, **146**, 837 (1940); Levy, *ibid.*, **166**, 740 (1950).

[32] Sheehan, Mader, and Cram, *J. Am. Chem. Soc.*, **68**, 2407 (1946).

**The Constitution of the Penicillins.** Although numerous structures were proposed for the penicillins, degradation studies and physical measurements progressively reduced the number of plausible formulas to the expressions I, III, and hybrids of the two forms, exemplified by II.[33]

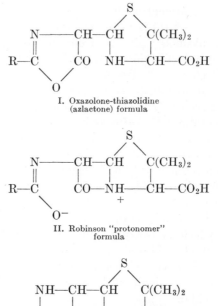

I. Oxazolone-thiazolidine
(azlactone) formula

II. Robinson "protonomer"
formula

III. β-Lactam formula

Impressive chemical evidence in favor of the β-lactam formula (III) could not be regarded as an unequivocal structural proof. Thermochemical data and especially evidence derived from infrared spectroscopic studies strongly supported III. Finally, the magnificent x-ray crystallographic investigations of Crowfoot and her colleagues were interpreted as definitely establishing the existence of the β-lactam structure in the crystal lattices of sodium, potassium, and rubidium benzylpenicillinates.[34] Figure 1 represents the stereochemical configuration of the benzylpenicillin ion or its mirror image in the crystals of the alkali salts; x-ray analysis does not distinguish between enantiomorphs.

[33] (a) For a scholarly discussion of the constitution of penicillins see ref. 8, Chapter 15; (b) for the chemistry of β-lactams (2-azetidinones) see ref. 8, Chapter 26; (c) for thiazolidines see ref. 8, Chapter 25; (d) for oxazolones (azlactones) see ref. 8, Chapter 21; and Carter, *Org. Reactions*, **3**, 198 (1946).

[34] Crowfoot and co-workers, ref. 8, pp. 310–366; Crowfoot, *Ann. Rev. Biochem.*, **17**, 115 (1948).

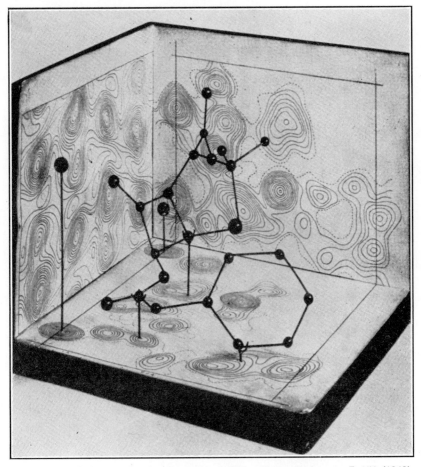

FIG. 1. Model of the molecule of benzylpenicillin. Chain, *Endeavour*, **7**, 156 (1948); courtesy of the publisher.

**Degradation of the Penicillins.** Treatment of benzylpenicillin (III, Flow Sheet I) with dilute alkali or the bacterial enzyme penicillinase [31] causes hydrolytic cleavage with the formation of the penicilloic acid (IV). Because of the flanking negative groupings, carbon dioxide is expelled from the $\alpha$-carboxyl group at room temperature to yield the penilloic acid (V), a thiazolidine which in turn is readily cleaved by the action of aqueous mercuric chloride to form phenylacetylaminoacetaldehyde (VI) and D-penicillamine (VII). D-Penicillamine, a hitherto unknown amino acid, is a moiety common to all "natural" and biosynthetic penicillins, irrespective of the precursors employed.

FLOW SHEET I. CERTAIN DEGRADATION AND REARRANGEMENT PRODUCTS OF BENZYLPENICILLIN ($R = C_6H_5CH_2-$)

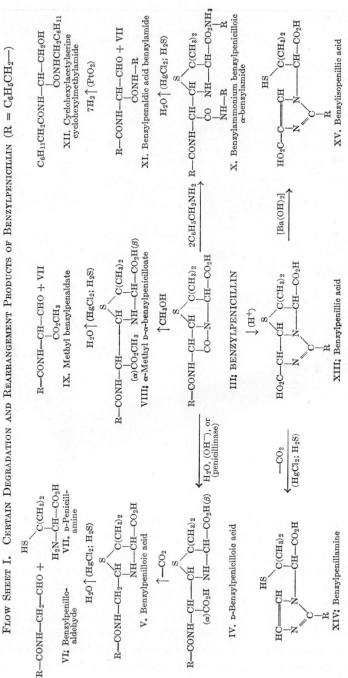

Methanol reacts with III to form α-methyl D-α-benzylpenicilloate (VIII), a general reaction for primary alcohols. Primary and secondary aliphatic amines likewise cleave the lactam ring to form α-amides, represented by X, unless a high insolubility of the amine salt initially formed affords protection from further attack. On standing at room temperature in aqueous solution below $pH$ 5 the penicillins undergo rearrangement to form the isomeric penillic acids (XIII), which contain a fused imidazoline-thiazolidine ring system. Derivatives X and XIII are useful for characterization of the penicillins. The structures of all the foregoing degradation and rearrangement products of penicillin have been well established by means of straightforward synthetic procedures.

The reductive desulfurization of sodium benzylpenicillinate (XVI, Fig. 2) to obtain the β-lactam XVII under such mild conditions that

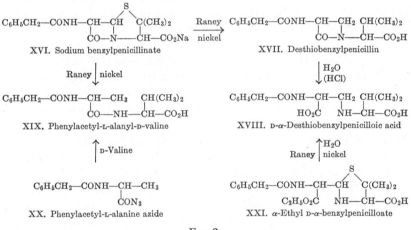

FIG. 2.

the involvement of an intramolecular rearrangement was highly improbable constituted the most convincing chemical evidence for the β-lactam formulation for the penicillins.[35] Acid hydrolysis of XVII yielded D-α-desthiobenzylpenicilloic acid (XVIII), which proved to be identical with an authentic specimen prepared by the treatment of α-ethyl D-α-benzylpenicilloate (XXI) with Raney nickel catalyst followed by hydrolysis. The structural proof for the other principal product

[35] (a) Kaczka and Folkers, ref. 8, pp. 243–268; Adkins, Brutschy, and McWhirter, J. Am. Chem. Soc., **70**, 2610 (1948). This important hydrogenolysis was originally accomplished by the chemists of Merck and Co. (b) For a review of the wide applications of this reaction in the structural elucidation of natural products, see McOmie, Ann. Repts. on Progress Chem. (Chem. Soc. London), **45**, 198 (1948); (c) Fletcher, Jr., and Richtmyer, Advances in Carbohydrate Chem., **5**, 1 (1950).

(XIX) of the hydrogenolysis served to establish the configuration of the asymmetric center to which the phenylacetamido grouping in penicillin is attached.   The phenylacetyl-L-alanyl-D-valine synthesized by causing phenylacetyl-L-alanine azide (XX) to condense with D-valine was shown to be identical with XIX.   It was not found possible to convert the lactam (XVII) into XIX with Raney nickel.   The rupture of the C—N bond in the formation of XIX, therefore, either preceded or occurred simultaneously with the scission of the C—S linkage; the alanyl derivative (XIX) was thus shown to be a primary degradation product of benzylpenicillin itself.

The sulfone (XXIII) and sulfoxide (XXIV) of methyl benzylpenicillinate (XXII, Flow Sheet II) afford substantial support for the β-lactam structure since it is known that oxidizing agents rupture a thiazolidine ring which is unprotected by N-acylation.[36]   Sodium benzylpenicillinate can also be converted into a crystalline sulfone in an excellent yield under conditions approaching neutrality.[37]   In fact, intact penicillins are not oxidized by iodine; the useful iodometric assay [38] depends upon preliminary degradation to the penicilloic acid (IV), a thiazolidine which then undergoes ring cleavage and oxidation to the corresponding sulfonic acid derivative.   It is of interest that an ethereal solution of the methyl ester (XXII) is isomerized by mercuric chloride to the oxazolone (XXV) and that XXVI represents another isomer containing a fused imidazolidine-thiazolidine nucleus different from the ring system found in the penillic acids (XIII).   Evidence for the thiohydrouracil structure assigned to the thiocyanate derivative (XXIX) [39] was adduced in part by its degradation to the uracil derivative (XXX) and by a direct synthesis of XXIX from the natural penicilloate (XXVIII). 5-Oxazolones (azlactones) in general interact with thiocyanate to form 1-acyl-2-thiohydantoins.   Certain β-lactams, on the other hand, gave rise to thiohydrouracils on treatment with thiocyanate.   Consequently, the formation of XXIX could be interpreted as favoring the β-lactam expression (III) for the penicillins.

**Penicillamine.**   Since the penillic acids (XIII) are degraded by acid hydrolysis to the corresponding penilloic acids (V), carbon dioxide, and D-penicillamine (VII), (XXXVIII), the last can be obtained by treatment of a penicillin with acid, alkali, primary alcohols, or primary amines, followed by precipitation with mercuric chloride (Flow Sheet I).

[36] Ratner and Clarke, *J. Am. Chem. Soc.*, **59**, 200 (1937); ref. 8, pp. 153, 157; Cavallito and Harley, *J. Org. Chem.*, **15**, 815 (1950).

[37] D. E. Cooper, unpublished observation.

[38] Alicino, *Ind. Eng. Chem. Anal. Ed.*, **18**, 619 (1946); Ministry of Health Conference, *Analyst*, **74**, 550 (1949).

[39] du Vigneaud and Melville, ref. 8, pp. 269–309.

FLOW SHEET II. CERTAIN DERIVATIVES AND REARRANGEMENT PRODUCTS OF METHYL BENZYLPENICILLINATE ($R = C_6H_5CH_2—$)

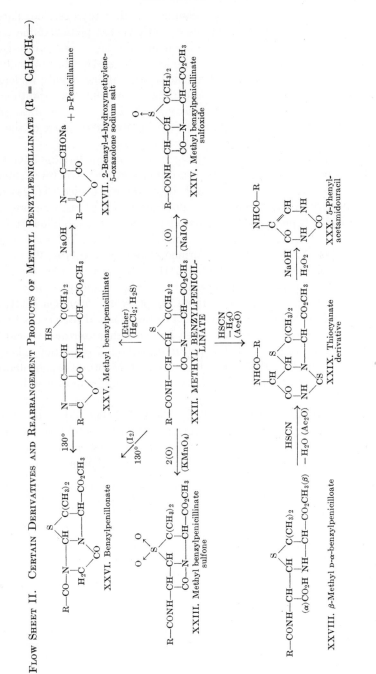

The chemical reactions of penicillamine ($\beta,\beta$-dimethylcysteine) parallel those of cysteine, with the notable exceptions that penicillamine (D- or L-isomer) is not vulnerable to amino acid oxidases, it is more resistant to chemical oxidation, and its disulfide is less susceptible to reducing agents than is cystine. Like cysteine, penicillamine readily undergoes cyclization with acetone and other carbonyl compounds to form thiazolidines.[36,39a] An eminently satisfactory method for the esterification of D-penicillamine (and other amino acids) involves treatment of the hydrochloride with an alkyl sulfite.[40]

Although several other preparative routes to penicillamine have been devised since the original synthesis, resolution, and structural elucidation were accomplished at Oxford,[41] the method of choice [42] is presented schematically in Flow Sheet III. DL-Valine (XXXI) can be prepared economically from isobutyraldehyde by means of a modified Strecker reaction.[43] The method is based on the fact that chloroacetylated amino acids (XXXII) are transformed smoothly into laterally unsaturated oxazolones (azlactones) (XXXIII) when heated with acetic anhydride (Bergmann rearrangement).[44] The addition of hydrogen sulfide to XXXIII takes place at room temperature without a catalyst.[45] The thiazolinecarboxylic acid (XXXIV) thus formed undergoes hydrolytic cleavage to yield XXXV when boiled with water alone; acid hydrolysis leads to XXXVI. The pictured method of resolution takes advantage of the fact that the brucine salt of N-formyl-D-penicillamine crystallizes first, from which XXXVIII is readily obtained by acid hydrolysis.

It is noteworthy that natural penicillamine belongs to the "unnatural" D-series of amino acids. Configurational proof was obtained by desulfurization of XXXIX with Raney nickel. The product was identified as N-phenylcarbamyl-D-valine (XL). L-Penicillamine inhibits the

[39a] Schubert, *J. Biol. Chem.*, **111**, 671 (1935); **114**, 341 (1936); **130**, 601 (1939); Micheel and Emde, *Ber.*, **72**, 1724 (1939).

[40] Phillips, U. S. pat. 2,460,191 [*C. A.*, **43**, 3030 (1949)].

[41] (a) Crooks, Jr., ref. 8, pp. 455–472; (b) Butenandt and co-workers, *Z. physiol. Chem.*, **282**, 268 (1947); (c) Süs, *Ann.*, **561**, 31 (1948); (d) Heilbron, Cook, and Catch, Brit. pat. 607,539 [*C. A.*, **43**, 4688 (1949)]; (e) American Cyanamid Co., Brit. pat. 609,722 [*C. A.*, **43**, 1796 (1949)]; (f) Chatterjee and co-workers, *J. Chem. Soc.*, 1337 (1948); (g) Sheehan and co-workers, U. S. pat. 2,477,148 [*C. A.*, **44**, 171 (1950)]; (h) Sheehan and Tishler U. S. pat. 2,477,149 [*C. A.*, **44**, 171 (1950)]; (i) American Cyanamid Co., Brit. pat. 615,628 [*C. A.*, **43**, 4687 (1949)].

[42] Sheehan and co-workers, U. S. pat. 2,496,416 [*C. A.*, **44**, 4510 (1950)]; U. S. pat. 2,496,417 [*C. A.*, **44**, 4511 (1950)].

[43] Reference 10, Report PB 79976, D-8 (May 1, 1944); ref. 8. pp. 458, 464.

[44] Reference 8, p. 457; Bergmann and Stern, *Ann.*, **448**, 20 (1926); Bergmann, Zervas, and Lebrecht, *Ber.*, **64**, 2315 (1931).

[45] Reference 8, p. 465; Gaubert, Brit. pat. 591,435 [*C. A.*, **42**, 592 (1948)].

FLOW SHEET III. SYNTHESIS OF PENICILLAMINE

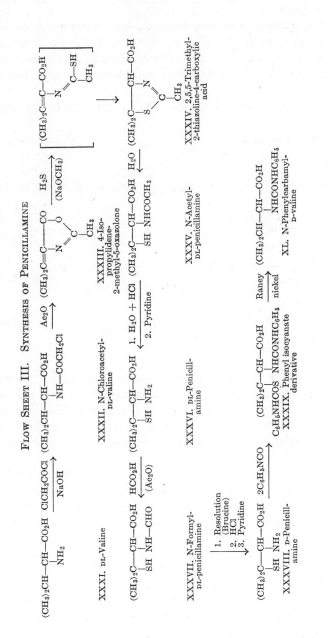

growth of rats under conditions where the enantiomorphic D-penicilla-mine is innocuous.[46]

**Synthetic Benzylpenicillin.** In an attempt to synthesize the oxazolone-thiazolidine structure (I, R = benzyl), which was the favored formula for penicillin in January, 1944, the Merck chemists caused the oxazo-lone (XLV, Fig. 3) to condense with D-penicillamine hydrochloride

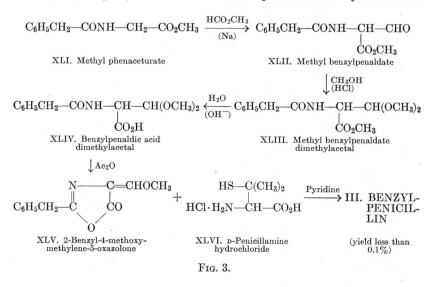

$$C_6H_5CH_2—CONH—CH_2—CO_2CH_3 \xrightarrow[\text{(Na)}]{\text{HCO}_2\text{CH}_3} C_6H_5CH_2—CONH—CH—CHO$$
$$\qquad\qquad\qquad\qquad\qquad CO_2CH_3$$

XLI. Methyl phenaceturate          XLII. Methyl benzylpenaldate

$$\downarrow \begin{array}{c} CH_3OH \\ (HCl) \end{array}$$

$$C_6H_5CH_2—CONH—CH—CH(OCH_3)_2 \xleftarrow[\text{(OH}^-)]{\text{H}_2\text{O}} C_6H_5CH_2—CONH—CH—CH(OCH_3)_2$$
$$\qquad\qquad CO_2H \qquad\qquad\qquad\qquad\qquad\qquad CO_2CH_3$$

XLIV. Benzylpenaldic acid          XLIII. Methyl benzylpenaldate
dimethylacetal                     dimethylacetal

$$\downarrow Ac_2O$$

XLV. 2-Benzyl-4-methoxy-          XLVI. D-Penicillamine          (yield less than
methylene-5-oxazolone             hydrochloride                  0.1%)

FIG. 3.

(XLVI). From this reaction they obtained repeatedly a product that showed a biological activity of approximately 0.5 unit per mg. when subjected to the standard assay for benzylpenicillin. The group at Oxford University independently discovered that penicillin-type ac-tivity was exhibited by the condensation product of 4-ethoxymethylene-2-styryl-5-oxazolone with D-penicillamine.

Convincing evidence that the active material present in the Merck reaction product was actually benzylpenicillin was deduced from (a) comparable chemical inactivation, (b) similarity of activity against dif-ferent microörganisms ("antibacterial spectrum"), (c) inactivation by penicillinase, and (d), most impressive of all, the isotope "tracer" tech-nique. DL-Penicillamine containing radioactive sulfur was condensed with the oxazolone (XLV); the product was diluted with natural benzyl-penicillin; the crystalline triethylammonium salt derived from the mix-ture was subjected to multiple recrystallizations and two transforma-tions without alteration of the content of the radioactive sulfur.[47] An

---

[46] Wilson and du Vigneaud, *Science,* **107,** 653 (1948).
[47] du Vigneaud and Wright, ref. 8, pp. 892–908.

intensive study of the reaction failed to increase significantly the micro yield of the synthetic product. Yet concentration of active material by methods based on the "countercurrent distribution" principle [48] led to the isolation of the pure triethylammonium salt of benzylpenicillin.[49]

More recently, Süs [50] has reported the conversion of synthetic DL-benzylpenicilloic acid (XLIX) into benzylpenicillin in a minute yield by means of phosphorus trichloride (Fig. 4). The crystalline intermedi-

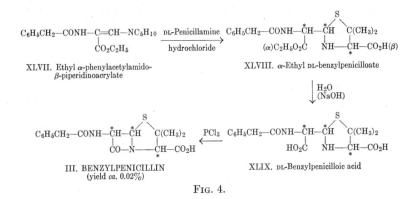

FIG. 4.

ate (XLVII) was prepared by causing piperidine to react with the homologous ethyl ester of XLII. The formation of III does not necessarily proceed by a direct cyclization of XLIX but may involve an oxazolone intermediate as in the original synthesis (Fig. 3).

**Stereochemical Aspects.** A synthesis of a penicillin by cyclization of the corresponding penicilloic acid (XLIX) or penicilloate (XLVIII) is complicated by the presence of the three asymmetric centers (marked *) within the molecule. Consequently, eight optical isomers are possible. Actually, all four diastereoisomeric penicilloates derived from D-penicill-amine have been isolated and arbitrarily designated as D-α-, D-β-, D-γ-, and D-δ-isomers. α-Ethyl D-α-benzylpenicilloate (XXI, Fig. 2), for example, is a direct reaction product of benzylpenicillin with alcohol. The condensation of D-penicillamine hydrochloride with an alkyl benzyl-penaldate, or derivative such as XLVII, yields a mixture of isomeric D-benzylpenicilloates. Because of probable concurrent isomerization mediated through enolization of the penaldate (or the double bond of the derivative) during this condensation, the configurations of the adjacent asymmetric carbon atoms in the resulting penicilloate are uncertain.

[48] Craig and co-workers, *J. Biol. Chem.*, **161**, 321 (1945).
[49] du Vigneaud and co-workers, *Science*, **104**, 431 (1946); ref. 8, pp. 1018–1024.
[50] Süs, *Ann.*, **571**, 201 (1951).

The configuration of the central asymmetric center in all the penicillo-ates, as in the penicillins, remains uncorrelated.[51]

**Other Synthetical Approaches to Penicillins.** The first straight-forward synthesis of compounds containing the unique $\beta$-lactam-thiazo-lidine ring system, represented by LIV, Fig. 5, was accomplished by

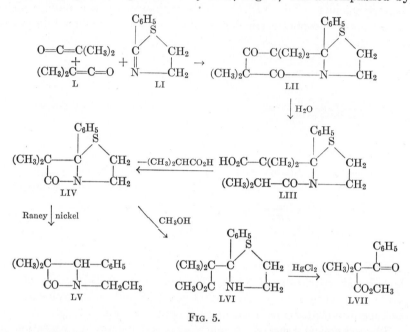

FIG. 5.

the addition of ketenes to thiazolines.[52] The use of diphenylketene in place of dimethylketene (L) in the reaction led directly to the triphen-ylated analog of LIV. In other cases the thiazoline (LI) combined with two molecules of the ketene with the formation of the intermediate piperidinedione (LII). Mild hydrolysis of LII yielded the $\beta$-acylamino acid (LIII), which lost isobutyric acid at its melting point to form the $\beta$-lactam (LIV). Staudinger and co-workers [53] originally described this novel route to monocyclic $\beta$-lactams via piperidinediones derived from the interaction of ketenes and Schiff bases.

Chemical evidence for the $\beta$-lactam-thiazolidine structure of LIV was obtained by reductive desulfurization with Raney nickel, which yielded

[51] Mozingo and Folkers, ref. 8, pp. 535–656.

[52] Ballard, Melstrom, and Smith, ref. 8, pp. 973–1003; Melstrom, in Elderfield, "Hetero-cyclic Compounds," John Wiley & Sons, New York (1950), Vol. 1, pp. 100–103; for an excellent account of the various attempted syntheses of penicillins see Bachmann and Cronyn, ref. 8, pp. 849–891.

[53] Staudinger, Klever, and Kober, *Ann.*, **374**, 1 (1910).

the lactam (LV), and by cleavage of the product of methanolysis (LVI) with mercuric chloride, which afforded methyl α-benzoylisobutyrate (LVII). Although LIV and congeners exhibited a low order of chemical reactivity in comparison with the chemical behavior of the penicillins, the infrared absorption spectra of these model compounds were found to show characteristic bands near 5.63 μ strikingly similar to the 5.62 μ band in the penicillin spectrum attributed to the labile carbonyl absorption.[23]

An ingenious total synthesis of a 5-phenylpenicillin methyl ester [54] (LXI, Fig. 6) has been achieved by Sheehan and associates.[55] The

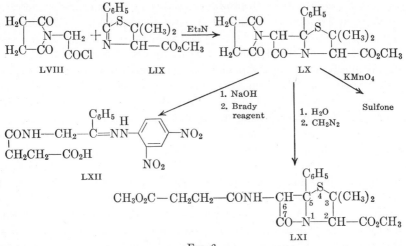

FIG. 6.

method consists in the gradual addition of triethylamine to a mixture of succinimidoacetyl chloride (LVIII) and racemic methyl 5,5-dimethyl-2-phenyl-2-thiazoline-4-carboxylate (LIX) under conditions of high dilution.[56] Phthalimidoacetyl and other diacylaminoacetyl chlorides have been used effectively in place of succinimidoacetyl chloride in the reaction with LIX and various thiazolines.

The β-lactam structures assigned to LX, its sulfone, and LXI were all strongly indicated on the basis of infrared absorption spectra. Per-

[54] Wolfrom, *J. Chem. Education*, **27**, 352 (1950), has introduced this numbering of the penicillin ring system and a systematic nomenclature for the penicillins, namely, 6-acylamino-3,3-dimethyl-7-oxo-4-thia-1-azabicyclo-[3.2.0]heptane-2-carboxylic acid.

[55] (a) Sheehan and co-workers, *J. Am. Chem. Soc.*, **72**, 3828 (1950); (b) Sheehan and Ryan, *ibid.*, **73**, 1204 (1951); and succeeding publications describing synthetical approaches to substituted penicillins and related compounds.

[56] Ziegler, Eberly, and Ohlinger, *Ann.*, **504**, 123 (1933).

manganate oxidation of LX produced the corresponding sulfone in high yield. Alkaline degradation of LX afforded N-phenacylsuccinamic acid, which was isolated as the 2,4-dinitrophenylhydrazone (LXII). Preferential hydrolysis of LX followed by esterification yielded crystalline methyl β-carbomethoxyethyl-5-phenylpenicillinate (LXI).

The formidable task of devising a method for the introduction of an acylamino group into the 6-position of the bicyclic system devoid of the stabilizing effect of an alkyl or aryl group attached to the 5-carbon atom remains to be achieved.

**Chemical Modifications of Penicillins.** p-Hydroxybenzylpenicillin (penicillin X) has been iodinated, brominated, and coupled with a variety of diazonium salts to produce derivatives showing higher activity *in vitro* on a molar basis than the parent compound.[57] The striking qualitative similarities of the modified penicillins, however, have overshadowed the observed quantitative differences. In general all other chemical alterations of the penicillins, including ester, amide, sulfoxide, and sulfone formation, isomerizations, and degradations, have either destroyed or apparently reduced antimicrobial activity without significantly broadening or shifting the antibacterial spectrum.

The lack of practical synthetic procedures has severely limited the study of the relationship of structure to activity. The condensation of the oxazolone (XLV) with certain α-amino-β-mercapto acids other than D-penicillamine, including DL-cysteine, DL-β-methylcysteine (isomers *A* and *B*), DL-β,β-diethylcysteine, and DL-β-ethyl-β-methylcysteine,[46, 58] in addition to β,β-pentamethylenecysteine,[59] has afforded products exhibiting typical penicillin-like activity in all cases. In the penicillin series, therefore, the characteristic geminal dimethyl grouping is not a specific requirement for antimicrobial activity. In contrast, under comparable conditions the reaction products obtained from XLV and β-phenylcysteine[59] and also from XLV and L-penicillamine[46] are antimicrobially inactive. Compound LXI and its hydrolysis products have shown no activity when subjected to conventional penicillin assay procedures. The question whether the inactivity of LXI is caused by the 5-phenyl substituent, an isomeric stereochemical configuration, or a combination of the two factors remains to be determined.

---

[57] Coghill, Stodola, and Wachtel, ref. 8, pp. 680–687; Stodola, Wachtel, and Coghill, U. S. pat. 2,504,161 [*C. A.*, **44**, 5918 (1950)].

[58] Carpenter and co-workers, *J. Biol. Chem.*, **176**, 915 (1948).

[59] Billimoria, Cook, and Heilbron, *J. Chem. Soc.*, 1437 (1949).

## STREPTOMYCIN

The isolation of streptomycin concentrates from cultures of *Streptomyces griseus* [60] was the outcome of a deliberate systematic search for an antibiotic exhibiting pronounced activity against Gram-negative and acid-fast bacteria. Experience gained with the production of penicillin and the clinical effectiveness of streptomycin and dihydrostreptomycin in the treatment of tuberculosis have jointly contributed to the expeditious development of commercial streptomycin.*

Although a literature of more than two thousand references on the subject of streptomycin has already accumulated, comprehensive reviews [7, 61] and a book [62] readily afford more complete information pertaining to the chemical aspects of this major antibiotic.

**Characteristics.** Streptomycin (LXIII) as the strongly alkaline levorotatory base, $C_{21}H_{39}N_7O_{12}$, or as a salt of an inorganic acid, is ex-

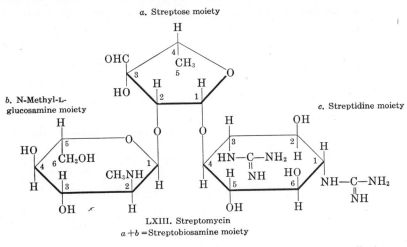

LXIII. Streptomycin
$a + b$ = Streptobiosamine moiety

tremely soluble in water and insoluble in organic solvents. It is unstable outside the $pH$ range 3–7. Purification is best achieved by the use of cation exchange resins. [63] The C-formyl group of streptomycin

[60] Schatz, Bugie, and Waksman, *Proc. Soc. Exptl. Biol. Med.*, **55**, 66 (1944).

* In 1946 the total production of streptomycin in the United States was about 2200 lb., valued at $6.40 per gram ($2900 per lb.) in October of that year. In 1950 approximately 157,800 lb. of dihydrostreptomycin base and 45,700 lb. of streptomycin base were produced and marketed as the sulfate and the hydrochloride (U. S. Tariff Commission report of April 26, 1951). In June, 1951, the wholesale price for these salts of streptomycin and its dihydro derivative had descended to $0.324 per gram ($147 per lb.) of the base.

[61] Lemieux and Wolfrom, *Advances in Carbohydrate Chem.*, **3**, 337 (1948).

[62] Waksman, "Streptomycin," Williams and Wilkins Co., Baltimore, Md. (1949).

[63] (a) Van Dolah, Christensen, and Shelton, U. S. pat. 2,528,022; (b) Taylor, U. S. pat. 2,528,188 [*C. A.*, **45**, 2158 (1951)]; (c) Howe, U. S. pat. 2,541,320 [*C. A.*, **45**, 4893 (1951)].

reacts with a variety of carbonyl reagents to form inactive derivatives, whereas catalytic hydrogenation to dihydrostreptomycin [64] appears to reduce neurotoxicity without diminishing antimicrobial activity. By reductive amination streptomycin has been converted into streptomycylamine and a variety of biologically active N-alkylstreptomycylamines.[65]

**Streptidine.** The presence of two guanido groups in the base named streptidine (LXIIIc), (LXIV), obtained by mild acid hydrolysis of streptomycin,[66-68] was shown by the isolation of guanidine after permanganate oxidation [69] and also by hydrolysis, which yielded a diurea derivative [69] following moderate treatment, and the corresponding diamine, designated streptamine,[67, 70] under more energetic conditions. Periodic acid oxidation [71] converted N,N'-dibenzoylstreptamine (LXV) into a dialdehyde which yielded $\alpha,\alpha'$-dibenzamido-$\beta$-hydroxyglutaric acid (LXVI) [72] on treatment with bromine water. The sequence thus proved streptidine (LXIV) to be a 1,3-diguanido-2,4,5,6-tetrahydroxycyclohexane.

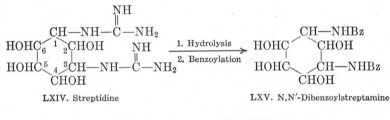

LXIV. Streptidine        LXV. N,N'-Dibenzoylstreptamine

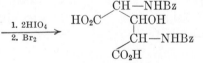

LXVI. $\alpha,\alpha'$-Dibenzamido-$\beta$-hydroxyglutaric acid

The lack of optical activity in streptidine (LXIV) indicated a *meso* configuration involving *cis* guanido groups. Although eight such *meso* forms are possible, streptamine has been synthesized from D-glucosa-

[64] Peck, Hoffhine, Jr., and Folkers, *J. Am. Chem. Soc.*, **68**, 1390 (1946); Peck, U. S. pat. 2,498,574 [*C. A.*, **44**, 6087 (1950)]; Carboni and Regna, U. S. pat. 2,522,858 [*C. A.*, **45**, 829 (1951)].

[65] Winsten and co-workers, *J. Am. Chem. Soc.*, **72**, 3969 (1950).

[66] Brink, Kuehl, Jr., and Folkers, *Science*, **102**, 506 (1945).

[67] Carter and co-workers, *ibid.*, **103**, 53 (1946).

[68] Peck and co-workers, *J. Am. Chem. Soc.*, **68**, 29 (1946).

[69] Peck and co-workers, *ibid.*, **68**, 776 (1946).

[70] Fried, Boyak, and Wintersteiner, *J. Biol. Chem.*, **162**, 391 (1946).

[71] Jackson, *Org. Reactions*, **2**, 341 (1944).

[72] Carter and co-workers, *Science*, **103**, 540 (1946).

mine and converted into streptidine; [73] thus, it is known with certainty that all the vicinal substituents of streptidine, with the exception of the hydroxyl group at position 2, are sterically *trans* as depicted in LXIIIc. In all probability, the configuration at position 2 is also *trans* because of the known nature of the cyclization employed in the elegant synthesis.[73]

**N-Methyl-L-glucosamine.** Treatment of streptomycin with methanol and hydrogen chloride (methanolysis) followed by acid hydrolysis and acetylation led to the isolation of a pentaacetate which yielded LXVII on hydrolysis. This hexosamine formed a phenylosazone which was converted into a phenylosotriazole (LXVIII) having the same melting point as D-glucose phenylosotriazole and an equal but opposite specific rotation. Oxidation of the hexosamine (LXVII) with mercuric oxide

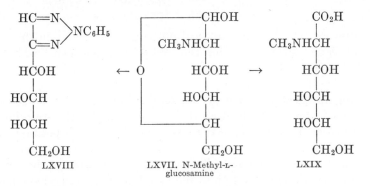

LXVIII                    LXVII. N-Methyl-L-                    LXIX
                              glucosamine

yielded an acid (LXIX) with the same melting point and an equal but opposite specific rotation as reported for N-methyl-D-glucosaminic acid. From these transformations it is evident that the hexosamine derived from streptomycin is N-methyl-L-glucosamine (LXVII),[74] a structure confirmed by its synthesis from L-arabinose.[74, 75]

Although the relatively unstable streptose moiety (LXIIIa) has not been isolated or synthesized, its structure has been elucidated,[76] and the locations of the glycosidic linkages have been determined by classical degradative procedures featuring desulfurizing hydrogenolysis,[35b, 35c, 77] periodate oxidation,[71] protective acylation, and hydrolysis.

**The Maltol Rearrangement.** The formation of maltol (LXX) on treatment of streptomycin with aqueous alkali [78] involves the expansion

[73] Wolfrom, Olin, and Polglase, *J. Am. Chem. Soc.*, **72**, 1724 (1950).

[74] Kuehl, Jr., and co-workers, *ibid.*, **68**, 536 (1946); **69**, 3032 (1947).

[75] Wolfrom, Thompson, and Hooper, *ibid.*, **68**, 2343 (1946).

[76] Kuehl, Jr., and co-workers, *ibid.*, **71**, 1445 (1949); Wolfrom and DeWalt, *ibid.*, **70**, 3148 (1948); Fried, Walz, and Wintersteiner, *ibid.*, **68**, 2746 (1946).

[77] Wolfrom and Karabinos, *ibid.*, **66**, 909 (1944).

[78] Schenck and Spielman, *ibid.*, **67**, 2276 (1945).

of a furanose ring (streptose moiety) into a γ-pyrone system. Maltol formation takes place only when the aldehyde group at position 1 of the streptose component (LXIIIa) is glycosidically combined and the 3-carbonyl is potentially free. Consequently, dihydrostreptomycin does

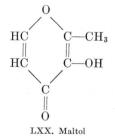

LXX. Maltol

not form maltol. Useful analytical procedures are based on this facile degradation. Mechanisms for the maltol rearrangement, which are supported by strikingly analogous ring enlargements, have been proposed.[61, 79]

**Configuration of the Glycosidic Linkages.** Folkers and his associates [80] have demonstrated conclusively that in streptomycin the streptobiosamine portion (LXIIIab) is linked glycosidically at either position 4 or 6 of streptidine. The hydrolytic cleavage of completely benzoylated streptomycin yielded an optically active heptabenzoylstreptidine, which was converted progressively into the mesyl derivative, the iodo derivative, heptabenzoyldesoxystreptidine, pentabenzoyldesoxystreptamine, and N,N'-dibenzoyldesoxystreptamine (LXXI). Treatment of LXXI with periodate gave α,γ-dibenzamido-β-hydroxyadipaldehyde (LXXII).

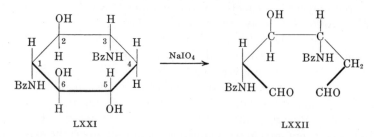

LXXI                                   LXXII

In their determination of the configurations of the glycosidic bonds in streptomycin, Wolfrom and his students [81] have taken into account the

---

[79] Fried in Elderfield, "Heterocyclic Compounds," John Wiley & Sons, New York (1950), Vol. I, p. 387.

[80] Kuehl, Jr., and co-workers, *J. Am. Chem. Soc.*, **70**, 2325 (1948); and earlier pertinent papers, to which references are given.

[81] Wolfrom, Cron, DeWalt, Husband, and Lemieux, *ibid.*, in press.

above proof of the unsymmetrical point of attachment of streptobiosamine to streptidine.  Hudson's rules of isorotation (see p. 1551 in Vol. II of this Treatise) applied to rotatory data pertaining to apposite derivatives of streptomycin have led to calculations which indicate that the configuration of the streptose-streptidine glycosidic union in streptomycin (LXIII) is $\beta$-L and that the N-methyl-L-glucosamine-streptose linkage is of the $\alpha$-L-type.

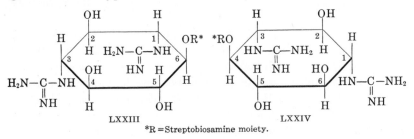

LXXIII                                    LXXIV

*R = Streptobiosamine moiety.

Wolfrom and co-workers [81] have drawn attention to the fact that, since the streptobiosamine moiety of streptomycin is optically active, positions 4 and 6 of the streptidine ring are not configurationally equivalent.  Formulas LXXIII and LXXIV, wherein R designates the optically active streptobiosamine component, portray diastereoisomers. The problem of which diastereoisomeric form represents the streptomycin molecule (LXIII) remains to be solved.

**Mannosidostreptomycin (Streptomycin B).**  A second substance isolated from commercial streptomycin by countercurrent distribution and chromatography has been named mannosidostreptomycin (streptomycin B).[82]  Degradation studies [83] have shown that mannosidostreptomycin can be regarded as a derivative of streptomycin wherein D-mannose is linked glycosidically at position 4 of the N-methyl-L-glucosamine moiety.  Mannosidostreptomycin, which is significantly less active antimicrobially than streptomycin, can be differentiated from it by paper partition chromatography, which indicates the existence of related compounds.[84]

**Hydroxystreptomycin.**  This substance, produced by *Streptomyces griseocarneus*, differs from streptomycin only in having a 5-hydroxymethyl group instead of a 5-methyl group in the streptose moiety (LXIIIa).[85]  The toxicity and antimicrobial activity of hydroxystreptomycin appear to parallel those of streptomycin.

[82] Fried and Titus, *ibid.*, **70**, 3615 (1948).

[83] Stavely and Fried, *ibid.*, **71**, 135 (1949); Peck and co-workers, *ibid.*, **70**, 3968 (1948).

[84] Winsten and Eigen, *ibid.*, **70**, 3333 (1948).

[85] Benedict and co-workers, *Science*, **112**, 77 (1950); Stodola and co-workers, *J. Am. Chem. Soc.*, **73**, 2290 (1951); Grundy and co-workers, *Arch. Biochem.*, **28**, 150 (1950).

### CHLORAMPHENICOL (CHLOROMYCETIN) [86]

Chloramphenicol (LXXV) is a chlorine-containing antibiotic produced by *Streptomyces venezuelae*.[87] It was independently isolated in crystalline form by two groups of investigators.[88] This antibiotic deserves special mention because of its outstanding effectiveness in rickettsial diseases such as scrub typhus and its notable activity against Gram-negative organisms, particularly those causing typhoid fever, brucellosis, and tularemia.

Chloramphenicol, $C_{11}H_{12}Cl_2N_2O_5$, is an intensely bitter, colorless, neutral compound which is remarkably stable in solution over the $pH$ range 3–9. Its ultraviolet absorption spectrum shows a single maximum at 278 m$\mu$, characteristic of a nitrobenzene derivative.[89] Acid hydrolysis of LXXV yielded dichloroacetic acid and a base (LXXVI) (Fig. 7) which was degraded by periodic acid oxidation [71] to $p$-nitrobenzaldehyde, formaldehyde, ammonia, and formic acid. These products indicated the presence of an aminodihydroxypropyl chain situated

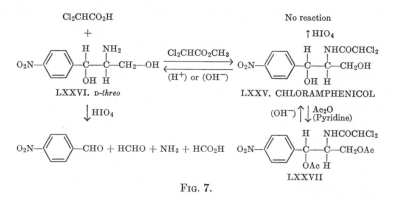

Fig. 7.

*para* to the nitrophenyl group. The failure of chloramphenicol to react with periodic acid eliminated the possibility of vicinal hydroxyl groups and definitely located the amino group in the 2-position of the side chain. A positive Van Slyke determination confirmed the presence

[86] Chloramphenicol is the generic name for LXXV. "Chloromycetin" is the trademark name of Parke, Davis & Co. for this compound. The systematic name approved by *Chemical Abstracts* is D-*threo*-$\alpha,\alpha$-dichloro-N-[$\beta$-hydroxy-$\alpha$-(hydroxymethyl)-$p$-nitrophenethyl]-acetamide [*C. A.*, **43**, 10300 (1949)]. D-(−)-*Threo*-1-$p$-nitrophenyl-2-dichloroacetamido-1,3-propanediol and D-*threo*-N-(1,1′-dihydroxy-1-$p$-nitrophenylisopropyl)-dichloroacetamide are other names for chloramphenicol encountered in the literature.

[87] Ehrlich and co-workers, *J. Bact.*, **56**, 467 (1948).

[88] Ehrlich and co-workers, *Science*, **106**, 417 (1947); Carter, Gottlieb, and Anderson, *ibid.*, **107**, 113 (1948).

[89] Bartz, *J. Biol. Chem.*, **172**, 445 (1948); Bartz, U. S. pat. 2,483,871 [*C. A.*, **44**, 4630 (1950)].

of the primary amino group in the base (LXXVI), and condensation of LXXVI with methyl dichloroacetate with resultant reconstitution of the antibiotic excluded the possibility of other transformations accompanying the hydrolysis. Alkaline deacetylation of the diacetyl derivative (LXXVII) at low temperature yielded chloramphenicol and afforded confirmatory evidence for the existence of two hydroxyl groups in the molecule. Thus the structure of chloramphenicol was known to be one of four optically active isomers of LXXV.[90]

A comparison of the physical and chemical properties of the base (LXXVI) derived from chloramphenicol with members of the ephedra series, the asymmetric centers of which have been related to mandelic acid and to alanine, indicated by analogy that the structure of chloramphenicol is D-(−)-threo-α,α-dichloro-N-[β-hydroxy-α-(hydroxymethyl)-n-nitrophenethyl]-acetamide (LXXV),[90] an "unnatural" configuration related to l-norpseudoephedrine rather than to the naturally occurring l-norephedrine. (See Ephedra Bases.)

Chloramphenicol enjoys the distinction of being the first major antibiotic for which practical syntheses have been devised; the first synthesis [91] is illustrated in Fig. 8. The sodium salt of 1-phenyl-2-nitro-1,3-

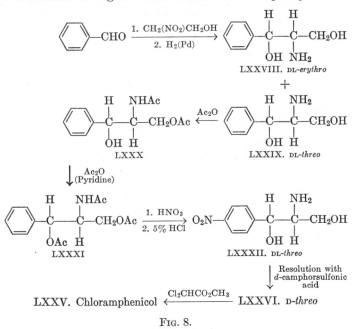

FIG. 8.

[90] Rebstock and co-workers, J. Am. Chem. Soc., **71**, 2458 (1949).

[91] (a) Controulis, Rebstock, and Crooks, Jr., ibid., **71**, 2463 (1949); (b) Crooks, Jr., and co-workers, U. S. pat. 2,483,884 [C. A., **45**, 179 (1951)]; (c) Crooks, Jr., and co-workers, U. S. pat. 2,483,885 [C. A., **45**, 633 (1951)].

propanediol, prepared by the condensation of benzaldehyde with crude β-nitroethanol, was hydrogenated in acetic acid by means of palladium oxide. By virtue of its insolubility in chloroform the crystalline *erythro* racemate (LXXVIII) was separated from DL-*threo*-1-phenyl-2-amino-1,3-propanediol (LXXIX). The *threo* racemate (LXXIX) was freed of the *erythro* form by recrystallization of the N,O-diacetyl derivative (LXXX) from absolute alcohol. The separation of the D-*threo* isomer (LXXVI) from its enantiomorph was achieved by treatment of the racemic base (LXXXII) with *d*-camphorsulfonic acid in isopropanol or, alternatively, with *d*-tartaric acid in methanol. On warming synthetic LXXVI with methyl dichloroacetate, chloramphenicol (LXXV) was produced.

Other attractive methods for the preparation of the key intermediate (LXXIX) include the condensation of an α-acylaminoacetophenone with formaldehyde followed by catalytic reduction of the carbonyl group [92] and the reduction of Erlenmeyer's β-phenylserine or its esters (LXXXIII) with lithium aluminum hydride.[93] Advantages of the lat-

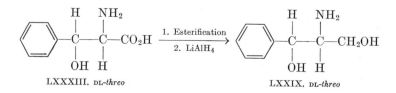

LXXXIII. DL-*threo*                    LXXIX. DL-*threo*

ter synthesis are noteworthy. The DL-β-phenylserine (LXXXIII) of Erlenmeyer is readily accessible from the base-promoted reaction between glycine and benzaldehyde.[93, 94] Moreover, it is known to possess largely the *threo* configuration.[95] Consequently, the reduction product is almost exclusively the desired DL-*threo*-1-phenyl-2-amino-1,3-propanediol (LXXIX).

The nitration process is circumvented in the synthesis of Long and Troutman [96] (Fig. 9), which has been adapted to the large-scale chemical production of chloramphenicol in competition with biological processes.[97] Treatment of the magnesiumethoxy derivative of ethyl malonate with *p*-nitrobenzoyl chloride followed by acid hydrolysis and de-

[92] Long and Troutman, *J. Am. Chem. Soc.*, **71**, 2469 (1949).

[93] Carrara and Weitnauer, *Gazz. chim. ital.*, **79**, 856 (1949) [*C. A.*, **44**, 7268 (1950)].

[94] Erlenmeyer, Jr., and Früstück, *Ann.*, **284**, 41 (1895); Ger. pat. 632,424 [*C. A.*, **30**, 6766 (1936)].

[95] (*a*) Vogler, *Helv. Chim. Acta*, **33**, 2111 (1950); (*b*) Billet, *Compt. rend.*, **230**, 1074 (1950).

[96] Long and Troutman, *J. Am. Chem. Soc.*, **71**, 2473 (1949).

[97] Olive, *Chem. Eng.*, **56**, No. 10, 107 (1949).

carboxylation of the condensation product yielded *p*-nitroacetophenone.*
Bromination of the ketone afforded LXXXIV, the starting material of
the commercial synthesis.[97] Acid hydrolysis of the hexamethylenetetramine salt derived from LXXXIV led to LXXXV, which was subsequently acetylated. The monohydroxymethylation of LXXXVI proceeded most expeditiously in the presence of sodium bicarbonate. The

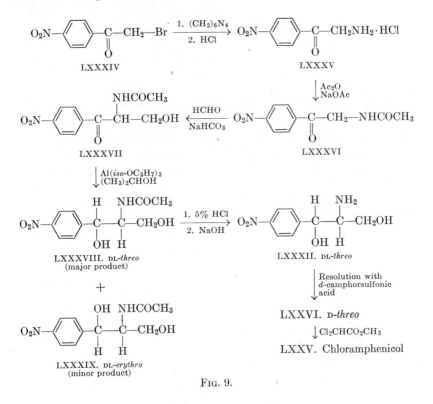

LXXXVIII. DL-*threo*
(major product)

LXXXIX. DL-*erythro*
(minor product)

LXXXII. DL-*threo*

LXXVI. D-*threo*

LXXV. Chloramphenicol

Fig. 9.

reduction of the ketone (LXXXVII) with aluminum isopropoxide [98]
produced favorable results only when water alone was employed for the
hydrolysis. An especially desirable feature of the synthesis is the fact
that the principal product of the reduction was found to be LXXXVIII,
the desired *threo* racemate, which can be easily separated from the
DL-*erythro* base (LXXXIX) by recrystallization.

* Wilkinson and Pedlow, U. S. pat. 2,573,080 (1951), have developed a remarkable
synthesis wherein (α-chloromethyl)benzyl methyl ether obtained readily from styrene,
chlorine, and methanol is converted into *p*-nitroacetophenone through successive nitration, dehydrohalogenation, and hydrolysis.
[98] Wilds, *Org. Reactions*, **2**, 178 (1944).

**Analogs and Derivatives.** An impressive variety of analogs of LXXV showing variations in the acyl group have been described.[99-103] In general, these variants have been reported to exhibit a low order of activity against *Shigella paradysenterie* (Sonnei). Replacement of the dichloroacetyl by an acetyl group, for example, causes a sevenfold decrease in potency.[101]

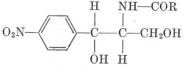

$$H \quad NH—COR$$
$$O_2N—\langle\bigcirc\rangle—C—C—CH_2OH$$
$$OH \quad H$$

LXXV. Chloramphenicol (R = CHCl₂)

Modifications involving the aryl moiety include *o*- and *m*-nitrophenyl,[99, 104, 105] halogen-containing phenyl,[99, 101, 106-109] alkyl- and alkoxyphenyl,[109] 1-naphthyl,[110] 2-furyl,[111] and 4-xenyl analogs.[112]

For many of these variants antimicrobial data have not been disclosed. A *para* substituent appears to be essential for significant activity. The *p*-bromophenyl analog is approximately one-fifth as active as chloramphenicol against several different microörganisms; [106] the corresponding chloro derivative is less active; the iodo and fluoro compounds are inert.[101] Replacement of the secondary hydroxyl by a keto group produced a powerful antifungal agent.[113] Replacement of the hydroxymethyl group by a carboxyl group caused complete inactivation; [114-116] replacement by hydrogen preserved antibacterial properties.[106] Phenylalaninol derivatives [117] and an inactive isomer of chlor-

[99] Crooks, Jr., Abstracts of the Second National Medicinal Chemistry Symposium of the American Chemical Society, Notre Dame, Indiana (1950), p. 39.

[100] Rebstock, *J. Am. Chem. Soc.*, **72**, 4800 (1950).

[101] Feitelson and co-workers, *J. Pharm. & Pharmacol.*, **3**, 149 (1951).

[102] Cestari and Bezzi, *Farm. sci. e tec.* (*Pavia*), **5**, 649 (1950) [*C. A.*, **45**, 4409 (1951)].

[103] Büchi, Contini, and Lieberherr, *Helv. Chim. Acta*, **34**, 274 (1951).

[104] Long and Jenesel, *J. Am. Chem. Soc.*, **72**, 4299 (1950).

[105] Buu-Hoï and Khôi, *Compt. rend.*, **229**, 1343 (1949).

[106] Buu-Hoï and co-workers, *J. Chem. Soc.*, 2766 (1950).

[107] Buu-Hoï and co-workers, *Compt. rend.*, **230**, 662 (1950).

[108] Bambas, Troutman, and Long, *J. Am. Chem. Soc.*, **72**, 4445 (1950).

[109] Buu-Hoï, Xuong, and Khôi, *J. Chem. Soc.*, 255 (1951).

[110] (a) Long and Troutman, *J. Am. Chem. Soc.*, **73**, 542 (1951); (b) Long and Troutman, U. S. pat. 2,516,130 (1950).

[111] (a) Long and Jenesel, U. S. pat. 2,547,712 [*C. A.*, **45**, 9564 (1951)]; (b) Hayes and Gever, *J. Org. Chem.*, **16**, 269 (1951).

[112] Bambas, U. S. pat. 2,516,098 (1950).

[113] Long and Troutman, *J. Am. Chem. Soc.*, **73**, 481 (1951).

[114] Huebner and Scholz, *ibid.*, **73**, 2089 (1951).

[115] Woolley, *J. Biol. Chem.*, **185**, 293 (1950).

[116] Billet, *Compt. rend.*, **231**, 293 (1950).

[117] Dornow and Winter, *Chem. Ber.*, **84**, 307 (1951).

amphenicol [118] have been described. Comparative antibacterial spectral data for the various analogs will be of special significance.

Although synthetic chloramphenicol showed 100% inhibition of *Shigella paradysenteriae* (Sonnei) when compared to the natural compound, the corresponding dichloroacetamides derived from the L-(+)-*threo* enantiomorph of LXXVI and the DL-*erythro* base gave bioassays showing less than 0.5% activity. It appears, therefore, that the D-*threo* configuration is highly specific for significant activity.

## AUREOMYCIN AND TERRAMYCIN

Comparative bacteriological studies on the major antibiotics aureomycin [119] and terramycin [120] reveal a striking similarity in their antibacterial spectra.[121] Both antibiotics are particularly effective in combating rickettsial diseases and certain infections caused by Gram-negative bacteria.

A comparison of the published physical and chemical properties of aureomycin [119,122] with those of terramycin [120,123] suggests that these compounds are intimately related chemically. Specifically, the molecular formula calculated from published analytical data for aureomycin is $C_{22}H_{23}ClN_2O_8$;[124] the formula for terramycin is $C_{22}H_{24-26}N_2O_9$.[125] Both antibiotics are yellow, crystalline, amphoteric compounds which parallel each other with respect to infrared and ultraviolet absorption spectra, specific rotation, solubility, and salt formation with acids and bases. For example, the ultraviolet absorption maxima for aureomycin at $pH$ 4.3 appear at 370 m$\mu$, 265 m$\mu$, and 251 m$\mu$, whereas the corresponding maxima for terramycin at $pH$ 4.5 are at 353 m$\mu$, 275 m$\mu$, and 247 m$\mu$.*

Terramycin gives positive ferric chloride, Pauly, Friedel-Crafts, Fehling, and Molisch tests,[125] the last indicating a carbohydrate component. The degradation of terramycin [126] in aqueous alkali has yielded ammonia

---

[118] Ruoff and Miller, *J. Am. Chem. Soc.*, **72**, 1417 (1950).

[119] Duggar, U. S. pat. 2,482,055 [*C. A.*, **44**, 8604 (1950)]; symposium of sixteen papers, *Ann. N. Y. Acad. Sci.*, **51**, 175 (1948).

[120] Sobin, Finlay, and Kane, U. S. pat. 2,516,080 [*C. A.*, **45**, 715 (1951)]; symposium of thirty-two papers, *Ann. N. Y. Acad. Sci.*, **53**, 221 (1950).

[121] Welch and co-workers, *J. Am. Pharm. Assoc., Sci. Ed.*, **39**, 185 (1950).

[122] Broschard and co-workers, *Science*, **109**, 199 (1949).

[123] Finlay and co-workers, *ibid.*, **111**, 85 (1950).

[124] (a) Dunitz and Leonard, *J. Am. Chem. Soc.*, **72**, 4276, footnote (1950); (b) Pepinsky and Watanabe, *Science*, **115**, 541 (1952).

[125] Regna and Solomons, *Ann. N. Y. Acad. Sci.*, **53**, 229 (1950).

* x-Ray crystallographic studies have established the isomorphism of the corresponding crystalline hydrochlorides (see ref. 124b).

[126] Pasternack and co-workers, *J. Am. Chem. Soc.*, **73**, 2400 (1951).

and dimethylamine. Alkaline hydrolysis in the presence of zinc has produced a tribasic acid, $C_{13}H_{12}O_6$; a phenolic lactone, $C_9H_8O_3$; acetic acid; and carbon dioxide. An alkaline fusion has afforded salicylic, m-hydroxybenzoic, and succinic acids.* Products of acid hydrolysis include an inactive base, $C_{22}H_{22}N_2O_8$; carbon dioxide; dimethylamine; and two compounds of the composition $C_{20}H_{15}NO_8$ and $C_{19}H_{14}O_7$, respectively. Treatment of terramycin with zinc and glacial acetic acid causes removal of the dimethylamino group with the formation of a yellow crystalline acid of the composition $C_{20}H_{19}NO_8$.

## POLYPEPTIDES

*Bacitracin*,[127] an antibiotic produced by a member of the *Bacillus subtilis* group, has been reported to be efficacious against penicillin-resistant staphylococci and synergistic with penicillin in the treatment of syphilis. The tendency to cause renal damage has limited its use. The subjection of commercial bacitracin to countercurrent distribution has yielded a crystalline, apparently homogeneous fraction,[128] from which several amino acids, including partially racemic D-isoleucine, were obtained by acid hydrolysis.

*Subtilin*, another peptide antibiotic elaborated by a strain of *Bacillus subtilis*, exhibits a low order of toxicity, but its activity appears largely confined to Gram-positive organisms. By means of countercurrent distribution processes, subtilin has been isolated in an essentially pure form.[129]

*Gramicidin*,[6, 130] *tyrocidine*,[6, 131] and *gramicidin S* [132] are all crystalline, cyclic polypeptides produced by strains of *Bacillus brevis*. *Tyrothricin* is the concentrate from which the neutral gramicidins and the basic tyrocidines can be fractionated. Evidence for the cyclopeptide structure rests on x-ray crystallographic data and the fact that electrometric titration fails to detect the presence of a free carboxyl group. It is of interest that amino acids possessing the "unnatural" D-configuration are found in all these substances and that gramicidin is known to contain both D- and L-valine within the molecule.[133] Although excessive toxicity

---

* Kuhn and Dury, *Chem. Ber.*, **84**, 848 (1951), have reported that treatment of terramycin with alkali also produces 6-acetylsalicylic acid; aureomycin yields 5-chlorosalicylic acid under comparable conditions.

[127] Johnson, Anker, and Meleney, *Science*, **102**, 376 (1945).

[128] Craig, Gregory, and Barry, *J. Clin. Invest.*, **28**, 1014 (1949).

[129] Brink, Mayfield, and Folkers, *J. Am. Chem. Soc.*, **73**, 330 (1951).

[130] Synge, *Biochem. J.*, **44**, 542 (1949); Gregory and Craig, *J. Biol. Chem.*, **172**, 839 (1948).

[131] Christensen, *ibid.*, **160**, 75 (1945).

[132] Consden and co-workers, *Biochem. J.*, **41**, 596 (1947).

[133] Hinman, Caron, and Christensen, *J. Am. Chem. Soc.*, **72**, 1620 (1950).

militates against their systemic administration, the marked stability of these antibiotics and their striking effectiveness against penicillin-resistant staphylococci are properties which favor widespread medical acceptance for topical application.  Methylol gramicidin, a product prepared from gramicidin and formaldehyde, appears to possess therapeutic advantages over gramicidin itself.[134]  The basic unit in *gramicidin S* is known to be a pentapeptide chain of the sequence -L-valyl-L-ornithyl-L-leucyl-D-phenylalanyl-L-prolyl-.[135]  Molecular-weight determinations based on an ingenious application of countercurrent distribution [136] have definitely established the cyclodecapeptide formula [132] for *gramicidin S*.

Strains of *Bacillus polymyxa* produce a series of closely related compounds designated *polymyxin* A (aerosporin) to E,[137] all containing L-threonine, L-$\alpha,\gamma$-diaminobutyric acid, and $(+)$-6-methyloctanoic acid. The polymyxins are differentiated by paper chromatography and by their amino acid compositions.  The crystalline 2-naphthalenesulfonates have proved invaluable in the isolation of homogeneous fractions. *Circulin*,[138] an antibiotic produced by *Bacillus circulans*, is reported to be a cyclopeptide of the composition $(C_{39}H_{74}N_{12}O_9)_n$, bearing a close chemical relationship to polymyxins A and E.  The group as a whole is remarkably active against Gram-negative pathogens but exhibits nephrotoxicity.

## CHEMICAL STRUCTURE AND ANTIBIOTIC ACTIVITY

A number of non-nitrogenous compounds of mold origin (Table II) possess highly reactive $\alpha,\beta$-unsaturated carbonyl systems.  Patulin (clavacin), citrinin, and penicillic acid are examples of unequivocal structure.*  Phoenicin and javanacin are hydroxyquinones.  Mold products of special interest are puberulic and puberlonic acid containing the aromatic cycloheptatrienolone (tropolone) ring system.[139]  On the other hand, some of the nitrogenous antibiotics produced by molds contain two nitrogen atoms in the molecule.  Gliotoxin, with its unique disulfide linkage, and aspergillic acid, a hydroxamic acid type, are fascinating examples.

A penicillin is an altered peptide which can be considered derived by

[134] Schales and Mann, *Arch. Biochem.*, **18**, 217 (1948).

[135] Harris and Work, *Biochem. J.*, **46**, 582 (1950).

[136] Battersby and Craig, *J. Am. Chem. Soc.*, **73**, 1887 (1951).

[137] *Ann. N. Y. Acad. Sci.*, **51**, 853 (1949); Wilkinson, *Nature*, **164**, 622 (1949).

[138] Peterson and Reineke, *J. Biol. Chem.*, **181**, 95 (1949).

* The structures of compounds marked by an asterisk in Table II have been established by synthesis.

[139] For a comprehensive review of the tropolones see Cook and Loudon, *Quart. Revs. (London)*, **5**, 99 (1951).

an intramolecular dehydration of the appropriate acyl-L-α-formylglycyl-D-β,β-dimethylcysteine.   It is a most remarkable fact (ref. 7a, p. 66) that not a single mold product with the exception of the penicillins would even qualify for trial in man as a systemic therapeutic agent. Furthermore, not only are the penicillins unique as mold metabolites, but also within the broad domain of their antibacterial spectra they are eminently the least toxic and most potent antimicrobial agents known.

The strongly basic streptomycin, the neutral chloramphenicol, and the amphoteric aureomycin and terramycin are all commercial antibiotics produced by the actinomycetes.   Cycloheximide (actidione) and vitamin $B_{12}$ are also elaborated by this versatile class of microörganisms. Chloramphenicol is a good example of the unexpected in the structure of a natural product.   Before its discovery no naturally occurring compound was known to contain a dichloroacetyl group or a nitro group.

Antimicrobial products of bacteria include the phenazine derivatives (hemipyocyanine, iodinin, pyocyanine, and chlororaphin), a tripyrrylmethane dye (prodigiosin), and the 4-quinolinols of the pyo series. The principal antibiotics produced by bacteria, however, are the complex polypeptides, some of which are cyclic.   The reports that the adrenocorticotrophic hormone (ACTH) can be enzymatically degraded to highly active peptides engenders the hope that the polypeptide antibiotics may ultimately yield non-toxic fragments of remarkable antimicrobial potency which are amenable to synthesis.

Relatively little is known concerning the mechanisms of antibiotic action.[140]   Harris and Work [141] have demonstrated that the presence of a D-amino acid moiety in a peptide does not guarantee antimicrobial activity.   Nevertheless, one of the few discernible characteristics common to all the commercial antibiotics of known structure to date is the existence of an unnatural configuration within the molecule, a feature which may be significant in view of the stereochemical specificity of common enzymes.

[140] Pratt and Dufrenoy, *Texas Repts. Biol. Med.*, **9**, 76 (1951).
[141] Harris and Work, *Biochem. J.*, **46**, 196 (1950).

## TABLE II

### OTHER ANTIBIOTICS ISOLATED IN PURE FORM

| Name, Formula, Structural Formula | Produced by | Description | Active against | References |
|---|---|---|---|---|
| Patulin (clavacin, clavatin, claviformin, expansine, penicidin) * $C_7H_6O_4$ | *Penicillium expansum, P. clariforme, P. patulum* | M.p. 111° Prisms or plates $[\alpha]_D$ nil UV max. 276 m$\mu$ | Many bacteria, some fungi | 142 |
| Puberulic acid $C_8H_6O_6$ | *Penicillium puberulum* | M.p. 316–318° Cream-colored powder | *Staph. aureus, B. anthracis* More active than puberulonic acid | 143 |
| Penicillic acid * $C_8H_{10}O_4$ | *Penicillium puberulum* | M.p. 86–87° (monohydrate, 58–64°) Needles $[\alpha]_D$ nil | Most bacteria | 144 |

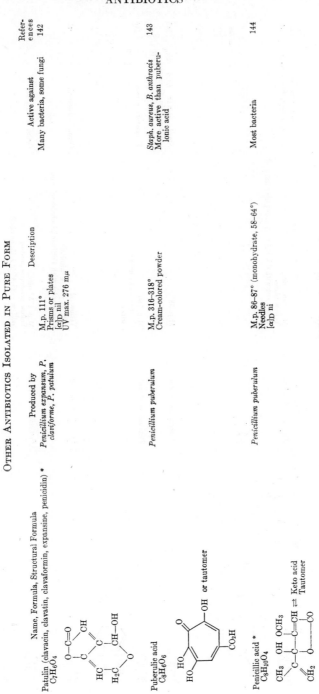

## TABLE II (Continued)

### OTHER ANTIBIOTICS ISOLATED IN PURE FORM

| Name, Formula, Structural Formula | Produced by | Description | Active against | References |
|---|---|---|---|---|
| Puberulonic acid $C_9H_4O_7$ | Penicillium puberulum | M.p. 296° (dec.)<br>Yellow plates<br>Treatment with dil. $H_2SO_4$ yields puberulic acid | Staph. aureus, B. anthracis | 143 |
| Mellein $C_{10}H_{10}O_3$ | Aspergillus melleus | M.p. 58° | Staph. aureus, Esch. coli, Myco. phlei, C. xerosis | 145 |
| Gladiolic acid $C_{11}H_{10}O_5$ | Penicillium gladioli | M.p. 160°<br>Colorless silky needles<br>$[\alpha]_D$ nil | Fungistatic action | 146 |
| Tardin $C_{11}H_{15}O_3$ | Penicillium tardum | Yellow oil<br>$[\alpha]_D^{20} = -11.4$ (alcohol)<br>Purple color with $FeCl_3$ in alcoholic solution | Gram + bacteria | 147 |
| Citrinin * $C_{13}H_{14}O_5$ | Penicillium citrinum | M.p. 175° (dec.)<br>Yellow prismatic needles<br>$[\alpha]_D^{18} = -37.4°$ (c 1.15, alcohol) | Gram + bacteria | 148 |

| Name | Source | Properties | Activity | Ref. |
|---|---|---|---|---|
| Phoenicin $C_{14}H_{10}O_6$ | *Penicillium rubrum, P. phoeniceum* | M.p. 230–231° Yellowish brown crystals | *Staph. aureus* | 149 |
| Frequentin $C_{14}H_{20}O_4$ (tentative) | *Penicillium frequentans* | M.p. 128° Colorless needles $[\alpha]_D^{25} = +68°$ (c 0.5, chloroform) | Fungi | 150 |
| Lactaroviolin $C_{15}H_{14}O$ | *Lactarius deliciosus* | M.p. 53° Purple-red crystals | Mycobacteria | 151 |
| Javanicin $C_{15}H_{14}O_6$ | *Fusarium javanicum* | M.p. 207.5–208° Red laths with coppery luster $[\alpha]_D$ nil | Gram + bacteria and myco-bacteria | 152 |
| Fuscin $C_{15}H_{16}O_5$ | *Oidiodendron fuscum* | M.p. 230° Orange plates $[\alpha]_D$ nil Intense purple solution in alkalies, purple-red color with alcoholic $FeCl_3$ | Gram + bacteria, some activity against Gram –, weak activity against mycobacteria | 153 |
| Hirsutic acid $C_{15}H_{20}O_4$ | *Stereum hirsutum* | M.p. 179.5° (uncorr.) $[\alpha]_D^{20} = +11.9°$ (abs. alcohol) | Gram + and – bacteria | 154 |
| Illudin M $C_{15}H_{20}O_3$ | | M.p. 130° $[\alpha]_D^{20} = -126°$ (alcohol) UV max. = 230, 320 m$\mu$ | *Mycobacterium smegma, Staph. aureus, Kleb. pneumoniae* | 155 |
| Illudin S $C_{15}H_{22}O_4$ | *Clitocybe illudens* | M.p. 124–125° $[\alpha]_D^{20} = -165°$ (alcohol) UV max. = 235, 328 m$\mu$ | | 155 |

## TABLE II (Continued)

### OTHER ANTIBIOTICS ISOLATED IN PURE FORM

| Name, Formula, Structural Formula | Produced by | Description | Active against | References |
|---|---|---|---|---|
| Marasmic acid $C_{16}H_{20}O_4$ | Marasmius conigenus | M.p. 165° (dec.), 174–175° (sealed in vacuo) $[\alpha]_D^{25} = +176°$ (c 1.4, acetone) | Active against Gram +, slight action against Gram − bacteria; Myco. smegma | 156 |
| Grifolin $C_{16}H_{28}O_2$ | Grifola confluens | M.p. 40° Colorless needles | Acid-fast bacteria; Staph. aureus, B. subtilis | 157 |
| Mycophenolic acid $C_{17}H_{20}O_6$ | Penicillium brevicompactum (P. stoloniferum) | M.p. 141° Colorless needles $[\alpha]_D$ nil | Action stronger against Gram + bacteria than Gram −; fungi | 158 |
| Thermophillin $C_{18}H_{18}O_9$ | Lenzites thermophila | M.p. 260° (dec.) (sealed tube) Golden plates | Staph. aureus | 159 |
| Viridin $C_{19}H_{16}O_6$    α-isomer    β-isomer | Trichoderma viride | M.p. 208–217° Colorless crystals $[\alpha]_D^{20} = -213.4°$ (chloroform) M.p. 140° $[\alpha]_D^{20} = -50.7°$ (chloroform) | Some fungi | 163 |
| Herquein $C_{19}H_{20}O_8$ | Penicillium herquei | M.p. 129° (dec.) Yellow-brown crystals | Gram + and − bacteria; myobacteria | 160 |
| Trichothecin $C_{19}H_{24}O_5$ | Trichothecium roseum | M.p. 118° Colorless needles $[\alpha]_D^{18} = +44°$ (c 1, chloroform) | Fungi | 161 |

Structural formula (Grifolin):

$$CH_3-\underset{CH_3}{\overset{CH_3}{C}}=CH-CH_2-CH_2-C=CH-CH=CH=CH-CH-CH-\underset{OH}{\overset{CH_3}{C}}-\underset{OH}{C}-C_2H_5$$

Structural formula (Mycophenolic acid):

OH, $C=CHCH_2$, $CH_2$, $CH_3$, $CH_2$, $CO_2H$, $CO$, $O$, $CH_2$, $CH_3$, or isomer

| Name / Formula | Source | Physical properties | Activity | No. |
|---|---|---|---|---|
| Rosein II $C_{19}H_{28}O_3$ | Trichothecium roseum | M.p. 186° $[\alpha]_D^{23} = +6°$ (c 2, chloroform or alcohol) | B. subtilis | 162 |
| Pleurotin $C_{20}H_{22}O_5$ | Pleurotus griseus | M.p. 200–215° (dec.) $[\alpha]_D^{23} = -20°$ (c 0.59, chloroform) UV max. 250 mμ | Gram + bacteria | 164 |
| Actinorhodin $C_{24}H_{22}O_{11}$ | Actinomyces sp. | Dec. 270° Red crystals; forms yellow triacetate, m.p. 260° (dec.) | Staph. | 165 |
| Fumagillin $C_{27}H_{36}O_7$ | Aspergillus fumigatus | M.p. 189–194° $[\alpha]_D^{25} = -26.6°$ (c 0.25, methanol) | Amebicide | 166 |
| Helvolic acid (fumigacin) $C_{32}H_{44}O_8$ | Aspergillus fumigatus mut. helvola | M.p. 210.5–211° Colorless needles Strongly levorotatory; $E_{1\,cm}^{1\%} = 300$ (230 mμ) | Gram + bacteria | 167 |
| a Glycolipide $C_{32}H_{60}O_{14}$ | Pseudomonas aeruginosa | M.p. 86° $[\alpha]_D = -84°$ (c 3, chloroform) | Myco. tuberculosis | 168 |
| Glutinosin $C_{48}H_{60}O_{16}$ | Metarrhizium glutinosum | M.p. above 300° Thin colorless plate $[\alpha]_D^{20} = +54°$ (benzene) | Mainly fungi, bacteria not affected | 169 |
| Griseofulvin (curling factor) $C_{17}H_{17}ClO_6$ | Penicillium griseofulvum, P. janczewskii | M.p. 220° Colorless octahedral crystals $[\alpha]_D^{17} = +370°$ (c 2, chloroform) | No effect on bacteria, powerful fungistatic agent | 170 |
| Geodin $C_{17}H_{12}Cl_2O_7$ | Aspergillus terreus | M.p. 235° Pale yellow needles Sublimes in vacuo $[\alpha]_{5461}^{20°} = +179°$ (c 0.8, chloroform) $[\alpha]_{5790}^{20°} = +149°$ | Gram + bacteria | 171 |

or alternative pseudo ester formula

## TABLE II (*Continued*)

### OTHER ANTIBIOTICS ISOLATED IN PURE FORM

| Name, Formula, Structural Formula | Produced by | Description | Active against | References |
|---|---|---|---|---|
| Ustin I $C_{21}H_{17}Cl_3O_6$ | *Aspergillus ustus* | M.p. 185–187° UV max. 325 m$\mu$ | Mycobacteria, Gram + cocci | 172 |
| Ustin II $C_{21}H_{18}Cl_2O_6$ | *Aspergillus ustus* | M.p. 214–216° UV absorption spectrum same as Ustin I | Mycobacteria, Gram + cocci | 172 |
| Lycomarasmine $C_9H_{15}N_3O_7$ | *Fusarium lycopersici* | M.p. 227–229° (dec.) White microcrystalline powder $[\alpha]_D = -42°$ to $-48°$ in aqueous soln. at pH 7.0 | Inhibited growth of *Lactobacillus casei* | 173 |
| Candidulin $C_{11}H_{15}NO_3$ or $C_{12}H_{17}NO_3$ | *Aspergillus candidus* | M.p. 88–89° $[\alpha]_D^{24} = +15°$ (chloroform) | Mycobacteria | 174 |
| Hemipyocyanine ($\alpha$-hydroxyphenazine) * $C_{12}H_8N_2O$ | *Pseudomonas pyocyanea* | M.p. 158° Yellow needles | Gram + and some Gram − bacteria, mycobacteria, fungi, yeasts | 175 |
| Iodinin $C_{12}H_8N_2O_4$ | *Chromobacterium iodinum* | M.p. 236° (with evolution of gas) Deep purple-colored crystals Liberates $I_2$ from KI in acetic acid | Gram + more susceptible than Gram − bacteria | 176 |

Lycomarasmine structural formula:

$$CH_3$$
$$H_2N-C=CH_2 \quad \quad HO_2C-CH-NH-CO-CH_2-NH-C-OH, \quad CO_2H$$

| | | |
|---|---|---|
| Aspergillic acid $C_{12}H_{20}N_2O_2$ | *Aspergillus flavus* | M.p. 97–99° <br> Pale yellow rods <br> $[\alpha]_D^{23} = +12°$ (alcohol) <br> UV absorption spectrum max. = 325 m$\mu$, $\epsilon$ = 8900 (alcohol); max. = 336 m$\mu$, $\epsilon$ = 10,500 (pH 8). | Both Gram − and Gram + bacteria, *Treponema pallidum*; fungistatic | 177 |

or the two alkyl groups are interchanged

| | | |
|---|---|---|
| Pyocyanine $C_{13}H_{10}N_2O$ | *Pseudomonas pyocyanea* | M.p. 133° <br> Deep blue needles <br> Reduces to colorless leuco compound | Bacteria, fungi | 178 |

or "phenol-betaine" tautomer

| | | |
|---|---|---|
| Chloroaphin $C_{13}H_{10}N_3O$ | *Pseudomonas chlororaphis* | M.p. 228–230° <br> Green crystals <br> Readily oxidized to oxychloroaphin <br> Sublimes in absence of oxygen | *Streptococcus hemolyticus* | 179 |

## TABLE II (*Continued*)

### OTHER ANTIBIOTICS ISOLATED IN PURE FORM

| Name, Formula, Structural Formula | Produced by | Description | Active against | References |
|---|---|---|---|---|
| Cycloheximide (actidione) $C_{15}H_{23}NO_4$ | Streptomyces griseus "Strain 4" | M.p. 119.5–121° Colorless plates $[\alpha]_D^{29} = -3.38°$ (c 9.47, alcohol) | Yeasts and some pathogenic fungi | 180 |
| Prodigiosin $C_{20}H_{25}N_3O$ $n\text{-}C_5H_{11}$ | Chromobacterium prodigiosum | Perchlorate M.p. 228° Vermilion | Bacteria; fungi; Protozoa | 181 |
| Streptothricin $C_{20}H_{34-36}N_8O_9$ | Streptomyces lavendulae | Reineckate M.p. 192–194° (dec.) Clusters of fine plates Hydrochloride $[\alpha]_D^{25} = -51.3°$ (c 1.4, water) | Inhibits both Gram + and Gram − bacteria. myoo-bacteria, yeasts, fungi | 182 |
| Myoelianamide $C_{22}H_{28}N_2O_5$ $C_{10}H_{17}O$ COCHNHCOCOCH₃  CONH₂ | Mycelium of Penicillium griseo-fulvum | M.p. 170–172° (dec.) Colorless, crystalline substance $[\alpha]_{5461}^{19} = -217°$ | Gram + bacteria | 183 |
| Enniatin B $C_{22}H_{38}N_2O_6$, R = $CH(CH_3)_2$ | Mycelium of strains of Fusaria | M.p. 174–176° | Myobacteria | 184 |

| Antibiotic | Source | Properties | Activity | Ref. |
|---|---|---|---|---|
| Enniatin C, $C_{24}H_{42}N_2O_6$, R = $CH_2CH(CH_3)_2$ | Myelium of strains of *Fusaria* | M.p. 152–153°, Sublimes in high vacuum | Myobacteria | 184 |
| Enniatin A, $C_{24}H_{42}N_2O_6$, R = $CH(CH_3)C_2H_5$ | *Fusarium orthoceras* var. *enniatum* | M.p. 122–122.5°, Colorless crystals, $[\alpha]_D^{20} = -92°$ (chloroform), Sublimes in high vacuum | Myobacteria and *Staph. aureus* | 184 |
| Sambucinin, $C_{24}H_{42}N_2O_7$ | *Fusarium sambucinum* | M.p. 85–86°, Colorless, neutral, optically active compound | Myobacteria | 185 |
| Picromycin (pikromycin), $C_{25}H_{43}NO_7$ | *Actinomyces* sp. | M.p. 169–170°, $[\alpha]_D^{24} = 8.2°$ (c 3.5, alcohol), $[\alpha]_D^{24} = -50.2°$ (c 6.3, chloroform), No characteristic UV absorption | *Staph. aureus* | 186 |
| Avenacein, $C_{25}H_{44}N_2O_7$ | *Fusarium avenaceum* | M.p. 139°, Colorless, neutral, optically active compound | Myobacteria | 185 |
| Fructigenin, $C_{26}H_{44-46}N_2O_7$ | *Fusarium fructigenum* | M.p. 129°, Colorless, neutral, optically active compound | Myobacteria | 185 |
| Lateritiin I, $C_{26}H_{46}N_2O_7$ | *Fusarium lateritium* | M.p. 121–122°, $[\alpha]_D^{20} = -95.6 \pm 2°$ (c 1, ethanol), Neutral substance | Myobacteria, action weaker against other bacteria | 187 |
| Proactinomycins A, $C_{27}H_{47}NO_8$; B, $C_{28}H_{49}NO_8$; C, $C_{24}H_{41}NO_6$ | *Proactinomyces* (*Nocardia*) *gardneri* | UV max. (in ether) A, 260 mμ; B, 265 mμ; C, 300 mμ | Gram + and − bacteria | 188 |
| Antimycin A, $C_{28}H_{40}N_2O_9$ | *Streptomyces* sp. | M.p. 130–140°, $[\alpha]_D^{25} = +64.8°$ (c 10, chloroform), UV max. = 225, 320 mμ | Yeasts and fungi | 189 |
| Borrelidin, $C_{28}H_{43}NO_5$ | *Streptomyces rochei* | M.p. 145–146°, $[\alpha]_D^{27} = -28°$ (alcohol), UV max. = 256 mμ, $E_{1\,cm.}^{1\%} = 550$ | *Borrelia* (spirochete) | 190 |

Enniatin general formula:

$$CH_3-N \quad \begin{matrix} N-CH_3 \\ CH(CH_3)_2 \end{matrix}$$

R

CH–CO–O–CH–CH–CO

CO–CH–O–CO–CH

R

$CH(CH_3)_2$

$CH(CH_3)_2$

## TABLE II (Continued)

### OTHER ANTIBIOTICS ISOLATED IN PURE FORM

| Name, Formula, Structural Formula | Produced by | Description | Active against | References |
|---|---|---|---|---|
| Fradicin $C_{30}H_{34}N_2O_4$ (tentative) | Streptomyces fradiae | Light greenish yellow $[\alpha]_D^{25} = +65°$ (c 1.0, 1,4-dioxane) UV max. = 293 mμ | Fungi | 191 |
| Pyo Ib $C_{31}H_{40}N_2O_2$ | Pseudomonas pyocyanea | M.p. 146.2–147° Colorless crystals | High activity for Gram + bacteria | 192 |
| Pyo Ic* $C_{36}H_{50}N_2O_2$ | Pseudomonas pyocyanea | M.p. 138–139° | Gram + bacteria | 192 |
| Pyo II $C_{34}H_{46}N_2O_4$ | Pseudomonas pyocyanea | M.p. 149–149.5° Yellow platelets | Gram + bacteria | 192 |
| Pyo III $C_{34}H_{44}N_2O_2$ | Pseudomonas pyocyanea | M.p. 152.8–153.5° Colorless prisms | Gram + bacteria | 192 |
| Pyo IV $C_{16}H_{23}NO_3$ | Pseudomonas pyocyanea | M.p. 131–132° or 139.5–140° Colorless needles having two allotropic forms Characteristic UV absorption spectrum | Gram + bacteria | 192 |
| Netropsin $C_{32}H_{48}N_{18}O_4$ | Streptomyces netropsis | Hydrochloride M.p. 168–172° (dec.) UV max. = 236, 296 mμ sulfate | Gram + and − bacteria | 193 |
| Actinomycin $C_{41}H_{58}N_8O_{11}$ | Streptomyces antibioticus | M.p. 255° (corr.) Red prisms $[\alpha]_D^{16} = -367°$ (c 0.25, alcohol) UV max. 237–240; 442–444 mμ | Gram + bacteria, Myco. tuberculosis | 194 |
| Violacein $C_{42}H_{35}N_5O_6$ | Chromobacterium violaceum | Violet-black pigment | Gram + bacteria, Protozoa | 195 |
| Actinomycin C (new) $C_{60}H_{83}N_{11}O_{16}$ | Streptomyces sp. | M.p. 252° (dec.) $[\alpha]_D^{17} = -309°$ ($\pm3°$) (c 0.25, alcohol) | Staph. aureus, Esch. coli | 196 |

| Compound | Source | Properties | Activity | Ref. |
|---|---|---|---|---|
| Aureothricin $C_{13}H_{13}N_3S_2O_3$ | Streptomyces sp. | M.p. 256° (dec.) Yellow crystals | Gram + and − bacteria | 197 |
| Gliotoxin $C_{13}H_{14}N_2O_4S_2$ | Gliocladium fimbriatum | M.p. 221° (dec.) $[\alpha]_D^{19} = -239°$ in chloroform, neutral substance Characteristic UV absorption spectrum | Mainly Gram + bacteria, actinomycetes, fungi | 198 |
| Chetonin (chaetomin) $C_{16}H_{17}N_3O_4S_2$ | Chaetomium cochliodes | M.p. 215° White powder $[\alpha]_D^{22} = +360°$ (c 1, chloroform) | Gram + bacteria | 199 |
| Sulfactin $C_{38}H_{55}N_{11}O_7S_4$ | Actinomyces strain resembling A. roseus | M.p. 245–275° (dec.) | Gram + bacteria | 200 |
| Xanthomycins $C_{29}H_{42}N_9O_7S_4Cr$ (Reineckate) or $C_{38}H_{57}N_{12}O_{13}S_4Cr$ (Reineckate) | Streptomyces sp. | M.p. 165–170° (dec.) Yellow-orange UV max. = 264–267, 325–327 mμ | Gram + bacteria | 201 |
| Grisein $C_{40}H_{61}N_{10}O_{20}SiFe$ | Streptomyces griseus | Red, amorphous powder UV max. = 265 mμ, $E_{1\ cm}^{1\%}$ 108 = 420 mμ, $E_{1\ cm}^{1\%}$ 28.9 | Gram + bacteria | 202 |
| Neomycin A | Streptomyces fradiae | M.p. 250–260° $[\alpha]_D^{25} = +83°$ (c 1.0, water) White amorphous powder UV max. = 370 mμ | Gram + and − bacteria; mycobacteria | 203 |
| Viomycin | Streptomyces puniceus, St. floridae | M.p. 252° (dec.) of microcrystalline sulfate $[\alpha]_D^{25} = -39.8°$ (c 1.0, water) UV max. = 268 mμ (0.1 N HCl) 268.5 mμ (pH 7) 282.5 mμ (0.1 N NaOH) | Gram + and − bacteria; mycobacteria | 204 |

(Provisional)

## REFERENCES FOR TABLE II

[142] *Patulin:** (a) Woodward and Singh, *J. Am. Chem. Soc.*, **72**, 1428 (1950); **71**, 758 (1949); (b) von Engel, Brzeski, and Plattner, *Helv. Chim. Acta*, **32**, 1166, 1752 (1949); (c) Dannbenn and Weisenborn, *J. Am. Chem. Soc.*, **71**, 3853 (1949); (d) Cohen, *Chemistry & Industry*, 640 (1949); (e) Hooper, Anderson, Skell, and Carter, *Science*, **99**, 16 (1944); (f) Atkinson and co-workers, *Australian J. Exptl. Biol. Med. Sci.*, **22**, 223 (1944); (g) Katzman and co-workers, *J. Biol. Chem.*, **154**, 475 (1944); (h) Chain, Florey, and Jennings, *Lancet*, **246**, 112 (1944); (i) Birkinshaw and co-workers, *ibid.*, **245**, 625 (1943); (j) Bergel and co-workers, *J. Chem. Soc.*, 415 (1944).

[143] *Puberulic acid and puberulonic acid:* (a) Johnson, Sheppard, and Todd, *J. Chem. Soc.*, 1139 (1951); (b) Corbett and co-workers, *ibid.*, 1 (1950); (c) Corbett, Johnson, and Todd, *ibid.*, 6 (1950); (d) McGowan, *Chemistry & Industry*, 205 (1947); (e) Birkinshaw and Raistrick, *Biochem. J.*, **26**, 441 (1932); (f) Barger and Dorrer, *ibid.*, **28**, 11 (1934).

[144] *Penicillic acid:* (a) Nineham and Raphael, *J. Chem. Soc.*, 118 (1949); (b) Raphael, *ibid.*, 1508 (1948); *(c) ibid.*, 805 (1947); (d) Munday, *Nature*, **163**, 443 (1949); *(e) Raphael, *ibid.*, **160**, 261 (1947); (f) Birkinshaw, Oxford, and Raistrick, *Biochem. J.*, **30**, 394 (1936).

[145] *Mellein:* Burton, *Nature*, **165**, 274 (1950).

[146] *Gladiolic acid:* (a) Brian and co-workers, *J. Gen. Microbiol.*, **2**, 341 (1948); (b) Brian and co-workers, *Nature*, **157**, 697 (1946).

[147] *Tardin:* Borodin, Philpot, and Florey, *Brit. J. Exptl. Path.*, **28**, 31 (1947).

[148] *Citrinin:* *(a) Johnson, Robertson, and Whalley, *J. Chem. Soc.*, 2971 (1950); (b) Cartwright, Robertson, and Whalley, *ibid.*, 1563 (1949); (c) Cartwright, Robertson, and Whalley, *Nature*, **163**, 94 (1949); (d) Brown and co-workers, *J. Chem. Soc.*, 859, 867 (1949); (e) Brown and co-workers, *Nature*, **162**, 72 (1948); (f) Frye, Wallis, and Daugherty, *J. Org. Chem.*, **14**, 397 (1949); (g) Sprenger and Ruoff, *ibid.*, **11**, 189 (1946); (h) Cram, *J. Am. Chem. Soc.*, **70**, 4244 (1948); (i) Schwenk, Schubert, and Stahl, *Arch. Biochem.*, **20**, 220 (1949); (j) Hetherington and Raistrick, *Trans. Roy. Soc. (London)*, **B220**, 269 (1931).

[149] *Phoenicin:* Burton, *Brit. J. Exptl. Path.*, **30**, 151 (1949); ref. 7a, p. 1518.

[150] *Frequentin:* Curtis, Hemming, and Smith, *Nature*, **167**, 557 (1951).

[151] *Lactaroviolin:* (a) Willstaedt and Zetterbug, *Svensk Kem. Tid.*, **58**, 306 (1946); (b) Willstaedt, *ibid.*, **58**, 243 (1946); (c) Karrer, Ruckstuhl, and Zbinden, *Helv. Chim. Acta*, **28**, 1176 (1945).

[152] *Javanicin:* Arnstein and Cook, *J. Chem. Soc.*, 1021 (1947).

[153] *Fuscin:* (a) Michael, *Biochem. J.*, **43**, 528 (1948); (b) Marcus, *ibid.*, **43**, 532 (1948).

[154] *Hirsutic acid:* Heatley, Jennings, and Florey, *Brit. J. Exptl. Path.*, **28**, 35 (1947).

[155] *Illudin S, Illudin M:* Anchel, Hervey, and Robbins, *Proc. Natl. Acad. Sci. U. S.*, **36**, 300 (1950).

[156] *Marasmic acid:* Kavanagh, Hervey, and Robbins, *ibid.*, **35**, 343 (1949).

[157] *Grifolin:* Hirata and Nakanishi, *J. Biol. Chem.*, **184**, 135 (1950).

[158] *Mycophenolic acid:* (a) Birkinshaw and co-workers, *Biochem. J.*, **43**, 216 (1948); (b) Clutterbuck and Raistrick, *ibid.*, **27**, 654 (1933).

[159] *Thermophillin:* Burton, *Nature*, **166**, 570 (1950).

[160] *Herquein:* Burton, *Brit. J. Exptl. Path.*, **30**, 151 (1949).

[161] *Trichothecin:* (a) Freeman and Gill, *Nature*, **166**, 698 (1950); (b) Freeman and Morrison, *ibid.*, **162**, 30 (1948).

[162] *Rosein II:* (a) Freeman, Morrison, and Michael, *Biochem. J.*, **45**, 191 (1949); (b) Freeman and Morrison, *ibid.*, **43**, xxiii (1948).

[163] *Viridin:* (a) Vischer, Howland, and Raudnitz, *Nature*, **165**, 528 (1950); (b) Brian, Curtis, Hemming, and McGowan, *Ann. Applied Biol.*, **33**, 190 (1946).

[164] *Pleurotin:* Robbins, Kavanagh, and Hervey, *Proc. Natl. Acad. Sci. U. S.*, **33**, 171 (1947).

[165] *Actinorhodin:* Brockmann, Pini, and Plotho, *Chem. Ber.*, **83**, 161 (1950).

[166] *Fumagillin:* (a) McCowen, Callender, and Lawlis, Jr., *Science,* **113,** 202 (1951); (b) Eble and Hanson, *Antibiotics and Chemotherapy,* **1,** 54 (1951).

[167] *Helvolic acid:* (a) Elliott and co-workers, *Federation Proc.,* **6,** 250 (1947); (b) Birkinshaw, Bracken, and Raistrick, *Biochem. J.,* **39,** 70 (1945); (c) Chain and Williams, *Brit. J. Exptl. Path.,* **24,** 108 (1943); (d) Menzel, Wintersteiner, and Hoogerheide, *J. Biol. Chem.,* **152,** 419 (1944).

[168] *a Glycolipide:* Jarvis and Johnson, *J. Am. Chem. Soc.,* **71,** 4124 (1949).

[169] *Glutinosin:* (a) Brian and McGowan, *Nature,* **157,** 334 (1946); (b) Brian, Curtis, and Hemming, *Proc. Roy. Soc. (London),* **B135,** 106 (1947).

[170] *Griseofulvin:* (a) Brian, Curtis, and Hemming, *Brit. Mycol. Soc. Trans.,* **32,** 30 (1949); (b) Grove and McGowan, *Nature,* **160,** 574 (1947).

[171] *Geodin:* (a) Raistrick, *Proc. Roy. Soc. (London),* **B136,** 481 (1950); (b) Calam and co-workers, *Biochem. J.,* **41,** 458 (1947); (c) *ibid.,* **33,** 579 (1939); (d) Clutterbuck, Koerber, and Raistrick, *ibid.,* **31,** 1089 (1937); (e) Raistrick and Smith, *ibid.,* **30,** 1315 (1936).

[172] *Ustin I and II:* (a) Hogeboom and Craig, *J. Biol. Chem.,* **162,** 363 (1946); (b) Doering and co-workers, *J. Am. Chem. Soc.,* **68,** 725 (1946).

[173] *Lyco-marasmine:* Plattner and Clauson-Kaas, *Experientia,* **1,** 195 (1945); ref. 7a, p. 1523.

[174] *Candidulin:* Stansly and Ananenko, *Arch. Biochem.,* **23,** 256 (1949).

[175] *Hemipyocyanine:** Wrede and Strack, *Z. physiol. Chem.,* **177,** 177 (1928); *Ber.,* **62,** 2051 (1929).

[176] *Iodinin:* (a) Clemo and Daglish, *J. Chem. Soc.,* 1481 (1950); (b) McIlwain, *ibid.,* 322 (1943); (c) Clemo and McIlwain, *ibid.,* 479 (1938).

[177] *Aspergillic acid:* (a) Dunn and co-workers, *ibid.,* 2707 (1949); (b) *ibid.,* Suppl. Issue No. 1, S126, 131 (1949); (c) Dunn and co-workers, *Nature,* **162,** 779 (1948); (d) Shaw, *J. Am. Chem. Soc.,* **71,** 67 (1949); (e) Shaw and McDowell, *ibid.,* **71,** 1691 (1949); (f) Dutcher and Wintersteiner, *J. Biol. Chem.,* **155,** 359 (1944); (g) Dutcher, *ibid.,* **171,** 321, 341 (1947).

[178] *Pyocyanine:* (a) Hillemann, *Ber.,* **71,** 46 (1938); (b) *Wrede and Strack, *Z. physiol. Chem.,* **181,** 58 (1929); (c) Wrede and Strack, *Ber.,* **62,** 2051 (1929); (d) Surrey, *Org. Syntheses,* **26,** 86 (1946).

[179] *Chlororaphin:* (a) McIlwain, *Nature,* **148,** 628 (1941); (b) Clemo and McIlwain, *J. Chem. Soc.,* 1991 (1934); (c) Kögl and Postowsky, *Ann.,* **480,** 280 (1930); (d) Kögl and Tönnis, *Ann.,* **497,** 265 (1932).

[180] *Cycloheximide (actidione):* (a) Kornfeld, Jones, and Parke, *J. Am. Chem. Soc.,* **71,** 150 (1949); (b) Kornfeld and Jones, *Science,* **108,** 437 (1948); (c) Ford and Leach, *J. Am. Chem. Soc.,* **70,** 1223 (1948); (d) Leach, Ford, and Whiffen, *ibid.,* **69,** 474 (1947).

[181] *Prodigiosin:* (a) Balamuth and Brent, *Proc. Soc. Exptl. Biol. Med.,* **75,** 374 (1950); (b) Hubbard and Rimington, *Biochem. J.,* **46,** 220 (1950); (c) Wrede and Rothhaus, *Z. physiol. Chem.,* **226,** 95 (1934); (d) Fisher and Gangl, *ibid.,* **267,** 201 (1941); (e) Wrede and Hettche, *Ber.,* **62,** 2678 (1929).

[182] *Streptothricin:* (a) Taylor, *Abstr. Second Natl. Med. Chem. Sym. Am. Chem. Soc.,* p. 33 (1950); (b) Swart, *J. Am. Chem. Soc.,* **71,** 2942 (1949); (c) Peck and co-workers, *ibid.,* **68,** 772 (1946); (d) Fried and Wintersteiner, *Science,* **101,** 613 (1945).

[183] *Mycelianamide:* Oxford and Raistrick, *Biochem. J.,* **42,** 323 (1948).

[184] *Enniatins:* (a) Plattner and Nager, *Helv. Chim. Acta,* **31,** 2192, 2203 (1948); (b) *Experientia,* **3,** 325 (1947); (c) Plattner, Nager, and Boller, *Helv. Chim. Acta,* **31,** 594 (1948); (d) Cook and co-workers, *Nature,* **160,** 31 (1947).

[185] *Sambucinin, Avenacein, and Fructigenin:* Cook and co-workers, *Nature,* **160,** 31 (1947).

[186] *Picromycin:* (a) Brockmann and Henkel, *Chem. Ber.,* **84,** 284 (1951); (b) Brockmann and Henkel, *Naturwissenschaften,* **37,** 138 (1950).

[187] *Lateritiin I:* (a) Cook, Cox, and Farmer, *J. Chem. Soc.,* 1022 (1949); (b) Cook and co-workers, *Nature,* **160,** 31 (1947).

[188] *Proactinomycins:* (a) Marston and Florey, *Brit. J. Exptl. Path.,* **30,** 407 (1949); (b) Marston, *ibid.,* **30,** 398 (1949); (c) Abraham, *ibid.,* **26,** 349 (1945); (d) Florey and co-workers, *ibid.,* **26,** 337 (1945); (e) Gardner and Chain, *ibid.,* **23,** 123 (1942).

[189] *Antimycin A:* (a) Kido and Spyhalski, *Science*, **112**, 172 (1950); (b) Ahmad, Schneider, and Strong, *Arch. Biochem.*, **28**, 281 (1950); (c) Dunshee and co-workers, *J. Am. Chem. Soc.*, **71**, 2436 (1949).

[190] *Borrelidin:* Berger, Jampolsky, and Goldberg, *Arch. Biochem.*, **22**, 477 (1949).

[191] *Fradicin:* (a) Hickey and Hidy, *Science*, **113**, 361 (1951); (b) Swart, Romano, and Waksman, *Proc. Soc. Exptl. Biol. Med.*, **73**, 376 (1950); (c) Swart, Hutchison, and Waksman, *Arch. Biochem.*, **24**, 92 (1949).

[192] *Pyo compounds:* *(a) Wells, *Federation Proc.*, **10**, 268 (1951); (b) Wells and co-workers, *ibid.*, **7**, 198 (1948); (c) Hays and co-workers, *J. Biol. Chem.*, **159**, 725 (1945).

[193] *Netropsin:* Finlay and co-workers, *J. Am. Chem. Soc.*, **73**, 341 (1951).

[194] *Actinomycin:* (a) Dalgliesh and co-workers, *J. Chem. Soc.*, 2946 (1950); (b) Waksman and Tishler, *J. Biol. Chem.*, **142**, 519 (1942); (c) Waksman and Woodruff, *J. Bact.*, **42**, 231 (1941).

[195] *Violacein:* (a) Beer and co-workers, *J. Chem. Soc.*, 885 (1949); (b) Lichstein and Van de Sand, *J. Bact.*, **52**, 145 (1946).

[196] *Actinomycin C:* (a) Brockmann and co-workers, *Chem. Ber.*, **84**, 260 (1951); (b) Brockmann and Grubhofer, *Naturwissenschaften*, **36**, 376 (1949).

[197] *Aureothricin:* (a) Umezawa, Maeda, and Kosaha, *Japan Med. J.*, **1**, 512 (1950); (b) Maeda, *J. Antibiotics*, **2**, 795 (1949).

[198] *Gliotoxin:* (a) Wintersteiner and Dutcher, *Ann. Rev. Biochem.*, **18**, 572 (1949); (b) Elvidge and Spring, *Nature*, **163**, 94 (1949); (c) Elvidge and Spring, *J. Chem. Soc.*, Suppl. Issue No. 1, S135 (1949); (d) Dutcher, Johnson, and Bruce, *J. Am. Chem. Soc.*, **67**, 1736 (1945) and preceding papers; (e) Johnson and Andreen, *ibid.*, **72**, 2862 (1950).

[199] *Chetomin:* Geiger, *Arch. Biochem.*, **21**, 125 (1949).

[200] *Sulfactin:* Junowicz-Kocholaty, Kocholaty, and Kelner, *J. Biol. Chem.*, **168**, 765 (1947).

[201] *Xanthomycins:* (a) Mold and Bartz, *J. Am. Chem. Soc.*, **72**, 1847 (1950); (b) Thorne and Peterson, *J. Biol. Chem.*, **176**, 413 (1948).

[202] *Grisein:* (a) Kuehl, Jr., and co-workers, *J. Am. Chem. Soc.*, **73**, 1770 (1951); (b) Reynolds and Waksman, *J. Bact.*, **55**, 739 (1948); (c) Reynolds, Schatz, and Waksman, *Proc. Soc. Exptl. Biol. Med.*, **55**, 66 (1944).

[203] *Neomycin:* (a) Leach and Teeters, *J. Am. Chem. Soc.*, **73**, 2794 (1951); (b) Leach and co-workers, *ibid.*, **73**, 2797 (1951); (c) Dutcher and co-workers, *ibid.*, **73**, 1384 (1951); (d) Kuehl, Jr., Bishop, and Folkers, *ibid.*, **73**, 881 (1951); (e) Wolfrom and Olin, *ibid.*, **72**, 1724 (1950); (f) Peck and co-workers, *ibid.*, **71**, 2590 (1949); (g) Swart, Hutchison, and Waksman, *Arch. Biochem.*, **24**, 92 (1949).

[204] *Viomycin:* (a) Finlay and co-workers, *Am. Rev. Tuberculosis*, **63**, 1 (1951); (b) Bartz and co-workers, *ibid.*, **63**, 4 (1951).

# INDEX